THE FIRESIDE BOOK OF
DOG
STORIES

Edited by

Jack Goodman

With an Introduction by

James Thurber

SIMON AND SCHUSTER
New York

About the Appearance of Books in Wartime

A recent ruling by the War Production Board has curtailed the use of paper by book publishers in 1943.

In line with this ruling and in order to conserve materials and manpower, we are co-operating by:

1. Using lighter-weight paper which reduces the bulk of ours books substantially.
2. Printing books with smaller margins and with more words to each page. Result: fewer pages per book.

Slimmer and smaller books will save paper and plate metal and labor. We are sure that readers will understand the publishers' desire to co-operate as fully as possible with the objectives of the War Production Board and our government.

PRINTED AND BOUND IN THE UNITED STATES OF AMERICA
BY KINGSPORT PRESS, INC., KINGSPORT, TENNESSEE

TO GEORGE

TABLE OF CONTENTS

INTRODUCTION

IN CONTEMPLATING a preface to this imposing collection of practically all the best pieces ever written about the dog, I was impelled at first to reach for the *Britannica* and other noble reference volumes, in order to do full and solemn justice to the subject, complete with historical facts and classical allusions.

In this state of mind, leafing through, among other things, *Plutarch's Lives*, I came upon the story of Xanthippus and his dog. It seems that the old Greek, fleeing Athens one time by ship, left his dog behind—or thought he left him behind. To his amazement and delight, the dog, in the finest whither-thou-goest tradition known to the animal kingdom, plunged into the sea and swam after the galley all the way to Salamis, a feat of which even a seal might well be proud. When the dog died, Xanthippus built a conspicuous tomb for it, high on a windy cliff, that men, infirm of purpose, weak of heart, might be reminded of the miracles which can be wrought by courage, loyalty, and resolution. So much for classical allusions. There will be no historical facts.

Man first gained superiority over the other animals not because of his mind, but because of his fingers. He could pick up rocks and throw them, and he could wield a club. Later he developed the spear and the bow and arrow. It is my theory that the other animals, realizing they were as good as cooked if they came within range of Man's weapons, decided to make friends with him. He probably tried to make a pet and companion out of each species in turn. (It never occurred to him, in those days, to play or go hunting with Woman, a peculiarity which has persisted down to the present time.)

It did not take Man long—probably not more than a hundred centuries—to discover that all the animals except the dog were impossible around the house.* One has but to spend a few days with an aardvark or a llama, command a water buffalo to sit up and beg, or try to housebreak a moose, to perceive how wisely Man set about his process of elimination and selection. When the first man brought the first dog to his cave (no doubt over and above his wife's protests), there began an association by which Man has enormously profited. It is conceivable that the primordial male held the female, as mate or mother, in no aspect of esteem whatsoever, and that the introduction of the dog into the family circle first infected him with that benign disease known as love. Certain it is that the American male of today, in that remarkable period between infancy and adolescence, goes through a phase, arguably atavistic, during which he views mother, sister, and the little girl next door with cold indifference, if not, indeed, outspoken disdain, the while he lavishes wholehearted affection on Rex or Rover. In his grief over the loss of a dog, a little boy stands for the first time on tiptoe, peering into the rueful morrow of manhood. After this most inconsolable of sorrows there is nothing life can do to him that he will not be able somehow to bear.

If Man has benefited immeasurably by his association with the dog, what, you may ask, has the dog got out of it? His scroll has, of course, been heavily charged with punishments: he has known the muzzle, the leash, and the tether; he has suffered the indignities of the show bench, the tin can on the tail, the ribbon in the hair; his love life with the other sex of his species has been regulated by the frigid hand of authority, his digestion ruined by the macaroons and marshmallows of doting women. The list of his woes could be continued indefinitely. But he has also had his fun, for he has been privileged to live with and study at close range the only creature with reason, the most unreasonable of creatures.

The dog has got more fun out of Man than Man has got out of the dog, for the clearly demonstrable reason that Man is the more laughable of the two animals. The dog has long been bemused by the singular activities and the curious practices of men, cocking his head inquiringly to one side, intently watching and listening to the strangest goings-on in the world. He has seen men sing together and

---

* There is no deliberate intention here to offend admirers of the cat, although I don't really much care whether I do or not.

fight one another in the same evening. He has watched them go to bed when it is time to get up, and get up when it is time to go to bed. He has observed them destroying the soil in vast areas, and nurturing it in small patches. He has stood by while men built strong and solid houses for rest and quiet, and then filled them with lights and bells and machinery. His sensitive nose, which can detect what's cooking in the next township, has caught at one and the same time the bewildering smells of the hospital and the munitions factory. He has seen men raise up great cities to heaven and then blow them to hell.

The effect upon the dog of his life with Man is discernible in his eyes, which frequently are capable of a greater range of expression than Man's. The eyes of the sensitive French poodle, for example, can shine with such an unalloyed glee and darken with so profound a gravity as to disconcert the masters of the earth, who have lost the key to so many of the simpler magics. Man has practiced for such a long time to mask his feelings and to regiment his emotions that some basic quality of naturalness has gone out of both his gaiety and his solemnity.

The dog is aware of this, I think. You can see it in his eyes sometimes when he lies and looks at you with a long, rueful gaze. He knows that the bare foot of Man has been too long away from the living earth, that he has been too busy with the construction of engines, which are, of all the things on earth, the farthest removed from the shape and intention of nature. I once owned a wise old poodle who used to try to acquaint me with the real facts of living. It was too late, though. I would hastily turn on the radio or run out and take a ride in the car.

The dog has seldom been successful in pulling Man up to its level of sagacity, but Man has frequently dragged the dog down to his. He has instructed it in sloth, gluttony, pride, and envy; he has made it, in some instances, neurotic; he has even taught it to drink. There once lived in Columbus, Ohio, on Franklin Avenue, a dog named Barge. He was an average kind of dog, medium in size and weight, ordinary in markings. His master and mistress and their two children made up a respectable middle-class family. Some of the young men in the neighborhood, however, pool-shooting, motorcycle-riding bravos, lured Barge into a saloon one day and set before him a saucer of beer. He lapped it up and liked it. From there it was but an easy step to whisky.

Barge was terribly funny, the boys thought, when he got stiff. He would bump into things, hiccup, grin foolishly, and even raise his muzzle on high in what passed for *Sweet Adeline*. Barge's coat became shabby, his gait uncertain, and his eyes misty. He took to staying out on the town all night, raising hell. His duties as watchdog in the home of his owners were completely neglected. One night, when Barge was off on one of his protracted bats, burglars broke in and made off with his mistress' best silver and cut glass.

Barge, staggering home around noon of the next day, sniffed disaster when he was still a block away. His owners were waiting for him, grimly on the front porch. They had not straightened up after the burglars. The sideboard drawers were pulled out, the floor littered with napkins and napkin rings. Barge's ears, chops, and tail fell as he was led sternly into the house to behold the result of his wicked way of life. He took one long, sad look around, and the cloudiness cleared from his head. He realized that he was not only a ne'er-do-well, but a wrongo. One must guard the house at night, warn the family of fire, pull drowning infants out of the lake. These were the sacred trusts, the inviolable laws. Man had dragged Barge very far down, but there was still a spark of doghood left in him. He ran quickly and quietly upstairs, jumped out of an open window, and killed himself. This is a true and solemn legend of Franklin Avenue.

The dog has come a long way with Man, and he is destined to follow him down all the pathways of the world to the end of time. This book contains much of Man's report on the dog, his tribute to it, his effort to understand the openhearted and inscrutable, the simple and complicated, animal. It is unfortunate that there can be no companion piece, set down by the dog, to complete the picture. He has not yet learned to communicate his thoughts to paper. But give him time. The planet has, after all, barely cooled off.

JAMES THURBER

Cornwall, N. Y.

EDITOR'S PREFACE

The paw print on the binding of this book is not a forgery. It is the genuine print, procured at some trouble and expense, of the right front paw of a large English bulldog named George. It was given unwillingly. In fact, George has been unco-operative about the whole idea of this book. He has quietly resented the amount of time the editor has spent reading masses of stories about literary dogs, time which could have been gainfully employed throwing a ball for a tangible, down-to-earth one who was right in front of him.

This is not a book of practical advice, but it is only friendly to offer a word of counsel to any reader who happens to require his dog's paw print. Do not use mud. The editor tried a rich mixture of earth and water, placed George's paw in it and then upon a piece of paper. The result was an indistinguishable blob on the paper and a lot more on carpets throughout the house when George happened to free himself and scuttled for safety. The best effect is obtained by soaking a piece of blotting paper with ink and proceeding from that point.

The reason for this discursive opening is that the editor is stalling for time. It is virtually impossible to write a preface for this kind of book without using the term "dog-lover." But ever since Jim Thurber once remarked, "I am not a dog-lover. To me, a dog-lover is a dog who is in love with another dog," the editor has been unable to use that phrase or to think of an effective substitute.

This, then, is a book of stories and articles about dogs, by and for people who are attached to them by leashes and other ties. There are stories about great danes and bull terriers, pointers, poodles, mutts. It wouldn't be accurate to say that in this collection every dog has his day, but quite a few kinds do have their half-hours.

There are omissions. Some have occurred because of copyright and permission problems, others because of the good or bad judgment of the editor. His simple yardstick in selection was to ask himself the question: "If I were a dog, would I want that one in?"

My thanks are due to Mrs. Lee Moore, for her generous co-operation, to E. G. Swem, Librarian of the College of William and Mary, and to Nina Bourne. And not only thanks are due, but acknowledgment of the fact that this book would have remained an idea were it not for the unfailing assistance of Elinor Green.

J. G.

THE FIRESIDE BOOK OF

DOG STORIES

For the Love of a Man

FROM "THE CALL OF THE WILD," BY

JACK LONDON

WHEN John Thornton froze his feet in the previous December, his partners had made him comfortable and left him to get well, going on themselves up the river to get out a raft of saw-logs for Dawson. He was still limping slightly at the time he rescued Buck, but with the continued warm weather even the slight limp left him. And here, lying by the river bank through the long spring days, watching the running water, listening lazily to the songs of birds and the hum of nature, Buck slowly won back his strength.

A rest comes very good after one has travelled three thousand miles, and it must be confessed that Buck waxed lazy as his wounds healed, his muscles swelled out, and the flesh came back to cover his bones. For that matter, they were all loafing—Buck, John Thornton, and Skeet and Nig—waiting for the raft to come that was to carry them down to Dawson. Skeet was a little Irish setter who early made friends with Buck, who, in a dying condition, was unable to resent her first advances. She had the doctor trait which some dogs possess, and as a mother cat washes her kittens, so she washed and cleansed Buck's wounds. Regularly, each morning after he had finished his breakfast, she performed her self-appointed task, till he came to look for her ministrations as much as he did for Thornton's. Nig, equally friendly, though less demonstrative, was a huge black dog, half bloodhound and half deerhound, with eyes that laughed and a boundless good nature.

To Buck's surprise these dogs manifested no jealousy toward him.

3

They seemed to share the kindliness and largeness of John Thornton. As Buck grew stronger they enticed him into all sorts of ridiculous games, in which Thornton himself could not forbear to join, and in this fashion Buck romped through his convalescence and into a new existence. Love, genuine passionate love, was his for the first time. This he had never experienced at Judge Miller's down in the sun-kissed Santa Clara Valley. With the Judge's sons, hunting and tramping, it had been a working partnership; with the Judge's grandsons, a sort of pompous guardianship; and with the Judge himself, a stately and dignified friendship. But love that was feverish and burning, that was adoration, that was madness, it had taken John Thornton to arouse.

This man had saved his life, which was something; but, further, he was the ideal master. Other men saw to the welfare of their dogs from a sense of duty and business expediency; he saw to the welfare of his as if they were his own children, because he could not help it. And he saw further. He never forgot a kindly greeting or a cheering word, and to sit down for a long talk with them ("gas" he called it) was as much his delight as theirs. He had a way of taking Buck's head roughly between his hands, and resting his own head upon Buck's, of shaking him back and forth, the while calling him ill names that to Buck were love names. Buck knew no greater joy than that rough embrace and the sound of murmured oaths, and at each jerk back and forth it seemed that his heart would be shaken out of his body so great was his ecstasy. And when, released, he sprang to his feet, his mouth laughing, his eyes eloquent, his throat vibrant with unuttered sound, and in that fashion remained without movement, John Thornton would reverently exclaim, "God! you can all but speak!"

Buck had a trick of love expression that was akin to hurt. He would often seize Thornton's hand in his mouth and close so fiercely that the flesh bore the impress of his teeth for some time afterward. And as Buck understood the oaths to be love words, so the man understood this feigned bite for a caress.

For the most part, however, Buck's love was expressed in adoration. While he went wild with happiness when Thornton touched him or spoke to him, he did not seek these tokens. Unlike Skeet, who was wont to shove her nose under Thornton's hand and nudge and nudge till petted, or Nig, who would stalk up and rest his great head on Thornton's knee, Buck was content to adore at a distance. He would lie by the hour, eager, alert, at Thornton's feet, looking up into his face, dwelling upon it, studying it, following with keenest interest each fleeting expression, every movement or change of feature. Or, as chance might have it, he would lie farther away, to the side or rear, watching the outlines of the man and the occasional movements of his body. And often, such was the communion in which they lived, the strength of Buck's gaze would draw John Thornton's head around, and he would return the gaze, without speech, his heart shining out of his eyes as Buck's heart shone out.

For a long time after his rescue, Buck did not like Thornton to get out of his sight. From the moment he left the tent to when he entered it again, Buck would follow at his heels. His transient masters since he had come into the Northland had bred in him a fear that no master could be permanent. He was afraid that Thornton would pass out of his life as Perrault and François and the Scotch half-breed had passed out. Even in the night, in his dreams, he was haunted by this fear. At such times he would shake off sleep and creep through the chill to the flap of the tent, where he would stand and listen to the sound of his master's breathing.

But in spite of this great love he bore John Thornton, which seemed to bespeak the soft civilizing influence, the strain of the primitive, which the Northland had aroused in him, remained alive and active. Faithfulness and devotion, things born of fire and roof, were his; yet he retained his wildness and wiliness. He was a thing of the wild, come in from the wild to sit by John Thornton's fire, rather than a dog of the soft Southland stamped with the marks of generations of civilization. Because of his very great love, he could not steal from this man, but from any other man, in any other camp, he did not hesitate an instant; while the cunning with which he stole enabled him to escape detection.

His face and body were scored by the teeth of many dogs, and he fought as fiercely as ever and more shrewdly. Skeet and Nig were too good-natured for quarrelling—besides, they belonged to John Thornton; but the strange dog, no matter what the breed or valor, swiftly acknowledged Buck's supremacy or found himself struggling for life with a terrible antagonist. And Buck was merciless. He had learned well the law of club and fang, and he never forewent an advantage or drew back from a foe he had started on the way to Death. He had lessoned from Spitz, and from the chief fighting dogs of the police and mail, and knew there was no middle course. He must master or be mastered; while to show mercy was a weakness. Mercy did not exist in the primordial life. It was misunderstood for fear, and such misunderstandings made for death. Kill or be killed, eat or be eaten, was the law; and this mandate, down out of the depths of Time, he obeyed.

He was older than the days he had seen and the breaths he had drawn. He linked the past with the present, and the eternity behind him throbbed through him in a mighty rhythm to which he swayed as the tides and seasons swayed. He sat by John Thornton's fire, a broad-breasted dog, white-fanged and long-furred; but behind him were the shades of all manner of dogs, half-wolves and wild wolves, urgent and prompting, tasting the savor of the meat he ate, thirsting for the water he drank, scenting the wind with him, listening with him and telling him the sounds made by the wild life in the forest, dictating his moods, directing his actions, lying down to sleep with him when he lay down, and dreaming with him and beyond him and becoming themselves the stuff of his dreams.

So peremptorily did these shades beckon him that each day mankind and the claims of mankind slipped farther from him. Deep in the forest a call was sounding, and as often as he heard this call, mysteriously thrilling and luring, he felt compelled to turn his back upon the fire and the beaten earth around it, and to plunge into the forest, and on and on, he knew not where or why; nor did he wonder where or why, the call sounding imperiously, deep in the forest. But as often as he gained the soft unbroken earth and the green shade, the love for John Thornton drew him back to the fire again.

Thornton alone held him. The rest of mankind was as nothing. Chance travellers might praise or pet him; but he was cold under it all, and from a too demonstrative man he would get up and walk away. When Thornton's partners, Hans and Pete, arrived on the long-expected raft, Buck refused to notice them till he learned they were close to Thornton; after that he tolerated them in a passive sort of way, accepting favors from them as though he favored them by accepting. They were of the same large type as Thornton, living close to the earth, thinking simply and seeing clearly; and ere they swung the raft into the big eddy by the saw-mill at Dawson, they understood Buck and his ways, and did not insist upon an intimacy such as obtained with Skeet and Nig.

For Thornton, however, his love seemed to grow and grow. He, alone among men, could put a pack upon Buck's back in the summer travelling. Nothing was too great for Buck to do, when Thornton commanded. One day (they had grub-staked themselves from the proceeds of the raft and left Dawson for the head-waters of the Tanana) the men and dogs were sitting on the crest of a cliff which fell away, straight down, to naked bed-rock three hundred feet below. John Thornton was sitting near the edge, Buck at his shoulder. A thoughtless whim seized Thornton, and he drew the attention of Hans and Pete to the experiment he had in mind. "Jump, Buck!" he commanded, sweeping his arm out and over the chasm. The next instant he was grappling with Buck on the extreme edge, while Hans and Pete were dragging them back into safety.

"It's uncanny," Pete said, after it was over and they had caught their speech.

Thornton shook his head. "No, it is splendid, and it is terrible, too. Do you know, it sometimes makes me afraid."

"I'm not hankering to be the man that lays hands on you while he's around," Pete announced conclusively, nodding his head toward Buck.

"Py jingo!" was Hans' contribution. "Not mineself either."

It was at Circle City, ere the year was out, that Pete's apprehensions were realized. "Black" Burton, a man evil-tempered and malicious, had been picking a quarrel with a tenderfoot at the bar, when Thornton stepped good-naturedly between. Buck, as was his custom, was lying in a corner, head on paws, watching his master's every action. Burton struck out, without warning, straight from the shoulder. Thornton was sent spinning, and saved himself from falling only by clutching the rail of the bar.

Those who were looking on heard what was neither bark nor yelp, but a something which is best described as a roar, and they saw Buck's body rise up in the air as he left the floor for Burton's throat. The man saved his life by instinctively throwing out his arm, but was hurled backward to the floor with Buck on top of him. Buck loosed his teeth from the flesh of the arm and drove in again for the throat. This time the man succeeded only in partly blocking, and his throat was torn open. Then the crowd was upon Buck, and he was driven off; but while a surgeon checked the bleeding, he prowled up and down, growling furiously, attempting to rush in, and being forced back by an array of hostile clubs. A "miners' meeting," called on the spot, decided that the dog had sufficient provocation, and Buck was discharged. But his reputation was made, and from that day his name spread through every camp in Alaska.

Later on, in the fall of the year, he saved John Thornton's life in quite another fashion. The three partners were lining a long and narrow poling-boat down a bad stretch of rapids on the Forty-Mile Creek. Hans and Pete moved along the bank, snubbing with a thin Manila rope from tree to tree, while Thornton remained in the boat, helping its descent by means of a pole, and shouting directions to the shore. Buck, on the bank, worried and anxious, kept abreast of the boat, his eyes never off his master.

At a particularly bad spot, where a ledge of barely submerged rocks jutted out into the river, Hans cast off the rope, and, while Thornton poled the boat out into the stream, ran down the bank with the end in his hand to snub the boat when it had cleared the ledge. This it did, and was flying down-stream in a current as swift as a mill-race, when Hans checked it with the rope and checked too suddenly. The boat flirted over and snubbed in to the bank bottom up, while Thornton, flung sheer out of it, was carried down-stream toward the worst part of the rapids, a stretch of wild water in which no swimmer could live.

Buck had sprung in on the instant, and at the end of three hundred yards, amid a mad swirl of water, he overhauled Thornton. When he felt him grasp his tail, Buck headed for the bank, swimming with all his splendid strength. But the progress shoreward was slow; the progress down-stream amazingly rapid. From below came the fatal roaring where the wild current went wilder and was rent in shreds and spray by the rocks which thrust through like the teeth of an enormous comb. The suck of the water as it took the beginning of the last steep pitch was frightful, and Thornton knew that the shore was impossible. He scraped furiously over a rock, bruised across a second, and struck a third with crushing force. He clutched its slippery top with both hands, releasing Buck, and above the roar of the churning water shouted: "Go, Buck! Go!"

Buck could not hold his own, and swept on down-stream, struggling desperately, but unable to win back. When he heard Thornton's command repeated, he partly reared out of the water, throwing his head high, as though for a last look, then turned obediently toward the bank. He swam powerfully and was dragged ashore by Pete and Hans at the very point where swimming ceased to be possible and destruction began.

They knew that the time a man could cling to a slippery rock in the face of that driving current was a matter of minutes, and they ran as fast as they could up the bank to a point far above where Thornton was hanging on. They attached the line with which they had been snubbing the boat to Buck's neck and shoulders, being careful that it should neither strangle him nor impede his swimming, and launched him into the stream. He struck out boldly, but not straight enough into the stream. He discovered the mistake too late, when Thornton was abreast of him and a bare half-dozen strokes away while he was being carried helplessly past.

Hans promptly snubbed with the rope, as though Buck were a boat. The rope thus tightening on him in the sweep of the current, he was jerked under the surface, and under the surface he remained till his body struck against the bank and he was hauled out. He was half drowned, and Hans and Pete threw themselves upon him, pounding the breath into him and the water out of him. He staggered to his feet and fell down. The faint sound of Thornton's voice came to them, and though they could not make out the words of it, they knew that he was in his extremity. His master's voice acted on Buck like an electric shock. He sprang to his feet and ran up the bank ahead of the men to the point of his previous departure.

Again the rope was attached and he was launched, and again he struck out, but this time straight into the stream. He had miscalculated once, but he would not be guilty of it a second time. Hans paid out the rope, permitting no slack, while Pete kept it clear of coils. Buck held on till he was on a line straight above Thornton; then he turned, and with the speed of an express train headed down upon him. Thornton saw him coming, and, as Buck struck him like a battering ram, with the whole force of the current behind him, he reached up and closed with both arms around the shaggy neck. Hans snubbed the rope around the tree, and Buck and Thornton were jerked under the water. Strangling, suffocating, sometimes one uppermost and sometimes the other, dragging over the jagged bottom, smashing against rocks and snags, they veered in to the bank.

Thornton came to, belly downward and being violently propelled back and forth across a drift log by Hans and Pete. His first glance was for Buck, over whose limp and apparently lifeless body Nig was setting up a howl, while Skeet was licking the wet face and closed eyes. Thornton was himself bruised and battered, and he went carefully over Buck's body, when he had been brought around, finding three broken ribs.

"That settles it," he announced. "We camp right here." And camp they did, till Buck's ribs knitted and he was able to travel.

That winter, at Dawson, Buck performed another exploit, not so heroic, perhaps, but one that put his name many notches higher on the totem-pole of Alaskan fame. This exploit was particularly gratifying to the three men; for they stood in need of the outfit which it furnished, and were enabled to make a long-desired trip into the virgin East, where miners had not yet appeared. It was brought about by a conversation in the Eldorado Saloon, in which men waxed boastful of their favorite dogs. Buck, because of his record, was the target for these men, and Thornton was driven stoutly to defend him. At the end of half an hour one man stated that his dog could start a sled with five hundred pounds and walk off with it; a second bragged six hundred for his dog; and a third seven hundred.

"Pooh! pooh!" said John Thornton. "Buck can start a thousand pounds."

"And break it out? and walk off with it for a hundred yards?" demanded Matthewson, a Bonanza King, he of the seven hundred vaunt.

"And break it out, and walk off with it for a hundred yards," John Thornton said coolly.

"Well," Matthewson said, slowly and deliberately, so that all could hear, "I've got a thousand dollars that says he can't. And there it is." So saying, he slammed a sack of gold dust of the size of a bologna sausage down upon the bar.

Nobody spoke. Thornton's bluff, if bluff it was, had been called. He could feel a flush of warm blood creeping up his face. His tongue had tricked him. He did not know whether Buck could start a thousand pounds. Half a ton! The enormousness of it appalled him. He had great faith in Buck's strength and had often thought him capable of starting such a load; but never, as now, had he faced the possibility of it, the eyes of a dozen men fixed upon him, silent and waiting. Further, he had no thousand dollars; nor had Hans or Pete.

"I've got a sled standing outside now, with twenty fifty-pound sacks of flour on it," Matthewson went on with brutal directness, "so don't let that hinder you."

Thornton did not reply. He did not know what to say. He glanced from face to face in the absent way of a man who has lost the power of thought and is seeking somewhere to find the thing that will start it going again. The face of Jim O'Brien, a Mastodon King and old-time comrade, caught his eyes. It was as a cue to him, seeming to rouse him to do what he would never have dreamed of doing.

"Can you lend me a thousand?" he asked, almost in a whisper.

"Sure," answered O'Brien, thumping down a plethoric sack by the side of Matthewson's. "Though it's little faith I'm having, John, that the beast can do the trick."

The Eldorado emptied its occupants into the street to see the test. The tables were deserted, and the dealers and game-keepers came forth to see the outcome of the wager and to lay odds. Several hundred men, furred and mittened, banked around the sled within easy distance. Matthewson's sled, loaded with a thousand pounds of flour, had been standing for a couple of hours, and in the intense cold (it was sixty below zero) the runners had frozen fast to the hard-packed snow. Men offered odds of two to one that Buck could not budge the sled. A quibble arose concerning the phrase "break out." O'Brien contended it was Thornton's privilege to knock the runners loose, leaving Buck to "break it out" from a dead standstill. Matthewson insisted that the phrase included breaking the runners from the frozen grip of the snow. A majority of the men who had witnessed the making of the bet decided in his favor, whereat the odds went up to three to one against Buck.

There were no takers. Not a man believed him capable of the feat. Thornton had been hurried into the wager, heavy with doubt; and now that he looked at the sled itself, the concrete fact, with the regular team of ten dogs curled up in the snow before it, the more impossible the task appeared. Matthewson waxed jubilant.

"Three to one!" he proclaimed. "I'll lay you another thousand at that figure, Thornton. What d'ye say?"

Thornton's doubt was strong in his face, but his fighting spirit was aroused—the fighting spirit that soars above odds, fails to recognize the impossible, and is deaf to all save the clamor for battle. He called Hans and Pete to him. Their sacks were slim, and with his own the three partners could rake together only two hundred dollars. In the ebb of their fortunes, this sum was their total capital; yet they laid it unhesitatingly against Matthewson's six hundred.

The team of ten dogs was unhitched, and Buck, with his own harness, was put into the sled. He had caught the contagion of the excitement, and he felt that in some way he must do a great thing for John Thornton. Murmurs of admiration at his splendid appearance went up. He was in perfect condition, without an ounce of superfluous flesh, and the one hundred and fifty pounds that he weighed were so many pounds of grit and virility. His furry coat shone with the sheen of silk. Down the neck and across the shoulders, his mane, in repose as it was, half bristled and seemed to lift with every movement, as though excess of vigor made each particular hair alive and active. The great breast and heavy fore legs were no more than in proportion with the rest of the body, where the muscles showed in tight rolls underneath the skin. Men felt these muscles and proclaimed them hard as iron, and the odds went down to two to one.

"Gad, sir! Gad, sir!" stuttered a member of the latest dynasty, a king of the Skookum Benches. "I offer you eight hundred for him, sir, before the test, sir; eight hundred just as he stands."

Thornton shook his head and stepped to Buck's side.

"You must stand off from him," Matthewson protested. "Free play and plenty of room."

The crowd fell silent; only could be heard the voices of the gamblers vainly offering two to one. Everybody acknowledged Buck a magnificent animal, but twenty fifty-pound sacks of flour bulked too large in their eyes for them to loosen their pouch-strings.

Thornton knelt down by Buck's side. He took his head in his two hands and rested cheek on cheek. He did not playfully shake him, as was his wont, or murmur soft love curses; but he whispered in his ear. "As you love me, Buck. As you love me," was what he whispered. Buck whined with suppressed eagerness.

The crowd was watching curiously. The affair was growing mysterious. It seemed like a conjuration. As Thornton got to his feet, Buck seized his mittened hand between his jaws, pressing in with his teeth and releasing slowly, half-reluctantly. It was the answer, in terms, not of speech, but of love. Thornton stepped well back.

"Now, Buck," he said.

Buck tightened the traces, then slacked them for a matter of several inches. It was the way he had learned.

"Gee!" Thornton's voice rang out, sharp in the tense silence.

Buck swung to the right, ending the movement in a plunge that took up the slack and with a sudden jerk arrested his one hundred and fifty pounds. The load quivered, and from under the runners arose a crisp crackling.

"Haw!" Thornton commanded.

Buck duplicated the manœuvre, this time to the left. The crackling turned into a snapping, the sled pivoting and the runners slipping and grating several inches to the side. The sled was broken out. Men were holding their breaths, intensely unconscious of the fact.

"Now, MUSH!"

Thornton's command cracked out like a pistol-shot. Buck threw himself forward, tightening the traces with a jarring lunge. His whole body was gathered compactly together in the tremendous effort, the muscles writhing and knotting like live things under the silky fur. His great chest was low to the ground, his head forward and down, while his feet were flying like mad, the claws scarring the hard-packed snow in parallel grooves. The sled swayed and trembled, half-started forward. One of his feet slipped, and one man groaned aloud. Then the sled lurched ahead in what appeared a rapid succession of jerks, though it never really came to a dead stop again . . . half an inch . . . an inch . . . two inches. . . . The jerks perceptibly diminished; as the sled gained momentum, he caught them up, till it was moving steadily along.

Men gasped and began to breathe again, unaware that for a moment they had ceased to breathe. Thornton was running behind, encouraging Buck with short, cheery words. The distance had been measured off, and as he neared the pile of firewood which marked the end of the hundred yards, a cheer began to grow and grow, which burst into a roar as he passed the firewood and halted at command. Every man was tearing himself loose, even Matthewson. Hats and mittens were flying in the air. Men were shaking hands, it did not matter with whom, and bubbling over in a general incoherent babel.

But Thornton fell on his knees beside Buck. Head was against head, and he was shaking him back and forth. Those who hurried up heard him cursing Buck, and he cursed him long and fervently, and softly and lovingly.

"Gad, sir! Gad, sir!" spluttered the Skookum Bench king. "I'll give you a thousand for him, sir, a thousand, sir—twelve hundred, sir."

Thornton rose to his feet. His eyes were wet. The tears were streaming frankly down his cheeks. "Sir," he said to the Skookum Bench king, "no, sir. You can go to hell, sir. It's the best I can do for you, sir."

Buck seized Thornton's hand in his teeth. Thornton shook him back and forth. As though animated by a common impulse, the onlookers drew back to a respectful distance; nor were they again indiscreet enough to interrupt.

Blue Milk

BY

BOOTH TARKINGTON

M R. AND MRS. STONE, little Orvie's parents, should not be blamed for a special prejudice they had. After all, they were only a young couple, took pride in the neatness of their house, didn't wish to incur bills for reupholstering furniture, and both were fond of Kitty, Mrs. Stone's cat. They loved their child more than they did Kitty or their furniture, no question; nevertheless, their steadfast refusal to add a pup to the family is comprehensible.

Orvie had more than a longing for a pup, he had a determination to possess one, gave his father and mother little rest from the topic and did all he could to impose his will upon theirs. Their great question had thus become whether it would be worse to have a pup or to have Orvie go on everlastingly asking for one. Then suddenly, without warning, he stopped.

Overnight he ceased to entreat, eschewed the subject completely, and yet was cheerful. This change in him was welcomed by his father; but his mother, who, of course, saw more of Orvie, could not feel it to be natural. She perceived a strangeness in the matter, something morbid, especially as the alteration was accompanied by peculiar manifestations. Disturbed, she spoke to her husband apprehensively.

"Nonsense!" he said. "Let's be grateful for a little peace and thank heaven he's got pups out of his head at last—at least for a little while! Home seems like a different place to me; I'd almost forgotten it could be restful. Two whole days—and he hasn't once asked for a pup!

15

I suppose it's too soon to hope; but maybe—maybe—maybe—oh, maybe he's forgotten pups altogether!"

"No." She shook her head. "You haven't watched him. Really it's very queer. Haven't you even noticed these peculiar noises he's making?"

"What peculiar noises?" Mr. Stone, preparing to leave the breakfast table, moved back his chair, but remained seated. "When does he make 'em?"

"Why, almost any time. He was making some just a few minutes ago before he finished his breakfast, and he made some more in the hall after he left the table. Didn't you notice?"

"Notice? I thought he was trying to hum some terrible kind of whining tune and not succeeding. Usually when children try to sing, they do make peculiar——"

"No," Mrs. Stone interrupted seriously. "He wasn't singing; he was making noises like a pup's whining and barking—at least he was trying to. He does it all the time. I haven't told you what happened last night when I put him to bed, because you didn't get home till so late, how could I? I don't even know what time you finally did get home, and really I think when you feel you have to go to these stag card parties all the time——"

"The first!" her husband said sternly. "The first since 'way last Easter—the only one in five months! Listen. You were talking about what happened when you put Orvie to bed last night. Can't you stick to the subject? Did he ask for a pup again?"

"No. He did the strangest thing I ever knew him to do. Right in the middle of his prayers, kneeling by the bed, he began to bark."

"What?"

"He did," Mrs. Stone insisted. "He'd just said, 'Bless Mamma and Papa' and then he made a noise like this: 'Muff! Muff! Muff!'" Untalented in mimicry, she gave a squeaky imitation of the sounds her son had made. "Yes, he seemed to be barking, or trying to, the way a very young pup does. Then he got into bed and did it some more."

Mr. Stone laughed. "I don't see anything very——"

"Don't you? Wait. I haven't told you the rest of it. After I'd put out the light and gone to my own room, I heard him doing it again; and then a little while later he began whining like a pup. He kept it up so long that I went back to his room and asked him what was the matter. He just said, 'Nothing, Mamma' and then made the whining sound again. I told him to stop doing that and go to sleep, and the minute I was out of the room he began again; and not until I opened the door and said 'Orvie!' did he stop. What's more, I'd heard him making sounds like that every now and then all yesterday. What do you think of it?"

"Nothing. Children often imitate animals; it's kind of an instinct. You hear 'em miaowing or barking or——"

"No," Mrs. Stone said. "Not the way Orvie's doing it. There are times when he sounds almost exactly like a real pup. He——" She paused, lifted a warning hand, and nodded her head toward the open window. "Listen!"

Her husband listened, and then, rising, went to the window and looked out. Upon the cement path just below, his son was passing round the house on his way to the back yard and apparently amusing himself as he went by barking and whining realistically in a small but accurately puplike voice. At the same time he seemed to be scratching himself intimately upon the body; for his right hand and forearm were thrust within the breast of his polka-dotted shirt waist, so that bulk and motion were visible in that locality. Disregarding this scratching, which, though it seemed vigorous, appeared to have no significance, Mr. Stone laughed again.

"Nonsense!" he said. "Orvie's just playing at something or other in his own imagination. Likely enough he's seen or heard some ventriloquist at a movie theater and maybe he's trying to learn to be one himself. Children imitate frogs and cows and dogs and cats and ventriloquists and——"

"No." Mrs. Stone remained serious. "There's something different about this and I'm afraid it might be getting deep-seated—something very peculiar."

Evidently she had a theory, or the beginnings of one; but her husband did not press her to explain it, and, more amused than disquieted, went out to the small garage in the rear of the yard, got into his car and set forth for his morning's work in good spirits. Little Orvie immediately came from the vicinity of the alley gate, where he had been lurking, entered the garage, closed the sliding door,

18

BLUE MILK

smiled happily and began to stroke the front of his polka-dotted waist, which still bulked and moved, though he had withdrawn his hand and forearm from within it.

"Good ole Ralph," he said affectionately. "Good ole Ralphie!"

One button of the polka-dotted waist was already unbuttoned, so to speak; Orvie unbuttoned two more and there promptly emerged upon his front the small black bright-eyed head and immature whiskers of a somewhat Scottish-seeming very young pup.

"Good ole Ralphie!" Orvie said, and fondly placed the pup upon the floor.

Then he went to the garage window and looked forth toward the house. Corbena, the colored cook, had just put a pan upon the top step of the rear veranda, Kitty's morning milk, though Kitty himself had not yet arrived from a night's excursion out amongst 'em, a too-frequent habit of his. Corbena retired within the kitchen, leaving the milk exposed, and little Orvie, opening a closet in the garage, brought therefrom two empty tomato cans.

One of these he half filled with fair water at a spigot, and the other he left empty; then he tenderly placed Ralph in a smallish wooden box inside the closet. This box was comfortable for the occupant, having been made soft and warm with rags and straw, and, though Orvie closed down its hinged lid securely, there were holes bored through the wood, here and there, so that the interior air remained, if not precisely fresh, at least breathable. For greater security, Orvie closed the closet door upon that precious box; then, with his two cans, he went forth, and, keeping an eye upon the screen door of the kitchen, made a chemical alteration of Kitty's morning milk.

When he returned to the garage, the tomato can that had held water was empty; but the other contained milk, and Ralph, released from box and closet, enjoyed it. Afterwards he was replaced in the open box, and little Orvie sat beside it upon the floor of the closet and stroked Ralph from nose to tail repeatedly, shook hands with Ralph gently, opened Ralph's mouth, looked long within, and then delicately examined the interiors of both Ralph's ears.

During this orgy of ineffable possession, little Orvie should have been painted by Sir Joshua Reynolds or even by Sir Thomas Lawrence, who carried further than did Sir Joshua the tradition that

children at times glow with an unearthly sweetness surpassing the
loveliness of flowers. Little Orvie, intrinsically, was anything but a
beautiful child; but if Sir Joshua or Sir Thomas had painted him as
he was at this moment, modernists would have execrated the portrait
for its prettiness.

The intricate insides of Ralph's ears added an element to little
Orvie's expression, the element of pride; and he shone with that radi-
ance of young motherhood in discovery that the first-born is not only
alive but consists of incredible structural miracles. Into little Orvie
there entered the conviction that Ralph, gloriously his own, was incomparably the most magnificently constructed as well as the strong-
est, handsomest, best-blooded and most unconquerable dog in the
whole world.

Such convictions take little account of facts; Orvie was of course
not affected by the circumstance that Ralph was a dubious stray, an
outcast wandering loosely upon the very streets a few days earlier. In
regard to another fact or circumstance, moreover, little Orvie's conviction was likewise obtuse. Ralph, in reality, was a girl; but Orvie
had no more doubt that Ralph was a boy than he had that he himself was a boy. His mind couldn't have entertained for one moment
a question upon the matter, and, to avoid unnecessary confusion, it
seems best for the rest of us to adopt Orvie's view, to regard Ralph
in that light and think of her as "he"—at least whenever that is not
impossible.

Suddenly the beauteousness of Orvie's expression vanished; he became alert, and his hand, pausing, permitted Ralph's left ear to
become less inside out and return to its customary posture. Two
voices were heard from without, a little distant; one was Kitty's and
the other Corbena's. Kitty miaowed clearly and persistently, and
Corbena responded with sympathetic inquiries, such as are addressed
to one in trouble. Orvie closed the lid upon little Ralph, stepped out
of the closet, closed it, too, went to the door of the garage, opened it
slightly and looked toward the house. His mother had just joined
Corbena and Kitty upon the back veranda.

"Yes'm," Corbena was saying. "Kitty ack thataway right along
lately, mew and miaow breakfast and supper, too, and don' look right
to me—Kitty kind o' gaunt-lookin'. Then look at that milk, gone and

done the same thing again. Look to me like the minute I pour it in the pan it up and turn bluish on me, so Kitty won't take more'n just a li'l some of it and commence miaowin' and mewin'. I thought maybe somep'n in the pan do it, so I changed pans; but no, ma'am, there that milk bluish again as ever!"

"Poor Kitty!" Mrs. Stone said. "She does seem to look rather thin. Corbena, are you sure the milk you put in the pan was——" She paused, and, instead of continuing her thought about the milk, stared in troubled fascination at her son, who was approaching from the garage.

Little Orvie, walking slowly, had the air of an absent-minded stroller concerned with the far-away. He did not look toward his mother, or Corbena or Kitty, seemed unaware of them and in a muse. At the same time, however, he allowed his lips to move slightly in the production of a dreamy sort of barking and whining: "Muff! Muff! Muff! Um-oo-ee! Um-oo-ee! Um-oo-ee!"

Kitty continued to miaow. Mrs. Stone and Corbena, saying nothing, stared at little Orvie.

"Muff! Muff! Muff!" he said dreamily. "Um-oo-ee! Um-oo-ee! Um-oo-ee!"

Then, continuing his apparently absent-minded barking and whining, and paying no attention to the three upon the veranda, he passed round the corner of the house and from their sight. "Dear me!" Mrs. Stone murmured. "What in the world's the matter with him?"

"Yes'm," Corbena agreed. "That child is somep'n more whut turn queer lately. The way he all time bark and whine like li'l pup look to me, Miz Stone, like maybe you better git doctor come and 'tend to him. Child can git out of his right mind same as grown people can."

"Nonsense!" Mrs. Stone said. "Don't be silly, Corbena. It's just one of those habits children get sometimes."

She spoke with some sharpness; nevertheless, her uneasiness about Orvie was increased by this additional barking and whining; for thus not infrequently do the most promising cerebrations of childhood fail to obtain recognition from adults. Little Orvie, if she had but known the truth, was for the first time in his life really using his mind.

Not forward in school, not quotable for bright saying, Orvie in his own field was accomplishing more than either of his parents would have dared to attempt in theirs. They were both more than four times his age; yet he had completely hoodwinked them, had introduced the forbidden stranger into their very house, not a large one, and, undetected, had repeatedly provided Ralph with food from their very table and from their Kitty's very pan. More, he had made Ralph his bedfellow, and the technic he here employed, though it necessarily involved risk, could not have been improved upon.

In the evenings while Orvie was at dinner, Ralph occupied a drawer in Orvie's bureau upstairs. Later, when Mrs. Stone had heard Orvie's prayers and seen him in bed, Orvie rose, took Ralph from the drawer, gave him more of Kitty's milk and then slept with him.

In the morning Orvie returned Ralph to the drawer, descended to breakfast, came up afterward and again removed Ralph from the drawer. Ralph then was borne outdoors in the concealment of little Orvie's shirt waist and thus carried to the box in the garage, whence, during the day, all manner of excursions became feasible. Thus the periods of greater danger—when Ralph occupied the bureau drawer —were reduced to a minimum; the only really crucial moments were those during which Mrs. Stone was putting Orvie to bed, and Orvie and Ralph had twice survived them encouragingly.

Here then was ingenuity, true thinking; Mr. and Mrs. Stone could not possibly have concealed a dog from him as he did from them. But, as if this were not enough, little Orvie's mind soared higher still. There were matters in which Ralph could not be made to understand the requisites for his own safety. As valet, so to say, Orvie did the best he could; but, in the detail of barking and whining, proved himself open to those inspirations sometimes called streaks of genius.

By barking and whining frequently himself, he accustomed his parents and Corbena to hear such sounds in and about the house, and thus planned to provide Ralph—if Ralph's own voice should sometimes be heard—with an alibi.

Such was little Orvie's single-hearted purpose, and such had been his skill in carrying it out that Ralph was now well into his third day of residence with Mr. and Mrs. Stone without their even dreaming they were that hospitable. Mentally, little Orvie was growing.

Intellectual progress, however, was anything but his mother's interpretation of what was the matter with him, and Mr. Stone also began to take a gloomy view of him at lunch that day. He sent an annoyed side glance in his son's direction. "Orvie, don't sing at the table."

"No, Papa," Orvie said, and barked reticently, as if to himself, "Muff!"

"Don't imitate animals either."

"Animals?" Orvie asked. "No, Papa. Muff! Um-oo-ee!"

"Orvard, did you hear me?"

"Yes, Papa." Orvie was silent; but, after a moment or two, ventured to bark again softly.

"Orvard!" Mr. Stone, staring imperiously at his son, became aware of the odd appearance of Orvie's plate. "Well, I declare!"

Mrs. Stone, preoccupied, looked up. "What's the matter?"

"His plate," her husband said. "Look at it! I just gave him a chop and French-fried potatoes and now there's nothing there. Not a thing! Why, he must eat like an anaconda!"

"Oh, no," Mrs. Stone protested gently; but she added, "You must learn not to gulp down your food, Orvie; it'll give you indigestion."

"Indigestion!" Orvie's father exclaimed, and he stared harder at the empty plate. "Why, even the bone's gone! Where is it? Orvie, did you drop that chop bone on the floor? Where is it?"

"Where's what, Papa?"

"That chop!" Mr. Stone got up and looked at the rug upon which the table stood. "No, there's nothing there. Where'd it go?"

"Where'd what go, Papa?"

"That chop!" Mr. Stone sat down at his place again. "That chop, or at least the bone! You could eat the chop; but you certainly couldn't eat the bone. Nobody could. What became of it? Did you see it fall?"

"Fall?" Orvie asked. "Fall, Papa?"

"Yes, fall! Fall, fall, fall! If it didn't fall off your plate, where did it go?"

"You mean my chop, Papa?"

"Yes, I do! What became of it?"

Orvie was thoughtful; then seemed to brighten a little. "Maybe it fell out the window, Papa."

"The window?" Mr. Stone breathed heavily. "Ten feet away and with a wire screen in it? Fell out of it?"

Orvie looked absent-minded. "Muff! Muff! Muff!" he said. "Um-oo-ee!"

"Oh, dear!" his father exclaimed, depressed. "Oh, dear me!"

"What, Papa?"

"Nothing!" Mr. Stone simply gave up thinking about the chop bone. Fathers and mothers, confronted frequently by the inexplicable, acquire this rather helpless habit of allowing mysteries to pass unsolved. Orvie applied himself to bread and milk, having just proved that for the sake of Ralph he was glad to deprive himself as well as Kitty. Unobserved legerdemain had removed the chop, with only one small bite out of it, to the interior of his shirt waist, where also were a handful of French-fried potatoes and a few of Ralph's hairs. Beneath Orvie's polka-dotted surface and about his upper middle, that is to say, little Orvie for two days had been far from neat. Bacon, toast, buttered bread, bits of steak and broiled chicken and even cereal had lain against him there during and after recent meals; he was no dietitian and fondly offered Ralph as wide a choice as he could.

"Muff!" he said, finishing his milk. "Um-oo-ee! I'm all through. Can I go out in the yard now, Mamma?"

She nodded gravely, not speaking; whereupon, uttering a few petty barks as he went, he ran outdoors. Mr. Stone, who had arrived after his wife and son had sat down to lunch, glanced across the table inquiringly. "Well, what's on your mind?" he asked, alluding to the preoccupation that had made her unusually silent.

"I'm really getting worried," she informed him. "Really, I mean. Something else happened this morning."

"Something else? Something else than what?"

"Than his barking," she said. "Listen, please. This summer I've been trying to have Orvie begin to cultivate self-reliance, so I've been having him look after his clothes, to a certain extent, himself. That is, he's supposed to hang them up when he takes them off, put what's soiled in the clothes basket and when he puts on fresh ones, get them out of his bureau drawer himself. This morning about eleven the laundry came and Corbena took Orvie's to his room to put in his bureau. I wish you'd seen what she found in the middle drawer! One of his best little white cambric waists with ruffled collars absolutely mangled—almost torn to pieces. She knew when she put it there last week it was in perfect condition. What's your explanation? What do you think made him do such a thing?"

"Who?" Mr. Stone asked. "Orvie? You don't mean he did it himself?"

She nodded solemnly. "He admitted it."

"What?"

"He did," Mrs. Stone said. "I called him in and he came in barking. I showed him the waist and asked him what had happened to it. First he said he thought Kitty must have done it; but when I showed him how absurd that was, he admitted he did it himself. I asked him how, and he said he 'guessed he must have gnawed it'! Those were his very words! What do you say to that?"

"I don't know, I'm sure. It seems odd, but——"

"Odd!" she exclaimed. "Don't you think maybe it's a case for one of these psychopathic doctors or whatever they call them? Corbena thinks it is. Corbena said herself we ought to get——"

"Never mind," Mr. Stone said. "I don't care what Corbena thinks we ought to do. Why did Orvie gnaw it? How did he explain doing such a thing?"

"He didn't explain it. When I asked him why he did it, he'd just say, 'What, Mamma?' and then make those noises, and that's what upset me the worst. Do you suppose it could be possible that a child could want something so long and talk about it so much and brood upon it so intensely that in time he'd—well, that in time he'd almost begin to have the delusion that he'd turned into the thing he'd wanted so much?"

"What?" Mr. Stone stared at his wife incredulously, and then, in despair over the elasticities of her imagination, laughed aloud. "Your theory is that Orvie's wanted a dog so long that now he's begun to believe he's a dog himself? So you want a psychoanalyst to prove to him that he's really a boy? Is that your idea?"

"No," she said, annoyed; but nevertheless added, "Still, it's certainly very strange. It's easy for you to make fun of me; but will you kindly tell me why he does all this barking and whining and why he gnawed his little cambric waist like that?"

"Good heavens! There's nothing very strange about a boy's playing to himself that he's a pup. You've heard him playing he's a whole railroad engine, haven't you?" This was spoken confidently; nevertheless, a meeting he had with his son, a few minutes later in the front yard, brought curious doubts into Mr. Stone's mind. As was his custom at noon, he had left his car before the house at the curbstone, and he was on his way to it when Orvie came from the back yard, barking indistinctly.

"Orvie! Where are you going?"

Until thus questioned, Orvie had not observed his father; he betrayed hesitation and embarrassment. Walking slowly, he again had his right hand inside his shirt waist and seemed to be scratching himself strongly. "What, Papa?" He paused at a distance from his father and turned partly away.

"Where are you going?"

"Only across the street to Freddie and Babe's house, Papa," Orvie said, and added quickly and with some emphasis, "Muff! Muff! Um-oo-ee! Um-oo-ee! Muff! Muff!"

"Come here," Mr. Stone said. "What do you want to bark all the time for like that? Come here!"

Orvie moved a few sidelong steps and paused, still keeping his shoulder and back toward his father as much as seemed plausible. The situation, indeed, appeared critical; for Ralph, whom he was carrying inside his shirt waist to show confidentially to the little cousins, Babe and Freddie, had all at once begun to feel lively. Ralph, in fact, was not only squirming in an almost unbearably tickling manner but was also chewing at his young master's fragile undergarment, rending it and at the same time abrading actual surfaces of the young master. To have so much going on sub rosa yet directly under Mr. Stone's eye, and simultaneously to maintain an air of aplomb, was difficult.

For more than two days Ralph had been accustomed to seclusions and inclosures; his adaptation of himself to these environments had hitherto been such a marvel of meekness, or inanity, that Orvie had been encouraged to believe the routine might be carried on permanently, or at least during his own lifetime. Now, however, Ralph, it seemed, desired to frolic, and did frolic—wished, too, a broader field and to gambol in the open air, though apparently he thought that his route thither lay not through the shirt waist but through Orvie. No doubt the legend of the Spartan boy who permitted the fox to gnaw his vitals arose from some such affair and was later poetically garbled; probably the Spartan boy's parents wouldn't let him have a fox.

"Stop scratching yourself!" Mr. Stone said. "Have you got chiggers? What's the matter with you?"

"Nothing, Papa. I——" Orvie interrupted himself, for to his horror Ralph, though briefly, became vocal in a slight bark, which had to be covered. Orvie turned his back upon his father and began to walk toward the street, barking loudly.

"Stop that!" Mr. Stone said. "Stop that silly barking, stand still and listen to me!"

"Yes, Papa." Orvie halted tentatively and looked back over his shoulder. "What you want, Papa? Muff! Muff! Um-oo-ee! Um-oo-ee! I got to go over to Babe and Freddie's now, Papa. Muff!"

"Listen to me!" Mr. Stone said, advancing. "Stop all this barking. At your age if you get a habit like that——"

"Yes, Papa. I—Muff!" Orvie said hurriedly, and moved on toward the sidewalk. "Muff! Muff! Ouch! I got to go now, Papa. Honest, I —Um-oo-ee! Papa, I——Muff! Muff!"

Mr. Stone let him go, and, frowning, watched him as he ran barking across the street and into the yard opposite. It could not be denied that little Orvie's behavior was peculiar, at least tinged with something suggestive of a kind of lunacy; and his father, stepping into the waiting automobile, nervously recalled the mystery of the chop bone at lunch. Could it be that Orvie had hidden that bone about his person, intending to bury it later and then dig it up, perhaps? A canine impersonation that would go to such lengths did seem almost unnaturally realistic, and Mr. Stone, as he drove down town, was in fact a little disturbed about his son.

That son, meanwhile, in Freddie's and Babe's yard, had stopped barking, and, after employing his voice for some time in an attempt at yodeling meant to let those within know that he waited for them

without, was joined upon the lawn by his two little cousins. He had
kept his happy secret to himself about as long as he could; his constantly swelling pride in Ralph, and in himself as owner, now resist-
lessly pressed him to excite the envy of pupless contemporaries.

"What you want, Orvie?" Babe inquired, and she added, "You
look awful dirty. Little Cousin M'ree from Kansas City and Cousin
Sadie and Cousin Josie are comin' to play with me this afternoon
pretty soon. You and Freddie better go somewheres and play by
yourselfs because the rest of us'll be all girls and clean."

"Listen," Orvie said. "Freddie, if I show you and Babe a secret
will you promise you'll never tell anybody?"

Interested, both Babe and Freddie promised.

"I mean you haf to promise you'll never tell anybody in the whole
world or you rather die," Orvie said; and, when they agreed to this,
he led them behind a clump of lilac bushes, opened his shirt waist
and displayed his treasure.

"Look there, ' he said. "Its name's Ralph."

Both Freddie and Babe were immediately ecstatic, though Babe
interrupted herself to tell Orvie he looked terrible inside the shirt
waist and ought to be ashamed to keep Ralph in such an awful place;
then shouting, she had something like a little fight with Freddie, as
both claimed the privilege simultaneously of holding Ralph against
their cheeks to feel how soft he was.

Orvie became nervous. "For good heavens goodnesses sakes hush
up!" he said, glancing toward the house. "Here! You give me back
my dog!" Decisively he took Ralph from them and restored him
into the interior of his shirt waist. "I guess I got enough trouble having Papa and Mamma not find out Ralph's my dog without your
making all this fuss!"

Babe resented the sequestration of Ralph; she wanted to play with
him, made efforts to obtain possession of him, and, when forcibly re-
pulsed, became threatening. "You just wait, Orvie Stone! Wait till
your papa and mamma find out you got a dog!"

Orvie had to remind her of the consequences of broken honor.
"You promised you'd never tell and you'll be a dirty ole story-teller
if you do and I'll tell everybody you are one too!"

"I won't tell, Orvie," Babe said coaxingly. "Orvie, please give me that dear little puppy."

"No!"

"I mean just to play with," Babe said. "Orvie, please let me play with that dear little puppy just half an hour. Please, Orvie——"

"No!"

"Of course he won't," Freddie said to Babe. "Orvie's going to let me have Ralph to play with now because I and Orvie are boys and——"

"No!" Orvie said, and buttoned up his shirt waist, inclosing Ralph from view.

At this, naturally, both Freddie and Babe were antagonized, and, as it happened that a sedan just then deposited three speckless little girls upon the sidewalk before the gate, the brother and sister ran to greet the newcomers and to speak at once unfavorably of Orvie, who remained behind the clump of lilacs.

" 'Lo, M'ree, 'lo, Josie, 'lo, Sadie," Babe said. "Dirty ole Orvie's here. He's over behind those bushes because he's got a secret."

"It's in his clo'es," Freddie explained. "It's a secret and I and Babe promised not to tell; but he's got it in his clo'es. Come on look at him and see if you can guess what it is; it's alive."

Little Marie from Kansas City, little Josie and little Sadie shouted with cruel pleasure. "Dirty ole Orvie!" they cried. "Come on! Come on! Come on!"

Thus Orvie, rushed upon, found himself driven from the shelter of the lilac bushes, and decided to leave for home. His five little cousins, however, made his departure difficult; they surrounded him, screaming merrily and spitefully, jostled him, poked him; and in this process the right forefinger of little Marie from Kansas City was electrified by the sensation of encountering a protuberance that squirmed.

She shrieked sincerely in horror. "Oh, oh, oh! He's got a rat in there! It's a rat or a cat or maybe a snake! Oh, you bad dirty little Orvie!"

"I am not!" Orvie cried. "It is not!" Infuriated, both on his own account and Ralph's, and, too, because he never did get on well with little Marie from Kansas City, he became indiscreet. "I have not got any ole rat or ole dirty cat or any snake in here! It's something I wouldn't let you touch even its tail if you cried your ole eyes out begging me!"

"Tail! Tail! Tail!" shouted little Josie and little Sadie, prodding insanely at Orvie. "It's got a tail! It's got a tail! It's got a tail!"

"Its name's Ralph!" Babe cried. "I didn't promise I wouldn't tell what its name was, Orvie. I'm not a story-teller for only tellin' what its name is."

Upon this, little Josie, little Sadie and little Marie from Kansas City were inspired to guess the rest. "It's a dog!" they cried simultaneously. "It's a dog!"

"Yes," Freddie said. "And his papa and mamma won't let him have one either. I didn't promise I wouldn't tell that, because everybody knows it anyways, Orvie."

"Story-tellers!" Orvie shouted at the top of his voice. "Babe and Freddie are dirty ole story-tellers and so's everybody else! You're all every one dirty ole story-tellers!"

"We are not! You're one yourself!" they all assured him, and then, as he bitterly hustled his way out from among them and ran to the street, they ran after him.

Little Marie made her voice piercing. "Orvie's got! Orvie's got! Orvie's got!" she cried, leaving what Orvie had to the imagination of dangerous adult listeners and terrifying him with this imminent menace to his secret. "Orvie's got! Orvie's got! Orvie's got!"

The others took it up. "Orvie's got! Orvie's got! Orvie's got!" they chanted delightedly, pursued him across the street and into his own yard. There he knew not where to turn. With the pack upon him, and the windows of the house open, so that at any moment his mother might hear, comprehend and look forth, he did not dare go to the garage to hide Ralph, nor to enter the house, nor to remain in the yard—nor to run away, when Freddie, Babe, Josie, Sadie and little Marie from Kansas City would certainly run whooping after him. All resources failed him.

"You go home!" he shouted, knowing helplessly how futile this assertion of his rights. "This is my yard and you got to everyone go home, you ole dirty story-tellers you! Go home!"

They enlarged their threat by a monosyllable. "Orvie's got a!" they chanted. "Orvie's got a! Orvie's got a! Orvie's got a!"

Corbena appeared at a kitchen window, obviously interested. Orvie, perceiving her and in terror lest the chanters should complete their chorus with the fatal word "dog," bawled incoherences at the top of his voice to drown them out. "Baw! Waw! Waw! Boo! Yoo! Yoo!"

Tauntingly little Marie chanted the first sound of the word "dog." "Orvie's got a duh!"

The rest took this up immediately. "Orvie's got a duh! Orvie's got a duh! Orvie's got a duh!"

"Baw! Waw! Waw! I have not! You're all story-tellers! Baw! Waw! Waw! Yoo! Yoo!"

They danced about him, encircling him. "Orvie's got a duh!" And then little Josie, the youngest of the group, piercingly added, "awg!" So that Orvie, though he bawled his loudest, feared Corbena might have heard the ruinous completion, "Orvie's got a duh—awg!"

Corbena had, in fact, heard just that. Her interest increased as she looked from the window and listened to the screeching. Then, returning to a polishing of the stove, she engaged herself in thought; but presently, looking forth again, saw that the five little cousins, following some new caprice, were racing back to the yard across the street.

Orvie, brooding, was walking toward the garage, and Corbena decided upon a line of conduct she would follow. No doubt she was influenced by an ill-founded partiality she had always felt for Kitty.

Kitty, as a matter of fact, was usually no bad hand at looking out for himself. True, he was subject to the seemingly haphazard misfortunes of life, as are we all, and the long arm of disastrous coincidence could at any time reach him; but he lived with a bold craftiness solely for himself and seldom failed to take care of Number 1. Orvie, entering the garage with Ralph in his bosom, or a little below, heard a sinisterly eloquent sound as he approached the door of the closet, which he had carelessly left open as he had the lid of the box also.

Ralph, rather overfed, had been indifferent to the chop and French-fried potatoes brought him from the lunch table, had allowed them to remain in the box almost untouched, and now, later, when he might have taken pleasure in them, another was doing that for him.

Kitty, though not aware to whom he owed the blueness of his daily milk, was getting even and didn't intend to be balked. Kitty, that is to say, was in Ralph's box eating Ralph's chop, and the eloquent sound Orvie heard as he came near was the police siren inside of Kitty turned on in nasty warning.

"Get out o' there!" Orvie cried indignantly, and accompanied his words with furious gestures. "Get out o' my dog's own box, you bad ole cat you!"

Kitty rose up out of the box in a tall, dangerous manner, sirening and with his teeth fixed in the chop and the bone projecting like a deformity ever to be part of him; anæsthetics and surgeons might remove this chop from him, he made clear, but nothing less should do it. Stepping testily, and with head and chop and rigid tail held high, he went forth with no undue haste, daring all hell to intercept him. He disappeared proudly into the golden light of outdoors.

"You bad ole cat you!" Intimidated, Orvie spoke feebly, though none the less bitterly; for this was the second time Kitty had been caught—so to speak—robbing Ralph's box. "You'll see, you ole cat you! I'll show you!"

Orvie didn't know how or what he was going to show Kitty, but later in the afternoon seized upon an opportunity to show him at least a little something. Having made a sketchy leash and collar out of a length of discarded clothesline, he gave Ralph some too-early lessons in "heeling" in the alley, and, returning, found Kitty again in the box. This time, however, Orvie neither bellowed nor made threatening gestures, but quietly closed the lid on Kitty. Kitty made a few objections; and then, after trifling with cold French-fried potatoes in the dark, philosophically took a nap until Orvie came back from another excursion, raised the lid and said severely, "There! That'll teach you, I guess, you ole cat you!"

Kitty yawned, left the box and walked languidly away; showed so much indifference, indeed, that Orvie was galled.

"You listen, you ole Kitty you!" he called fiercely. "Next time I catch you in my dog's box I'm goin' to slam the lid down and fasten it and keep you in there all day! You better look out!"

Kitty paid not the slightest attention and even had the hardihood to return within the hour, seat himself in Orvie's presence, look at the box and miaow inquiringly.

"You——" Orvie began; but a summons into the house prevented him from further expressing his emotion. Corbena called loudly from the kitchen door.

"Li'l Orvie! You out 'n 'at garage? You come in here. You' mamma want you ri' now."

Orvie put Ralph in the box, fastened the lid down, closed the door of the closet and noisily gave himself the pleasure of seeing Kitty precede him into the house.

"Shame!" Corbena said, holding open the screen door of the kitchen for Kitty, but closing it before Orvie arrived. "Shame on you to holler and chase Kitty thataway! No, you ain' go' come in my kitchen and holler and chase Kitty some more. You go round and go in front door and walk upstairs to you' mamma. Go on now! I got somep'n else to do 'cept argue!"

Her words held a meaning hidden from little Orvie, a meaning that would have chilled his blood had he understood it; and, while he was following the route she had insisted upon, and being kept upstairs for a sufficient time by his mother, Corbena completed a brief but thorough investigation. Mrs. Stone, who made a pretext to have little Orvie change his clothes under her own eye, also learned much; and, when Mr. Stone arrived at the house after his day's work, she met him at the front door, drew him into the living room and told him all.

"Two days!" she said, approaching the conclusion of her narrative. "Three days really by this time, and two nights! In the daytime he keeps it in that box in the garage whenever he hasn't got it out playing with it; though when he slips it into the house and up to his room he must carry it inside his waist—I wish you'd seen conditions there!—and Corbena found a rope collar and leash that he leads it by, probably in the alley. Then, when he comes in and goes upstairs to wash his hands and face before dinner, he hides it in his bureau drawer—that's what happened to his cambric ruffled waist—then, after I put him in bed, he gets up and takes it out of the drawer and sleeps with it. Oh, there's no doubt about it! Corbena and I worked it all out. What makes us sure he's had this dog for two whole days without our knowing it, Corbena remembered it was day before yesterday he brought down that box from the attic and carried it out to the garage. What on earth do you think?"

"I don't know." Mr. Stone sighed; then blew out an audible breath suggesting a faint kind of laughter. "In a way it's almost a relief—I mean, to know that he hasn't been getting woozy in the head on account of this dog mania of his. Of course that's why he's been barking—in the hope we mightn't notice if the dog himself barked. Not so dumb, you know! Really seems to show he has ideas—peculiar ones, but at least ideas. What have you done about it? What have you said to Orvie?"

"Nothing. He doesn't dream we even suspect. I waited to see what you'd say, so we could decide together."

"I see." Mr. Stone pondered. "What sort of a dog is he?"

"He?" Mrs. Stone uttered a half-hushed outcry. "It isn't! Corbena says it's very small but terribly mongrel, and the worst of it is it's a she!"

"Well, that settles it," Mr. Stone said. "Of course that settles it."

"Yes, of course; but how am I to——"

"Wait," he said. "Let me handle this. I see just what to do."

"Do you?" Mrs. Stone was doubtful. "If you simply mean to call Orvie in and take that dog away from him and tell him he can't have it, I won't answer for the shock to his nervous system. I don't think it should be managed that way."

"Neither do I!" her husband protested. "Don't you think I have any regard for the child's feelings? Don't you suppose I know it's one thing to tell him he can't have a dog and quite another thing to take a dog away from him after he's actually got one? Naturally, I intend to use some diplomacy."

"What kind of diplomacy? I don't see——"

"Listen," he interrupted. "We don't want to get Orvie all harrowed up, or to be harrowed up ourselves. We'll simply let him believe the pup's got out of the box, wandered away and got lost. If we do that, why, of course Orvie'll think maybe he'll find it again some day, so he won't feel too badly about it. For a while he'll poke around looking for it and whistling, of course; then he'll forget all about it."

"I hope so."

"Of course he will," Mr. Stone said. "We won't say a thing to Orvie, and you mustn't let Corbena speak of it to him, either. What's more, he can have the pup sleep with him tonight and we'll let him have another morning and most of the afternoon, too, for that matter, playing with it—pretty near a whole day—and then, toward evening, it'll simply be missing and he won't have so very long to worry about it before bedtime comes and he goes to sleep. Next morning when he wakes up, he'll hardly think of it at all."

"I hope so," she said again. "I do hope so!"

"Why, certainly!" Mr. Stone reassured her. "Tomorrow after lunch I'll have Elmore Jones come down to my office and I'll give him a couple of dollars to drive up here later in his car and take the pup quietly away."

"Elmore Jones? You mean that awful old colored man who used to be a sort of gardener at your father's and stole the lawn mower?"

"That was when Elmore was drinking," Mr. Stone explained, and laughed, though he was a little nettled by the criticism of his judgment she seemed to imply. "Father was rather hard on him about that and the rest of us give Elmore little jobs when we can, to help him out. He's got an old car now that he uses as a sort of a truck, and he's perfectly reliable."

"But if he comes in here and walks out to the garage and takes the pup out of that box, and Orvie sees him——"

"Oh, dear me!" Mr. Stone sighed. "Orvie won't be here to see him —not unless you let him. I'll instruct Elmore Jones to come and get the pup tomorrow afternoon at five o'clock exactly; and you can arrange for Orvie to be across the street at Babe's and Freddie's, playing with them, from half-past four to half-past five, can't you?"

"Yes," she said thoughtfully, then looked more cheerful. "Why, yes, I believe that would work out all right. I'll tell Winnie about it this evening and ask her to make sort of a little party of it. I'll get her to ask some of the other children and I'll take Orvie over there myself, between four and half past, and tell him he can stay till almost six o'clock. I'll ask Winnie to have cookies and lemonade and little games, so he'll have a nice happy time; and that way, it seems to me, with a long happy day and a little party to remember—and of course just thinking his pup's lost and may come back some time—why, probably, he won't be much upset."

"Of course he won't," her husband agreed. "Besides that, it isn't as if we were doing anything rather cruel to this pup, because Elmore Jones'll simply take it out in the country twenty-five or thirty miles and leave it near some farmhouse or other, where people usually are glad to have a dog and——"

"Yes," Mrs. Stone said, almost with enthusiasm. "People who live 'way out in the country like that are kind to dogs. They're nearly always glad to find one and give it a good home; so of course we're really not——"

"No, of course we're not. It isn't like telling Elmore Jones to take Orvie's pup out and drown it. No; we're doing the best we can under the circumstances, and I really don't think Orvie'll mind at all."

"No," Mrs. Stone agreed. "I don't think he will, either—not to speak of."

Then, though both parents were thoughtful and perhaps slightly apprehensive, not to say remorseful, they ended by stimulating themselves with something like an exchange of congratulations upon having discovered a plan that would depress their little son's spirits in the least possible degree. On the following afternoon, however, at about ten minutes before six, when Mr. Stone came into the house, he found his wife in a pathetic mood. She was looking out of one of the living-room windows and didn't turn when he approached her.

"How—how did it go?" he asked somewhat hesitantly. "How did Orvie take it?"

"I don't know." She sniffled abruptly, turned and allowed him to see that her eyes were moist and not free from reproachfulness. "Oh, your plan was carried out—carried out quite perfectly! Your old Elmore Jones was here at five. I heard him in the kitchen and Corbena telling him what to do; so it's gone. Orvie's just come back from Winnie's. He's upstairs."

"What did he say?"

"Nothing," Mrs. Stone replied huskily. "Of course he knows, because this is the time he always takes it upstairs and puts it in the bureau drawer, so of course he's been out there—to the empty box. I kept out of his way—just listened to him running upstairs—I felt I simply couldn't face him. I do wonder if you've been really right in doing this to him. I do wonder."

"I!" her husband exclaimed. "Wonder if I'm really right? Me? Didn't you tell me——" He paused. Corbena stood in the doorway.

"Dinner serve'," she said, glanced about the room questioningly and added in a solemn voice, addressing herself to Mrs. Stone, "Milk in 'at pan I set on back porch fer Kitty done gone blue on me again."

"Blue?" Mr. Stone said. "Blue milk? What do you mean, Corbena?"

Corbena's solemnity increased. "Blue," she said. "Milk blue again. Elmore Jones come five o'clock like Miz Stone tell me he goin' to; but he ain't no right bright nice-actin' colored man, Elmore Jones ain't. He come in my kitchen, say he goin' be rich man soon. I say, 'Don' blow all 'at gin in my face, Elmore Jones! Go on open the closet in the garage, git that pup out that box in the closet and go on away from here.' He say, yes'm that box whut he come fer, not me, and shambled on out. I tooken a look in my oven, then I heard him shut the garage door and I went and looked out and he was goin' out the alley gate wif 'at box under his arm. 'I got him!' Elmore Jones holler at me. 'He in here all right,' Elmore Jones holler. Then I heard Elmore Jones's ole clatterbox automobile buzz-chuggin' away. How fur you tell Elmore to go, Mr. Stone?"

"Why, I told him to go twenty-five or thirty——"

Corbena, though interrupting, seemed merely to meditate aloud. "Li'l Orvie come back from his aunt's house 'cross the street li'l while after you tooken him over there this afternoon, Miz Stone. Then he gone back again. I see him pass my kitchen window; and, come to 'member, I didn' tooken no notice then, but seem to me now like he was actin' like he scratchin' hisself under his li'l shirt." Corbena paused and again looked about the room questioningly. "Kitty nowhere in here, Miz Stone?"

"Kitty? No."

"No, Kitty certainly ain't here," Corbena said. "Elmore Jones tell me Mr. Stone done hand him fi'-dolluh bill; tell me he ain't spen' more'n half of it. Miz Stone, you see poor Kitty anywheres at all since about four o'clock?"

"No!" Mrs. Stone gasped. "Oh, my goodness!"

Mr. Stone, staring haggardly, strode out into the hall and halfway up the stairs, but there he paused.

His ascending footsteps must have been heard overhead, for, as he halted, little Orvie's voice promptly became audible.

"Muff! Muff! Muff!" The barking grew louder as Orvie approached the head of the stairway to descend for dinner. "Muff! Um-oo-ee! Um-oo-ee! Um-oo-ee!"

Artistically, the imitated whining was of course plaintive; yet the voice that produced it had never sounded more contented. "Muff! Muff!" said little Orvie: "Um-oo-ee!"

Mr. Stone returned down the stairs he had just impetuously ascended and made a pitiable effort to seem unconscious of how his wife and Corbena were looking at him.

Memories

BY

JOHN GALSWORTHY

WE SET out to meet him at Waterloo Station on a dull day of February—I, who had owned his impetuous mother, knowing a
little what to expect, while to my companion he would be all original.
We stood there waiting (for the Salisbury train was late), and wondering with a warm, half-fearful eagerness what sort of new thread
Life was going to twine into our skein. I think our chief dread was
that he might have light eyes—those yellow Chinese eyes of the
common, parti-colored spaniel. And each new minute of the train's
tardiness increased our anxious compassion: His first journey; his
first separation from his mother; this black two-months' baby! Then
the train ran in, and we hastened to look for him. "Have you a dog
for us?"

"A dog! Not in this van. Ask the rear-guard."

"Have you a dog for us?"

"That's right. From Salisbury. Here's your wild beast, sir!"

From behind a wooden crate we saw a long black muzzled nose
poking round at us, and heard a faint hoarse whimpering.

I remember my first thought:

"Isn't his nose too long?"

But to my companion's heart it went at once, because it was swollen from crying and being pressed against things that he could not
see through. We took him out, soft, wobbly, tearful; set him down on
his four as yet not quite simultaneous legs, and regarded him. Or,
rather, my companion did, having her head on one side, and a quaver-

ing smile; and I regarded her, knowing that I should thereby get a truer impression of him.

He wandered a little round our legs, neither wagging his tail nor licking at our hands; then he looked up, and my companion said: "He's an angel!"

I was not so certain. He seemed hammer-headed, with no eyes at all, and little connection between his head, his body, and his legs. His ears were very long, as long as his poor nose; and gleaming down in the blackness of him I could see the same white star that disgraced his mother's chest.

Picking him up, we carried him to a four-wheeled cab, and took his muzzle off. His little dark-brown eyes were resolutely fixed on distance, and by his refusal to even smell the biscuits we had brought to make him happy, we knew that the human being had not yet come into a life that had contained so far only a mother, a wood-shed, and four other soft, wobbly, black, hammer-headed angels, smelling of themselves, and warmth, and wood shavings. It was pleasant to feel that to us he would surrender an untouched love, that is, if he would surrender anything. Suppose he did not take to us!

And just then something must have stirred in him, for he turned up his swollen nose and stared at my companion, and a little later rubbed the dry pinkness of his tongue against my thumb. In that look, and that unconscious restless lick, he was trying hard to leave unhappiness behind, trying hard to feel that these new creatures with stroking paws and queer scents were his mother; yet all the time he knew, I am sure, that they were something bigger, more permanently, desperately, his. The first sense of being owned, perhaps (who knows) of owning, had stirred in him. He would never again be quite the same unconscious creature.

A little way from the end of our journey we got out and dismissed the cab. He could not too soon know the scents and pavements of this London where the chief of his life must pass. I can see now his first bumble down that wide, backwater of a street, how continually and suddenly he sat down to make sure of his own legs, how continually he lost our heels. He showed us then in full perfection what was afterwards to be an inconvenient—if endearing—characteristic: At any call or whistle he would look in precisely the opposite direction.

How many times all through his life have I not seen him, at my whistle, start violently and turn his tail to me, then, with nose thrown searchingly from side to side, begin to canter toward the horizon!

In that first walk, we met, fortunately, but one vehicle, a brewer's dray; he chose that moment to attend to the more serious affairs of life, sitting quietly before the horses' feet and requiring to be moved by hand. From the beginning he had his dignity, and was extremely difficult to lift, owing to the length of his middle distance.

What strange feellngs must have stirred in his little white soul when he first smelled carpet! But it was all so strange to him that day —I doubt if he felt more than I did when I first travelled to my private school, reading "Tales of a Grandfather," and plied with tracts and sherry by my father's man of business.

That night, indeed, for several nights, he slept with me, keeping me too warm down my back, and waking me now and then with quaint sleepy whimperings. Indeed, all through his life he flew a good deal in his sleep, fighting dogs and seeing ghosts, running after rabbits and thrown sticks; and to the last one never quite knew whether or no to rouse him when his four black feet began to jerk and quiver. His dreams were like our dreams, both good and bad; happy sometimes, sometimes tragic to weeping point.

He ceased to sleep with me the day we discovered that he was a perfect little colony, whose settlers were of an active species which I have never seen again. After that he had many beds, for circumstance ordained that his life should be nomadic, and it is to this I trace that philosophic indifference to place or property, which marked him out from most of his own kind. He learned early that for a black dog with long silky ears, a feathered tail, and head of great dignity, there was no home whatsoever, away from those creatures with special scents, who took liberties with his name, and alone of all created things were privileged to smack him with a slipper. He would sleep anywhere, so long as it was in their room, or so close outside it as to make no matter, for it was with him a principle that what he did not smell did not exist. I would I could hear again those long rubber-lipped snufflings of recognition underneath the door, with which each morning he would regale and reassure a spirit that grew with age more and more nervous and delicate about this matter of propinquity! For he was a dog of fixed ideas, things stamped on his mind were indelible; as, for example, his duty toward cats, for whom he had really a perverse affection, which had led to that first disastrous moment of his life, when he was brought up, poor bewildered puppy, from a brief excursion to the kitchen, with one eye closed and his cheek torn! He bore to his grave that jagged scratch across the eye. It was in dread of a repetition of this tragedy that he was instructed at the word "Cats" to rush forward with a special "tow-row-row-ing," which he never used toward any other form of creature. To the end he cherished a hope that he would reach the cat, but never did; and if he had, we knew he would only have stood and wagged his tail; but I well remember once, when he returned, important, from some such sally, how dreadfully my companion startled a cat-loving friend by murmuring in her most honeyed voice: "Well, my darling, have you been killing pussies in the garden?"

His eye and nose were impeccable in their sense of form; indeed, he was very English in that matter: People must be just so; things smell properly; and affairs go on in the one right way. He could tolerate neither creatures in ragged clothes, nor children on their hands and knees, nor postmen, because, with their bags, they swelled-up on one side, and carried lanterns on their stomachs. He would never let the harmless creatures pass without religious barks. Naturally a believer in authority and routine, and distrusting spiritual adventure, he yet had curious fads that seemed to have nested in him, quite outside of all principle. He would, for instance, follow neither carriages nor horses, and if we tried to make him, at once left for home, where he would sit with nose raised to Heaven, emitting through it a most lugubrious, shrill noise. Then again, one must not place a stick, a slipper, a glove, or anything with which he could play, upon one's head—since such an action reduced him at once to frenzy. For so conservative a dog, his environment was sadly anarchistic. He never complained in words of our shifting habits, but curled his head round over his left paw and pressed his chin very hard against the ground whenever he smelled packing. What necessity—he seemed continually to be saying—what real necessity is there for change of any kind whatever? Here we were all together, and one day was like another, so that I knew where I was—and now *you* only know what will happen next; and *I*–I can't tell you whether I shall be with you when it happens! What strange, grieving minutes a dog passes at such times in the underground of his subconsciousness, refusing realisation, yet all the time only too well divining. Some careless word, some unmuted compassion in voice, the stealthy wrapping of a pair of boots, the unaccustomed shutting of a door that ought to be open, the removal from a down-stair room of an object always there—one tiny thing, and he knows for certain that he is not going too. He fights against the knowledge just as we do against what we cannot bear; he gives up hope, but not effort, protesting in the only way he knows of, and now and then heaving a great sigh. Those sighs of a dog! They go to the heart so much more deeply than the sighs of our own kind, because they are utterly unintended, regardless of effect, emerging from one who, heaving them, knows not that they have escaped him!

The words: "Yes—going too!" spoken in a certain tone, would call up in his eyes a still-questioning half-happiness, and from his tail a quiet flutter, but did not quite serve to put to rest either his doubt or his feeling that it was all unnecessary—until the cab arrived. Then he would pour himself out of door or window, and be found in the bottom of the vehicle, looking severely away from an admiring cabman. Once settled on our feet he travelled with philosophy, but no digestion.

I think no dog was ever more indifferent to an outside world of human creatures; yet few dogs have made more conquests—especially among strange women, through whom, however, he had a habit of looking—very discouraging. He had, natheless, one or two particular friends, and a few persons whom he knew he had seen before, but, broadly speaking, there were in his world of men, only his mistress, and—the almighty.

Each August, till he was six, he was sent for health, and the assuagement of his hereditary instincts, up to a Scotch shooting, where he carried many birds in a very tender manner. Once he was compelled by Fate to remain there nearly a year; and we went up ourselves to fetch him home. Down the long avenue toward the keeper's cottage we walked. It was high autumn; there had been frost already, for the ground was fine with red and yellow leaves; and presently we saw himself coming, professionally questing among those leaves, and preceding his dear keeper with the businesslike self-containment of a sportsman; not too fat, glossy as a raven's wing, swinging his ears and sporran like a little Highlander. We approached him silently. Suddenly his nose went up from its imagined trail, and he came rushing at our legs. From him, as a garment drops from a man, dropped all his strange soberness; he became in a single instant one fluttering eagerness. He leaped from life to life in one bound, without hesitation, without regret. Not one sigh, not one look back, not the faintest token of gratitude or regret at leaving those good people who had tended him for a whole year, buttered oat-cake for him, allowed him to choose each night exactly where he would sleep. No, he just marched out beside us, as close as ever he could get, drawing us on in spirit, and not even attending to the scents, until the lodge gates were passed.

It was strictly in accordance with the perversity of things, and something in the nature of calamity that he had not been ours one year, when there came over me a dreadful but overmastering aversion from killing those birds and creatures of which he was so fond as soon as they were dead. And so I never knew him as a sportsman; for during that first year he was only an unbroken puppy, tied to my waist for fear of accidents, and carefully pulling me off every shot. They tell me he developed a lovely nose and perfect mouth, large enough to hold gingerly the biggest hare. I well believe it, remembering the qualities of his mother, whose character, however, in stability he far surpassed. But, as *he* grew every year more devoted to dead grouse and birds and rabbits, *I* liked them more and more alive; it was the only real breach between us, and we kept it out of sight. Ah! well; it is consoling to reflect that I should infallibly have ruined his sporting qualities, lacking that peculiar habit of meaning what one says, so necessary to keep dogs virtuous. But surely to have had him with me, quivering and alert, with his solemn, eager face, would have given a new joy to those crisp mornings when the hope of wings coming to the gun makes poignant in the sportsman, as nothing else will, an almost sensual love of Nature, a fierce delight in the soft glow of leaves, in the white birch stems and tracery of sparse twigs against blue sky, in the scents of sap and grass and gum and heather flowers;

stivers the hair of him with keenness for interpreting each sound, and fills the very fern or moss he kneels on, the very trunk he leans against, with strange vibration.

Slowly Fate prepares for each of us the religion that lies coiled in our most secret nerves; with such we cannot trifle, we do not even try! But how shall a man grudge any one sensations he has so keenly felt? Let such as have never known those curious delights uphold the hand of horror—for me there can be no such luxury. If I could, I would still perhaps be knowing them; but when once the joy of life in those winged and furry things has knocked at the very portals of one's spirit, the thought that by pressing a little iron twig one will rive that joy out of their vitals is too hard to bear. Call it æstheticism, squeamishness, namby-pamby sentimentalism, what you will—it is stronger than oneself!

Yes, after one had once watched with an eye that did not merely see, the thirsty gaping of a slowly dying bird, or a rabbit dragging a broken leg to a hole where he would lie for hours thinking of the fern to which he should never more come forth—after that, there was always the following little matter of arithmetic: Given, that all those who had been shooting were "good-fair" shots—which, Heaven knew, they never were—they yet missed one at least in four, and did not miss it very much; so that if seventy-five things were slain, there were also twenty-five that had been fired at, and, of those twenty-five, twelve and a half had "gotten it" somewhere in their bodies, and would "likely" die at their great leisure.

This was the sum that brought about the only cleavage in our lives; and so, as he grew older, and trying to part from each other we no longer could, he ceased going to Scotland. But after that I often felt, and especially when we heard guns, how the best and most secret instincts of him were being stifled. But what was to be done? In that which was left of a clay pigeon he would take not the faintest interest—the scent of it was paltry. Yet always, even in his most cosseted and idle days, he managed to preserve the grave preoccupation of one professionally concerned with retrieving things that smell; and consoled himself with pastimes such as cricket, which he played in a manner highly specialised, following the ball up the moment it left the bowler's hand, and sometimes retrieving it before it reached the batsman. When remonstrated with, he would consider a little, hanging out a pink tongue and looking rather too eagerly at the ball, then canter slowly out to a sort of forward short leg. Why he always chose that particular position it is difficult to say; possibly he could lurk there better than anywhere else, the batsman's eye not being on him, and the bowler's not too much. As a fieldsman he was perfect, but for an occasional belief that he was not merely short leg, but slip, point, mid-off, and wicket-keep; and perhaps a tendency to make the ball a little "jubey." But he worked tremendously, watching every movement; for he knew the game thoroughly, and seldom delayed it more than three minutes when he secured the ball. And if that ball were really lost, then indeed he took over the proceedings with an intensity and quiet vigor that destroyed many shrubs, and the solemn satisfaction which comes from being in the very centre of the stage.

But his most passionate delight was swimming in anything except the sea, for which, with its unpleasant noise and habit of tasting salt, he had little affection. I see him now, cleaving the Serpentine, with his air of "the world well lost," striving to reach my stick before it had touched water. Being only a large spaniel, too small for mere heroism, he saved no lives in the water but his own—and that, on one occasion, before our very eyes, from a dark trout stream, which was trying to wash him down into a black hole among the boulders.

The call of the wild—Spring running—whatever it is—that besets men and dogs, seldom attained full mastery over him; but one could often see it struggling against his devotion to the scent of us, and, watching that dumb contest, I have time and again wondered how far this civilisation of ours was justifiably imposed on him; how far the love for us that we had so carefully implanted could ever replace in him the satisfaction of his primitive wild yearnings. He was like a man, naturally polygamous, married to one loved woman.

It was surely not for nothing that Rover is dog's most common name, and would be ours, but for our too tenacious fear of losing something, to admit, even to ourselves, that we are hankering. There was a man who said: Strange that two such queerly opposite qualities as courage and hypocrisy are the leading characteristics of the Anglo-Saxon! But is not hypocrisy just a product of tenacity, which is again the lower part of courage? Is not hypocrisy but an active sense of property in one's good name, the clutching close of respectability at any price, the feeling that one must not part, even at the cost of truth, with what he has sweated so to gain? And so we Anglo-Saxons will not answer to the name of Rover, and treat our dogs so that they, too, hardly know their natures.

The history of his one wandering, for which no respectable reason can be assigned, will never, of course, be known. It was in London, of an October evening, when we were told he had slipped out and was not anywhere. Then began those four distressful hours of searching for that black needle in that blacker bundle of hay. Hours of real dismay and suffering—for it is suffering, indeed, to feel a loved thing swallowed up in that hopeless maze of London streets. Stolen or run over? Which was worst? The neighboring police stations visited, the Dog's Home notified, an order for five hundred "Lost Dog" bills placed in the printer's hands, the streets patrolled! And then, in a lull snatched for food, and still endeavoring to preserve some aspect of assurance, we heard the bark which meant: "Here is a door I cannot open!" We hurried forth, and there he was on the top doorstep—busy, unashamed, giving no explanations, asking for his supper; and very shortly after him came his five hundred "Lost Dog" bills. Long I sat looking at him that night after my companion had gone up, thinking of the evening, some years before, when there followed us that shadow of a spaniel who had been lost for eleven days. And my heart turned over within me. But he! He was asleep, for he knew not remorse.

Ah! and there was that other time, when it was reported to me, returning home at night, that he had gone out to find me; and I went forth again, disturbed, and whistling his special call to the empty fields. Suddenly out of the darkness I heard a rushing, and he came furiously dashing against my heels for he alone knew where he had been lurking and saying to himself: I will not go in till he comes! I could not scold, there was something too lyrical in the return of that live, lonely, rushing piece of blackness through the blacker night. After all, the vagary was but a variation in his practice when one was away at bed-time, of passionately scratching up his bed in protest, till it resembled nothing; for, in spite of his long and solemn face and the silkiness of his ears, there was much in him yet of the cave bear—he dug graves on the smallest provocations, in which he never buried anything. He was not a "clever" dog; and guiltless of all tricks. Nor was he ever "shown." We did not even dream of subjecting him to this indignity. Was our dog a clown, a hobby, a fad, a fashion, a feather in our caps—that we should subject him to periodic pennings in stuffy halls, that we should harry his faithful soul with such tom-foolery? He never even heard us talk about his lineage, deplore the length of his nose, or call him "clever-looking." We should have been ashamed to let him smell about us the tar-brush of a sense of property, to let him think we looked on him as an asset to earn us pelf or glory. We wished that there should be between us the spirit that was between the sheep-dog and that farmer, who, when asked his dog's age, touched the old creature's head, and answered thus: "Teresa" (his daughter) "was born in November, and this one in August." That sheep-dog had seen eighteen years when the great white day came for him, and his spirit passed away up, to cling with the wood-smoke round the dark rafters of the kitchen where he had lain so vast a time beside his master's boots. No, no! If a man does not soon pass beyond the thought: "By what shall this dog profit me?" into the large state of simple gladness to be with dog, he shall never know the very essence of that companionship which depends not on the points of dog, but on some strange and subtle mingling of mute spirits. For it is by muteness that a dog becomes for one so utterly beyond value; with him one is at peace, where words play no tortur-ing tricks. When he just sits, loving, and knows that he is being loved, those are the moments that I think are precious to a dog; when, with his adoring soul coming through his eyes, he feels that you are really thinking of him. But he is touchingly tolerant of one's other occupa-tions. The subject of these memories always knew when one was too absorbed in work to be so close to him as he thought proper; yet he never tried to hinder or distract, or asked for attention. It dinged his mood, of course, so that the red under his eyes and the folds of his crumply cheeks—which seemed to speak of a touch of bloodhound introduced a long way back into his breeding—grew deeper and more manifest. If he could have spoken at such times, he would have said:

"I have been a long time alone, and I cannot always be asleep; but you know best, and I must not criticise."

He did not at all mind one's being absorbed in other humans; he seemed to enjoy the sounds of conversation lifting round him, and to know when they were sensible. He could not, for instance, stand actors or actresses giving readings of their parts, perceiving at once that the same had no connection with the minds and real feelings of the speakers; and, having wandered a little to show his disapproval, he would go to the door and stare at it till it opened and let him out. Once or twice, it is true, when an actor of large voice was declaiming an emotional passage, he so far relented as to go up to him and pant in his face. Music, too, made him restless, inclined to sigh, and to ask questions. Sometimes, at its first sound, he would cross to the window and remain there looking for Her. At others, he would simply go and lie on the loud pedal, and we never could tell whether it was from sentiment, or because he thought that in this way he heard less. At one special Nocturne of Chopin's he always whimpered. He *was*, indeed, of rather Polish temperament—very gay when he was gay, dark and brooding when he was not.

On the whole, perhaps his life was uneventful for so far-travelling a dog, though it held its moments of eccentricity, as when he leaped through the window of a four-wheeler into Kensington, or sat on a Dartmoor adder. But that was fortunately of a Sunday afternoon—when adder and all were torpid, so nothing happened, till a friend, who was following, lifted him off the creature with his large boot.

If only one could have known more of his private life—more of his relations with his own kind! I fancy he was always rather a dark dog to them, having so many thoughts about us that he could not share with any one, and being naturally fastidious, except with ladies, for whom he had a chivalrous and catholic taste, so that they often turned and snapped at him. He had, however, but one lasting love affair, for a liver-colored lass of our village, not quite of his own caste, but a wholesome if somewhat elderly girl, with loving and sphinx-like eyes. Their children, alas, were not for this world, and soon departed.

Nor was he a fighting dog; but once attacked, he lacked a sense of values, being unable to distinguish between dogs that he could beat and dogs with whom he had "no earthly." It was, in fact, as well to interfere at once, especially in the matter of retrievers, for he never forgot having in his youth been attacked by a retriever from behind. No, he never forgot, and never forgave, an enemy. Only a month before that day of which I cannot speak, being very old and ill, he engaged an Irish terrier on whose impudence he had long had his eye, and routed him. And how a battle cheered his spirit! He was certainly no Christian; but, allowing for essential dog, he was very much a gentleman. And I do think that most of us who live on this earth these days would rather leave it with that label on us than the other. For to be a Christian, as Tolstoy understood the word—and no one else in our time has had logic and love of truth enough to give it coherent meaning—is (to be quite sincere) not suited to men of Western blood. Whereas—to be a gentleman! It is a far cry, but perhaps it can be done. In him, at all events, there was no pettiness, no meanness, and no cruelty, and though he fell below his ideal at times, this never altered the true look of his eyes, nor the simple loyalty in his soul.

But what a crowd of memories come back, bringing with them the perfume of fallen days! What delights and glamour, what long hours of effort, discouragements, and secret fears did he not watch over— our black familiar; and with the sight and scent and touch of him, deepen or assuage! How many thousand walks did we not go together, so that we still turn to see if he is following at his padding gait, attentive to the invisible trails. Not the least hard thing to bear when they go from us, these quiet friends, is that they carry away with them so many years of our own lives. Yet, if they find warmth therein, who would grudge them those years that they have so guarded? Nothing else of us can they take to lie upon with outstretched paws and chin pressed to the ground; and, whatever they take, be sure they have deserved.

Do they know, as we do, that their time must come? Yes, they know, at rare moments. No other way can I interpret those pauses of his latter life, when, propped on his forefeet, he would sit for long minutes quite motionless—his head drooped, utterly withdrawn; then turn those eyes of his and look at me. That look said more plainly than all words could: "Yes, I know that I must go!" If *we* have spirits

that persist—*they* have. If *we* know, after our departure, who we
were—*they* do. No one, I think, who really longs for truth, can ever
glibly say which it will be for dog and man—persistence or extinction
of our consciousness. There is but one thing certain—the childish-
ness of fretting over that eternal question. Whichever it be, it must
be right, the only possible thing. He felt that too, I know; but then,
like his master, he was what is called a pessimist.

My companion tells me that, since he left us, he has once come
back. It was Old Year's Night, and she was sad, when he came to her
in visible shape of his black body, passing round the dining-table
from the window-end, to his proper place beneath the table, at her
feet. She saw him quite clearly; she heard the padding tap-tap of his
paws and very toe-nails; she felt his warmth brushing hard against
the front of her skirt. She thought then that he would settle down
upon her feet, but something disturbed him, and he stood pausing,
pressed against her, then moved out toward where I generally sit, but
was not sitting that night. She saw him stand there, as if considering;
then at some sound or laugh, she became self-conscious, and slowly,
very slowly, he was no longer there. Had he some message, some
counsel to give, something he would say, that last night of the last
year of all those he had watched over us? Will he come back again?

No stone stands over where he lies. It is on our hearts that his life
is engraved.

The Hound and the Hat

BY

JAMES THURBER

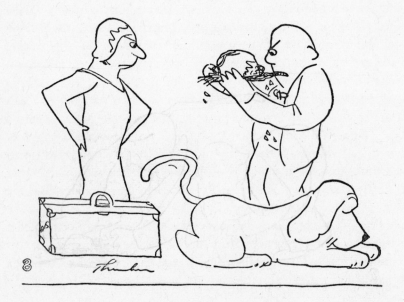

The Dog That Bit People

FROM "MY LIFE AND HARD TIMES," BY

JAMES THURBER

PROBABLY no one man should have as many dogs in his life as I have had, but there was more pleasure than distress in them for me except in the case of an Airedale named Muggs. He gave me more trouble than all the other fifty-four or five put together, although my moment of keenest embarrassment was the time a Scotch terrier named Jeannie, who had just had six puppies in the clothes closet of a fourth floor apartment in New York, had the unexpected seventh and last at the corner of Eleventh Street and Fifth Avenue during a walk she had insisted on taking. Then, too, there was the prize-winning French poodle, a great big black poodle—none of your little, untroublesome white miniatures—who got sick riding in the rumble seat of a car with me on her way to the Greenwich Dog Show. She had a red rubber bib tucked around her throat and, since a rain storm came up when we were half way through the Bronx, I had to hold over her a small green umbrella, really more of a parasol. The rain beat down fearfully and suddenly the driver of the car drove into a big garage, filled with mechanics. It happened so quickly that I forgot to put the umbrella down and I will always remember, with sickening distress, the look of incredulity mixed with hatred that came over the face of the particular hardened garage man that came over to see what we wanted, when he took a look at me and the poodle. All garage men, and people of that intolerant stripe, hate poodles with their curious hair cut, especially the pom-pons that you have got to leave on their hips if you expect the dogs to win a prize.

59

But the Airedale, as I have said, was the worst of all my dogs. He really wasn't my dog, as a matter of fact: I came home from a vacation one summer to find that my brother Roy had bought him while I was away. A big, burly, choleric dog, he always acted as if he thought I wasn't one of the family. There was a slight advantage in being one of the family, for he didn't bite the family as often as he bit strangers. Still, in the years that we had him he bit everybody but mother, and he made a pass at her once but missed. That was during the month when we suddenly had mice, and Muggs refused to do anything about them. Nobody ever had mice exactly like the mice we had that month. They acted like pet mice, almost like mice somebody had trained. They were so friendly that one night when mother entertained at dinner the Friraliras, a club she and my father had belonged to for twenty years, she put down a lot of little dishes with food in them on the pantry floor so that the mice would be satisfied with that and wouldn't come into the dining room. Muggs stayed out in the pantry with the mice, lying on the floor, growling to himself—not at the mice, but about all the people in the next room that he would have liked to get at. Mother slipped out into the pantry once to see how everything was going. Everything was going fine. It made her so mad to see Muggs lying there, oblivious of the mice—they came running up to her—that she slapped him and he slashed at her, but didn't make it. He was sorry immediately, mother said. He was always sorry, she said, after he bit someone, but we could not understand how she figured this out. He didn't act sorry.

Mother used to send a box of candy every Christmas to the people the Airedale bit. The list finally contained forty or more names. Nobody could understand why we didn't get rid of the dog. I didn't understand it very well myself, but we didn't get rid of him. I think that one or two people tried to poison Muggs—he acted poisoned once in a while—and old Major Moberly fired at him once with his service revolver near the Seneca Hotel in East Broad Street—but Muggs lived to be almost eleven years old and even when he could hardly get around he bit a Congressman who had called to see my father on business. My mother had never liked the Congressman— she said the signs of his horoscope showed he couldn't be trusted (he was Saturn with the moon in Virgo)—but she sent him a box of candy that Christmas. He sent it right back, probably because he suspected it was trick candy. Mother persuaded herself it was all for the best that the dog had bitten him, even though father lost an important business association because of it. "I wouldn't be associated with such a man," mother said. "Muggs could read him like a book."

We used to take turns feeding Muggs to be on his good side, but that didn't always work. He was never in a very good humor, even after a meal. Nobody knew exactly what was the matter with him, but whatever it was it made him irascible, especially in the mornings. Roy never felt very well in the morning, either, especially before breakfast, and once when he came downstairs and found that Muggs had moodily chewed up the morning paper he hit him in the face with a grapefruit and then jumped up on the dining room table, scattering dishes and silverware and spilling the coffee. Muggs' first free leap carried him all the way across the table and into a brass fire screen in front of the gas grate but he was back on his feet in a moment and in the end he got Roy and gave him a pretty vicious bite in the leg. Then he was all over it; he never bit anyone more than once at a time. Mother always mentioned that as an argument in his favor; she said he had a quick temper but that he didn't hold a grudge. She was forever defending him. I think she liked him because he wasn't well. "He's not strong," she would say, pityingly, but that was inaccurate; he may not have been well but he was terribly strong.

One time my mother went to the Chittenden Hotel to call on a woman mental healer who was lecturing in Columbus on the subject of "Harmonious Vibrations." She wanted to find out if it was possible to get harmonious vibrations into a dog. "He's a large tan-colored Airedale," mother explained. The woman said that she had never treated a dog but she advised my mother to hold the thought that he did not bite and would not bite. Mother was holding the thought the very next morning when Muggs got the iceman but she blamed that slip-up on the iceman. "If you didn't think he would bite you, he wouldn't," mother told him. He stomped out of the house in a terrible jangle of vibrations.

One morning when Muggs bit me slightly, more or less in passing, I reached down and grabbed his short stumpy tail and hoisted him

into the air. It was a foolhardy thing to do and the last time I saw
my mother, about six months ago, she said she didn't know what possessed me. I don't either, except that I was pretty mad. As long as I
held the dog off the floor by his tail he couldn't get at me, but he
twisted and jerked so, snarling all the time, that I realized I couldn't
hold him that way very long. I carried him to the kitchen and flung
him onto the floor and shut the door on him just as he crashed against
it. But I forgot about the backstairs. Muggs went up the backstairs
and down the frontstairs and had me cornered in the living room. I
managed to get up onto the mantelpiece above the fireplace, but it
gave way and came down with a tremendous crash throwing a large
marble clock, several vases, and myself heavily to the floor. Muggs
was so alarmed by the racket that when I picked myself up he had
disappeared. We couldn't find him anywhere, although we whistled
and shouted, until old Mrs. Detweiler called after dinner that night.
Muggs had bitten her once, in the leg, and she came into the living
room only after we assured her that Muggs had run away. She had
just seated herself when, with a great growling and scratching of
claws, Muggs emerged from under a davenport where he had been
quietly hiding all the time, and bit her again. Mother examined the
bite and put arnica on it and told Mrs. Detweiler that it was only a
bruise. "He just bumped you," she said. But Mrs. Detweiler left the
house in a nasty state of mind.

Lots of people reported our Airedale to the police but my father
held a municipal office at the time and was on friendly terms with
the police. Even so, the cops had been out a couple of times—once
when Muggs bit Mrs. Rufus Sturtevant and again when he bit Lieu-
tenant-Governor Malloy—but mother told them that it hadn't been
Muggs' fault but the fault of the people who were bitten. "When he
starts for them, they scream," she explained, "and that excites him."
The cops suggested that it might be a good idea to tie the dog up, but
mother said that it mortified him to be tied up and that he wouldn't
eat when he was tied up.

Muggs at his meals was an unusual sight. Because of the fact that
if you reached toward the floor he would bite you, we usually put
his food plate on top of an old kitchen table with a bench alongside
the table. Muggs would stand on the bench and eat. I remember that

my mother's Uncle Horatio, who boasted that he was the third man
up Missionary Ridge, was splutteringly indignant when he found out
that we fed the dog on a table because we were afraid to put his plate
on the floor. He said he wasn't afraid of any dog that ever lived and
that he would put the dog's plate on the floor if we would give it to
him. Roy said that if Uncle Horatio had fed Muggs on the ground
just before the battle he would have been the first man up Missionary
Ridge. Uncle Horatio was furious. "Bring him in! Bring him in
now!" he shouted. "I'll feed the —— on the floor!" Roy was all for
giving him a chance, but my father wouldn't hear of it. He said that
Muggs had already been fed. "I'll feed him again!" bawled Uncle
Horatio. We had quite a time quieting him.

In his last year Muggs used to spend practically all of his time outdoors. He didn't like to stay in the house for some reason or other—
perhaps it held too many unpleasant memories for him. Anyway, it
was hard to get him to come in and as a result the garbage man, the
iceman, and the laundryman wouldn't come near the house. We had
to haul the garbage down to the corner, take the laundry out and
bring it back, and meet the iceman a block from home. After this had
gone on for some time we hit on an ingenious arrangement for getting the dog in the house so that we could lock him up while the gas
meter was read, and so on. Muggs was afraid of only one thing, an
electrical storm. Thunder and lightning frightened him out of his
senses (I think he thought a storm had broken the day the mantelpiece fell). He would rush into the house and hide under a bed or in
a clothes closet. So we fixed up a thunder machine out of a long narrow piece of sheet iron with a wooden handle on one end. Mother
would shake this vigorously when she wanted to get Muggs into the
house. It made an excellent imitation of thunder, but I suppose it was
the most roundabout system for running a household that was ever
devised. It took a lot out of mother.

A few months before Muggs died, he got to "seeing things." He
would rise slowly from the floor, growling low, and stalk stiff-legged
and menacing toward nothing at all. Sometimes the Thing would be
just a little to the right or left of a visitor. Once a Fuller Brush sales-
man got hysterics. Muggs came wandering into the room like Hamlet
following his father's ghost. His eyes were fixed on a spot just to the

left of the Fuller Brush man, who stood it until Muggs was about three slow, creeping paces from him. Then he shouted. Muggs wavered on past him into the hallway grumbling to himself but the Fuller man went on shouting. I think mother had to throw a pan of cold water on him before he stopped. That was the way she used to stop us boys when we got into fights.

Muggs died quite suddenly one night. Mother wanted to bury him in the family lot under a marble stone with some such inscription as "Flights of angels sing thee to thy rest" but we persuaded her it was against the law. In the end we just put up a smooth board above his grave along a lonely road. On the board I wrote with an indelible pencil "Cave Canem." Mother was quite pleased with the simple classic dignity of the old Latin epitaph.

Snapshot of a Dog

BY

JAMES THURBER

I RAN across a dim photograph of him the other day. He's been dead 25 years. His name was Rex (my two brothers and I named him) and he was a bull terrier. "An American bull terrier," we used to say, proudly; none of your English bulls. He had one brindle eye that sometimes made him look like a clown and sometimes reminded you of a politician with derby hat and cigar. The rest of him was white except for a brindle saddle and a brindle stocking on a hind leg. Nevertheless, there was a nobility about him. He was big and muscular and beautifully made. He never lost his dignity even when trying to accomplish the extravagant tasks my brother and I used to set for him.

One of these was the bringing of a ten-foot wooden rail into the yard through the back gate. We would throw it out into the alley and tell him to get it. Rex was as powerful as a wrestler, and he would catch the rail at the balance, lift it clear of the ground, and trot with great confidence toward the gate. Of course, the gate being only four feet wide, he couldn't bring the rail in broadside. He found that out when he got a few terrific jolts, but he wouldn't give up. He finally figured out how to do it, by dragging the rail, holding onto one end, growling. He got a great, wagging satisfaction out of his work.

He was a tremendous fighter, but he never started fights. He never went for a dog's throat but for one of its ears (that teaches a dog a lesson), and he would get his grip, close his eyes, and hold on. He could hold on for hours. His longest fight lasted from dusk to almost pitch-dark, one Sunday. It was fought with a large, snarly nonde-script belonging to a large colored man. When Rex finally got his ear grip, the brief whirlwind of snarling turned to screeching. It was frightening to listen to and to watch. The Negro boldly picked the dogs up, swung them around his head, and finally let them fly like a hammer in a hammer throw, but although they landed ten feet away, with a great plump, Rex still held on. Working their way to the middle of the car tracks, two or three streetcars were held up by the fight. A motorman tried to pry Rex's jaws open with a switch rod; somebody lighted a stick and held it to Rex's tail but he paid no attention. Rex's joy of battle, when battle was joined, was almost tranquil. He had a kind of pleasant expression during fights, his eyes closed in what would have seemed to be sleep had it not been for the turmoil of the struggle. The Fire Department finally had to be sent for and a powerful stream of water turned on the dogs for several moments before Rex finally let go.

The story of that Homeric fight got all around town, and some of our relatives considered it a blot on the family name. They insisted that we get rid of Rex, but nobody could have made us give him up. We would have left town with him first. It would have been different, perhaps, if he had ever looked for trouble. But he had a gentle disposition. He never bit a person in the ten strenuous years that he lived, nor ever growled at anyone except prowlers.

Swimming was his favorite recreation. The first time he ever saw a body of water, he trotted nervously along the steep bank for a while, fell to barking wildly, and finally plunged in from a height of eight feet or more. I shall always remember that shining, virgin dive. Then he swam upstream and back just for the pleasure of it, like a man. It was fun to see him battle upstream against a stiff current, growling every foot of the way. He had as much fun in the water as any person I have ever known. You didn't have to throw a stick into the water to get him to go in. Of course, he would bring back a stick if you did throw one in. He would have brought back a piano if you had thrown one in.

That reminds me of the night he went a-roving in the light of the moon and brought back a small chest of drawers he had found somewhere—how far from the house nobody ever knew. There were no

drawers in the chest when he got it home, and it wasn't a good one
—just an old cheap piece abandoned on a trash heap. Still it was something he wanted, probably because it presented a nice problem in
transportation. We first knew about his achievement when, deep in
the night, we heard sounds as if two or three people were trying to
tear the house down. We came downstairs and turned on the porch
light. Rex was on the top step, trying to pull the thing up, but it had
caught and he was just holding his own. I suppose he would have
held his own until dawn if we hadn't helped him. Next day we carted
the chest miles away and threw it out. If we had thrown it out nearby,
he would have brought it home again, as a small token of his integrity
in such matters.

There was in his world no such thing as the impossible. Even death
couldn't beat him down. He died, it is true, but only, as one of his
admirers said, after "straight-arming the death angel" for more than
an hour. Late one afternoon he wandered home, too slowly and
uncertainly to be the Rex that had trotted briskly homeward up our
avenue for ten years. I think we all knew when he came through the
gate that he was dying. He had apparently taken a terrible beating,
probably from the owner of some dog he had got into a fight with.
His head and body were scarred, and some of the brass studs of his
heavy collar were sprung loose. He licked at our hands and, staggering, fell, but got up again. We could see that he was looking for
someone. One of his three masters was not home. He did not get
home for an hour. During that hour the bull terrier fought against
death as he had fought against the cold, strong current of the creek.
When the person he was waiting for did come through the gate,
whistling, ceasing to whistle, Rex walked a few wabbly paces toward
him, touched his hand with his muzzle, and fell down again. This
time he didn't get up.

Dandy

THE STORY OF A DOG, BY

W. H. HUDSON

HE WAS of mixed breed, and was supposed to have a strain of Dandy Dinmont blood which gave him his name. A big ungainly animal with a rough shaggy coat of blue-gray hair and white on his neck and clumsy paws. He looked like a Sussex sheep dog with legs reduced to half their proper length. He was, when I first knew him, getting old and increasingly deaf and dim of sight, otherwise in the best of health and spirits, or at all events very good-tempered.

Until I knew Dandy I had always supposed that the story of Ludlam's dog was pure invention, and I dare say that is the general opinion about it; but Dandy made me reconsider the subject, and eventually I came to believe that Ludlam's dog did exist once upon a time, centuries ago perhaps, and that if he had been the laziest dog in the world Dandy was not far behind him in that respect. It is true he did not lean his head against a wall to bark; he exhibited his laziness in other ways. He barked often, though never at strangers; he welcomed every visitor, even the tax-collector, with tail-waggings and a smile. He spent a good deal of his time in the large kitchen, where he had a sofa to sleep on, and when the two cats of the house wanted an hour's rest they would coil themselves up on Dandy's broad shaggy side, preferring that bed to cushion or rug. They were like a warm blanket over him, and it was a sort of mutual benefit society. After an hour's sleep Dandy would go out for a short constitutional as far as the neighboring thoroughfare, where he would

68

blunder against people, wag his tail to everybody, and then come back. He had six or eight or more outings each day, and, owing to doors and gates being closed and to his lazy disposition, he had much trouble in getting out and in. First he would sit down in the hall and bark, bark, bark, until some one would come to open the door for him, whereupon he would slowly waddle down the garden path, and if he found the gate closed he would again sit down and start barking. And the bark, bark would go on until some one came to let him out. But if after he had barked about twenty or thirty times no one came, he would deliberately open the gate himself, which he could do perfectly well, and let himself out. In twenty minutes or so he would be back at the gate and barking for admission once more, and finally, if no one paid any attention, letting himself in.

Dandy always had something to eat at meal-times, but he too liked a snack between meals once or twice a day. The dog-biscuits were kept in an open box on the lower dresser shelf, so that he could get one "whenever he felt so disposed," but he didn't like the trouble this arrangement gave him, so he would sit down and start barking, and as he had a bark which was both deep and loud, after it had been repeated a dozen times at intervals of five seconds, any person who happened to be in or near the kitchen was glad to give him his biscuit for the sake of peace and quietness. If no one gave it him, he would then take it out himself and eat it.

Now it came to pass that during the last year of the war dog-biscuits, like many other articles of food for man and beast, grew scarce, and were finally not to be had at all. At all events, that was what happened in Dandy's town of Penzance. He missed his biscuits greatly and often reminded us of it by barking; then, lest we should think he was barking about something else, he would go and sniff and paw at the empty box. He perhaps thought it was pure forgetfulness on the part of those of the house who went every morning to do the marketing and had fallen into the habit of returning without dog-biscuits in the basket. One day during that last winter of scarcity and anxiety I went to the kitchen and found the floor strewn all over with the fragments of Dandy's biscuit-box. Dandy himself had done it; he had dragged the box from its place out into the middle of the floor, and then deliberately set himself to bite and tear it into small pieces and scatter them about. He was caught at it just as he was finishing the job, and the kindly person who surprised him in the act suggested that the reason of his breaking up the box in that way was that he got something of the biscuit flavor by biting the pieces. My own theory was that as the box was there to hold biscuits and now held none, he had come to regard it as useless—as having lost its function, so to speak—also that its presence there was an insult to his intelligence, a constant temptation to make a fool of himself by visiting it half a dozen times a day only to find it empty as usual. Better, then, to get rid of it altogether, and no doubt when he did it he put a little temper into the business!

Dandy, from the time I first knew him, was strictly teetotal, but in former and distant days he had been rather fond of his glass. If a person held up a glass of beer before him, I was told, he wagged his tail in joyful anticipation, and a little beer was always given him at mealtime. Then he had an experience, which, after a little hesitation, I have thought it best to relate, as it is perhaps the most curious incident in Dandy's somewhat uneventful life.

One day Dandy, who after the manner of his kind, had attached himself to the person who was always willing to take him out for a stroll, followed his friend to a neighboring public-house, where the said friend had to discuss some business matter with the landlord. They went into the taproom, and Dandy, finding that the business was going to be a rather long affair, settled himself down to have a nap. Now it chanced that a barrel of beer which had just been broached had a leaky tap, and the landlord had set a basin on the floor to catch the waste. Dandy, waking from his nap and hearing the trickling sound, got up, and going to the basin quenched his thirst, after which he resumed his nap. By-and-by he woke again and had a second drink, and altogether he woke and had a drink five or six times; then, the business being concluded, they went out together, but no sooner were they out in the fresh air than Dandy began to exhibit signs of inebriation. He swerved from side to side, colliding with the passers-by, and finally fell off the pavement into the swift stream of water which at that point runs in the gutter at one side of the street. Getting out of the water, he started again, trying to keep close to the wall to save himself from another ducking. People looked curiously at him, and by-and-by they began to ask what the matter was. "Is your dog going to have a fit—or what is it?" they asked. Dandy's friend said he didn't know; something was the matter, no doubt, and he would take him home as quickly as possible and see to it.

When they finally got to the house Dandy staggered to the sofa, and succeeded in climbing on to it and, throwing himself on his cushion, went fast to sleep, and slept on without a break until the following morning. Then he rose quite refreshed and appeared to have forgotten all about it; but that day when at dinner-time some one said "Dandy" and held up a glass of beer, instead of wagging his tail as usual he dropped it between his legs and turned away in evident disgust. And from that time onward he would never touch it with his tongue, and it was plain that when they tried to tempt him, setting beer before him and smilingly inviting him to drink, he knew they were mocking him, and before turning away he would emit a low growl and show his teeth. It was the one thing that put him out and would make him angry with his friends and life companions.

I should not have related this incident if Dandy had been alive. But he is no longer with us. He was old—half-way between fifteen and sixteen: it seemed as though he had waited to see the end of the war, since no sooner was the armistice proclaimed than he began to decline rapidly. Gone deaf and blind, he still insisted on taking several constitutionals every day, and would bark as usual at the gate, and if no one came to let him out or admit him, he would open it for himself as before. This went on till January, 1919, when some of the boys he knew were coming back to Penzance and to the house. Then he established himself on his sofa, and we knew that his end was near, for there he would sleep all day and all night, declining food. It is customary in this country to chloroform a dog and give him a dose of strychnine to "put him out of his misery." But it was not necessary in this case, as he was not in misery; not a groan did he ever emit, waking or sleeping; and if you put a hand on him he would look up and wag his tail just to let you know that it was well with him. And in his sleep he passed away—a perfect case of euthanasia—and was buried in the large garden near the second apple-tree.

Verdun Belle

BY

ALEXANDER WOOLLCOTT

I FIRST heard the saga of Verdun Belle's adventure as it was being told one June afternoon under a drowsy apple tree in the troubled valley of the Marne.

The story began in a chill, grimy Lorraine village, where, in hovels and haymows, a disconsolate detachment of United States marines lay waiting the order to go up into that maze of trenches of which the crumbling traces still weave a haunted web around the citadel bearing the immortal name of Verdun.

Into this village at dusk one day in the early spring of 1918 there came out of space a shabby, lonesome dog—a squat setter of indiscreet, complex and unguessable ancestry.

One watching her as she trotted intently along the aromatic village street would have sworn that she had an important engagement with the mayor and was, regretfully, a little late.

At the end of the street she came to where a young buck private lounged glumly on a doorstep. Halting in her tracks, she sat down to contemplate him. Then, satisfied seemingly by what she sensed and saw, she came over and flopped down beside him in a most companionable manner, settling herself comfortably as if she had come at last to her long journey's end. His pleased hand reached over and played with one silken chocolate-colored ear.

Somehow that gesture sealed a compact between those two. There was thereafter no doubt in either's mind that they belonged to each other for better or for worse, in sickness and in health, through weal and woe, world without end.

She ate when and what he ate. She slept beside him in the day, her muzzle resting on his leg so that he could not get up in the night and go forgetfully back to America without her noticing it.

To the uninitiated onlookers her enthusiasm may not have been immediately explicable. In the eyes of his top sergeant and his company clerk he may well have seemed an undistinguished warrior, freckle-faced and immensely indifferent to the business of making the world safe for democracy.

Verdun Belle thought him the most charming person in all the world. There was a loose popular notion that she had joined up with the company as mascot and belonged to them all. She affably let them think so, but she had her own ideas on the subject.

When they moved up into the line she went along and was so obviously trench-broken that they guessed she had already served a hitch with some French regiment in that once desperate region.

They even built up the not implausible theory that she had come to them lonely from the grave of some little soldier in faded horizon blue.

Certainly she knew trench ways, knew in the narrowest of passages how to keep out from underfoot and was so well aware of the dangers of the parapet that a plate of chicken bones up there would not have interested her. She even knew what gas was, and after a reminding whiff of it became more than reconciled to the regulation gas mask, which they patiently wrecked for all subsequent human use because an unimaginative War Department had not foreseen the peculiar anatomical specifications of Verdun Belle.

In May, when the outfit was engaged in the exhausting activities which the High Command was pleased to describe as "resting," Belle thought it a convenient time to present an interested but amply forewarned regiment with seven wriggling casuals, some black and white and mottled as a mackerel sky, some splotched with the same brown as her own.

These newcomers complicated the domestic economy of the leathernecks' haymow, but they did not become an acute problem until that memorable night late in the month when breathless word bade these troops be up and away.

The Second Division of the A.E.F. was always being thus picked

up by the scruff of the neck and flung across France. This time the
enemy had snapped up Soissons and Rheims and were pushing with
dreadful ease and speed toward the remembering Marne.

Foch had called upon the Americans to help stem the tide. Ahead
of the marines, as they scrambled across the monotonous plain of the
Champagne, there lay amid the ripening wheat fields a mean and hilly
patch of timber called Belleau Wood. Verdun Belle went along.

The leatherneck had solved the problem of the puppies by drowning four and placing the other three in a basket he had begged from
a village woman.

His notion that he could carry the basket would have come as a
shock to whatever functionary back in Washington designed the
marine pack, which, with its neat assortment of food supplies, extra
clothing, emergency restoratives, and gruesome implements for destruction, had been so painstakingly calculated to exhaust the capacity of the human back. But in his need the young marine somehow
contrived to add an item not in the regulations—namely, one basket
containing three unweaned and faintly resentful puppies.

By night and by day the troop movement was made, now in little
wheezing trains, now in swarming lorries, now afoot.

Sometimes Belle's crony rode. Sometimes (under pressure of
popular clamor against the room he was taking up) he would yield
up his place to the basket and jog along with his hand on the tailboard,
with Belle trotting behind him.

All the soldiers in Christendom seemed to be moving across France
to some nameless crossroads over the hill. Obviously this was no
mere shift from one quiet sector to another. They were going to war.

Everyone had assured the stubborn youngster that he would not
be able to manage, and now misgivings settled on him like crows.

He guessed that Verdun Belle must be wondering too. He turned
to assure her that everything would be all right. She was not there.
Ahead of him, behind him, there was no sign of her. No one within
call had seen her quit the line. He kept telling himself she would show
up. But the day went and the night came without her.

He jettisoned the basket and pouched the pups in his forest-green
shirt in the manner of kangaroos. In the morning one of the three

was dead. And the problem of transporting the other two was now tangled by the circumstance that he had to feed them.

An immensely interested old woman in the village where they halted at sunup, vastly amused by this spectacle of a soldier trying to carry two nursing puppies to war, volunteered some milk for the cup of his mess kit, and with much jeering advice from all sides, and, by dint of the eye-dropper from his pack, he tried sheepishly to be a mother to the two waifs. The attempt was not shiningly successful.

He itched to pitch them over the fence. But if Verdun Belle had not been run over by some thundering camion, if she lived she would find him, and then what would he say when her eyes asked what he had done with the pups?

So, as the order was shouted to fall in, he hitched his pack to his back and stuffed his charges back into his shirt.

Now, in the morning light, the highway was choked. Down from the lines in agonized, grotesque rout came the stream of French life from the threatened countryside, jumbled fragments of fleeing French regiments. But America was coming up the road.

It was a week in which the world held its breath.

The battle was close at hand now. Field hospitals, jostling in the river of traffic, sought space to pitch their tents. The top sergeant of one such outfit was riding on the driver's seat of an ambulance. Marines in endless number were moving up fast.

It was one of these who, in a moment's halt, fell out of line, leaped to the step of the blockaded ambulance, and looked eagerly into the medico top sergeant's eyes.

"Say, buddy," whispered the youngster, "take care of these for me. I lost their mother in the jam."

The Top found his hands closing on two drowsy pups.

All that day the field-hospital personnel was harried by the task of providing nourishment for the two casuals who had been thus unexpectedly attached to them for rations. Once established in a farmhouse (from which they were promptly shelled out), the Top went over the possible provender and found that the pups were not yet equal to a diet of bread, corn syrup and corned willy. A stray cow, loosed from her moorings in the great flight, was browsing tentatively in the next field, and two orderlies who had carelessly reminisced of life on their farms back home were detailed to induce her cooperation.

But the bombardment had brought out a certain moody goatishness in this cow, and she would not let them come near her. After a hot and maddening chase that lasted two hours, the two milkmen reported a complete failure to their disgusted chief.

The problem was still unsolved at sundown, and the pups lay faint in their bed of absorbent cotton out in the garden, when, bringing up the rear of a detachment of marines that straggled past, there trotted a brown-and-white setter.

"It would be swell if she had milk in her," the top sergeant said reflectively, wondering how he could salvage the mascot of an outfit on the march.

But his larcenous thoughts were waste. At the gate she halted dead in her tracks, flung her head high to sniff the air, wheeled sharp to the left and became just a streak of brown and white against the ground. The entire staff came out and formed a jostling circle to watch the family reunion.

After that it was tacitly assumed that these casuals belonged. When the hospital was ordered to shift further back beyond the reach of the whining shells, Verdun Belle and the pups were intrusted to an ambulance driver and went along in style. They all moved—bag, baggage and livestock—into the deserted little Château of the Guardian Angel, of which the front windows were curtained against the eyes and dust of the road, but of which the rear windows looked out across drooping fruit trees upon a sleepy, murmurous, multi-colored valley, fair as the Garden of the Lord.

The operating tables, with acetylene torches to light them, were set up in what had been a tool shed. Cots were strewn in the orchard alongside. Thereafter for a month there was never rest in that hospital.

The surgeons and orderlies spelled each other at times, snatching morsels of sleep and returning a few hours later to relieve the others. But Verdun Belle took no time off. Between cat naps in the corner, due attentions to her restive brood and an occasional snack for herself, she managed somehow to be on hand for every ambulance, cursorily examining each casualty as he was lifted to the ground.

Then, in the four o'clock dark of one morning, the orderly bending over a stretcher that had just been rested on the ground was hit by something that half bowled him over.

The projectile was Verdun Belle. Every quivering inch of her proclaimed to all concerned that here was a case she was personally in charge of. From nose to tail tip she was taut with excitement, and a kind of eager whimpering bubbled up out of her as if she ached to sit back on her haunches and roar to the star-spangled sky but was really too busy at the moment to indulge herself in any release so satisfying to her soul. For here was this mess of a leatherneck of hers to be washed up first. So like him to get all dirty the moment her back was turned! The first thing he knew as he came to was the feel of a rough pink tongue cleaning his ears.

I saw them all next day. An ambling passer-by, I came upon two cots shoved together under an apple tree. Belle and her ravenous pups occupied one of these. On the other the young marine—a gas case, I think, but maybe his stupor was shell shock and perhaps he had merely had a crack on the head—was deep in a dreamless sleep. Before drifting off he had taken the comforting precaution to reach out one hand and close it tight on a silken ear.

Later that day he told me all about his dog. I doubt if I ever knew his name, but some quirk of memory makes me think his home was in West Philadelphia and that he had joined up with the marines when he came out of school.

I went my way before dark and never saw them again, nor ever heard tell what became of the boy and his dog. I never knew when, if ever, he was shipped back into the fight, nor where, if ever, those two met again. It is, you see, a story without an end, though there must be those here and there in this country who witnessed and could set down for us the chapter that has never been written.

I hope there was something prophetic in the closing paragraph of the anonymous account of Verdun Belle which appeared the next week in the A.E.F. newspaper, The Stars and Stripes. That paragraph was a benison which ran in this wise:

Before long they would have to ship him on to the evacuation
hospital, on from there to the base hospital, on and on and on. It was
not very clear to anyone how another separation could be prevented.
It was a perplexing question, but they knew in their hearts they could
safely leave the answer to someone else. They could leave it to
Verdun Belle.

Gulliver the Great

BY

WALTER A. DYER

I T WAS a mild evening in early spring, and the magnolias were in
bloom. We motored around the park, turned up a side street, and
finally came to a throbbing standstill before the Churchwarden
Club.

There was nothing about its exterior to indicate that it was a club-
house at all, but within there was an indefinable atmosphere of early
Victorian comfort. There was something about it that suggested
Mr. Pickwick. Old prints of horses and ships and battles hung upon
the walls, and the oak was dark and old. There seemed to be no
decorative scheme or keynote, and yet the atmosphere was utterly
distinctive. It was my first visit to the Churchwarden Club, of which
my quaint, old-fashioned Uncle Ford had long been a member, and
I was charmed.

We dined in the rathskeller, the walls of which were completely
covered with long churchwarden pipes, arranged in the most intricate and marvelous patterns; and after our mutton-chop and ale and
plum pudding, we filled with the choicest of tobaccos the pipes which
the old major-domo brought us.

Then came Jacob R. Enderby to smoke with us.

Tall and spare he was, with long, straight, black hair, large, aqui-
line nose, and piercing eyes. I disgraced myself by staring at him. I
didn't know such a man existed in New York, and yet I couldn't
decide whether his habitat should be Arizona or Cape Cod.

Enderby and Uncle Ford were deep in a discussion of the states-

79

manship of James G. Blaine, when a waiter summoned my uncle to
the telephone.

I neglected to state that my uncle, in his prosaic hours, is a phy-
sician; and this was a call. I knew it the moment I saw the waiter
approaching. I was disappointed and disgusted.

Uncle Ford saw this and laughed.

"Cheer up!" said he. "You needn't come with me to visit the sick.
I'll be back in an hour, and meanwhile Mr. Enderby will take care
of you; won't you, Jake?"

For answer Enderby arose, and refilling his pipe took me by the
arm, while my uncle got into his overcoat. As he passed us on the
way out he whispered in my ear:

"Talk about dogs."

I heard and nodded.

Enderby led me to the lounge or loafing-room, an oak-paneled
apartment in the rear of the floor above, with huge leather chairs
and a seat in the bay window. Save for a gray-haired old chap dozing
over a copy of *Simplicissimus*, the room was deserted.

But no sooner had Enderby seated himself on the window-seat
than there was a rush and a commotion, and a short, glad bark, and
Nubbins, the steward's bull-terrier, bounded in and landed at Enderby's side with canine expressions of great joy.

I reached forward to pat him, but he paid absolutely no attention
to me.

At last his wrigglings subsided, and he settled down with his head
on Enderby's knee, the picture of content. Then I recalled my Uncle's parting injunction.

"Friend of yours?" I suggested.

Enderby smiled. "Yes," he said, "we're friends, I guess. And the
funny part of it is that he doesn't pay any attention to any one else
except his master. They all act that way with me, dogs do." And
he pulled Nubbins's stubby ears.

"Natural attraction, I suppose," said I.

"Yes, it is," he answered, with the modest frankness of a big man.
"It's a thing hard to explain, though there's a sort of reason for it in
my case."

I pushed toward him a little tobacco-laden teak-wood stand hopefully. He refilled and lighted.

"It's an extraordinary thing, even so," he said, puffing. "Every dog nowadays seems to look upon me as his long-lost master, but it wasn't always so. I hated dogs and they hated me."

Not wishing to say "Really" or "Indeed" to this big, outdoor man, I simply grunted my surprise.

"Yes, we were born enemies. More than that, I was afraid of dogs. A little fuzzy toy dog, ambling up to me in a room full of company, with his tail wagging, gave me the shudders. I couldn't touch the beast. And as for big dogs outdoors, I feared them like the plague. I would go blocks out of my way to avoid one.

"I don't remember being particularly cowardly about other things, but I just couldn't help this. It was in my blood, for some reason or other. It was the bane of my existence. I couldn't see what the brutes were put in the world for, or how any one could have anything to do with them.

"All the dogs reciprocated. They disliked and distrusted me. The most docile old Brunos would growl and show their teeth when I came near."

"Did the change come suddenly?" I asked.

"Quite. It was in 1901. I accepted a commission from an importing and trading company to go to the Philippines to do a little quiet exploring, and spent four months in the sickly place. Then I got the fever, and when I recovered I couldn't get out of there too soon.

"I reached Manila just in time to see the mail steamer disappearing around the point, and I was mad. There would be another in six days, but I couldn't wait. I was just crazy to get back home.

"I made inquiries and learned of an old tramp steamer, named the *Old Squaw*, making ready to leave for Honolulu on the following day with a cargo of hemp and stuff, and a bunch of Moros for some show in the States, and I booked passage on that.

"She was the worst old tub you ever saw. I didn't learn much about her, but I verily believe her to have been a condemned excursion boat. She wouldn't have been allowed to run to Coney Island.

"She was battered and unpainted, and she wallowed horribly. I don't believe she could have reached Honolulu much before the regular boat, but I couldn't wait, and I took her.

"I made myself as comfortable as possible, bribed the cook to insure myself against starvation, and swung a hammock on the forward deck as far as possible from the worst of the vile smells.

"But we hadn't lost sight of Manila Bay when I discovered that there was a dog aboard—and such a dog! I had never seen one that sent me into such a panic as this one, and he had free range of the ship. A Great Dane he was, named Gulliver, and he was the pride of the captain's rum-soaked heart.

"With all my fear, I realized he was a magnificent animal, but I looked on him as a gigantic devil. Without exception, he was the biggest dog I ever saw, and as muscular as a lion. He lacked some points that show judges set store by, but he had the size and the build.

"I had seen Vohl's Vulcan and the Württemberg breed, but they were fox-terriers compared with Gulliver. His tail was as big around as my arm, and the cook lived in terror of his getting into the galley and wagging it; and he had a mouth that looked to me like the crater of Mauna Loa, and a voice that shook the planking when he spoke.

"I first caught sight of him appearing from behind a huge coil of cordage in the stern. He stretched and yawned, and I nearly died of fright.

"I caught up a belaying-pin, though little good that would have done me. I think he saw me do it, and doubtless he set me down for an enemy then and there.

"We were well out of the harbor, and there was no turning back, but I would have given my right hand to be off that boat. I fully expected him to eat me up, and I slept with that belaying-pin sticking into my ribs in the hammock, and with my revolver loaded and handy.

"Fortunately, Gulliver's dislike for me took the form of sublime contempt. He knew I was afraid of him, and he despised me for it. He was a great pet with the captain and crew, and even the Moros treated him with admiring respect when they were allowed on deck. I couldn't understand it. I would as soon have made a pet of a hungry boa-constrictor.

"On the third day out the poor old boiler burst and the *Old Squaw* caught fire. She was dry and rotten inside and she burned like tinder. No attempt was made to extinguish the flames, which got into the hemp in the hold in short order.

"The smoke was stifling, and in a jiffy all hands were struggling with the boats. The Moros came tumbling up from below and added to the confusion with their terrified yells.

"The davits were old and rusty, and the men were soon fighting among themselves. One boat dropped stern foremost, filled, and sank immediately, and the *Old Squaw* herself was visibly settling.

"I saw there was no chance of getting away in the boats, and I recalled a life-raft on the deck forward near my hammock. It was a sort of catamaran—a double platform on a pair of hollow, watertight, cylindrical buoys. It wasn't twenty feet long and about half as broad, but it would have to do. I fancy it was a forgotten relic of the old excursion-boat days.

"There was no time to lose, for the *Old Squaw* was bound to sink presently. Besides, I was aft with the rest, and the flames were licking up the deck and running-gear in the waist of the boat.

"The galley, which was amidships near the engine-room, had received the full force of the explosion, and the cook lay moaning in the lee scuppers with a small water-cask thumping against his chest. I couldn't stop to help the man, but I did kick the cask away.

"It seemed to be nearly full, and it occurred to me that I should need it. I glanced quickly around, and luckily found a tin of biscuits that had also been blown out of the galley. I picked this up, and rolling the cask of water ahead of me as rapidly as I could, I made my way through the hot, stifling smoke to the bow of the boat.

"I kicked at the life-raft; it seemed to be sound, and I lashed the biscuits and water to it. I also threw on a coil of rope and a piece of sail-cloth. I saw nothing else about that could possibly be of any value to me. I abandoned my trunk for fear it would only prove troublesome.

"Then I hacked the raft loose with my knife and shoved it over the bulwark. Apparently no one had seen me, for there was no one else forward of the sheet of flame that now cut the boat in two.

"The raft was a mighty heavy affair, but I managed to raise one end to the rail. I don't believe I would ever have been able to heave it over under any circumstances, but I didn't have to.

"I felt a great upheaval, and the prow of the *Old Squaw* went up into the air. I grabbed the ropes that I had lashed the food on with and clung to the raft. The deck became almost perpendicular, and it was a miracle that the raft didn't slide down with me into the flames. Somehow it stuck where it was.

"Then the boat sank with a great roar, and for about a thousand years, it seemed to me, I was under water. I didn't do anything, I couldn't think.

"I was only conscious of a tremendous weight of water and a feeling that I would burst open. Instinct alone made me cling to the raft.

"When it finally brought me to the surface I was as nearly dead as I care to be. I lay there on the thing in a half-conscious condition for an endless time. If my life had depended on my doing something, I would have been lost.

"Then gradually I came to, and began to spit out salt water and gasp for breath. I gathered my wits together and sat up. My hands were absolutely numb, and I had to loosen the grip of my fingers with the help of my toes. Odd sensation.

"Then I looked about me. My biscuits and water and rope were safe, but the sail-cloth had vanished. I remember that this annoyed me hugely at the time, though I don't know what earthly good it would have been.

"The sea was fairly calm, and I could see all about. Not a human being was visible, only a few floating bits of wreckage. Every man on board must have gone down with the ship and drowned, except myself.

"Then I caught sight of something that made my heart stand still. The huge head of Gulliver was coming rapidly toward me through the water!

"The dog was swimming strongly, and must have leaped from the *Old Squaw* before she sank. My raft was the only thing afloat large enough to hold him, and he knew it.

"I drew my revolver, but it was soaking wet and useless. Then I sat down on the cracker tin and gritted my teeth and waited. I had been alarmed, I must admit, when the boiler blew up and the panic began, but that was nothing to the terror that seized me now.

"Here I was all alone on the top of the Pacific Ocean with a horrible demon making for me as fast as he could swim. My mind was benumbed, and I could think of nothing to do. I trembled and my teeth rattled. I prayed for a shark, but no shark came.

"Soon Gulliver reached the raft and placed one of his forepaws on it and then the other. The top of it stood six or eight inches above the water, and it took a great effort for the dog to raise himself. I wanted to kick him back, but I didn't dare to move.

"Gulliver struggled mightily. Again and again he reared his great shoulders above the sea, only to be cast back, scratching and kicking, at a lurch of the raft.

"Finally a wave favored him, and he caught the edge of the under platform with one of his hind feet. With a stupendous effort he heaved his huge bulk over the edge and lay sprawling at my feet, panting and trembling."

Enderby paused and gazed out of the window with a big sigh, as though the recital of his story had brought back some of the horror of his remarkable experience.

Nubbins looked up inquiringly, and then snuggled closer to his friend, while Enderby smoothed the white head.

"Well," he continued, "there we were. You can't possibly imagine how I felt unless you, too, have been afflicted with dog-fear. It was awful. And I hated the brute so. I could have torn him limb from limb if I had had the strength. But he was vastly more powerful than I. I could only fear him.

"By and by he got up and shook himself. I cowered on my cracker-tin, but he only looked at me contemptuously, went to the other end of the raft, and lay down to wait patiently for deliverance.

"We remained this way until nightfall. The sea was comparatively calm, and we seemed to be drifting but slowly. We were in the path of ships likely to be passing one way or the other, and I would have been hopeful of the outcome if it had not been for my feared and hated companion.

"I began to feel faint, and opened the cracker-tin. The biscuits were wet with salt water, but I ate a couple, and left the tin open to

dry them. Gulliver looked around, and I shut the tin hastily. But
the dog never moved. He was not disposed to ask any favors. By
kicking the sides of the cask and prying with my knife, I managed
to get the bung out and took a drink. Then I settled myself on the
raft with my back against the cask, and longed for a smoke.

"The gentle motion of the raft produced a lulling effect on my
exhausted nerves, and I began to nod, only to awake with a start,
with fear gripping at my heart. I dared not sleep. I don't know what
I thought Gulliver would do to me, for I did not understand dogs,
but I felt that I must watch him constantly. In the starlight I could
see that his eyes were open. Gulliver was watchful too.

"All night long I kept up a running fight with drowsiness. I dozed
at intervals, but never for long at a time. It was a horrible night, and
I cannot tell you how I longed for day and welcomed it when it came.

"I must have slept toward dawn, for I suddenly became conscious
of broad daylight. I roused myself, stood up, and swung my arms
and legs to stir up circulation, for the night had been chilly. Gulliver
arose, too, and stood silently watching me until I ceased for fear.
When he had settled down again I got my breakfast out of the
cracker-tin. Gulliver was restless, and was evidently interested.

" 'He must be hungry,' I thought, and then a new fear caught me.
I had only to wait until he became very hungry and then he would
surely attack me. I concluded that it would be wiser to feed him, and
I tossed him a biscuit.

"I expected to see him grab it ravenously, and wondered as soon
as I had thrown it if the taste of food would only serve to make him
more ferocious. But at first he would not touch it. He only lay there
with his great head on his paws and glowered at me. Distrust was
plainly visible in his face. I had never realized before that a dog's
face could express the subtler emotions.

"His gaze fascinated me, and I could not take my eyes from his.
The bulk of him was tremendous as he lay there, and I noticed the
big, swelling muscles of his jaw. At last he arose, sniffed suspiciously
at the biscuit, and looked up at me again.

" 'It's all right; eat it!' I cried.

"The sound of my own voice frightened me. I had not intended to speak to him. But in spite of my strained tone he seemed somewhat reassured.

"He took a little nibble, and then swallowed the biscuit after one or two crunches, and looked up expectantly. I threw him another and he ate that.

" 'That's all,' said I. 'We must be sparing of them.'

"I was amazed to discover how perfectly he understood. He lay down again and licked his chops.

"Late in the afternoon I saw a line of smoke on the horizon, and soon a steamer hove into view. I stood up and waved my coat frantically, but to no purpose. Gulliver stood up and looked from me to the steamer, apparently much interested.

" 'Too far off,' I said to Gulliver. 'I hope the next one will come nearer.'

"At midday I dined, and fed Gulliver. This time he took the two biscuits quite without reserve and whacked his great tail against the raft. It seemed to me that his attitude was less hostile, and I wondered at it.

"When I took my drink from the cask, Gulliver showed signs of interest.

" 'I suppose dogs get thirsty, too,' I said aloud.

"Gulliver rapped with his tail. I looked about for some sort of receptacle, and finally pulled off my shoe, filled it with water, and shoved it toward him with my foot. He drank gratefully.

"During the afternoon I sighted another ship, but it was too distant to notice me. However, the sea remained calm and I did not despair.

"After we had had supper, I settled back against my cask, resolved to keep awake, for still I did not trust Gulliver. The sun set suddenly and the stars came out, and I found myself strangely lonesome. It seemed as though I had been alone out there on the Pacific for weeks. The miles and miles of heaving waters, almost on a level with my eye, were beginning to get on my nerves. I longed for someone to talk to, and wished I had dragged the half-breed cook along with me for company. I sighed loudly, and Gulliver raised his head.

" 'Lonesome out here, isn't it?' I said, simply to hear the sound of my own voice.

"Then for the first time Gulliver spoke. He made a deep sound in his throat, but it wasn't a growl, and with all my ignorance of dog language I knew it.

"Then I began to talk. I talked about everything—the people back home and all that—and Gulliver listened. I know more about dogs now, and I know that the best way to make friends with a dog is to talk to him. He can't talk back, but he can understand a heap more than you think he can.

"Finally Gulliver, who had kept his distance all this time, arose and came toward me. My words died in my throat. What was he going to do? To my immense relief he did nothing but sink down at my feet with a grunt and curl his huge body into a semicircle. He had dignity, Gulliver had. He wanted to be friendly, but he would not presume. However, I had lost interest in conversation, and sat watching him and wondering.

"In spite of my firm resolution, I fell asleep at length from sheer exhaustion, and never woke until daybreak. The sky was clouded and our raft was pitching. Gulliver was standing in the middle of the raft, looking at me in evident alarm. I glanced over my shoulder, and the blackness of the horizon told me that a storm was coming, and coming soon.

"I made fast our slender provender, tied the end of a line about my own waist for safety, and waited.

"In a short time the storm struck us in all its tropical fury. The raft pitched and tossed, now high up at one end, and now at the other, and sometimes almost engulfed in the waves.

"Gulliver was having a desperate time to keep aboard. His blunt claws slipped on the wet deck of the raft, and he fell and slid about dangerously. The thought flashed across my mind that the storm might prove to be a blessing in disguise, and that I might soon be rid of the brute.

"As I clung there to the lashings, I saw him slip down to the further end of the raft, his hind quarters actually over the edge. A wave swept over him, but still he clung, panting madly. Then the raft righted itself for a moment, and as he hung there he gave me a look I shall never forget—a look of fear, of pleading, of reproach, and yet of silent courage. And with all my stupidity I read that look. Somehow it told me that I was the master, after all, and he the dog. I could

not resist it. Cautiously I raised myself and loosened the spare rope
I had saved. As the raft tipped the other way Gulliver regained his
footing and came sliding toward me.

"Quickly I passed the rope around his body, and as the raft dived
again I hung on to the rope with one hand, retaining my own hold
with the other. Gulliver's great weight nearly pulled my arm from
its socket, but he helped mightily, and during the next moment of
equilibrium I took another turn about his body and made the end of
the rope fast.

"The storm passed as swiftly as it had come, and though it left us
drenched and exhausted, we were both safe.

"That evening Gulliver crept close to me as I talked, and I let him.
Loneliness will make a man do strange things.

"On the fifth day, when our provisions were nearly gone, and I
had begun to feel the sinking dullness of despair, I sighted a steamer
apparently coming directly toward us. Instantly I felt new life in
my limbs and around my heart, and while the boat was yet miles
away I began to shout and to wave my coat.

" 'I believe she's coming, old man!' I cried to Gulliver. 'I believe
she's coming!'

"I soon wearied of this foolishness and sat down to wait. Gulliver
came close and sat beside me, and for the first time I put my hand on
him. He looked up at me and rapped furiously with his tail. I patted
his head—a little gingerly, I must confess.

"It was a big, smooth head, and it felt solid and strong. I passed
my hand down his neck, his back, his flanks. He seemed to quiver
with joy. He leaned his huge body against me. Then he bowed his
head and licked my shoe.

"A feeling of intense shame and unworthiness came over me, with
the realization of how completely I had misunderstood him. Why
should this great, powerful creature lick my shoe? It was incredible.

"Then, somehow, everything changed. Fear and distrust left me,
and a feeling of comradeship and understanding took their place. We
two had been through so much together. A dog was no longer a
frightful beast to me; he was a dog! I cannot think of a nobler word.
And Gulliver had licked my shoe! Doubtless it was only the fineness
of his perception that had prevented him from licking my hand. I

might have resented that. I put my arms suddenly around Gulliver's neck and hugged him, I loved that dog!

"Slowly, slowly, the steamer crawled along, but still kept to her course. When she was about a mile away, however, I saw that she would not pass as close to us as I had hoped; so I began once more my waving and yelling. She came nearer, nearer, but still showed no sign of observing us.

"She was abreast of us, and passing. I was in a frenzy!

"She was so near that I could make out the figure of the captain on the bridge, and other figures on the deck below. It seemed as though they must see us, though I realized how low in the water we stood, and how pitifully weak and hoarse my voice was. I had been a fool to waste it. Then an idea struck me.

"'Speak!' I cried to Gulliver, who stood watching beside me. 'Speak, old man!'

"Gulliver needed no second bidding. A roar like that of all the bulls of Bashan rolled out over the blue Pacific. Again and again Gulliver gave voice, deep, full, powerful. His great side heaved with the mighty effort, his red, cavernous mouth open, and his head raised high.

"'Good, old man!' I cried. 'Good!' And again that magnificent voice boomed forth.

"Then something happened on board the steamer. The figures came to the side. I waved my coat and danced. Then they saw us.

"I was pretty well done up when they took us aboard, and I slept for twenty-four hours straight. When I awoke there sat Gulliver by my bunk, and when I turned to look at him he lifted a great paw and put it on my arm."

Enderby ceased, and there was silence in the room save for the light snoring of Nubbins.

"You took him home with you, I suppose?" I asked.

Enderby nodded.

"And you have him still?" I certainly wanted to have a look at that dog.

But he did not answer. I saw an expression of great sadness come into his eyes as he gazed out of the window, and I knew that Jacob Enderby had finished his story.

The Bar Sinister

BY

RICHARD HARDING DAVIS

THE Master was walking most unsteady, his legs tripping each other. After the fifth or sixth round, my legs often go the same way.

But even when the Master's legs bend and twist a bit, you mustn't think he can't reach you. Indeed, that is the time he kicks most frequent. So I kept behind him in the shadow, or ran in the middle of the street. He stopped at many public houses with swinging doors, those doors that are cut so high from the sidewalk that you can look in under them, and see if the Master is inside. At night, when I peep beneath them, the man at the counter will see me first and say, "Here's the Kid, Jerry, come to take you home. Get a move on you"; and the Master will stumble out and follow me. It's lucky for us I'm so white, for, no matter how dark the night, he can always see me ahead, just out of reach of his boot. At night the Master certainly does see most amazing. Sometimes he sees two or four of me, and walks in a circle, so that I have to take him by the leg of his trousers and lead him into the right road. One night, when he was very nasty-tempered and I was coaxing him along, two men passed us, and one of them says, "Look at that brute!" and the other asks, "Which?" and they both laugh. The Master he cursed them good and proper.

But this night, whenever we stopped at a public house, the Master's pals left it and went on with us to the next. They spoke quite civil to me, and when the Master tried a flying kick, they gives him a shove. "Do you want us to lose our money?" says the pals.

91

I had had nothing to eat for a day and a night, and just before we set out the Master gives me a wash under the hydrant. Whenever I am locked up until all the slop-pans in our alley are empty, and made to take a bath, and the Master's pals speak civil and feel my ribs, I know something is going to happen. And that night, when every time they see a policeman under a lamp-post, they dodged across the street, and when at the last one of them picked me up and hid me under his jacket, I began to tremble; for I knew what it meant. It meant that I was to fight again for the Master.

I don't fight because I like fighting. I fight because if I didn't the other dog would find my throat, and the Master would lose his stakes, and I would be very sorry for him, and ashamed. Dogs can pass me and I can pass dogs, and I'd never pick a fight with none of them. When I see two dogs standing on their hind legs in the streets, claw-ing each other's ears, and snapping for each other's windpipes, or howling and swearing and rolling in the mud, I feel sorry they should act so, and pretend not to notice. If he'd let me, I'd like to pass the time of day with every dog I meet. But there's something about me that no nice dog can abide. When I trot up to nice dogs, nodding and grinning, to make friends, they always tell me to be off. "Go to the devil!" they bark at me. "Get out!" And when I walk away they shout "Mongrel!" and "Gutter-dog!" and sometimes, after my back is turned, they rush me. I could kill most of them with three shakes, breaking the backbone of the little ones and squeezing the throat of the big ones. But what's the good? They *are* nice dogs; that's why I try to make up to them: and, though it's not for them to say it, I *am* a street-dog, and if I try to push into the company of my betters, I suppose it's their right to teach me my place.

Of course they don't know I'm the best fighting bull-terrier of my weight in Montreal. That's why it wouldn't be fair for me to take notice of what they shout. They don't know that if I once locked my jaws on them I'd carry away whatever I touched. The night I fought Kelley's White Rat, I wouldn't loosen up until the Master made a noose in my leash and strangled me; and, as for that Ottawa dog, if the handlers hadn't thrown red pepper down my nose I *never* would have let go of him. I don't think the handlers treated me quite right that time, but maybe they didn't know the Ottawa dog was dead. I did.

I learned my fighting from my mother when I was very young. We slept in a lumber-yard on the river-front, and by day hunted for food along the wharves. When we got it, the other tramp-dogs would try to take it off us, and then it was wonderful to see mother fly at them and drive them away. All I know of fighting I learned from mother, watching her picking the ash-heaps for me when I was too little to fight for myself. No one ever was so good to me as mother. When it snowed and the ice was in the St. Lawrence, she used to hunt alone, and bring me back new bones, and she'd sit and laugh to see me trying to swallow 'em whole. I was just a puppy then; my teeth was falling out. When I was able to fight we kept the whole river-range to ourselves. I had the genuine long "punishing" jaw, so mother said, and there wasn't a man or a dog that dared worry us. Those were happy days, those were; and we lived well, share and share alike, and when we wanted a bit of fun, we chased the fat old wharf-rats! My, how they would squeal!

Then the trouble came. It was no trouble to me. I was too young to care then. But mother took it so to heart that she grew ailing, and wouldn't go abroad with me by day. It was the same old scandal that they're always bringing up against me. I was so young then that I didn't know. I couldn't see any difference between mother—and other mothers.

But one day a pack of curs we drove off snarled back some new names at her, and mother dropped her head and ran, just as though they had whipped us. After that she wouldn't go out with me except in the dark, and one day she went away and never came back, and, though I hunted for her in every court and alley and back street of Montreal, I never found her.

One night, a month after mother ran away, I asked Guardian, the old blind mastiff, whose Master is the night watchman on our slip, what it all meant. And he told me.

"Every dog in Montreal knows," he says, "except you; and every Master knows. So I think it's time you knew."

Then he tells me that my father, who had treated mother so bad, was a great and noble gentleman from London. "Your father had

twenty-two registered ancestors, had your father," old Guardian
says, "and in him was the best bull-terrier blood of England, the most
ancientest, the most royal; the winning 'blue-ribbon' blood, that
breeds champions. He had sleepy pink eyes and thin pink lips, and
he was as white all over as his own white teeth, and under his white
skin you could see his muscles, hard and smooth, like the links of
a steel chain. When your father stood still, and tipped his nose in
the air, it was just as though he was saying, 'Oh, yes, you common
dogs and men, you may well stare. It must be a rare treat for you
colonials to see real English royalty.' He certainly was pleased with
hisself, was your father. He looked just as proud and haughty as one
of them stone dogs in Victoria Park—them as is cut out of white
marble. And you're like him," says the old mastiff—"by that, of
course, meaning you're white, same as him. That's the only likeness.
But, you see, the trouble is, Kid—well, you see, Kid, the trouble is—
your mother—"

"That will do," I said, for then I understood without his telling
me, and I got up and walked away, holding my head and tail high
in the air.

But I was, oh, so miserable, and I wanted to see mother that very
minute, and tell her that I didn't care.

Mother is what I am, a street-dog; there's no royal blood in
mother's veins, nor is she like that father of mine, nor—and that's the
worst—she's not even like me. For while I, when I'm washed for a
fight, am as white as clean snow, she—and this is our trouble—she,
my mother, is a black-and-tan.

When mother hid herself from me, I was twelve months old and
able to take care of myself, and as, after mother left me, the wharves
were never the same, I moved uptown and met the Master. Before
he came, lots of other men-folks had tried to make up to me, and to
whistle me home. But they either tried patting me or coaxing me
with a piece of meat; so I didn't take to 'em. But one day the Master
pulled me out of a street-fight by the hind legs, and kicked me good.

"You want to fight, do you?" says he. "I'll give you all the *fighting*
you want!" he says, and he kicks me again. So I knew he was my
Master, and I followed him home. Since that day I've pulled off
many fights for him, and they've brought dogs from all over the

province to have a go at me; but up to that night none, under thirty pounds, had ever downed me.

But that night, so soon as they carried me into the ring, I saw the dog was overweight, and that I was no match for him. It was asking too much of a puppy. The Master should have known I couldn't do it. Not that I mean to blame the Master, for when sober, which he sometimes was—though not, as you might say, his habit—he was most kind to me, and let me out to find food, if I could get it, and only kicked me when I didn't pick him up at night and lead him home.

But kicks will stiffen the muscles, and starving a dog so as to get him ugly-tempered for a fight may make him nasty, but it's weakening to his insides, and it causes the legs to wobble.

The ring was in a hall back of a public house. There was a red-hot whitewashed stove in one corner, and the ring in the other. I lay in the Master's lap, wrapped in my blanket, and, spite of the stove, shivering awful; but I always shiver before a fight: I can't help gettin' excited. While the men-folks were a-flashing their money and taking their last drink at the bar, a little Irish groom in gaiters came up to me and give me the back of his hand to smell, and scratched me behind the ears.

"You poor little pup," says he; "you haven't no show," he says. "That brute in the tap-room he'll eat your heart out."

"That's what *you* think," says the Master, snarling. "I'll lay you a quid the Kid chews him up."

The groom he shook his head, but kept looking at me so sorry-like that I begun to get a bit sad myself. He seemed like he couldn't bear to leave off a-patting of me, and he says, speaking low just like he would to a man-folk, "Well, good luck to you, little pup," which I thought so civil of him that I reached up and licked his hand. I don't do that to many men. And the Master he knew I didn't, and took on dreadful.

"What 'ave you got on the back of your hand?" says he, jumping up.

"Soap!" says the groom, quick as a rat. "That's more than you've got on yours. Do you want to smell of it?" and he sticks his fist under the Master's nose. But the pals pushed in between 'em.

"He tried to poison the Kid!" shouts the Master.

"Oh, one fight at a time," says the referee. "Get into the ring, Jerry. We're waiting." So we went into the ring.

I never could just remember what did happen in that ring. He give me no time to spring. He fell on me like a horse. I couldn't keep my feet against him, and though, as I saw, he could get his hold when he liked, he wanted to chew me over a bit first. I was wondering if they'd be able to pry him off me, when, in the third round, he took his hold; and I begun to drown, just as I did when I fell into the river off the Red C slip. He closed deeper and deeper on my throat, and everything went black and red and bursting; and then, when I were sure I were dead, the handlers pulled him off, and the Master gave me a kick that brought me to. But I couldn't move none, or even wink, both eyes being shut with lumps.

"He's a cur!" yells the Master, "a sneaking, cowardly cur! He lost the fight for me," says he, "because he's a —— —— —— cowardly cur." And he kicks me again in the lower ribs, so that I go sliding across the sawdust. "There's gratitude fer yer," yells the Master. "I've fed that dog, and nussed that dog and housed him like a prince; and now he puts his tail between his legs and sells me out, he does. He's a coward! I've done with him, I am. I'd sell him for a pipeful of tobacco." He picked me up by the tail, and swung me for the men-folks to see. "Does any gentleman here want to buy a dog," he says, "to make into sausage-meat?" he says. "That's all he's good for."

Then I heard the little Irish groom say, "I'll give you ten bob for the dog."

And another voice says, "Ah, don't you do it; the dog's same as dead—mebbe he is dead."

"Ten shillings!" says the Master, and his voice sobers a bit; "make it two pounds and he's yours."

But the pals rushed in again.

"Don't you be a fool, Jerry," they say. "You'll be sorry for this when you're sober. The Kid's worth a fiver."

One of my eyes was not so swelled up as the other, and as I hung by my tail, I opened it, and saw one of the pals take the groom by the shoulder.

"You ought to give 'im five pounds for that dog, mate," he says;

"that's no ordinary dog. That dog's got good blood in him, that dog has. Why, his father—that very dog's father—"

I thought he never would go on. He waited like he wanted to be sure the groom was listening.

"That very dog's father," says the pal, "is Regent Royal, son of Champion Regent Monarch, champion bull-terrier of England for four years."

I was sore, and torn, and chewed most awful, but what the pal said sounded so fine that I wanted to wag my tail, only couldn't, owing to my hanging from it.

But the Master calls out: "Yes, his father was Regent Royal; who's saying he wasn't? but the pup's a cowardly cur, that's what his pup is. And why? I'll tell you why: because his mother was a black-and-tan street-dog, that's why!"

I don't see how I got the strength, but, someway, I threw myself out of the Master's grip and fell at his feet, and turned over and fastened all my teeth in his ankle, just across the bone.

When I woke, after the pals had kicked me off him, I was in the smoking-car of a railroad-train, lying in the lap of the little groom, and he was rubbing my open wounds with a greasy yellow stuff, exquisite to the smell and most agreeable to lick off.

PART II

"Well, what's your name—Nolan? Well, Nolan, these references are satisfactory," said the young gentleman my new Master called "Mr. Wyndham, sir." "I'll take you on as second man. You can begin to-day."

My new Master shuffled his feet and put his finger to his forehead. "Thank you, sir," says he. Then he choked like he had swallowed a fish-bone. "I have a little dawg, sir," says he.

"You can't keep him," says "Mr. Wyndham, sir," very short.

" 'E's only a puppy, sir," says my new Master; " 'e wouldn't go outside the stables, sir."

"It's not that," says "Mr. Wyndham, sir." "I have a large kennel of very fine dogs; they're the best of their breed in America. I don't allow strange dogs on the premises."

The Master shakes his head, and motions me with his cap, and I crept out from behind the door. "I'm sorry, sir," says the Master. "Then I can't take the place. I can't get along without the dawg, sir."

"Mr. Wyndham, sir," looked at me that fierce that I guessed he was going to whip me, so I turned over on my back and begged with my legs and tail.

"Why, you beat him!" says "Mr. Wyndham, sir," very stern.

"No fear!" the Master says, getting very red. "The party I bought him off taught him that. He never learnt that from me!" He picked me up in his arms, and to show "Mr. Wyndham, sir," how well I loved the Master, I bit his chin and hands.

"Mr. Wyndham, sir," turned over the letters the Master had given him. "Well, these references certainly are very strong," he says. "I guess I'll let the dog stay. Only see you keep him away from the kennels—or you'll both go."

"Thank you, sir," says the Master, grinning like a cat when she's safe behind the area railing.

"He's not a bad bull-terrier," says "Mr. Wyndham, sir," feeling my head. "Not that I know much about the smooth-coated breeds. My dogs are St. Bernards." He stopped patting me and held up my nose. "What's the matter with his ears?" he says. "They're chewed to pieces. Is this a fighting dog?" he asks, quick and rough-like.

I could have laughed. If he hadn't been holding my nose, I certainly would have had a good grin at him. Me the best under thirty pounds in the Province of Quebec, and him asking if I was a fighting dog! I ran to the Master and hung down my head modest-like, waiting for him to tell my list of battles; but the Master he coughs in his cap most painful. "Fightin' dawg, sir!" he cries. "Lor' bless you, sir, the Kid don't know the word. 'E's just a puppy, sir, same as you see; a pet dog, so to speak. 'E's a regular old lady's lap-dog, the Kid is."

"Well, you keep him away from my St. Bernards," says "Mr. Wyndham, sir," "or they might make a mouthful of him."

"Yes, sir; that they might," says the Master. But when we gets outside he slaps his knee and laughs inside hisself, and winks at me most sociable.

The Master's new home was in the country, in a province they called Long Island. There was a high stone wall about his home with

big iron gates to it, same as Godfrey's brewery; and there was a house
with five red roofs; and the stables, where I lived, was cleaner than
the aërated bakery-shop. And then there was the kennels; but they
was like nothing else in this world that ever I see. For the first days
I couldn't sleep of nights for fear some one would catch me lying
in such a cleaned-up place, and would chase me out of it; and when
I did fall to sleep I'd dream I was back in the old Master's attic, shivering under the rusty stove, which never had no coals in it, with the
Master flat on his back on the cold floor, with his clothes on. And I'd
wake up scared and whimpering, and find myself on the new Master's
cot with his hand on the quilt beside me; and I'd see the glow of the
big stove, and hear the high-quality horses below-stairs stamping in
their straw-lined boxes, and I'd snoop the sweet smell of hay and
harness-soap and go to sleep again.

The stables was my jail, so the Master said, but I don't ask no better
home than that jail.

"Now, Kid," says he, sitting on the top of a bucket upside down,
"you've got to understand this. When I whistle it means you're not
to go out of this 'ere yard. These stables is your jail. If you leave 'em
I'll have to leave 'em too, and over the seas, in the County Mayo, an
old mother will 'ave to leave her bit of a cottage. For two pounds I
must be sending her every month, or she'll have naught to eat, nor
no thatch over 'er head. I can't lose my place, Kid, so see you don't
lose it for me. You must keep away from the kennels," says he;
"they're not for the likes of you. The kennels are for the quality.
I wouldn't take a litter of them woolly dogs for one wag of your
tail, Kid, but for all that they are your betters, same as the gentry up
in the big house are my betters. I know my place and keep away from
the gentry, and you keep away from the champions."

So I never goes out of the stables. All day I just lay in the sun on
the stone flags, licking my jaws, and watching the grooms wash down
the carriages, and the only care I had was to see they didn't get gay
and turn the hose on me. There wasn't even a single rat to plague
me. Such stables I never did see.

"Nolan," says the head groom, "some day that dog of yours will
give you the slip. You can't keep a street-dog tied up all his life. It's
against his natur'." The head groom is a nice old gentleman, but he

doesn't know everything. Just as though I'd been a street-dog because I liked it! As if I'd rather poke for my vittles in ash-heaps than
have 'em handed me in a wash-basin, and would sooner bite and
fight than be polite and sociable. If I'd had mother there I couldn't
have asked for nothing more. But I'd think of her snooping in the
gutters, or freezing of nights under the bridges, or, what's worst of
all, running through the hot streets with her tongue down, so wild
and crazy for a drink that the people would shout "mad dog" at her
and stone her. Water's so good that I don't blame the men-folks for
locking it up inside their houses; but when the hot days come, I think
they might remember that those are the dog-days, and leave a little
water outside in a trough, like they do for the horses. Then we
wouldn't go mad, and the policemen wouldn't shoot us. I had so
much of everything I wanted that it made me think a lot of the days
when I hadn't nothing, and if I could have given what I had to
mother, as she used to share with me, I'd have been the happiest dog
in the land. Not that I wasn't happy then, and most grateful to the
Master, too, and if I'd only minded him, the trouble wouldn't have
come again.

But one day the coachman says that the little lady they called Miss
Dorothy had come back from school, and that same morning she
runs over to the stables to pat her ponies, and she sees me.

"Oh, what a nice little, white little dog!" said she. "Whose little
dog are you?" says she.

"That's my dog, miss," says the Master. " 'Is name is Kid." And I
ran up to her most polite, and licks her fingers, for I never see so
pretty and kind a lady.

"You must come with me and call on my new puppies," says she,
picking me up in her arms, and starting off with me.

"Oh, but please, miss," cries Nolan, "Mr. Wyndham give orders
that the Kid's not to go to the kennels."

"That'll be all right," says the little lady; "they're my kennels too.
And the puppies will like to play with him."

You wouldn't believe me if I was to tell you of the style of them
quality-dogs. If I hadn't seen it myself I wouldn't have believed it
neither. The Viceroy of Canada don't live no better. There was forty
of them, but each one had his own house and a yard—most exclusive

—and a cot and a drinking-basin all to hisself. They had servants standing round waiting to feed 'em when they was hungry, and valets to wash 'em; and they had their hair combed and brushed like the grooms must when they go out on the box. Even the puppies had overcoats with their names on 'em in blue letters, and the name of each of those they called champions was painted up fine over his front door just like it was a public house or a veterinary's. They were the biggest St. Bernards I ever did see. I could have walked under them if they'd have let me. But they were very proud and haughty dogs, and looked only once at me, and then sniffed in the air. The little lady's own dog was an old gentleman bull-dog. He'd come along with us, and when he notices how taken aback I was with all I see, 'e turned quite kind and affable and showed me about.

"Jimmy Jocks," Miss Dorothy called him, but, owing to his weight, he walked most dignified and slow, waddling like a duck, as you might say, and looked much too proud and handsome for such a silly name.

"That's the runway, and that's the trophy-house," says he to me, "and that over there is the hospital, where you have to go if you get distemper, and the vet gives you beastly medicine."

"And which of these is your 'ouse, sir?" asks I, wishing to be respectful. But he looked that hurt and haughty. "I don't live in the kennels," says he, most contemptuous. "I am a house-dog. I sleep in Miss Dorothy's room. And at lunch I'm let in with the family, if the visitors don't mind. They 'most always do, but they're too polite to say so. Besides," says he, smiling most condescending, "visitors are always afraid of me. It's because I'm so ugly," says he. "I suppose," says he, screwing up his wrinkles and speaking very slow and impressive, "I suppose I'm the ugliest bull-dog in America"; and as he seemed to be so pleased to think hisself so, I said, "Yes, sir; you certainly are the ugliest ever I see," at which he nodded his head most approving.

"But I couldn't hurt 'em, as you say," he goes on, though I hadn't said nothing like that, being too polite. "I'm too old," he says; "I haven't any teeth. The last time one of those grizzly bears," said he, glaring at the big St. Bernards, "took a hold of me, he nearly was my death," says he. I thought his eyes would pop out of his head, he seemed so wrought up about it. "He rolled me around in the dirt, he did," says Jimmy Jocks, "an' I couldn't get up. It was low," says Jimmy Jocks, making a face like he had a bad taste in his mouth. "Low, that's what I call it—bad form, you understand, young man, not done in my set—and—and low." He growled 'way down in his stomach, and puffed hisself out, panting and blowing like he had been on a run.

"I'm not a street fighter," he says, scowling at a St. Bernard marked "Champion." "And when my rheumatism is not troubling me," he says, "I endeavor to be civil to all dogs, so long as they are gentlemen."

"Yes, sir," said I, for even to me he had been most affable.

At this we had come to a little house off by itself, and Jimmy Jocks invites me in. "This is their trophy-room," he says, "where they keep their prizes. Mine," he says, rather grandlike, "are on the sideboard." Not knowing what a sideboard might be, I said, "Indeed, sir, that must be very gratifying." But he only wrinkled up his chops as much as to say, "It is my right."

The trophy-room was as wonderful as any public house I ever see. On the walls was pictures of nothing but beautiful St. Bernard dogs, and rows and rows of blue and red and yellow ribbons; and when I asked Jimmy Jocks why they was so many more of blue than of the others, he laughs and says, "Because these kennels always win." And there was many shining cups on the shelves, which Jimmy Jocks told me were prizes won by the champions.

"Now, sir, might I ask you, sir," says I, "wot is a champion?"

At that he panted and breathed so hard I thought he would bust hisself. "My dear young friend!" says he, "wherever have you been educated? A champion is a—a champion," he says. "He must win nine blue ribbons in the 'open' class. You follow me—that is—against all comers. Then he has the title before his name, and they put his photograph in the sporting papers. You know, of course, that *I* am a champion," says he. "I am Champion Woodstock Wizard III, and the two other Woodstock Wizards, my father and uncle, were both champions."

"But I thought your name was Jimmy Jocks," I said.

He laughs right out at that.

"That's my kennel name, not my registered name," he says. "Why, certainly, you know that every dog has two names. Now, for instance, what's your registered name and number?" says he.

"I've got only one name," I says. "Just Kid."

Woodstock Wizard puffs at that and wrinkles up his forehead and pops out his eyes.

"Who are your people?" says he. "Where is your home?"

"At the stable, sir," I said. "My Master is the second groom."

At that Woodstock Wizard III looks at me for quite a bit without winking, and stares all around the room over my head.

"Oh, well," says he at last, "you're a very civil young dog," says he, "and I blame no one for what he can't help," which I thought most fair and liberal. "And I have known many bull-terriers that were champions," says he, "though as a rule they mostly run with fire-engines and to fighting. For me, I wouldn't care to run through the streets after a hose-cart, nor to fight," says he: "but each to his taste."

I could not help thinking that if Woodstock Wizard III tried to follow a fire-engine he would die of apoplexy, and seeing he'd lost his teeth, it was lucky he had no taste for fighting; but, after his being so condescending, I didn't say nothing.

"Anyway," says he, "every smooth-coated dog is better than any hairy old camel like those St. Bernards, and if ever you're hungry down at the stables, young man, come up to the house and I'll give you a bone. I can't eat them myself, but I bury them around the garden from force of habit and in case a friend should drop in. Ah, I see my mistress coming," he says, "and I bid you good day. I regret," he says, "that our different social position prevents our meeting frequent, for you're a worthy young dog with a proper respect for your betters, and in this country there's precious few of them have that." Then he waddles off, leaving me alone and very sad, for he was the first dog in many days that had spoke to me. But since he showed, seeing that I was a stable-dog, he didn't want my company, I waited for him to get well away. It was not a cheerful place to wait, the trophy-house. The pictures of the champions seemed to scowl at me, and ask what right such as I had even to admire them, and the blue and gold ribbons and the silver cups made me very miserable. I had never won no blue ribbons or silver cups, only stakes for the old Master to spend in the publics; and I hadn't won them for being a beautiful high-quality dog, but just for fighting—which, of course, as Woodstock Wizard III says, is low. So I started for the stables, with my head down and my tail between my legs, feeling sorry I had ever left the Master. But I had more reason to be sorry before I got back to him.

The trophy-house was quite a bit from the kennels, and as I left it I see Miss Dorothy and Woodstock Wizard III walking back toward them, and, also, that a big St. Bernard, his name was Champion Red Elfberg, had broke his chain and was running their way. When he reaches old Jimmy Jocks he lets out a roar like a grain-steamer in a fog, and he makes three leaps for him. Old Jimmy Jocks was about a fourth his size; but he plants his feet and curves his back, and his hair goes up around his neck like a collar. But he never had no show at no time, for the grizzly bear, as Jimmy Jocks had called him, lights on old Jimmy's back and tries to break it, and old Jimmy Jocks snaps his gums and claws the grass, panting and groaning awful. But he can't do nothing, and the grizzly bear just rolls him under him, biting and tearing cruel. The odds was all that Woodstock Wizard III was going to be killed; I had fought enough to see that: but not knowing the rules of the game among champions, I didn't like to interfere between two gentlemen who might be settling a private affair, and, as it were, take it as presuming of me. So I stood by, though I was shaking terrible, and holding myself in like I was on a leash. But that Woodstock Wizard III, who was underneath, sees me through the dust, and calls very faint, "Help, you!" he says. "Take him in the hind leg," he says. "He's murdering me," he says. And then the little Miss Dorothy, who was crying, and calling to the kennel-men, catches at the Red Elfberg's hind legs to pull him off, and the brute, keeping his front pats well in Jimmy's stomach, turns his big head and snaps at her. So that was all I asked for, thank you. I went up under him. It was really nothing. He stood so high that I had only to take off about three feet from him and come in from the side, and my long "punishing jaw," as mother was always talking about, locked on his woolly throat, and my back teeth met. I couldn't shake him, but I shook myself, and every time I shook my-

self there was thirty pounds of weight tore at his windpipes. I
couldn't see nothing for his long hair, but I heard Jimmy Jocks puffing and blowing on one side, and munching the brute's leg with his
old gums. Jimmy was an old sport that day, was Jimmy, or Woodstock Wizard III, as I should say. When the Red Elfberg was out
and down I had to run, or those kennel-men would have had my life.
They chased me right into the stables; and from under the hay I
watched the head groom take down a carriage-whip and order them
to the right about. Luckily Master and the young grooms were
out, or that day there'd have been fighting for everybody.

Well, it nearly did for me and the Master. "Mr. Wyndham, sir,"
comes raging to the stables. I'd half killed his best prize-winner, he
says, and had oughter be shot, and he gives the Master his notice.
But Miss Dorothy she follows him, and says it was his Red Elfberg
what began the fight, and that I'd saved Jimmy's life, and that old
Jimmy Jocks was worth more to her than all the St. Bernards in the
Swiss mountains—wherever they may be. And that I was her
champion, anyway. Then she cried over me most beautiful, and over
Jimmy Jocks, too, who was that tied up in bandages he couldn't even
waddle. So when he heard that side of it, "Mr. Wyndham, sir," told
us that if Nolan put me on a chain we could stay. So it came out
all right for everybody but me. I was glad the Master kept his place,
but I'd never worn a chain before, and it disheartened me. But that
was the least of it. For the quality-dogs couldn't forgive my whipping their champion, and they came to the fence between the kennels
and the stables, and laughed through the bars, barking most cruel
words at me. I couldn't understand how they found it out, but they
knew. After the fight Jimmy Jocks was most condescending to me,
and he said the grooms had boasted to the kennel-men that I was a
son of Regent Royal, and that when the kennel-men asked who was
my mother they had had to tell them that too. Perhaps that was the
way of it, but, however, the scandal got out, and every one of the
quality-dogs knew that I was a street-dog and the son of a black-
and-tan.

"These misalliances will occur," said Jimmy Jocks, in his old-
fashioned way; "but no well-bred dog," says he, looking most scornful at the St. Bernards, who were howling behind the palings, "would

refer to your misfortune before you, certainly not cast it in your face. I myself remember your father's father, when he made his début at the Crystal Palace. He took four blue ribbons and three specials."

But no sooner than Jimmy would leave me the St. Bernards would take to howling again, insulting mother and insulting me. And when I tore at my chain, they, seeing they were safe, would howl the more. It was never the same after that; the laughs and the jeers cut into my heart, and the chain bore heavy on my spirit. I was so sad that sometimes I wished I was back in the gutter again, where no one was better than me, and some nights I wished I was dead. If it hadn't been for the Master being so kind, and that it would have looked like I was blaming mother, I would have twisted my leash and hanged myself.

About a month after my fight, the word was passed through the kennels that the New York Show was coming, and such goings on as followed I never did see. If each of them had been matched to fight for a thousand pounds and the gate, they couldn't have trained more conscientious. But perhaps that's just my envy. The kennel-men rubbed 'em and scrubbed 'em, and trims their hair and curls and combs it, and some dogs they fatted and some they starved. No one talked of nothing but the Show, and the chances "our kennels" had against the other kennels, and if this one of our champions would win over that one, and whether them as hoped to be champions had better show in the "open" or the "limit" class, and whether this dog would beat his own dad, or whether his little puppy sister couldn't beat the two of 'em. Even the grooms had their money up, and day or night you heard nothing but praises of "our" dogs, until I, being so far out of it, couldn't have felt meaner if I had been running the streets with a can to my tail. I knew shows were not for such as me, and so all day I lay stretched at the end of my chain, pretending I was asleep, and only too glad that they had something so important to think of that they could leave me alone.

But one day, before the Show opened, Miss Dorothy came to the stables with "Mr. Wyndham, sir," and seeing me chained up and so miserable, she takes me in her arms.

"You poor little tyke!" says she. "It's cruel to tie him up so; he's eating his heart out, Nolan," she says. "I don't know nothing about bull-terriers," says she, "but I think Kid's got good points," says she, "and you ought to show him. Jimmy Jocks has three legs on the Rensselaer Cup now, and I'm going to show him this time, so that he can get the fourth; and, if you wish, I'll enter your dog too. How would you like that, Kid?" says she. "How would you like to see the most beautiful dogs in the world? Maybe you'd meet a pal or two," says she. "It would cheer you up, wouldn't it, Kid?" says she. But I was so upset I could only wag my tail most violent. "He says it would!" says she, though, being that excited, I hadn't said nothing.

So "Mr. Wyndham, sir," laughs, and takes out a piece of blue paper and sits down at the head groom's table.

"What's the name of the father of your dog, Nolan?" says he. And Nolan says: "The man I got him off told me he was a son of Champion Regent Royal, sir. But it don't seem likely, does it?" says Nolan.

"It does not!" says "Mr. Wyndham, sir," short-like.

"Aren't you sure, Nolan?" says Miss Dorothy.

"No, miss," says the Master.

"Sire unknown," says Mr. Wyndham, sir," and writes it down.

"Date of birth?" asks "Mr. Wyndham, sir."

"I—I—unknown, sir," says Nolan. And "Mr. Wyndham, sir," writes it down.

"Breeder?" says "Mr. Wyndham, sir."

"Unknown," says Nolan, getting very red around the jaws, and I drops my head and tail. And "Mr. Wyndham, sir," writes that down.

"Mother's name?" says "Mr. Wyndham, sir."

"She was a—unknown," says the Master. And I licks his hand.

"Dam unknown," says "Mr. Wyndham, sir," and writes it down. Then he takes the paper and reads out loud: " 'Sire unknown, dam unknown, breeder unknown, date of birth unknown.' You'd better call him the 'Great Unknown,' " says he. "Who's paying his entrance fee?"

"I am," says Miss Dorothy.

Two weeks after we all got on a train for New York, Jimmy Jocks and me following Nolan in the smoking-car, and twenty-two of the St. Bernards in boxes and crates and on chains and leashes. Such a barking and howling I never did hear; and when they sees me going, too, they laughs fit to kill.

"Wot is this—a circus?" says the railroad man.

But I had no heart in it. I hated to go. I knew I was no "show" dog, even though Miss Dorothy and the Master did their best to keep me from shaming them. For before we set out Miss Dorothy brings a man from town who scrubbed and rubbed me, and sand-papered my tail, which hurt most awful, and shaved my ears with the Master's razor, so you could 'most see clear through 'em, and sprinkles me over with pipe-clay, till I shines like a Tommy's cross-belts.

"Upon my word!" says Jimmy Jocks when he first sees me. "Wot a swell you are! You're the image of your grand-dad when he made his début at the Crystal Palace. He took four firsts and three specials." But I knew he was only trying to throw heart into me. They might scrub, and they might rub, and they might pipe-clay, but they couldn't pipe-clay the insides of me, and they was black-and-tan.

Then we came to a garden, which it was not, but the biggest hall in the world. Inside there was lines of benches a few miles long, and on them sat every dog in America. If all the dog-snatchers in Montreal had worked night and day for a year, they couldn't have caught so many dogs. And they was all shouting and barking and howling so vicious that my heart stopped beating. For at first I thought they was all enraged at my presuming to intrude. But after I got in my place they kept at it just the same, barking at every dog as he come in: daring him to fight, and ordering him out, and asking him what breed of dog he thought he was, anyway. Jimmy Jocks was chained just behind me, and he said he never see so fine a show. "That's a hot class you're in, my lad," he says, looking over into my street, where there were thirty bull-terriers. They was all as white as cream, and each so beautiful that if I could have broke my chain I would have run all the way home and hid myself under the horse-trough.

All night long they talked and sang, and passed greetings with old pals, and the homesick puppies howled dismal. Them that couldn't sleep wouldn't let no others sleep, and all the electric lights burned in the roof, and in my eyes. I could hear Jimmy Jocks snoring peaceful, but I could only doze by jerks, and when I dozed I dreamed horrible.

All the dogs in the hall seemed coming at me for daring to intrude, with their jaws red and open, and their eyes blazing like the lights in the roof. "You're a street-dog! Get out, you street-dog!" they yells. And as they drives me out, the pipe-clay drops off me, and they laugh and shriek; and when I looks down I see that I have turned into a black-and-tan.

They was most awful dreams, and next morning, when Miss Dorothy comes and gives me water in a pan, I begs and begs her to take me home; but she can't understand. "How well Kid is!" she says. And when I jumps into the Master's arms and pulls to break my chain, he says, "If he knew all as he had against him, miss, he wouldn't be so gay." And from a book they reads out the names of the beautiful high-bred terriers which I have got to meet. And I can't make 'em understand that I only want to run away and hide myself where no one will see me.

Then suddenly men comes hurrying down our street and begins to brush the beautiful bull-terriers; and the Master rubs me with a towel so excited that his hands trembles awful, and Miss Dorothy tweaks my ears between her gloves, so that the blood runs to 'em, and they turn pink and stand up straight and sharp.

"Now, then, Nolan," says she, her voice shaking just like his fingers, "keep his head up—and never let the judge lose sight of him." When I hears that my legs breaks under me, for I knows all about judges. Twice the old Master goes up before the judge for fighting me with other dogs, and the judge promises him if he ever does it again he'll chain him up in jail. I knew he'd find me out. A judge can't be fooled by no pipe-clay. He can see right through you, and he reads your insides.

The judging-ring, which is where the judge holds out, was so like a fighting-pit that when I come in it, and find six other dogs there, I springs into position, so that when they lets us go I can defend myself. But the Master smooths down my hair and whispers, "Hold 'ard, Kid, hold 'ard. This ain't a fight," says he. "Look your prettiest," he whispers. "Please, Kid, look your prettiest"; and he pulls my leash so tight that I can't touch my pats to the sawdust, and my nose goes up in the air. There was millions of people a-watching us from the railings, and three of our kennel-men, too, making fun of the Master and me, and Miss Dorothy with her chin just reaching to the rail, and her eyes so big that I thought she was a-going to cry. It was awful to think that when the judge stood up and exposed me, all those people, and Miss Dorothy, would be there to see me driven from the Show.

The judge he was a fierce-looking man with specs on his nose, and a red beard. When I first come in he didn't see me, owing to my being too quick for him and dodging behind the Master. But when the Master drags me round and I pulls at the sawdust to keep back, the judge looks at us careless-like, and then stops and glares through his specs, and I knew it was all up with me.

"Are there any more?" asks the judge to the gentleman at the gate, but never taking his specs from me.

The man at the gate looks in his book. "Seven in the novice class," says he. "They're all here. You can go ahead," and he shuts the gate.

The judge he doesn't hesitate a moment. He just waves his hand toward the corner of the ring. "Take him away," he says to the Master, "over there, and keep him away"; and he turns and looks most solemn at the six beautiful bull-terriers. I don't know how I crawled to that corner. I wanted to scratch under the sawdust and dig myself a grave. The kennel-men they slapped the rail with their hands and laughed at the Master like they would fall over. They pointed at me in the corner, and their sides just shaked. But little Miss Dorothy she presses her lips tight against the rail, and I see tears rolling from her eyes. The Master he hangs his head like he had been whipped. I felt most sorry for him than all. He was so red, and he was letting on not to see the kennel-men, and blinking his eyes. If the judge had ordered me right out it wouldn't have disgraced us so, but it was keeping me there while he was judging the high-bred dogs that hurt so hard. With all those people staring, too. And his doing it so quick, without no doubt nor questions. You can't fool the judges. They see inside you.

But he couldn't make up his mind about them high-bred dogs. He scowls at 'em, and he glares at 'em, first with his head on the one side and then on the other. And he feels of 'em, and orders 'em to run about. And Nolan leans against the rails, with his head hung down, and pats me. And Miss Dorothy comes over beside him, but don't say nothing, only wipes her eye with her finger. A man on the other side of the rail he says to the Master, "The judge don't like your dog?"

"No," says the Master.

"Have you ever shown him before?" says the man.

"No," says the Master, "and I'll never show him again. He's my dog," says the Master, "and he suits me! And I don't care what no judges think." And when he says them kind words, I licks his hand most grateful.

The judge had two of the six dogs on a little platform in the middle of the ring, and he had chased the four other dogs into the corners, where they was licking their chops, and letting on they didn't care, same as Nolan was.

The two dogs on the platform was so beautiful that the judge hisself couldn't tell which was the best of 'em, even when he stoops down and holds their heads together. But at last he gives a sigh, and brushes the sawdust off his knees, and goes to the table in the ring, where there was a man keeping score, and heaps and heaps of blue and gold and red and yellow ribbons. And the judge picks up a bunch of 'em and walks to the two gentlemen who was holding the beautiful dogs, and he says to each, "What's his number?" and he hands each gentleman a ribbon. And then he turned sharp and comes straight at the Master.

"What's his number?" says the judge. And Master was so scared that he couldn't make no answer.

But Miss Dorothy claps her hands and cries out like she was laughing, "Three twenty-six," and the judge writes it down and shoves Master the blue ribbon.

I bit the Master, and I jumps and bit Miss Dorothy, and I waggled so hard that the Master couldn't hold me. When I get to the gate Miss Dorothy snatches me up and kisses me between the ears, right before millions of people, and they both hold me so tight that I didn't know which of them was carrying of me. But one thing I knew, for I listened hard, as it was the judge hisself as said it.

"Did you see that puppy I gave first to?" says the judge to the gentleman at the gate.

"I did. He was a bit out of his class," says the gate gentleman.

"He certainly was!" says the judge, and they both laughed.

But I didn't care. They couldn't hurt me then, not with Nolan holding the blue ribbon and Miss Dorothy hugging my ears, and the kennel-men sneaking away, each looking like he'd been caught with his nose under the lid of the slop-can.

We sat down together, and we all three just talked as fast as we could. They was so pleased that I couldn't help feeling proud myself, and I barked and leaped about so gay that all the bull-terriers in our street stretched on their chains and howled at me.

"Just look at him!" says one of those I had beat. "What's he giving hisself airs about?"

"Because he's got one blue ribbon!" says another of 'em. "Why, when I was a puppy I used to eat 'em, and if that judge could ever learn to know a toy from a mastiff, I'd have had this one."

But Jimmy Jocks he leaned over from his bench and says, "Well done, Kid. Didn't I tell you so?" What he 'ad told me was that I might get a "commended," but I didn't remind him.

"Didn't I tell you," says Jimmy Jocks, "that I saw your grandfather make his début at the Crystal—"

"Yes, sir, you did, sir," says I, for I have no love for the men of my family.

A gentleman with a showing-leash around his neck comes up just then and looks at me very critical. "Nice dog you've got, Miss Wyndham," says he; "would you care to sell him?"

"He's not my dog," says Miss Dorothy, holding me tight. "I wish he were."

"He's not for sale, sir," says the Master, and I was *that* glad.

"Oh, he's yours, is he?" says the gentleman, looking hard at Nolan. "Well, I'll give you a hundred dollars for him," says he, careless-like.

"Thank you, sir; he's not for sale," says Nolan, but his eyes get very big. The gentleman he walked away; but I watches him, and he talks to a man in a golf-cap, and by and by the man comes along our street, looking at all the dogs, and stops in front of me.

"This your dog?" says he to Nolan. "Pity he's so leggy," says he. "If he had a good tail, and a longer stop, and his ears were set higher, he'd be a good dog. As he is, I'll give you fifty dollars for him."

But, before the Master could speak, Miss Dorothy laughs and says: "You're Mr. Polk's kennel-man, I believe. Well, you tell Mr. Polk from me that the dog's not for sale now any more than he was five minutes ago, and that when he is, he'll have to bid against me for him."

The man looks foolish at that, but he turns to Nolan quicklike. "I'll give you three hundred for him," he says.

"Oh, indeed!" whispers Miss Dorothy, like she was talking to herself. "That's it, is it?" And she turns and looks at me just as though she had never seen me before. Nolan he was a-gaping, too, with his mouth open. But he holds me tight.

"He's not for sale," he growls, like he was frightened; and the man looks black and walks away.

"Why, Nolan!" cries Miss Dorothy, "Mr. Polk knows more about bull-terriers than any amateur in America. What can he mean? Why, Kid is no more than a puppy! Three hundred dollars for a puppy!"

"And he ain't no thoroughbred, neither!" cries the Master. "He's 'Unknown,' ain't he? Kid can't help it, of course, but his mother, miss—"

I dropped my head. I couldn't bear he should tell Miss Dorothy. I couldn't bear she should know I had stolen my blue ribbon.

But the Master never told, for at that a gentleman runs up, calling, "Three twenty-six, three twenty-six!" And Miss Dorothy says, "Here he is; what is it?"

"The Winners' class," says the gentleman. "Hurry, please; the judge is waiting for him."

Nolan tries to get me off the chain on to a showing-leash, but he shakes so, he only chokes me. "What is it, miss?" he says. "What is it?"

"The Winners' class," says Miss Dorothy. "The judge wants him with the winners of the other classes—to decide which is the best. It's only a form," says she. "He has the champions against him now."

"Yes," says the gentleman, as he hurries us to the ring. "I'm afraid it's only a form for your dog, but the judge wants all the winners, puppy class even."

We had got to the gate, and the gentleman there was writing down my number.

"Who won the open?" asks Miss Dorothy.

"Oh, who would?" laughs the gentleman. "The old champion, of course. He's won for three years now. There he is. Isn't he wonderful?" says he; and he points to a dog that's standing proud and haughty on the platform in the middle of the ring.

I never see so beautiful a dog—so fine and clean and noble, so white like he had rolled hisself in flour, holding his nose up and his eyes shut, same as though no one was worth looking at. Aside of him we other dogs, even though we had a blue ribbon apiece, seemed like lumps of mud. He was a royal gentleman, a king, he was. His master didn't have to hold his head with no leash. He held it hisself, standing as still as an iron dog on a lawn, like he knew all the people was looking at him. And so they was, and no one around the ring pointed at no other dog but him.

"Oh, what a picture!" cried Miss Dorothy. "He's like a marble figure by a great artist—one who loved dogs. Who is he?" says she, looking in her book. "I don't keep up with terriers."

"Oh, you know him," says the gentleman. "He is the champion of champions, Regent Royal."

The Master's face went red.

"And this is Regent Royal's son," cries he, and he pulls me quick into the ring, and plants me on the platform next my father.

I trembled so that I near fell. My legs twisted like a leash. But my father he never looked at me. He only smiled the same sleepy smile, and he still kept his eyes half shut, like as no one, no, not even his own son, was worth his lookin' at.

The judge he didn't let me stay beside my father, but, one by one, he placed the other dogs next to him and measured and felt and pulled at them. And each one he put down, but he never put my father down. And then he comes over and picks up me and sets me back on the platform, shoulder to shoulder with the Champion Regent Royal, and goes down on his knees, and looks into our eyes.

The gentleman with my father he laughs, and says to the judge, "Thinking of keeping us here all day, John?" But the judge he doesn't hear him, and goes behind us and runs his hand down my side, and holds back my ears, and takes my jaws between his fingers. The crowd around the ring is very deep now, and nobody says nothing. The gentleman at the score-table, he is leaning forward, with his elbows on his knees and his eyes very wide, and the gentleman at the gate is whispering quick to Miss Dorothy, who has turned white. I stood as stiff as stone. I didn't even breathe. But out of the corner of my eye I could see my father licking his pink chops, and yawning just a little, like he was bored.

The judge he had stopped looking fierce and was looking solemn. Something inside him seemed a-troubling him awful. The more he stares at us now, the more solemn he gets, and when he touches us he does it gentle, like he was patting us. For a long time he kneels in the sawdust, looking at my father and at me, and no one around the ring says nothing to nobody.

Then the judge takes a breath and touches me sudden. "It's his," he says. But he lays his hand just as quick on my father. "I'm sorry," says he.

The gentleman holding my father cries:

"Do you mean to tell me—"

And the judge he answers, "I mean the other is the better dog." He takes my father's head between his hands and looks down at him most sorrowful. "The king is dead," says he. "Long live the king! Good-by, Regent," he says.

The crowd around the railings clapped their hands, and some laughed scornful, and every one talks fast, and I start for the gate, so dizzy that I can't see my way. But my father pushes in front of me, walking very daintily, and smiling sleepy, same as he had just been waked, with his head high and his eyes shut, looking at nobody.

So that is how I "came by my inheritance," as Miss Dorothy calls it; and just for that, though I couldn't feel where I was any different, the crowd follows me to my bench, and pats me, and coos at me, like I was a baby in a baby-carriage. And the handlers have to hold 'em back so that the gentlemen from the papers can make pictures of me, and Nolan walks me up and down so proud, and the men shake their heads and says, "He certainly is the true type, he is!" And the pretty ladies ask Miss Dorothy, who sits beside me letting me lick her gloves to show the crowd what friends we is, "Aren't you afraid he'll bite you?" And Jimmy Jocks calls to me, "Didn't I tell you so? I always knew you were one of us. Blood will out, Kid; blood will out. I saw your grandfather," says he, "make his début at the Crystal Palace. But he was never the dog you are!"

After that, if I could have asked for it, there was nothing I couldn't get. You might have thought I was a snow-dog, and they was afeard I'd melt. If I wet my pats, Nolan gave me a hot bath and chained me to the stove; if I couldn't eat my food, being stuffed full by the cook —for I am a house-dog now, and let in to lunch, whether there is visitors or not—Nolan would run to bring the vet. It was all tommy rot, as Jimmy says, but meant most kind. I couldn't scratch myself comfortable, without Nolan giving me nasty drinks, and rubbing me outside till it burnt awful; and I wasn't let to eat bones for fear of spoiling my "beautiful" mouth, what mother used to call my "punishing jaw"; and my food was cooked special on a gas-stove; and Miss Dorothy gives me an overcoat, cut very stylish like the champions', to wear when we goes out carriage-driving.

After the next Show, where I takes three blue ribbons, four silver cups, two medals, and brings home forty-five dollars for Nolan, they gives me a "registered" name, same as Jimmy's. Miss Dorothy wanted to call me "Regent Heir Apparent"; but I was *that* glad when Nolan says, "No; Kid don't owe nothing to his father, only to you and hisself. So, if you please, miss, we'll call him Wyndham Kid." And so they did, and you can see it on my overcoat in blue letters, and painted top of my kennel. It was all too hard to understand. For days I just sat and wondered if I was really me, and how it all come about, and why everybody was so kind. But oh, it was so good they was, for if they hadn't been I'd never have got the thing I most wished after. But, because they was kind, and not liking to deny me nothing, they gave it me, and it was more to me than anything in the world.

It came about one day when we was out driving. We was in the cart they calls the dog-cart because it's the one Miss Dorothy keeps to take Jimmy and me for an airing. Nolan was up behind, and me, in my new overcoat, was sitting beside Miss Dorothy. I was admiring the view, and thinking how good it was to have a horse pull you about so that you needn't get yourself splashed and have to be washed, when I hears a dog calling loud for help, and I pricks up my ears and looks over the horse's head. And I sees something that makes me tremble down to my toes. In the road before us three big dogs was chasing a little old lady-dog. She had a string to her tail, where some boys had tied a can, and she was dirty with mud and ashes, and

torn most awful. She was too far done up to get away, and too old
to help herself, but she was making a fight for her life, snapping her
old gums savage, and dying game. All this I see in a wink, and then
the three dogs pinned her down, and I can't stand it no longer, and
clears the wheel and lands in the road on my head. It was my stylish
overcoat done that, and I cursed it proper, but I gets my pats again
quick, and makes a rush for the fighting. Behind me I hear Miss
Dorothy cry: "They'll kill that old dog. Wait, take my whip. Beat
them off her! The Kid can take care of himself"; and I hear Nolan
fall into the road, and the horse come to a stop. The old lady-dog was
down, and the three was eating her vicious; but as I come up, scattering the pebbles, she hears, and thinking it's one more of them, she
lifts her head, and my heart breaks open like some one had sunk his
teeth in it. For, under the ashes and the dirt and the blood, I can see
who it is, and I know that my mother has come back to me.

I gives a yell that throws them three dogs off their legs.

"Mother!" I cries. "I'm the Kid," I cries. "I'm coming to you.
Mother, I'm coming!"

And I shoots over her at the throat of the big dog, and the other
two they sinks their teeth into that stylish overcoat and tears it off me,
and that sets me free, and I lets them have it. I never had so fine a fight
as that! What with mother being there to see, and not having been
let to mix up in no fights since I become a prize-winner, it just naturally did me good, and it wasn't three shakes before I had 'em yelping. Quick as a wink, mother she jumps in to help me, and I just
laughed to see her. It was so like old times. And Nolan he made me
laugh, too. He was like a hen on a bank, shaking the butt of his whip,
but not daring to cut in for fear of hitting me.

"Stop it, Kid," he says, "stop it. Do you want to be all torn up?"
says he. "Think of the Boston show," says he. "Think of Chicago.
Think of Danbury. Don't you never want to be a champion?" How
was I to think of all them places when I had three dogs to cut up at
the same time? But in a minute two of 'em begs for mercy, and
mother and me lets 'em run away. The big one he ain't able to run
away. Then mother and me we dances and jumps, and barks and
laughs, and bites each other and rolls each other in the road. There
never was two dogs so happy as we. And Nolan he whistles and

calls and begs me to come to him; but I just laugh and play larks with mother.

"Now, you come with me," says I, "to my new home, and never try to run away again." And I shows her our house with the five red roofs, set on the top of the hill. But mother trembles awful, and says: "They'd never let me in such a place. Does the Viceroy live there, Kid?" says she. And I laugh at her. "No; I do," I says. "And if they won't let you live there, too, you and me will go back to the streets together, for we must never be parted no more." So we trots up the hill side by side, with Nolan trying to catch me, and Miss Dorothy laughing at him from the cart.

"The Kid's made friends with the poor old dog," says she. "Maybe he knew her long ago when he ran the streets himself. Put her in here beside me, and see if he doesn't follow."

So when I hears that I tells mother to go with Nolan and sit in the cart; but she says no—that she'd soil the pretty lady's frock; but I tells her to do as I say, and so Nolan lifts her, trembling still, into the cart, and I runs alongside, barking joyful.

When we drives into the stables I takes mother to my kennel, and tells her to go inside it and make herself at home. "Oh, but he won't let me!" says she.

"Who won't let you?" says I, keeping my eye on Nolan, and growling a bit nasty, just to show I was meaning to have my way.

"Why, Wyndham Kid," says she, looking up at the name on my kennel.

"But I'm Wyndham Kid!" says I.

"You!" cries mother. "You! Is my little Kid the great Wyndham Kid the dogs all talk about?" And at that, she being very old, and sick, and nervous, as mothers are, just drops down in the straw and weeps bitter.

Well, there ain't much more than that to tell. Miss Dorothy she settled it.

"If the Kid wants the poor old thing in the stables," says she, "let her stay.

"You see," says she, "she's a black-and-tan, and his mother was a black-and-tan, and maybe that's what makes Kid feel so friendly toward her," says she.

"Indeed, for me," says Nolan, "she can have the best there is. I'd never drive out no dog that asks for a crust nor a shelter," he says. "But what will Mr. Wyndham do?"

"He'll do what I say," says Miss Dorothy, "and if I say she's to stay, she will stay, and I say—she's to stay!"

And so mother and Nolan and me found a home. Mother was scared at first—not being used to kind people; but she was so gentle and loving that the grooms got fonder of her than of me, and tried to make me jealous by patting of her and giving her the pick of the vittles. But that was the wrong way to hurt my feelings. That's all, I think. Mother is so happy here that I tell her we ought to call it the Happy Hunting Grounds, because no one hunts you, and there is nothing to hunt; it just all comes to you. And so we live in peace, mother sleeping all day in the sun, or behind the stove in the head groom's office, being fed twice a day regular by Nolan, and all the day by the other grooms most irregular. And as for me, I go hurrying around the country to the bench-shows, winning money and cups for Nolan, and taking the blue ribbons away from father.

The Coming of Riquet

BY

ANATOLE FRANCE

Seated at his table one morning in front of the window, against which the leaves of the plane tree quivered, M. Bergeret, who was trying to discover how the ships of Aeneas had been changed into nymphs, heard a tap at the door, and forthwith his servant entered, carrying in front of her, opossum-like, a tiny creature whose black head peeped out from the folds of her apron, which she had turned up to form a pocket. With a look of anxiety and hope upon her face, she remained motionless for a moment, then she placed the little thing upon the carpet at her master's feet.

"What's that?" asked M. Bergeret.

It was a little dog of doubtful breed, having something of the terrier in him, and a well-set head, a short, smooth coat of a dark tan color, and a tiny little stump of a tail. His body retained its puppy-like softness, and he went sniffling at the carpet.

"Angélique," said M. Bergeret, "take this animal back to its owner."

"It has no owner, Monsieur."

M. Bergeret looked silently at the little creature, who had come to examine his slippers, and was giving little sniffs of approval. M. Bergeret was a philologist, which perhaps explains why at this juncture he asked a vain question.

"What is he called?"

"Monsieur," replied Angélique, "he has no name."

M. Bergeret seemed put out at this answer: he looked at the dog sadly, with a disheartened air.

Then the little animal placed its two front paws on M. Bergeret's slipper, and, holding it thus, began innocently to nibble at it. With a sudden access of compassion M. Bergeret took the tiny nameless creature upon his knee. The dog looked at him intently, and M. Bergeret was pleased at his confiding expression.

"What beautiful eyes!" he cried.

The dog's eyes were indeed beautiful, the pupils of a golden-flecked chestnut set in warm white. And his gaze spoke of simple, mysterious thoughts, common alike to the thoughtful beasts and simple men of the earth.

Tired, perhaps, with the intellectual effort he had made for the purpose of entering into communication with a human being, he closed his beautiful eyes, and, yawning widely, revealed his pink mouth, his curled-up tongue, and his array of dazzling teeth.

M. Bergeret put his hand into the dog's mouth, and allowed him to lick it, at which old Angélique gave a smile of relief.

"A more affectionate little creature doesn't breathe," she said.

"The dog," said M. Bergeret, "is a religious animal. In his savage state he worships the moon and the lights that float upon the waters. These are his gods, to whom he appeals at night with long-drawn howls. In the domesticated state he seeks by his caresses to conciliate those powerful genii who dispense the good things of this world—to wit, men. He worships and honors men by the accomplishment of the rites passed down to him by his ancestors: he licks their hands, jumps against their legs, and when they show signs of anger towards him he approaches them crawling on his belly as a sign of humility, to appease their wrath."

"All dogs are not the friends of man," remarked Angélique. "Some of them bite the hand that feeds them."

"Those are the ungodly, blasphemous dogs," returned M. Bergeret, "insensate creatures like Ajax, the son of Telamon, who wounded the hand of the golden Aphrodite. These sacrilegious creatures die a dreadful death, or lead wandering and miserable lives. They are not to be confounded with those dogs who, espousing the quarrel of their own particular god, wage war upon his enemy, the neighboring god. They are heroes. Such, for example, is the dog of Lafolie, the butcher, who fixed his sharp teeth into the leg of the

tramp Pied-d'Alouette. For it is a fact that dogs fight among themselves like men, and Turk, with his snub nose, serves his god Lafolie
against the robber gods, in the same way that Israel helped Jehovah
to destroy Chamos and Moloch."

The puppy, however, having decided that M. Bergeret's remarks
were the reverse of interesting, curled up his feet and stretched out
his head, ready to go to sleep upon the knees that harbored him.

"Where did you find him?" asked M. Bergeret.

"Well, Monsieur, it was M. Dellion's *chef* gave him to me."

"With the result," continued M. Bergeret, "that we now have this
soul to care for."

"What soul?" asked Angélique.

"This canine soul. An animal is, properly speaking, a soul; I do
not say an immortal soul. And yet, when I come to consider the posi-
tions this poor little beast and I myself occupy in the scheme of
things, I recognize in both exactly the same right to immortality."

After considerable hesitation, old Angélique, with a painful effort
that made her upper lip curl up and reveal her two remaining teeth,
said:

"If Monsieur does not want a dog, I will return him to M. Dellion's
chef; but you may safely keep him, I assure you. You won't see or
hear him."

She had hardly finished her sentence when the puppy, hearing a
heavy van rolling down the street, sat bolt upright on M. Bergeret's
knees, and began to bark both loud and long, so that the window-
panes resounded with the noise.

M. Bergeret smiled.

"He's a watch-dog," said Angélique, by way of excuse. "They are
by far the most faithful."

"Have you given him anything to eat?" asked M. Bergeret.

"Of course," returned Angélique.

"What does he eat?"

"Monsieur must be aware that dogs eat bread and meat."

Somewhat piqued, M. Bergeret retorted that in her eagerness she
might very likely have taken him away from his mother before he
was old enough to leave her, upon which he was lifted up again and

re-examined, only to make sure of the fact that he was at least six months old.

M. Bergeret put him down on the carpet, and regarded him with interest.

"Isn't he pretty?" said the servant.

"No, he is not pretty," replied M. Bergeret. "But he is engaging, and has beautiful eyes. That is what people used to say about me," added the professor, "when I was three times as old, and not half as intelligent. Since then I have no doubt acquired an outlook upon the universe which he will never attain. But, in comparison with the Absolute, I may say that my knowledge equals his in the smallness of its extent. Like his, it is a geometrical point in the infinite." Then, addressing the little creature who was sniffing the waste-paper basket, he went on: "Smell it out, sniff it well, take from the outside world all the knowledge that can reach your simple brain through the medium of that black truffle-like nose of yours. And what though I at the same time observe, and compare, and study? We shall never know, neither the one nor the other of us, why we have been put into this world, and what we are doing in it. What are we here for, eh?"

As he had spoken rather loudly, the puppy looked at him anxiously, and M. Bergeret, returning to the thought which had first filled his mind, said to the servant:

"We must give him a name."

With her hands folded in front of her she replied laughingly that that would not be a difficult matter.

Upon which M. Bergeret made the private reflection that to the simple all things are simple, but that clear-sighted souls, who look upon things from many and divers aspects, invisible to the vulgar mind, experience the greatest difficulty in coming to a decision about even the most trivial matters. And he cudgelled his brains, trying to hit upon a name for the little living thing that was busily engaged in nibbling the fringe of the carpet.

"All the names of dogs," thought he, "preserved in the ancient treatises of the huntsmen of old, such as Fouilloux, and in the verses of our sylvan poets such as La Fontaine—Finaud, Miraut, Briffaut, Ravaud, and such-like names, are given to sporting dogs, who are the aristocracy of the kennel, the chivalry of the canine race. The dog of Ulysses was called Argos, and he was a hunter too, so Homer tells us. 'In his youth he hunted the little hares of Ithaca, but now he was old and hunted no more.' What we require is something quite different. The names given by old maids to their lap-dogs would be more suitable, were they not usually pretentious and absurd. Azor, for instance, is ridiculous!"

So M. Bergeret ruminated, calling to memory many a dog name, without being able to decide, however, on one that pleased him. He would have liked to invent a name, but lacked the imagination.

"What day is it?" he asked at last.

"The ninth," replied Angélique. "Thursday, the ninth."

"Well, then!" said M. Bergeret, "can't we call the dog Thursday, like Robinson Crusoe who called his man Friday, for the same reason?"

"As Monsieur pleases," said Angélique. "But it isn't very pretty."

"Very well," said M. Bergeret, "find a name for the creature yourself, for, after all, you brought him here."

"Oh, no," said the servant. "I couldn't find a name for him; I'm not clever enough. When I saw him lying on the straw in the kitchen, I called him Riquet, and he came up and played about under my skirts."

"You called him Riquet, did you?" cried M. Bergeret. "Why didn't you say so before? Riquet he is and Riquet he shall remain; that's settled. Now be off with you, and take Riquet with you. I want to work."

"Monsieur," returned Angélique, "I am going to leave the puppy with you; I will come for him when I get back from market."

"You could quite well take him to market with you," retorted M. Bergeret.

"Monsieur, I am going to church as well."

It was quite true that she really was going to church at Saint-Exupère, to ask for a Mass to be said for the repose of her husband's soul. She did that regularly once a year, not that she had even been informed of the decease of Borniche, who had never communicated with her since his desertion, but it was a settled thing in the good woman's mind that Borniche was dead. She had therefore no fear of his coming to rob her of the little she had, and did her best to fix things up to his advantage in the other world, so long as he left her in peace in this one.

"Eh!" ejaculated M. Bergeret. "Shut him up in the kitchen or some other convenient place, and do not wor——"

He did not finish his sentence, for Angélique had vanished, purposely pretending not to hear, that she might leave Riquet with his master. She wanted them to grow used to one another, and she also wanted to give poor, friendless M. Bergeret a companion. Having closed the door behind her, she went along the corridor and down the steps.

M. Bergeret set to work again and plunged head foremost into his *Virgilius nauticus*. He loved the work; it rested his thoughts, and became a kind of game that suited him, for he played it all by himself. On the table beside him were several boxes filled with pegs, which he fixed into little squares of cardboard to represent the fleet of Aeneas. Now while he was thus occupied he felt something like tiny fists tapping at his legs. Riquet, whom he had quite forgotten, was standing on his hind legs patting his master's knees, and wagging his little stump of a tail. When he tired of this, he let his paws slide down the trouser leg, then got up and began his coaxing over again. And M. Bergeret, turning away from the printed lore before him, saw two brown eyes gazing up at him lovingly.

"What gives a human beauty to the gaze of this dog," he thought, "is probably that it varies unceasingly, being by turns bright and vivacious, or serious and sorrowful; because through these eyes his little dumb soul finds expression for thought that lacks nothing in depth nor sequence. My father was very fond of cats, and, consequently, I liked them too. He used to declare that cats are the wise man's best companions, for they respect his studious hours. Bajazet, his Persian cat, would sit at night for hours at a stretch, motionless and majestic, perched on a corner of his table. I still remember the agate eyes of Bajazet, but those jewel-like orbs concealed all thought, that owl-like stare was cold, and hard, and wicked. How much do I prefer the melting gaze of the dog!"

Riquet, however, was agitating his paws in frantic fashion, and M. Bergeret, who was anxious to return to his philological amusements, said kindly, but shortly:

"Lie down, Riquet!"

Upon which Riquet went and thrust his nose against the door through which Angélique had passed out. And there he remained, uttering from time to time plaintive, meek little cries. After a while he began to scratch, making a gentle rasping noise on the polished floor with his nails. Then the whining began again followed by more scratching. Disturbed by these sounds, M. Bergeret sternly bade him keep still.

Riquet peered at him sorrowfully with his brown eyes, then, sitting down, he looked at M. Bergeret again, rose, returned to the door, sniffed underneath it, and wailed afresh.

"Do you want to go out?" asked M. Bergeret.

Putting down his pen, he went to the door, which he held a few inches open. After making sure that he was running no risk of hurting himself on the way out, Riquet slipped through the doorway and marched off with a composure that was scarcely polite. On returning to his table, M. Bergeret, sensitive man that he was, pondered over the dog's action. He said to himself:

"I was on the point of reproaching the animal for going without saying either good-bye or thank you, and expecting him to apologize for leaving me. It was the beautiful human expression of his eyes that made me so foolish. I was beginning to look upon him as one of my own kind."

After making this reflection M. Bergeret applied himself anew to the metamorphosis of the ships of Aeneas, a legend both pretty and popular, but perhaps a trifle too simple in itself for expression in such noble language. M. Bergeret, however, saw nothing incongruous in it. He knew that the nursery tales have furnished material for nearly all epics, and that Virgil had carefully collected together in his poem the riddles, the puns, the uncouth stories, and the puerile imaginings of his forefathers; that Homer, his master and the master of all the bards, had done little more than tell over again what the good wives of Ionia and the fishermen of the islands had been narrating for more than a thousand years before him. Besides, for the time being, this was the least of his worries; he had another far more important preoccupation. An expression, met with in the course of the charming story of the metamorphosis, did not appear sufficiently plain to him. That was what was worrying him.

"Bergeret, my friend," he said to himself, "this is where you must open your eyes and show your sense. Remember that Virgil always expresses himself with extreme precision when writing on the technique of the arts; remember that he went yachting at Baïae, that he was an expert in naval construction, and that therefore his language, in this passage, must have a precise and definite signification."

And M. Bergeret carefully consulted a great number of texts, in order to throw a light upon the word which he could not understand, and which he had to explain. He was almost on the point of grasping the solution, or, at any rate, he had caught a glimpse of it, when he heard a noise like the rattling of chains at his door, a noise which, although not alarming, struck him as curious. The disturbance was presently accompanied by a shrill whining, and M. Bergeret, interrupted in his philological investigations, immediately concluded that these importunate wails must emanate from Riquet.

As a matter of fact, after having looked vainly all over the house for Angélique, Riquet had been seized with a desire to see M. Bergeret again. Solitude was as painful to him as human society was dear. In order to put an end to the noise, and also because he had a secret desire to see Riquet again, M. Bergeret got up from his arm-chair and opened the door, and Riquet re-entered the study with the same coolness with which he had quitted it, but as soon as he saw the door close behind him he assumed a melancholy expression, and began to wander up and down the room like a soul in torment.

He had a sudden way of appearing to find something of interest beneath the chairs and tables, and would sniff long and noisily; then he would walk aimlessly about or sit down in a corner with an air of great humility, like the beggars who are to be seen in church porches. Finally he began to bark at a cast of Hermes which stood upon the mantel-shelf, whereupon M. Bergeret addressed him in words full of just reproach.

"Riquet! such vain agitation, such sniffing and barking were better suited to a stable than to the study of a professor, and they lead one to suppose that your ancestors lived with horses whose straw litters they shared. I do not reproach you with that. It is only natural you should have inherited their habits, manners, and tendencies as well as their close-cropped coat, their sausage-like body, and their long, thin nose. I do not speak of your beautiful eyes, for there are few men, few dogs even, who can open such beauties to the light of day. But, leaving all that aside, you are a mongrel, my friend, a mongrel from your short, bandy legs to your head. Again I am far from despising you for that. What I want you to understand is that if you desire to live with me, you will have to drop your mongrel manners and behave like a *scholar*, in other words, to remain silent and quiet, to respect work, after the manner of Bajazet, who of a night would sit for four hours without stirring, and watch my father's pen skimming over the paper. He was a silent and tactful creature. How different is your own character, my friend! Since you came into this chamber of study your hoarse voice, your unseemly snufflings and your whines, that sound like steam whistles, have constantly confused my thoughts and interrupted my reflections. And now you have made me lose the drift of an important passage in Servius, referring to the construction of one of the ships of Aeneas. Know then, Riquet, my friend, that this is the house of silence and the abode of meditation, and that if you are anxious to stay here you must become literary. Be quiet!"

Thus spoke M. Bergeret. Riquet, who had listened to him with mute astonishment, approached his master, and with suppliant gesture placed a timid paw upon the knee, which he seemed to revere in a fashion that savored of long ago. Then a kind thought struck M. Bergeret. He picked him up by the scruff of his neck, and put him upon the cushions of the ample easy chair in which he was sitting. Turning himself round three times, Riquet lay down, and then remained perfectly still and silent. He was quite happy. M. Bergeret was grateful to him, and as he ran through Servius he occasionally stroked the close-cropped coat, which, without being soft, was smooth and very pleasant to the touch. Riquet fell into a gentle doze, and communicated to his master the generous warmth of his body, the subtle, gentle heat of a living, breathing thing. And from that moment M. Bergeret found more pleasure in his *Virgilius nauticus*.

From floor to ceiling his study was lined with deal shelves, bearing books arranged in methodical order. One glance, and all that remains to us of Latin thought was ready to his hand. The Greeks lay half-way up. In a quiet corner, easy to access, were Rabelais, the excellent story-tellers of the *Cent nouvelles nouvelles*, Bonaventure des Périers, Guillaume Bouchet, and all the old French "conteurs," whom M. Bergeret considered better adapted to humanity than writings in the more heroic style, and who were the favorite reading of his leisure. He possessed them in cheap modern editions only, but he had discovered a poor bookbinder in the town who covered his volumes with leaves from a book of anthems, and it gave M. Bergeret the keenest pleasure to see these free-spoken gentlemen thus clad in Requiems and Misereres. This was the sole luxury and the only peculiarity of his austere library. The other books were paper-backed or bound in poor and worn-out bindings. The gentle friendly manner in which they were handled by their owner gave them the look of tools set out in a busy man's workshop. The books of archaeology and art found a resting-place on the highest shelves, not by any means out of contempt, but because they were not so often used.

Now, while M. Bergeret worked at his *Virgilius nauticus* and shared his chair with Riquet, he found, as chance would have it, that it was necessary to consult Ottfried Müller's little *Manual*, which happened to be on one of the topmost shelves.

There was no need of one of those tall ladders on wheels topped by railings and a shelf, to enable him to reach the book; there were ladders of this description in the town library, and they had been used by all the great book-lovers of the eighteenth and nineteenth centuries; indeed, several of the latter had fallen from them, and thus died honorable deaths, in the manner spoken of in the pamphlet entitled: *Des bibliophiles qui moururent en tombant de leur échelle*. No, indeed! M. Bergeret had no need of anything of the sort. A small pair of folding steps would have served his purpose excellently well, and he had once seen some in the shop of Clérambaut, the cabinet-maker, in the Rue de Josde. They folded up, and looked just the thing, with their bevelled uprights each pierced with a trefoil as a grip for the hand. M. Bergeret would have given anything to possess them, but the state of his finances, which were somewhat involved, forced him to abandon the idea. No one knew better than he did that financial ills are not mortal, but, for all that, he had no steps in his study.

In place of such a pair of steps he used an old cane-bottomed chair, the back of which had been broken, leaving only two horns or antennae, which had shown themselves to be more dangerous than useful. So they had been cut to the level of the seat, and the chair had become a stool. There were two reasons why this stool was ill-fitted to the use to which M. Bergeret was wont to put it. In the first place the woven-cane seat had grown slack with long use, and now contained a large hollow, making one's foothold precarious. In the second place the stool was too low, and it was hardly possible when standing upon it to reach the books on the highest shelf, even with the finger-tips. What generally happened was that in the endeavor to grasp one book, several others fell out; and it depended upon their being bound or paper-covered whether they lay with broken corners, or sprawled with leaves spread like a fan or a concertina.

Now, with the intention of getting down the *Manual* of Ottfried Müller, M. Bergeret quitted the chair he was sharing with Riquet, who, rolled into a ball with his head tight pressed to his body, lay in warm comfort, opening one voluptuous eye, which he re-closed as quickly. Then M. Bergeret drew the stool from the dark corner where it was hidden and placed it where it was required, hoisted himself upon it, and managed, by making his arm as long as possible, and straining upon tiptoe, to touch, first with one, then with two fingers, the back of a book which he judged to be the one he was needing. As for the thumb, it remained below the shelf and rendered no assistance whatever. M. Bergeret, who found it therefore exceedingly difficult to draw out the book, made the reflection that the reason why the hand is a precious implement is on account of the position of the thumb, and that no being could rise to be an artist who had four feet and no hands.

"It is to the hand," he reflected, "that men owe their power of becoming engineers, painters, writers, and manipulators of all kinds of things. If they had not a thumb as well as their other fingers, they would be as incapable as I am at this moment, and they could never have changed the face of the earth as they have done. Beyond a doubt it is the shape of the hand that has assured to man the conquest of the world."

Then, almost simultaneously, M. Bergeret remembered that monkeys, who possess four hands, have not, for all that, created the arts, nor disposed that earth to their use, and he erased from his mind the theory upon which he had just embarked. However, he did the best he could with his four fingers. It must be known that Ottfried Müller's *Manual* is composed of three volumes and an atlas. M. Bergeret wanted volume one. He pulled out first the second volume, then the atlas, then volume three, and finally the book that he required. At last he held it in his hands. All that now remained for him to do was to descend, and this he was about to do when the cane seat gave way beneath his foot, which passed through it. He lost his balance and fell to the ground, not as heavily as might have been feared, for he broke his fall by grasping at one of the uprights of the bookshelf.

He was on the ground, however, full of astonishment, and wearing on one leg the broken chair; his whole body was permeated and as though constricted by a pain that spread all over it, and that presently settled itself more particularly in the region of the left elbow and hip upon which he had fallen. But, as his anatomy was not seriously damaged, he gathered his wits together; he had got so far as to realize that he must draw his right leg out of the stool in which it had so unfortunately become entangled, and that he must be careful to raise himself up on his right side, which was unhurt. He was even trying to put this into execution when he felt a warm breath upon his cheek, and turning his eyes, which fright and pain had for the moment fixed, he saw close to his cheek Riquet's little face.

At the sound of the fall Riquet had jumped down from the chair and run to his unfortunate master; he was now standing near him in a state of great excitement; then he commenced to run round him. First he came near out of sympathy, then he retreated out of fear of some mysterious danger. He understood perfectly well that a misfortune had taken place, but he was neither thoughtful nor clever enough to discover what it was; hence his anxiety. His fidelity drew him to his suffering friend, and his prudence stopped him on the very brink of the fatal spot. Encouraged at length by the calm and silence which eventually reigned, he licked M. Bergeret's neck and looked at him with eyes of fear and of love. The fallen master smiled, and the dog licked the end of his nose. It was a great comfort to M. Bergeret, who freed his right leg, stood erect, and limped good-humoredly back to his chair.

Riquet was there before him. All that could be seen of his eyes was a gleam between the narrow slit of the half-closed lids. He seemed to have forgotten all about the adventure that a moment before had so stirred them both. The little creature lived in the present, with no thought of time that had run its course; not that he was wanting in memory, inasmuch as he could remember, not his own past alone, but the faraway past of his ancestors, and his little head was a rich storehouse of useful knowledge; but he took no pleasure in remembrance, and memory was not for him, as it was for M. Bergeret, a divine muse.

Gently stroking the short, smooth coat of his companion, M. Bergeret addressed him in the following affectionate terms:

"Dog! at the price of the repose which is dear to your heart, you came to me when I was dismayed and brought low. You did not laugh, as any young person of my own species would have done. It is true that however joyous or terrible nature may appear to you at times, she never inspires you with a sense of the ridiculous. And it is for that very reason, because of your innocent gravity, that you are the surest friend a man can have. In the first instance I inspired confidence and admiration in you, and now you show me pity.

"Dog! when we first met on the highway of life, we came from the two poles of creation; we belong to different species. I refer to this with no desire to take advantage of it, but rather with a strong sense of universal brotherhood. We have hardly been acquainted two hours, and my hand has never yet fed you. What can be the meaning of the obscure love for me that has sprung up in your little heart? The sympathy you bestow on me is a charming mystery, and I accept it. Sleep, friend, in the place that you have chosen!"

Having thus spoken, M. Bergeret turned over the leaves of Ottfried Müller's *Manual*, which with marvelous instinct he had kept in his hand both during and after his fall. He turned over the pages, and could not find what he sought.

Every moment, however, seemed to increase the pain he was feeling.

"I believe," he thought, "that the whole of my left side is bruised and my hip swollen. I have a suspicion that my right leg is grazed all over and my left elbow aches and burns, but shall I cavil at pain that has led me to the discovery of a friend?"

His reflections were running thus when old Angélique, breathless and perspiring, entered the study. She first opened the door, and then she knocked, for she never permitted herself to enter without knocking. If she had not done so before she opened the door, she did it after, for she had good manners, and knew what was expected of her. She went in therefore, knocked, and said:

"Monsieur, I have come to relieve you of the dog."

M. Bergeret heard these words with decided annoyance. He had not as yet inquired into his claims to Riquet, and now realized that he had none. The thought that Madame Borniche might take the animal away from him filled him with sadness, yet, after all, Riquet did belong to her. Affecting indifference, he replied:

"He's asleep; let him sleep!"

"Where is he? I don't see him," remarked old Angélique.

"Here he is," answered M. Bergeret. "In my chair."

With her two hands clasped over her portly figure, old Angélique smiled, and, in a tone of gentle mockery, ventured:

"I wonder what pleasure the creature can find in sleeping there behind Monsieur!"

"That," retorted M. Bergeret, "is his business."

Then, as he was of inquiring mind, he immediately sought of Riquet his reasons for the selection of his resting-place, and lighting on them, replied with his accustomed candor:

"I keep him warm, and my presence affords a sense of security; my comrade is a chilly and homely little animal." Then he added: "Do you know, Angélique? I will go out presently and buy him a collar."

The Odyssey of Runyon Jones

BY

NORMAN CORWIN

First broadcast on June 8, 1941, as the sixth of "Twenty-six by Corwin," under the direction of the author. Runyon was played by Larry Robinson, Father Time by Roy Fant, Mother Nature by Hester Sondergaard, the Giant by Arthur Vinton. Alexander Semmler composed and conducted the original musical score.

Music: Introductory cue; plenty of harp and strings for glitter.

RUNYON (*timidly*). Is this the department of lost dogs?

CLERK. Yes.

RUNYON. I'm looking for my dog.

CLERK (*perfunctorily*). Your name?

RUNYON. Runyon Jones.

CLERK. Runyon?

RUNYON. Yes, sir. It's a terrible name, but Mother says I will like it when I grow up because it's distinguished, she says. The other boys call me Onion.

CLERK. What's the name of your dog?

RUNYON. Pootzy.

CLERK. Pootzy?

RUNYON. Yes, sir. He's very smart, sir.

CLERK. When did you lose him?

RUNYON. Yesterday morning.

CLERK. Where?

RUNYON. Right outside my house. He was chasing an automobile.

134

CLERK. Why?

RUNYON. He wanted to bite the tires, I think.

CLERK. Front or rear?

RUNYON. All of them.

CLERK. What happened?

RUNYON. The car ran over him.

CLERK. And then?

RUNYON. He was killed, sir.

CLERK. Then you're on the wrong floor. This is the Department of *Lost* Dogs. What you want is the Department of *Deceased* Dogs.

RUNYON. Where is that, sir?

CLERK. Two flights up. Here, take this slip and hand it to the man at the desk.

RUNYON. Thank you, sir.

Music: Transitional cue. It should combine the elements of timidity and hope.

RUNYON. Is this the Department of Diseased Dogs?

SECOND CLERK. *Deceased*, not diseased. Let me see that slip.

RUNYON. Yes, sir.

SECOND CLERK. Mm. Pootzy. Are you Runyon Jones?

RUNYON. Yes, sir.

SECOND CLERK. Just a minute; let me look at the file.

Sound of file case opening, cards flipped.

SECOND CLERK (*to himself; scarcely audible, mumbling*). Pootzy Jones . . . one and a half years old . . . inveterate auto chaser . . . leash . . . attitude . . . mm. (*To Runyon.*) Young man, I don't think there's anything we can do for you.

RUNYON (*terribly downhearted*). You can't find Pootzy?

SECOND CLERK. Ordinarily, in a good many cases, when a boy's dog dies from old age or natural causes, or is merely run over while chasing a cat in line of duty, or is fatally wounded in a fight with other dogs, we can make arrangements with St. Bernard, the head of Dog Heaven, for the return of the animal on a limited basis.

RUNYON. What's a limited basis?

SECOND CLERK. *But*—in the case of Pootzy, he is down in the files as an inveterate auto chaser and tire nipper, Class 4. Also, it is known that he has resisted leashes, that he bit a dog-catcher on August eleventh last, and that he stayed out all night on three separate occasions. I'm sorry to say he's *not* in Dog Heaven.

RUNYON (*freshly disappointed*). No? Gosh! (*Almost at point of tears.*) Are you sure, Mister? Couldn't he have snuck in when nobody was looking?

SECOND CLERK (*firmly*). He is not in Dog Heaven, and that settles that.

RUNYON. Well, where is he, then?

SECOND CLERK. In the place where all ill-behaved curs are punished. Curgatory.

RUNYON. Where's that? I'll go there.

SECOND CLERK. Oh, no. Impossible.

RUNYON. But he won't chase any more automobiles—I *swear* it! Look—honest. I'll spit on my hand and touch my forehead three times. (*Spitting.*) Pft—foo.

SECOND CLERK. What's that mean?

RUNYON. That's the secret oath of the Elmwood Street A.C., which means pledge of honor.

SECOND CLERK. Nevertheless it will be impossible.

RUNYON. But Pootzy will be lonely without me. I *have* to find him.

SECOND CLERK. Please go now. I am busy.

RUNYON. But, gee whiz—I came all the way here . . .

SECOND CLERK. Now go quietly, Mr. Jones, or I shall have to call an officer.

RUNYON (*making a scene*). I *won't* go! I won't go without Pootzy! You've got him somewhere, and you're hiding him on me!

SECOND CLERK. Now listen here.

RUNYON. I *won't* listen! You give my dog back or I'll kick you in the shins! (*Calling.*) Pootzy! *Pootzy!* . . . You locked him up, and you won't let me have him because you want to keep him for yourself. I know!

SECOND CLERK. Here! Here! Stop kicking me! Stop that! (*Projecting.*) Officer! Officer! Come here!

RUNYON. (*Continues to protest, ad lib, as the Officer hurries on.*)

OFFICER (*approaching*). What *is* this? What's going on here?

RUNYON and CLERK. (*Both begin to explain, talking at the same time. Finally the Officer shushes them.*)

OFFICER. I think you'd both better explain the matter to the Superintendent of the Division.

SECOND CLERK (*indignantly*). I certainly will! I'm not going to stand for being kicked in the shins by any young brat who happens to come along. No wonder his dog's in Curgatory—I can see where the animal learned its bad manners.

RUNYON (*beside himself; almost crying*). You take that back! I did not teach Pootzy his bad manners. He taught himself!

OFFICER. Quiet, both of you, and follow me. We'll explain it all to the Super.

Music: Transitional cue—an argumentative piece scored for distinct voices at high and low instrumentation. An emphatic statement concludes the piece.

SUPER (*a kindly sort—the right man for the position*). I see. Well, there are things to be said for both sides. Now, first of all, I suggest that you two shake hands and apologize to each other.

RUNYON. Well, all right. I'm sorry I kicked you in the shins, Mister.

SECOND CLERK. That's all right. (*Clears his throat.*) I may possibly have lost my temper a bit, too.

SUPER. Yes. And now, Mr. Jones, let me explain what the clerk was trying to tell you. We do not keep any dogs here on the premises. The most we can do is to refer applications to the right parties. It so happens we have connections with Dog Heaven through our good friend St. Bernard. But unfortunately there is no contact whatsoever—none at all—with Curgatory.

RUNYON. Well, isn't there any way of getting to Curgatory, sir? Because I'll go myself if you'll only tell me how to get there, sir. I got *here* by myself.

SUPER (*to Clerk*). Clerk, there's obviously quite an attachment to the dog in this case, and . . .

RUNYON. He was attached to a leash, but he kept breaking away on account of he liked to run fast.

SUPER. Yes. Mm. Now, Mr. Jones, I think you're a likely lad, and so I'm going to tell you frankly that the chances of your ever getting Pootzy back are (*gravely*) very, very slim.

RUNYON (*again disappointed*). They are? Why is that, sir?

SUPER. Because Curgatory is a great, great distance away and extremely hard to get to. In fact, nobody *we* know seems to know just how one does get there. But if you're determined to try to get Pootzy back, and you're willing to take risks and chances . . .

RUNYON (*eagerly*). Yes, sir, I'll do anything. Gee whizzickers, if you only knew Pootzy . . .

SUPER. Then I'll tell you how to get to somebody who *may* know somebody who knows somebody else who can send you to the right place so that you *might* be able to find out how to *set out* for Curgatory.

RUNYON. Gosh, would you, sir?

SUPER. Glad to. Clerk, get me Form 5—the blue slip—and also applications for the interdivisional visa and interdepartmental passport. Then clip on the transfer coupons and the pink manifest.

CLERK. Yes, sir.

SUPER. Now, Mr. Jones, this is what you do. There is only one person I know who can possibly set you on the right track, and that's the head of the Division of Time. We call him Father Time. His place is quite far, and you'll have to make several changes before you get there. That's what all the tickets are for.

RUNYON. Shall I say you sent me?

SUPER. Oh, that won't do much good! He's very busy and won't have much time to talk to you. Tell him quickly what you are after, and if he can assist you, he'll tell you quickly. He hates to waste time.

CLERK. The papers, sir.

Sound of papers.

SUPER. Very good. Mr. Jones, will you fill out this blank, and sign these two, while I stamp these documents?

RUNYON. Yes, sir.

While they are busy at their respective tasks (sound of stamping), the Super speaks in a very low, casual manner to the Clerk.

SUPER. Er—Clerk—see that he gets put safely on the Golden Escalator with instructions to change at the Inter-Heaven Junction for the Nebula Express.

CLERK. Wouldn't it be better for him to take the Westbound Taurus Special? That crosses the Meridian two light-hours ahead of the Neb.

SUPER. Yes, but then he'd have to wait at Asterion for the Ecliptic Local. It's better the other way.

CLERK. Maybe you're right.

SUPER. Have you finished, Mr. Jones?

RUNYON. Yes, sir. I got an inkspot all over this sheet here. Will that make any difference?

SUPER. No, no. Well, Mr. Jones, I guess that does it!

RUNYON (*optimistic*). Thank you, Mr. Superintendent. Gosh, Pootzy's sure gonna be glad to see me.

SUPER (*cautioning*). Ah—don't be too sure you'll find him, because you're liable to be disappointed, you know. But good luck anyway.

RUNYON (*not knowing what to say*). Well—thank you.

CLERK (*with professional cheer, markedly in contrast to his earlier manner*). Now, young man, if you come with me, I'll see that you get on to the Golden Escalator.

RUNYON. All right, I'm coming.

Music: Cue descriptive of Runyon's celestial journey. Score for separate celeste mike, supported by strings; give tempo of perpetuum mobile; at length retard into rhythm of:

Assorted tick-tocks, including bells and chimes which keep striking under the following scene at various perspectives in the studio, some quite far off. After this is established:

TIME. And you mean to say you came all the way here to ask if I know anybody who can help you find a dog named Pootzy?

RUNYON. Yes, Father Time.

TIME. Don't you realize I'm very busy?

RUNYON. Yes, Father Time, but it won't take you long to tell me whether—

TIME. Quiet! I've got to listen for time signals.

A bong.

TIME. Aha! That means that the eclipse of three moons on Jupiter was right on time.

RUNYON (*progressively timid*). He was a little dog, about so big . . .

VOICE (*booming out—use P.A.*). When you hear the time signal it will be exactly half past one-sixty-two on Uranus.

TIME. Fah! That was thirty-seven thousandths of a second late! Miss Chrono, make a note of that. We'll have to make it up in the year seven billion, three hundred two.

CHRONO. Yes, sir.

TIME. Now what was it you wanted, little man?

RUNYON. Well, sir, could you tell me how I could get to Curgatory, because my dog Pootzy . . .

TIME. Oh, yes. Was he a delinquent dog?

RUNYON. No, sir, a mongrel.

VOICE (*P.A.*). When you hear the musical note it will be the hundred seventy-second millionth anniversary of the birth of the first dinosaur.

Great booming note of the Chinese gong; reverberation on the board.

TIME. Miss Chrono, remind me to send an anniversary message of felicitations to M.N.

CHRONO. Yes, sir. Can I have time to go to lunch?

TIME. Later, later. (*To Runyon.*) Where did you say the dog was?

RUNYON. In Curgatory. I just want to know how to get there.

TIME. Aha! Well, now, the only way . . .

Loud buzzer close on mike. Receiver off.

TIME. Now who's that?

CHRONO. Main office. Chrono speaking.

TIME. My, my! Look at that green clock. It's getting toward morning on Neptune already.

CHRONO. Yes, I'll tell him. Keep your shirt on, he's right here.

TIME (*testily*). Who's that? Who's that on the phone?

CHRONO. Our agent on Alcyone. He says they need a shipment of sand very badly.

TIME. Why?

CHRONO. The sands of time are running low through the Archipelago of the Pleiades.

TIME. Tell him we're digging some new pits on Mercury and that he'll have his order in two shakes of a comet's tail.

CHRONO. (*Still off, relays Time's message and hangs up while:*)

TIME. Finest platinum sand in the system. Uh . . . (*With surprise.*) What are *you* doing here?

RUNYON. Don't you remember, Father Time? I'm the one who is looking for my dog. I came . . .

TIME. Oh, yes, yes! Mr. Bones!

RUNYON. Jones.

TIME. You're from Earth, aren't you?

RUNYON. Yes, sir.

TIME (*sharply*). Well, then, I want you to know that I am heartily ashamed of the kind of time they have down there in Greenwich.

RUNYON. Yes, sir.

TIME. And I want you to understand why.

RUNYON. Yes, sir.

TIME. Because it's so *mean!* It's *pretty mean* time! [1]

RUNYON. Yes, sir.

TIME. And now about you and your dog. I don't know where Curgatory is at all. It used to be on Sirius, the Dog Star, but the neighbors on Furud and Murzim and Adhara complained about the piteous howling and whining that came from there; so they had to move.

RUNYON (*fearing the worst*). Er—why was there howling and whining?

----

[1] The notes will be found on pages 151-53.

TIME. Because all the dogs in Curgatory are tortured, of course.

RUNYON. Does—does it hurt them bad?

TIME (*laughs*). Well, naturally! What a question! Why, I've heard there are fleas in Curgatory as big as a lion! That's only one of the attractions.

RUNYON (*very tentatively*). Uh—well—is there some way I could find out how to get there?

TIME. Well, the only one I know who could possibly help you is M.N.

RUNYON. M.N.?

TIME. Don't you know anything, lad? Mother Nature!

RUNYON. Oh.

Celeste chord, amplified to a startling degree.

TIME. Well, well, there goes the vernal equinox on Aldebaran. Now, Mr. Pootzy . . .

RUNYON. No, that's my dog.

TIME. Quiet, Pootzy! . . . Now here's how you get to M.N.'s place . . .

VOICE (*P.A.*). When you hear the note of the bass bautant, that will be time for all visitors—(*significantly*) who weren't invited—to get ready to leave.

Music: Bass Bautant,[1] followed by variation on previous inter-stellar movement cue. This sustains briefly under the following scene.
Establish background of bird noises.

MOTHER NATURE (*laughing*). Pootzy? What a funny name!

RUNYON. Yes, ma'am.

MOTHER NATURE. And you came here to ask me . . .

RUNYON. Well, Father Time said you might know where it is.

MOTHER NATURE. Well, I don't, little boy, but let me think. (*Pause.*) I'll tell you who might. Just off the main skyway between Castor and Pollux, before you get to the red light of Mekbuda, there's a harpy who . . .

[1] See notes on pages 151-53.

BLOSSOM. Excuse me, Mrs. Nature, but these papers have to be signed right away if you want to get them on the Solar Limited.

MOTHER NATURE. Yes. Excuse me, Runyon.

RUNYON. Yes, ma'am.

MOTHER NATURE (*low, to herself*). Formal complaint about an earthquake in California . . . test specimen of a new metal for the mountains of East Orion . . . new species of ant for the Antilles . . . replace two worn rings on Saturn . . . a petition of twenty-six butterflies of the order Rhopalocera demanding less time in chrysalis and more on the wing . . . requisition for ersatz beans to take the place of butter beans . . . rain wanted in the Panhandle . . . There! That's finished.

> BLOSSOM (*idle talk*). Hello.
>
> RUNYON. Hello.
>
> BLOSSOM. You from Betelguese?
>
> RUNYON. No, ma'am, I'm from Des Moines.
>
> BLOSSOM. Looking for a job?
>
> RUNYON. No, ma'am. I want to find my dog.
>
> BLOSSOM. Oh. Curgatory?
>
> RUNYON. Yes'm.
>
> BLOSSOM. Too bad. No chance.

(*to the girl*). Here, Blossom, take these and see that they— Wait a minute. What's that you have in your hand?

BLOSSOM. A vacuum bottle, ma'am. Some warm nectar in case I get hungry on the way, and . . .

MOTHER NATURE (*furious*). Don't you know I *abhor* a vacuum? Give me that!

Smashing of glass.

MOTHER NATURE. Now, Blossom, don't let me lose my patience with you again. If you get hungry, there's plenty to drink in the Milky Way!

BLOSSOM. Yes, Mrs. Nature.

MOTHER NATURE (*immediately calm again*). Now, Runyon—as I was saying, this harpy is a very strange spirit, full of lots of esoteric knowledge and . . .

RUNYON. Does he know where I can find Pootzy?

MOTHER NATURE. That I can't tell you. But there's no harm asking. Incidentally, it's a she, not a he. In fact, she's more commonly known as an *it*.

RUNYON. Does it bite?

MOTHER NATURE. Oh, no! But you may have difficulty understanding it, because of the way this harpy talks. You'll have to hold this little charm—oh, now where did I put it—yes, here it is—you'll have to hold this in your left hand while the harpy talks, in order to make out anything at all.

RUNYON. Gee, isn't it pretty? It's like an aggie in marbles.

MOTHER NATURE. Yes, it's the most charming charm I have. Don't lose it, now, because it has the power of translating the harpy's language into your own.

RUNYON. No, ma'am, I won't lose it. I'll take care of it like as if it was Pootzy.

Music: Transitional cue, segueing to harp solo. Throughout this scene the harp holds a conversation with Runyon, and its phrases should be as much like conversation as possible—monosyllabic, but at times questioning and expository, as the speech of Runyon indicates.

HARP. (*After a cadenza, a questioning phrase.*)

RUNYON. Yes, sir. I mean yes, ma'am. I mean yes, It.

HARP. (*Phrase.*)

RUNYON. Pootzy.

HARP. (*Phrase in which strings are plucked six times, as though spelling out something.*)

RUNYON. No. P-o-o-t-z-y.

HARP. (*Phrase.*)

RUNYON. Chasing an automobile.

HARP. (*Phrase.*)

RUNYON. Yes'm—sir, I mean . . .

HARP. (*Phrase broadening into sostenuto tones in lower register.*)

RUNYON (*fearfully*). A giant?

HARP (*Phrase—"Yes."*)

RUNYON. But does he bite?

HARP. (*Reassuring phrases.*)

RUNYON (*still not too certain this is safe*). Does he know where Pootzy is?

HARP. (*Phrase*—"Maybe.")

RUNYON. You don't know where he is? Gosh, nobody seems to know where Curgatory is. I hope the giant does. How do I get there, Miss Harpy? I mean, Mr.—I mean, The Harpy?

HARP. (*Cadenza of a most expository nature, broadening into:*)

Music: Full orchestra in transitional cue. The music here should convey a sense of bigness and grotesqueness.

RUNYON (*sounding very little*). And so he ran under the automobile before I could get him, Mr. Giant. And that's how he got killed.

GIANT (*a great voice tremendously built up by amplification—laughing*). So you've come here expecting me to tell you where Curgatory is!

RUNYON. Yes, sir. If you know, I mean.

GIANT. Of course I know!

RUNYON (*in a transport of delight*). You *do?* Oh, gee, will you tell me, please! Oh, gee gosh jiminy heck! Then you know where Pootzy is!

GIANT (*laughs*). Do you think I'm gonna tell a little squirt where Curgatory is? Why, I haven't told anybody anything for sixty-seven million years, and I don't see why I should start in now!

RUNYON (*who can't understand how anybody, even a Giant, could be mean enough to withhold information leading to the whereabouts of Pootzy*). But it's Pootzy, don't you understand— Pootzy! Pootzy's there. If you tell me, I can go *get* him.

GIANT (*derisively*). Pootzy! Pshaw! I don't care if *Tootsy's* there. Now beat it, small fry; I got worries of my own—me with my two heads to feed and four sets of teeth, two uppers and two lowers, to clean every night! G'wan, beat it.

RUNYON. Please, Mr. Giant, *please!*

GIANT. What did you ever do for *me?*

RUNYON. Nothing, but I'll do anything you want me to, if I get Pootzy back.

GIANT. Haw, haw! As if you *could* do something for me! G'wan now, scram before I squash you with my little finger.

RUNYON. But listen to me . . .

GIANT. Don't take up my valuable time. Who sent you here in the first place, anyway?

RUNYON. The harpy.

GIANT (*bellowing*). The *harpy?*

RUNYON. Yes, sir.

GIANT. You don't say! Mmmmm. Step on my thumbnail here, and don't slip—I want to talk to you very confidentially. Come up here near my ear. Now—what do you know about the harpy?

RUNYON (*fade in, advancing on mike rapidly*). Well, it told me how to get here. It gave me full directions.

GIANT (*angry*). It? What are you talking about?

RUNYON. The harpy, sir.

GIANT. *Miss* Harpy to you, bunny!

RUNYON. Yes, sir. (*Gulps.*)

GIANT (*low again*). Well, how the Hecuba could you understand her?

RUNYON. Why, that was easy.

GIANT. Easy! I've been trying to get next to that creature for the last four million years, and every time I ask her for a date, she gives me queer talk. I can't make her out. I think she's stringing me along.

RUNYON. You mean she talks like this?

Music: A shot of harp talk.

GIANT (*astounded*). Yeah! Say! How'd you do that?

RUNYON. Well, I'll tell you how if you tell me how to reach Curgatory.

GIANT. Oh, businessman, eh?

RUNYON. No, I just want to swap you, that's all.

GIANT. Well, all right; tell me how.

RUNYON. Oh, no. First you tell me how to get to Curgatory.

GIANT. Hm. (*Growls.*) Well, that's fair enough. Mind you, you're not fooling me now. What you tell me better work!

RUNYON. Sure. It works like a charm, no foolin'.

GIANT. All right, then. Now (*fading*) get this, kid: first you go up through that cloud of meteor dust there on the trimtram, and then you change at San Sunspot for the Sidereal Ferry . . . (*Crossing under:*)

Music: Transitional cue, similar to the first in combining a feeling of timidity and hope.
A long-drawn wolf cry.

RUNYON (*frightened*). What was that?

OFFICER. That was merely the soul of a wolf passing by the Curgatorium.

RUNYON. Does—does it bite?

OFFICER. Don't be alarmed, Mr. Jones. You see, the near-by wolves who occupy what is known as Lupine Limbo resent certain of the policies in practice here in Curgatory, to say nothing of the smell.

RUNYON. They do?

Bell.

OFFICER. Ah, that means the board of directors has reached a decision on your application. We can go in now.

Creaking of heavy door.

CHAIRMAN. Mr. Jones, will you sit here?

RUNYON. Thank you.

CHAIRMAN. Gentlemen of the board, this is Mr. Runyon Jones of Earth, whose request to be reunited with his dog Pootzy—number seventeen billion, six million twelve—we have just discussed.

BOARD. (*Ad-lib greetings.*)

CHAIRMAN. Jones, we have gone into this matter most carefully.

RUNYON. That's good.

CHAIRMAN. We fully appreciate the pains to which you have gone, and the trouble . . .

RUNYON. Oh, it was nothin'.

CHAIRMAN. . . . you have taken. We are also aware of the unusual devotion you have shown the said Pootzy, and all these factors have entered into our decision.

RUNYON. Yes, sir. Then can I see Pootzy and have him back?

CHAIRMAN. The unanimous decision of the board of directors is that you may not.

RUNYON. What? You mean I can't see . . .

CHAIRMAN. Sorry, but it is entirely contrary to the established rules and regulations of the institution. If we made an exception for you, it might lead to all kinds of complications.

RUNYON (*trying hard to fight back his tears*). Jiminy, can't I see Pootzy for just a minute?

CHAIRMAN. Sorry, Jones.

RUNYON. Not even for a teeny-weeny *second?* Just to peek at him through the bars and whistle once? Just like this? (*He tries to whistle, but cries instead.*)

CHAIRMAN. We are all very sorry, Jones, but nothing can be done for you. Incidentally, it may be of some consolation to you to know that there are no bars in Curgatory.

RUNYON (*coming up for air*). That's good. (*He sniffles.*) Do you torture Pootzy bad? He's got a lame foot, you know. I hope you don't hurt him awful.

CHAIRMAN. Just a moment, Jones. I am proud to say we do not torture any dogs in Curgatory. Where did you get that terrible idea?

RUNYON. Father Time told me.

General indignation mixed with amusement.

CHAIRMAN. Father Time? Why, don't take stock in anything he says, Jones. (*Confidentially.*) I shouldn't like this to get back to Father Time, but between you and us—strictly entre nous—that job of his seems to have got the better of him. He's more or less known as a—a crackpot.

DIRECTOR. That torture talk is nonsense.

SECOND DIRECTOR. Yes, indeed. . . . Well, we've got a big docket to clear. Hadn't we better show Jones how to get back to the Sidereal Ferry?

CHAIRMAN. Yes, Jones. I'm afraid that closes the case. Sorry.

RUNYON. Can I say just one more thing, gentlemen?

CHAIRMAN. Well, you'll have to make it fast.

RUNYON (*pleading in desperation*). Pootzy is a good dog. He didn't mean to bite no tires. He just wanted to race the cars to show me how fast he could run. And he could of run faster if he wasn't lame in the leg. And the time he bit the dog-catcher, the big bum . . .

CHAIRMAN. Jones! That's no kind of language.

RUNYON (*mad and miserable*). Well, he *was* a big bum! He hurt Pootzy, and Pootzy wasn't doin' no harm to nobody; he was just chasing a cat. And about his staying out all night, that was because he saw me talking to Eddie Mazer's bulldog, and he got jealous. You can't blame a dog for that, can you? Honest, Pootzy is the best dog in the world, or else would I have come all this way for him?

FIRST DIRECTOR. What about the day the auto ran over him and killed him? Didn't he break away from your leash?

RUNYON. No, sir, the leash broke.

CHAIRMAN (*severely*). Are you sure of that, Jones? (*For a moment there is no answer.*) Jones . . . ?

RUNYON (*defeated*). No, sir.

FIRST DIRECTOR. Then the said Pootzy did break away?

RUNYON (*now crying*). Yes, sir.

CHAIRMAN. Well, there you are. Again, please understand that we are sorry, but there is nothing we can do.

Gavel.

CHAIRMAN. Next item, gentlemen.

OFFICER. This way out, Mr. Jones.

RUNYON. Good-bye. And tell Pootzy I—I . . . (*He can't finish.*)

CHAIRMAN. Yes. I'll tell him.

RUNYON (*going off*). Good-bye. (*Shouting.*) Good-bye, Pootzy! Can you hear me?

CHAIRMAN (*gravely*). No, he cannot. I will tell him good-bye for you.

RUNYON. Thank you, sir.

FIRST DIRECTOR. Wait a minute, Jones. Where did you get that mark over your right eye?

RUNYON. Oh, this? Oh, that's nothing. I got that in the accident.

CHAIRMAN. What accident?

RUNYON. When I tried to prevent Pootzy from being run over.

FIRST DIRECTOR. And?

RUNYON. And nothing.

CHAIRMAN. Well, didn't you reach Pootzy in time?

RUNYON. No, sir. Almost—but, you see, the car ran over me first.

THE BOARD (*shocked*). It did?

RUNYON. Yes, sir. That's how *I* got killed.

CHAIRMAN. Well, now . . . (*He clears his throat uncomfortably.*) Ahem—just a moment, Jones.

BOARD. (*An indistinguishable ad-lib conference. At length:*)

CHAIRMAN. Jones, the status of the case is changed by the fact that you gave your life to save your dog. That comes under the Priorities Ruling affecting the Seventh Clause of the Constitution of Curgatory.

RUNYON (*not getting it*). I see. Well, good-bye, gentlemen.

BOARD. (*Ad-libs under:*)

CHAIRMAN. No, no—you don't understand! You can have the said Pootzy back!

RUNYON (*incredulously*). I can see Pootzy?

CHAIRMAN. Yes, sir! We'll release the said Pootzy from Curgatory in your custody.

RUNYON. You mean—now?

CHAIRMAN (*pleased as Punch—no, more so*). Yes. The officer will take you.

OFFICER. Come, Mr. Jones.

RUNYON. Yes, right away. Gee.

Door closes. Footsteps on stone for ten seconds.

OFFICER. He's down at the end of the long corridor.

More footsteps. At length:

OFFICER. Well, here we are. He's right inside that door.

RUNYON (*hardly able to control his voice*). Is he? Right inside there?

OFFICER. Yes. Just open the door and walk right in.

RUNYON. Er—wait a minute.

OFFICER. What's the matter?

RUNYON. Do I look all right?
OFFICER (*chuckling*). Oh, yes, Mr. Jones.

Clear, clean sound of doorknob and the beginning of the door opening, whereat there is an immediate dissolve into:

Music: Conclusion

THE ODYSSEY OF RUNYON JONES

The impulse to write this dog story came from my association with an English setter named Nick, who lived down the hill. Apparently he had a falling out with his owners, because he wouldn't speak to them unless they were prepared to back up any statement they made with genuine hamburger. He was a faker and a showoff, and a furious barker after anything which couldn't bark back. Once he refused to enter my house when I was giving shelter to a neighbor's kittens. He hated them and wouldn't go near them, and looked at me with such baleful accusation that I had to drop everything and have a long talk with him. Nick was erratic and irregular, a Grand Hotel of fleas, and all the things a well-bred dog shouldn't be, but his personality was so winning that, had he been Pootzy, an odyssey such as Jones' would seem well worth the effort.

Casting. Without a sensitive and versatile Runyon, you might as well all go home. He should be between nine and twelve and sound earnest, purposeful, persistent. Don't, under any circumstances, employ a Runyon who sounds fresh or oversmart or whining. So many radio kids sound that way, although as a class they are better than the horrible Hollywood junior brigade. Kingsley Colton, in the days when he played Stinky in "My Client Curley," had the right quality; and so did Larry Robinson, who performed the role of Runyon the night it was done for the first time.

Father Time must of course be old to be credible. Roy Fant achieved a toothless quality which conveyed the idea that he had been on the job for a long while. The character of Time should justify the "crackpot" comment which is made later by the Chairman of the Board of Curgatory.

Mother Nature is a busy but not overbearing executive type: the efficient controller of all things natural; the kindly helper; the disciplinarian. M.N.'s assistant, Blossom, is a silly child. Those who know Florence Robinson's strange pixie quality will understand what is needed in that role.

The Giant is a stock giant. Arthur Vinton played him with humor and vitality, deepening an already deep voice, and rolling his speech in a wondrous way.

Acting. Everybody whom Runyon meets in his travels treats him as an adult, never as a child. Nobody wastes sympathy, except perhaps the Superintendent, who is aware of the boy's unusual attachment to his dog. Father Time is too daft to care much; Mother Nature is accustomed to all kinds of strange petitions; the Giant has worries of his own; the personnel of Curgatory is polite but firm, always addressing the boy as Jones. None of the characters should be travestied.

Sound. The only problem is that of the background for the Father Time sequence. I found that the best effect was achieved by slowing down a recording of a cuckoo clock. At normal speed this effect was a pleasant *ding*, followed by a cheerful *cuckoo*, but I reduced it to a speed so low that the ding became a tremendous and deep-chested BONG, and the optimistic chirrup of the cuckoo became a lugubrious two-note wail of a melancholy whistling buoy. This succeeded somehow in creating an effect of great space, of mysterious gyrations, of the weird inner workings of the solar system.

Rehearsal Routine. The chief production worries are the blending of sound, music, and speech in the Time sequence and the interview between the Giant and Runyon. The former can best be accomplished by using a separate microphone for each element, being careful not to allow the background of sound to override speech. This scene will be soupy unless one works hard to maintain clear perspectives.

In the Giant scene, complete isolation is necessary if Runyon is to sound small and the Giant big. I placed Runyon in a dead booth and reduced the level of his microphone on the control board, while the Giant had the whole studio to himself, and an echo chamber to boot.

Additional Notes. 1. In a recording of the first of two broadcasts of this program on the same night (one went to the West only), it was found that nobody got the allusion to G.M.T. Seems silly, but the point had to be repeated—punched, as the boys say.

2. There's no such thing. Chatterton, the poet, coined the instrument in one of his poems, and I have appropriated it to confound musicians. Alex Semmler settled for a bassoon, which is what I meant in the first place, I placed the bassoon in the dead booth, on a public-address microphone whose amplifier fed into the wide space of the studio proper; it made quite a frightful sound, which was what I wanted.

Brag Dog

BY

VEREEN BELL

Eph was outside when it happened. He was sitting under the china-berry tree, writing in the dirt with a nail, trying, as usual, to study out some way to buy the wheel chair for Addie May. Of course she knew nothing at all about any wheel chair, but Eph guessed that Addie May'd be mighty happy if she could just glide out on the porch to talk to a passer-by, and then glide back in when the flies got too bad, without anybody's having to leave their work to tote her.

It was just then that Cleotha came in the house, and there the puppy was, chewing up her only half fit'n pair of go-to-meetin' shoes. She let go a stick of cordwood at him, and her daughter, little Valentine, screamed like she was stabbed. The puppy was knocked clean under the bed. Eph expected to drag him out cold dead, but before he could kneel down, the puppy came wobbling out, bleeding at the mouth, and one ear torn half off. The puppy sat down, his head tilted to favor his injured ear, and, licking his mouth, he regarded them in puzzlement, blinking that blind, white eye. He wagged his tail uncertainly.

Eph never had felt quite so roused up about anything. "You ever do dat again, Cleotha, and you gwine git hurt. Fum now on, you bees on prohibition, so you better be keerful, you hear me?"

Little naked Valentine had dropped the shriveled ear of raw corn she had been eating and went to the puppy. Eph knelt beside them, and the puppy began gnawing at his hand as if nothing had happened.

"Ol' hardhead," Eph said tenderly. " 'E got a skull just like a rock in de river."

After that the puppy's name was Hardhead. Mr. Floyd Jessup had given the puppy to Eph. They had been fishing on the lake, and not catching anything. Mr. Floyd didn't mind, though; he kept whipping the fly rod, and popping the bass bug among the lily bonnets.

"How're you making out these days, Eph?" he asked after a while.

Eph hesitated a moment. His crop was no good, because it had been so almighty dry. He hardly had food enough for his family, much less his stock—you could hang your hat on the mule's hip bones. The lake was down low, too, so that the fish weren't biting and hardly anybody wanted a boatman any more. At home, Cleotha was a file-tongue she-cat, and Addie May, his wife, was crippled these eight years, and not long ago the good Lord had taken their boy, Luck, away from them. Luck had been a first-class hand at tractors and such, and Eph concluded that some of the heavenly machinery had got itself out of fix and they'd just naturally had to call Luck in on the case.

But Eph couldn't bother Mr. Floyd with all that, so he answered, "Tol'able, Mr. Floyd, just tol'able."

"Haven't you a little granddaughter?"

"Yes, suh; Valentine."

"I've got a pointer puppy you can have, Eph. The kid will enjoy him, I guess. A cat scratched his eyes nearly out. One of them's gone, and he'll be blind in the other one within a month or so. But she can have the fun of him for that length of time."

Eph thought it would be fine for Valentine to have a puppy to play with, even a half-blind puppy. So the next time Mr. Floyd came fishing, he brought the puppy with him. That night on the way home the puppy chewed contentedly on Eph's ragged coat, not seeming to mind having one eye milky like a white marble and the other with webby stuff over it.

It was dark when Eph got home, and Addie May and Cleotha and little Valentine were all in bed, but Eph roused them with a shout.

"Guess what I brung home!" he said into the darkness.

"I bet it ain't nothin' to eat," Cleotha said pessimistically.

"I know what it is," Valentine said suddenly, " 'cause it's already in the bed with me. It's a little old dog."

Cleotha came out of the bed with an angry bound, and lit a lamp. "A dog?" she shouted. Sure enough, it was a dog, in the bed with Valentine, giving her happy face a lathering.

"Father reserve us!" Cleotha said. "We ain't got a dust a' meal ner a drop a' grease in de house, and de old fool done brung home another mouth to feed."

Addie May turned painfully, so she could get a look at the puppy. "He's purty, ain't he?"

"Purty? I'll purty 'im," Cleotha said in a tight-lipped rage.

The puppy was lucky to be alive next morning. Three or four times during the night Cleotha had tried to slip out and put an end to that extra hungry mouth. But every time Addie May heard her, and called Eph. Sometimes Eph wondered if Addie May ever really went to sleep any more.

Eph lay awake and thought about the wheel chair. "If'n I was makin' any money," he thought, "I could bury a dime er fi'teen cents a week and in two years er maybe three er four, I'd dig up enough to pay for hit, cash. But I ain't makin' no money."

His brain began to ache from a confusion of thought. It wasn't possible for an old nigger like him to buy a wheel chair for his crippled wife. Yet he wanted it so bad he was tempted to call on the good Lord to pass a miracle. He was even tempted to point out to Him how wrong things had been going, with Luck dying, and Addie May getting crippled, and little Valentine being half hungry all the time; but he was afraid the Lord might think he was criticizing, so he kept his mouth shut.

With morning, rain came. Not a gulley-washer, the kind they needed to bring the lake up, but enough of one to help the corn some. By late summer they had bread to eat with their greens, and occasionally Eph would get his old Long Tom single-barreled full-choke shotgun and kill a rabbit or a crow for dinner.

Eph and little Valentine saw to it that the puppy got a little something to eat all the time. He seemed to prosper on corn bread and greens; in fact, his bones grew faster than his flesh, it looked like, giving him a gawky, thick-legged appearance.

The dog's good eye got better instead of worse, and gradually the spidery film over it was gone and the puppy could see almost as good as anybody.

"Well, now, let me see," Eph said, puzzled. "I guess I got to take de Hardhead back to Mr. Floyd."

"How come?" Cleotha asked.

"Well, he ain't went complete blind like Mr. Floyd thought. He goan make a bird dog now."

"You old fool, didn't Mr. Floyd gi'm to you? We gwine sell dat dog and git some money for him, maybe two dollars er two and a quarter. He's sho your dog."

But Eph thought he ought to take him back, so he rose before Valentine woke next morning, and he and the puppy started sadly to Tallahassee. When he finally got there, they went straight to Mr. Floyd's enormous country house on the other side of town.

"You walked twenty miles from the lake with this dog?" Mr. Floyd asked. "You lunatic, I gave you that dog. Now, you keep him."

"Yes, suh, but I feel kinda gilted 'bout him re-gittin' back his sights. He ought to be your little dog, Mr. Floyd."

"I gave him to you, understand? And listen, I don't want to hear of you selling that dog for two or three dollars. He's worth thirty right now, if that eye's all right. Take him to the kennels and let my dog man give him a distemper shot and some worm medicine and a square meal." He drew out a dollar bill and gave it to Eph. "That's bus money back, understand? I don't want you walking down here again, keeping a bird-dog puppy out in the hot sun all day."

Afterward, on the way to the department store, Eph had a curious mixture of feelings. Now that he was about to get the wheel chair, his fingers trembled violently in glad excitement. At the same time, the thought of parting with Hardhead put a sickness in his heart. He hurried into the store before he could change his mind.

"How much your w'eel chairs costes, suh?"

"We got one for twenty-five dollars," the clerk told him.

It was beautiful, with rubber tires and shiny bright wood and black spokes.

Eph didn't hesitate. "Well, dis yere's a thutty-dollar puppy, and I wants to turn him in on dat w'eel chair."

The clerk looked at Hardhead's gaunt frame and unsightly imperfections, and he had to put his hand over his mouth. "I'm afraid we couldn't do that, old man," he said. "Tell you what, though; you train that puppy and he'll be easier to sell. Won't make much difference what he looks like then."

Eph went out with the curious mixture of feelings, only this time they were backward. His hand on Hardhead's scrawny neck was glad. At the same time his whole insides seemed touched by his disappointment. He hadn't got the wheel chair.

Eph told Cleotha what Mr. Floyd had said about harming the puppy. " 'E says if'n you boddered dis puppy, he gwine have you put in de callyboots, in de blackest corner of hit."

Addie May had them put her out on the porch, so she could tell passers-by about Eph's trip from town. They sat her down carefully. Addie May looked at her yard and said, "If'n I had me a nickel, I'd buy me some flar seed, and I'd plant 'em right around this ere poach. Zeenies. Blue uns and yaller uns and pank uns." It wasn't often that Addie May let on about wanting anything. The next nickel Eph got his hand on, he was sure going to buy her some zinnia seed.

All afternoon Addie May sat there, speaking to the people who occasionally went by with fish poles and sacks on their way to the lake.

"Mawnin', Miz Davis," they would say to her, "how you?"

"Just tol'able," Addie May would answer. "It's sho Lawd hot, ain't it?"

"Ain't it?"

"Eph went to Ta'hassee, yestiddy, right in de b'ilin' sun."

"Did? W'en 'e comin' back, Miz Davis?"

" 'E come back yestiddy," Addie May would say casually. "On de bust."

Mr. Floyd had given Eph about a dozen cans of dog food to feed the Hardhead. "Feed him a can every three or four days, to sort of balance his diet. A dog needs more than corn bread, you know."

But when Eph came in from pulling fodder one afternoon, Cleotha had found the dog food. She cooked two cans of it in the frying pan. It looked like beef hash.

"Dat ain't people's sump'm-to-eat," Eph said. "Dat's dog rations."

"It eats good," Cleotha said complacently.

Eph dubiously took a spoonful of the stuff and sampled it, and it wasn't bad, sure enough. They had dog food for supper, but Eph couldn't eat any of it, knowing he wasn't supposed to. After supper, he went out and fed Hardhead corn bread and pot licker and tried to explain as best he could.

"It doan seem eggsactly fair," Eph admitted, "but at the same time we been sharin' up wid you, so I guess you don't objeck to sharin' up wid us, specially since you don't know nothin' 'bout it nohow."

The lake got into such a shape that nobody fished it any more, and Eph had lots of time to spend trying to make his eroded clay farm land grow something. Hardhead always went with him plowing. While Eph plodded up and down the dry furrows, Hardhead would crouch under the sassafras bushes along the rail and wait for the birds. Presently they would come fluttering in, one or two at a time —larks and bluebirds and grassbirds, prospecting in Eph's plowed earth. Suddenly Hardhead, now a half-grown, long-legged dog, would come bounding out and circle the field with whippet-like speed, raising a considerable dust, and chase every bird out of the field. Then he went back to the sassafras bushes, panting, and waited for them to come back into the field again.

Eph watched his antics with pride. "Yes, suh, you got de bird-dog instank. W'en de fust frost comes, you and me is gwine a bird huntin', and I gwine learn you your bird-dog manners." A trained dog would bring a fine price, he thought with a sudden unhappiness.

Along about the first week in December, Eph got his old Long Tom down from the rafters, and the five shells he had saved.

Eph said, as they walked out of the yard, "All right, now git out and go. And recollect 'bout dis, Hardhead. Fum now on, I ain't your sugar tit to chaw on. I de Boss Man, and w'en I holler, you got to hear my voice."

Hardhead ran about excitedly, going faster and faster. Every now and then a field lark would jump up in front of him, and Hardhead would chase it, springing up in the air after the bird. Suddenly the dog cut short one of his absurdly long casts with a flash point, then moved in boldly and held.

Eph grinned in pleasure. "I hope dee's sup'm dere. I kin tolerate a bird-eatin' dog er a flushin' dog, but I can't abide no false pointer."

Hardhead's ears moved, listening to the man's voice. The muscles in his big-boned hind legs quivered. Eph came up until he stood beside the dog. Slowly he stroked the dog from his head to the tip of his shaking tail, and talked to him soothingly.

"Yes, suh, dat's de way a brag dog behaves hisself, and you's de brag dog fo' sho." He saddened momentarily. "Doggone, I do wish ol' Luck was here now, a-lookin'. Me and you and Luck could had us some ideal hunts together, couldn't us, now?"

Hardhead's tremors gradually passed. Eph stopped stroking him and stepped in front of him. A rabbit came out in great frightened bounds. Hardhead went after him with a happy yelp. Eph chuckled.

"Chase him plumb out de county, and see do I keer," he said. "You in grammy school now, and you ain't sposed to be reading de high-school books." He walked on in the direction the dog had gone. "Anyhow, dat ol' rabbit did smell like a pa'tridge. He even fooled me."

That night, he told his family, "We gwine have us a ideal bird dog."

"How much he goan be wuth w'en you git 'em trained up?" Cleotha asked interestedly. "Ten or twelve dollars, you reckon?"

"Sheh, gal. Time I work on him three-four months, I 'spect he be wuth forty dollars."

"Y'ain't plannin' to seel him off?" Addie May asked. Little Valentine began to pucker up around the mouth like she had eaten a green persimmon.

"I ain't sure," Eph said unhappily.

"Yes, you is," Cleotha said ominously. "I ain't goin' round raggedy w'en dey's a forty-dollar dog in de yard!"

"Maybe he turn out bad," Addie May said hopefully. "If'n he ain't a bird dog, he ain't wuth nothin', is he, Eph?"

"Ain't wuth a nickel," Eph agreed.

"In dat case," Cleotha said, "be better to knock 'im in de haid, and den dey'll be one lesser hongry mouth to feed."

For a while, Hardhead improved. But approaching maturity, he became a wild dog. Soon as they left the yard, Hardhead lit out, fast as he could run. For maybe ten minutes he was in sight, then he'd disappear in the distance, going hell-a-lickety. Eph's shouting never seemed to mean a thing to him. And that would be the last Eph saw of him that day usually. Sometimes Eph would see him find birds 'way off. He flushed them immediately, without hesitation, and chased them out of sight.

Finally Eph thought of putting a drag chain on Hardhead. The dog stood patiently while it was being attached, blinking that white-marble eye and twitching his mutilated ear and grinning in excitement. He ran somewhat one-sided, but he still ran wild, and presently he would be out of sight.

"Dang your fool time," Eph finally said when the dog came in one night, brier-scratched and happy, "how come you don't listen at me? I hope you run dem legs off up to de yelbows." The dog got up and came to Eph, and began biting imaginary fleas on the Negro's leg. "Git away fum here," Eph said. He was thinking about the lost wheel chair, and Hardhead's worthlessness made him sicklike. His hand fell upon the dog's big head, and he softened. "If de truth be told, you jist ain't no bird dog. You jist ain't got it into you. You jist a high-class yard dog, and fum now on dat's all you claims to be."

Cleotha, standing behind him, said, "I heered you say he wasn't no bird dog."

From then on, Cleotha was out to get rid of that hungry mouth, and several times, when Eph was in the field, she almost did it. Hardhead knew well enough how Cleotha felt about him, and he never let her get close to him. When he saw her coming, he got up and moved elsewhere. Being one-eyed didn't seem to make him any less alert. Sometimes Cleotha would come out with a plate of corn bread and pot licker in her outstretched hand, and a stick of cordwood behind her back, but hungry as he was, Hardhead wasn't fooled. He wagged his tail politely and went under the sagging old barn.

When Mr. Floyd came back from Europe, the first thing he did
was to drive to the lake to fish with Eph. In the past year the rains
had done fine, and the bass were roiling the water.

"I guess you didn't know I was going to be your neighbor, Eph,"
Mr. Floyd said. "I'm buying the old Humphrey plantation that
joins your little farm. Ten thousand acres of it. Plenty of birds on
that place."

"Oh, Lawd, de birds on dat Humphrey place!" Eph said.

"By the way, what ever happened to that bird-dog puppy I gave
you about three years ago?"

"We still got 'im, and proud of 'im. 'Course Cleotha, she don't
keer 'bout him mightily. But ol' Hardhead, 'e de best yard dog in
Floridy."

"Is that so?" Mr. Floyd asked. "How is he on birds?"

Eph sighed, " 'E ain't no' count as a bird dog, Mr. Floyd. We jist
got him for a pet dog, sort of."

"Gun shy?"

"Oh, no, suh; 'e like to hear de guns."

"What's wrong with him?"

" 'E's a pure wild dog in de woods, Mr. Floyd. Sometime I wish
you could see de way 'e lickety-splits, like a fitified dog. Den, too,
'e hardheaded as a light'rd knot."

"Does he find birds?"

"Well, I can't rightly say what-all he do do. I don't see him but
jist a very few minutes, once I let 'im go. Ev'y now and den I see
him find a covey. Den—blip!—he done fleshed 'em."

"Did you ever try hunting him from horseback?" Mr. Floyd
asked.

"No, suh. Ner muleback either, 'cause ol' Kate's backbone would
split me right in two."

"I want to see that dog hunt, Eph. Bring him over to the place
Monday morning. We'll have a horse saddled for you."

Monday, Mr. Floyd told Mr. Mac, his dog man, to get out Bob,
one of his best pointers. The horses were saddled when Hardhead
arrived, followed at the end of a taut plowline by Eph.

Eph wiped his face with the back of his hand. "Dis lunytic done drug me two miles," he said. "W'en I gits back, I gwine hitch 'im up to de plow, and let ol' Kate loafer a w'ile."

Mr. Floyd looked at Hardhead. He saw a seventy-pound liver-and-white pointer with a great chest, long, big-boned legs, and a lithe waist hardly bigger than your two fists together. His ribs flared out under his tough hide like keg staves, and you could tell that fat would no more stay on him than it would stay on a white-hot stove. Eph tied him to a tree, and when the dog finally decided that the tree was too sturdy to be moved, he half-crouched at the end of his rope, panting excitedly and blinking at them with that milky eye.

They took the two dogs down to Blue Pasture on leash, and Mr. Floyd said, "All right, let's see what they'll do. Leave that check cord on Hardhead."

The dogs were released. "Better watch de big fool close right now, suh," Eph said, " 'cause you ain't gwine see him for long, dog bite his bullheaded time."

Mr. Floyd's dog, Bob, made a long swinging cast toward the branch at the left of Blue Pasture. But Hardhead split the middle, going wide open like a racing greyhound, the fifty-foot check cord they'd tied to him dancing and leaping wildly into the air. The horses spurred after him, and they did well to keep him in sight for fifteen minutes. Once they saw him swing with startling abruptness from a dead run to a cold point, never having slowed or put his nose to the ground. For that one instant, his work was perfect. There he stood, with his tail pointing at the pine tops and his head up as if he were looking over a stump, and that crooked ear twisted lopsided on top of his head. It lasted only a second. Hardhead ducked his head and bolted, busting the covey into twenty frightened pieces, slashing at them with his teeth. He came in with such a lightning rush he even caught one of the birds. He gave it a quick crunch, flung it aside, and then went helling it after the others, chasing them out of sight.

"See dere how 'e do?" Eph said. "Ain't no 'count as a bird dog. But round de house he minds good, and he keeps de possums out de chicken house and de pigs out de yard, and he's a ideal play-pretty for Valentine."

That night when they came in, Mr. Floyd asked, "Well, Mac, what do you think?"

"It'll be a hell of a job to break him, Mr. Floyd," the dog man answered, "but if we can do it, he'll be one everlastin' pistol ball."

"That's what I think, too," Mr. Floyd said. "Eph, you've got a dog we figure can run in field trials. He's your dog, but I want to see a winner that was bred in my kennels; and I'm going to let you and Mac try to break him. I need another man around the kennels anyway, and from now you're working for me—and you better keep your lazy bones in a hustle."

That night as Hardhead dragged Eph home at a trot, the Negro said, "Now, ain't you sump'm! Mr. Floyd done made up his mind dat you a field-trial dog, and 'e want us to train you up. But 'e gwine find out just how hardhead you is, 'fo' he gits through, and he gwine be plumb disagusted. But I ain't. It ain't gwine make de fust bit of diffe'nce. You gwine still be de ol' nigger's brag dog, even if it ain't nothin' but de brag yard dog."

They went to work trying to break Hardhead, but he seemed to get wilder. In the woods they could never get near him. He ran wild as a buck deer and he never held a point for more than twenty seconds. They couldn't train him when they couldn't touch him. Sometimes Hardhead would come back that night, and then again he might be gone three days. After a day of fruitless search in the woods, they would wake up to find the dog lying wearily by the house, muddy and brier-slashed, and twitching in his sleep as he chased dream quail. One time he showed up with blood spots here and there on him. They dug the shot out, and found them to be No. 4's. Whoever let go at him had meant to kill him. They investigated and found out Hardhead had run down a yearling calf and killed it, just for the fun of it. The calf belonged to Mr. Donnelson, a farmer friend of Mr. Floyd's who lived fifteen miles away. Mr. Floyd paid for the calf and got everything straightened out.

"Damn his wild soul," he said afterward, "my ten thousand acres just cramped his style. He wanted room to stretch out and hunt."

Eph thought of the trick that they used finally to break Hardhead. Down in the Blue Pasture there were two coveys that Hardhead knew, and he inevitably went straight to them, first off, and sent them a-scattering. One day they took another bird dog out and located the two coveys precisely, without flushing them. Then Mr. Mac hid in the brush near the first covey, and Eph hid near the second covey, nearly a quarter mile down the pasture. Presently, far up the woods, they heard Mr. Floyd's shout, and they knew Hardhead was loose. Then Mr. Mac could see him coming, his big feet drumming on the ground like a wild mustang's hoofs. Hardhead got wind of this first covey and swerved in and flash-pointed.

Mr. Mac made a dive for the trailing check cord. He got it just as Hardhead lunged forward to pop the birds. "Whoa!" he yelled, and braced himself, but when the big dog hit the end of the cord the man was jerked to his knees.

Hardhead turned a complete end-over-end flip, and hopped to his feet with an expression of mixed incredulity and frustration, his tongue hanging out sideways. He got another whiff of the quail, and stiffened. Then he tried to bust into 'em again, and Mr. Mac turned him tail over head again. Every time Hardhead moved he got snatched back on his tail. Mr. Mac made him stand there twenty minutes, with the birds not ten yards from him. Then he walked in and flushed the birds, shooting one of them down. He made Hardhead stand another minute, then let him go retrieve the bird the way he'd learned to do it in the yard. He retrieved with tender mouth, too, because the last bird he bit had had nails in it.

When Mr. Mac sent him on, he headed straight as a bullet for that second covey. He held his point a good bit longer this time, and when he did charge, Eph was on the other end of the cord, and Hardhead hit the ground again.

Later, when they were talking about it, they laughed about the look on Hardhead's face after he'd been stopped by the cord.

Mr. Mac observed, "He come up with a surprised expression, and he said to me: 'Well, Judas Priest, is that what you been wanting me to do all this time?'"

Eph shook his head. "Dat ain't what he said to me. After nearbout snatching my arms out de sockeys, de ol' scoun'l looked at me, a-spittin' de dirt out'n his mouth, and he said, plain as day, 'Well, you finely cotched me, but I sho give you a time of it!'"

When they had worked on him a few more months, they ran him at

Quitman, at the Continentals—"Mr. Gerald Livin'ston's trials," Eph
called them afterward—but Hardhead was too wild. Mr. Mac handled him, and Eph scouted. Hardhead found two coveys and held
them stanchly. Then he got lost. The time was up when Eph finally
found Hardhead three miles off the course, on point.

At Shuqualak, Mississippi, Hardhead won second. A big lemon
pointer named Kentucky Buckaroo beat him, a hardgoing young
dog that had been burning up the field-trial circuit.

"Buck's the next champion, absolutely," they said.

After Shuqualak, Mr. Floyd came to Eph and handed him two
hundred-dollar bills.

Eph's eyes widened. "W'at's dis yere for, Mr. Floyd?"

"That's what you get for having the next-best dog in the trials."

"Father, do!" Eph whispered. "I didn't know dey gave you no
money for jist bird huntin'. Dese Sugar Log people is sho fine folks."

Mr. Floyd started to go, then turned back. "When we get back,
I've got a brood bitch I'm going to send over to your place. We
want to be getting some Hardhead puppies."

Grand Junction, Tennessee, on field-trial week is dog men's paradise. Any talk but bird-dog talk is beside the point. The great old
dogs live again; dogs like Mary Montrose, who first won the National when she was a derby, and Becky Broomhill and Feagin's
Mohawk Pal, both of whom also won it three times; John Proctor,
champion and famous sire, whose blood has run hot as ever in his
descendants, like Comanche Rap, and Ferris Jake, who won the
1921 championship, and Muscle Shoals Jake, who missed the championship, but took everything else, and his son, Air Pilot, who was
headed for the top until automobile fumes in a garage ruined his nose,
and his son, Air Pilot's Sam, who won in 1937, twenty-one years
after his great-great-great-grandfather, John Proctor.

The wealthy dog owners are there, Johnsons and Teagles and
Fleischmanns and Sages, and such, and field-trial judges like Hobart
Ames, who owns the course, and Dr. Benton King, a little man on a
big horse; and the professional handlers, the real dog men—the
Farriors, father and son, and Ches Harris, who has won more cham-
pionships than any other living handler, and Dewey English and
Clyde Morton and the Bevan Brothers and all the rest of them.

Eph had never seen so many handsome saddle horses in his life. He held Hardhead's collar and said, "Yes, suh, Hardhead, if'n you win next-best ag'in, we goan buy Addie May that sump'm-another!"

The first day was perfect, clear and brittle-cold and breathless. Hardhead was paired with a dog from Oklahoma who hunted well the first half of the long heat, then tired and slowed. Hardhead got off to a bad start, ambling too wide and getting lost, but Eph found him; from then on he hunted the course at a ground-eating pace.

"I'll bet he's in the second series," Mr. Mac said after the heat, as he put the leash on Hardhead's collar.

"He sure hustled," Mr. Floyd grinned. "Take him to the dog truck, Eph."

But it was Hardhead who took Eph to the dog truck. After three hours of the hardest bird hunting, most dogs would have been content to trot wearily at heel. Hardhead hunched his gaunt shoulders, stretched the leash taut as a fiddle string, and pulled.

Two or three men were watching. One of them asked Eph, "Hey, George, ain't that the one they call Hardhead? The one they just took up?"

Jogging along, Eph grinned and said, "Dis de ol' fool hisse'f, gen'lemen."

"I'll bet a hundred to two on that dog against the field," the man said to his friends, "provided they call him back for the second series."

"You think I didn't see the way he drug that nigger by here?" one of the others said. "You trying to catch a fish?"

"I throwed out my net."

But when night of the second day came, there was a new favorite. He was a yellow pointer from Oklahoma, and his name was Ambling Sam. When he ran he outhunted everything that had been put down, finding five coveys and nailing them tight. He traveled wide and fast, with a happy, light-hearted style, and he handled like a show dog.

Eight dogs were called back for the second series, but everybody was pretty sure that the real race was between Hardhead, Ambling Sam and Kentucky Buckaroo. Hardhead and Buck were paired in the last brace. In the brace preceding them, Ambling Sam threw his chances away. After hunting nicely for two hours—though not so spectacularly as he had in his previous run—he jumped a doe deer, forgot his training, and chased her clean out of the country.

The judges called the last brace. Mr. Mac and Mr. Floyd and Eph took Hardhead out of the dog truck and gave him a tiny bit of water. The dog yawned nervously and looked things over, his leathery muscles quivering and his one good eye glinting fiercely.

Mr. Floyd pulled at his cigarette and whispered, "Look at him. He's right today."

Mr. Mac gave Eph a hard glance. "Don't lose him, Eph. He's sure hot. He can be the best dog in the world today—or he can be the wildest."

They brought him out front, Mr. Mac leaning back as the dog strained mulelike against the rope. Eph held the rope until Mr. Mac found the leash snap. "All right, I got him," he said, unsnapping the rope. He muttered, "He's hot as a pistol, Eph. Don't lose him now."

Buck stood waiting, eager, too, but well-mannered. A smooth-turned bird dog, Buck made an odd contrast with the gaunt, big-boned Hardhead, with his wild impatience and his bad eye and ear.

"Let 'im go!" the starting judge said.

Both dogs broke fast, but Hardhead jumped with the suppressed power of a spring out of a clock. He ran furiously, straining almost agonizingly for a longer stride. Easily losing Buckaroo, he was still going like this when he hit game, five minutes later. He was right in the middle of the covey in one bound, and they exploded around him. For one split second he seemed about to lunge forward after them. But he stood, on point, until the judges came.

"It's a stop to flush," one of them said. "I saw the birds."

Mr. Mac sent Hardhead on. The dog resumed his wicked wind-scorching stride. He swung out to the right, skirting a cornfield and leaving a vapor of dust behind him.

"Go hard, dog," Eph muttered, "but don't come up on no birds till you run off some o' dat hot."

Then Hardhead found two coveys within five minutes. The first he almost flushed again. Running wild, he suddenly stopped his front feet dead. His rear end kept going, swinging him around, and when he had stopped he was on birds.

Eph rode to the edge of the woods and shouted to the judges, waving his battered hat.

The brown body of the gallery shifted and broke, and the riders galloped to the point. Mr. Mac dismounted, his little twenty-eight-gauge gun in his left hand, and his quirt in the other. Hardhead stood frozen, his tail good and his front quarters still in the slight crouch in which he had stopped. Mr. Mac walked rapidly out front, kicking the bushes and flinging his quirt against the grass. When the birds got up, he fired the gun with one hand, watching to see that Hardhead didn't break.

The next find was a bit on the spectacular side. Slicing rapidly across a thinly covered grass field, Hardhead picked up a vagrant scent and wheeled at right angles. He didn't slow down, but his head was higher as he read the wind. The birds were feeding quietly two hundred yards away. He drew on them boldly, cockily, and abruptly pointed with high head and tail and all feet planted solid. Two birds were not eight feet from him, their frightened little black eyes shining as they squatted motionlessly in a barren furrow in plain view of everybody. Mr. Mac flushed the covey.

Kentucky Buckaroo had come to be known as one of the biggest going dogs on the field-trial circuit. Hardhead was bigger. Buck made several good finds, and handled nicely, but it was Hardhead that everybody watched. In the distance they saw the Negro ride out to the edge of the woods and wave his hand, and again his shout of point drifted clearly down.

"That big dog's got 'em again," a brown man called. When the judge rode up, Mr. Mac dismounted and walked toward the motionless dog. Before he got close to him, Hardhead left the point and ran fifty yards out into the sedge and pointed again.

"Dey runnin' fum 'im," Eph thought nervously. This time the birds held, and Mr. Mac's boots exploded them out. Hardhead stood to wing and shot, and was sent on.

Eph grinned his relief. "De reason dat ol' head's so hard is 'cause she's packed plumb tight with brains!"

Hardhead swung out into the woods again, going like a ball of light through the cold shadows. An ice-water brook wandered down the woods; Eph hoped the dog would stop and drink, and get a few seconds of rest. Hardhead drank, but he did it galloping up the shallow stream, splashing the chilled waters on the damp leaves of the banks. Then he jumped out and headed for the cornfield.

In ten minutes he was out of Eph's sight. Twenty minutes later Hardhead was lost and Mr. Mac had joined the search. They quirted their horses, riding high in the saddle and intently studying every distant whitish object that might be a pointer on birds.

"Dog take my sorry time," Eph thought fearfully, "I done gone and let 'im lost hisse'f!"

Another ten minutes they searched, without success. If they didn't find him before taking-up time, Hardhead was out of it. "Lemme find 'im, Lord, lemme find 'im," Eph kept muttering. Then he thought of Luck, and he said, "If'n you kin look any better fum where you is, Luck, glance round and see do you see 'im."

A man shouted, "Hey, Mac, yon's your dog!"

Eph saw him, a mile away, beyond the gallery, slashing his way down a rise, moving with incredible swiftness, as always. At the bottom of the rise, Kentucky Buckaroo stood on point; even that far away, Eph could tell the judges were watching to see what Hardhead would do.

When Hardhead was two hundred yards away, he saw the point and stopped on the hillside, stylishly honoring; he held until the birds were flushed and Buck sent on.

"For a dog with one eye," a man was saying as Eph approached the gallery again, "he can see a damn long way."

"That's the most dog you'll ever look at, bud," another answered. "I've watched 'em all from Eugene M right on down, and that hard-headed son of a gun right yonder's my pick."

"Comanche Frank would've showed him a thing or two."

"Comanche Frank, hell."

"You wait a while. This race isn't over. See if your Hardhead is still balling the jack like that after three hours of it."

That's what the judges were watching too. Buckaroo was running a good race, and finding birds; and ordinarily his performance would have won. But Hardhead was too much dog. He had covered more ground, found more birds, and handled as well as Buck.

The gallery rode in quiet excitement. Hardhead was far out to the left, almost, it seemed, on the horizon. Buck was on the right and closer in. Buck cut across in front of the gallery. Ahead of him was a ravine, ten feet or so across. Buck slid down one side and galloped up the other, hardly slowing.

"Buck can't be very tired," somebody said, "the way he come out of that hole like a bat out of hell."

While the riders looked for a place to cross the ravine, Hardhead came back in, his big feet thrumming on the red earth. Before he even reached the place, it was apparent that he was going to cross the ravine at exactly the same place Buck had crossed. Everybody stopped—the judges and reporters and spectators and dog men—to see if Hardhead would reveal any weariness in crossing that deep ravine.

The dog came on, that torn ear lying inside out on his head the way it did sometimes. For a split second it seemed that Hardhead didn't even see the ravine. Then he was there. He left the ground. In mid-air his tail gave a convulsive flirt that seemed to send him over. That unbelievable leap carried him across with two feet to spare. Within a few minutes he had overtaken Buckaroo and was headed for the horizon again.

The judges looked at their watches. Doctor King said, "You can take your dogs up."

Addie May didn't know exactly what to make of the wheel chair. A lot of the neighbors heard that Eph had bought it, and they were there when it came.

"How you do it, Eph?" Addie May said uncertainly.

"You jist gits in it and rolls right around," Eph said happily.

Addie May hesitated. "Ise scared of hit."

Eph laughed. "Hit's plumb harmless, honey."

They sat her in it, and she rolled carefully across the room, and, with growing confidence, turned it around and came back.

"Doggone," said Joe Ben Brown, "I gwine borry dat to ride to de store in!"

Cleotha looked at Eph angrily. "I see you aims to just th'ow dat best-dog money away."

Eph paid no attention to her. "How you likes it, Addie May?"

"Hit's sho Lord purty," she said, almost ready to cry in her happiness. "We'll put us a sheet over hit to keep it nice, and just let comp'ny set in it."

"Honey, dat ain't no comp'ny chair. Dat's your ev'yday chair, and you kin roll right where you pleases," Eph said. Hardhead came up and hasseled the chair with his flaring nostrils, and his tail give a perfunctory wag. "Look at de ol' scoun'l," Eph said, "he know he done bought you dat fancy sump'm."

A Dog's Nervous System

BY

E. B. WHITE

I WOULD like to hand down a dissenting opinion in the case of the Camel ad which shows a Boston terrier relaxing. I can string along with cigarette manufacturers to a certain degree, but when it comes to the temperament and habits of terriers, I shall stand my ground.

The ad says: "A dog's nervous system resembles our own." I don't think a dog's nervous system resembles my own in the least. A dog's nervous system is in a class by itself. If it resembles anything at all, it resembles the New York Edison Company's power plant. This is particularly true of Boston terriers, and if the Camel people don't know that, they have never been around dogs.

The ad says: "But when a dog's nerves tire, he obeys his instincts —he relaxes." This, I admit, is true. But I should like to call attention to the fact that it sometimes takes days, even weeks, before a dog's nerves tire. In the case of terriers it can run into months.

I knew a Boston terrier once (he is now dead and, so far as I know, relaxed) whose nerves stayed keyed up from the twenty-fifth of one June to the sixth of the following July, without one minute's peace for anybody in the family. He was an old dog and he was blind in one eye, but his infirmities caused no diminution in his nervous power. During the period of which I speak, the famous period of his greatest excitation, he not only raised a type of general hell which startled even his closest friends and observers, but he gave a mighty clever excuse. He said it was love.

"I'm in love," he would scream. (He could scream just like a hurt child.) "I'm in love and I'm going *crazy*."

Day and night it was all the same. I tried everything to soothe him. I tried darkness, cold water dashed in the face, the lash, long quiet talks, warm milk administered internally, threats, promises, and close confinement in remote locations. At last, after about a week of it, I went down the road and had a chat with the lady who owned the object of our terrier's affection. It was she who finally cleared up the situation.

"Oh," she said, wearily, "if it's that bad, let him out."

I hadn't thought of anything as simple as that myself, but I am a creature of infinite reserve. As a matter of record, it turned out to be not so simple—the terrier got run over by a motor car one night while returning from his amorous adventures, suffering a complete paralysis of the hip but no assuagement of the nervous system; and the little Scotty bitch returned to Washington, D.C., and a Caesarian.

I am not through with the Camel people yet. Love is not the only thing that can keep a dog's nerves in a state of perpetual jangle. A dog, more than any other creature, it seems to me, gets interested in one subject, theme, or object, in life, and pursues it with a fixity of purpose which would be inspiring to Man if it weren't so troublesome. One dog gets absorbed in one thing, another dog in another. When I was a boy there was a smooth-haired fox terrier (in those days nobody ever heard of a fox terrier that *wasn't* smooth-haired) who became interested, rather late in life, in a certain stone. The stone was about the size of an egg. As far as I could see, it was like a million other stones—but to him it was the Stone Supreme.

He kept it with him day and night, slept with it, ate with it, played with it, analyzed it, took it on little trips (you would often see him three blocks from home, trotting along on some shady errand, his stone safe in his jaws). He used to lie by the hour on the porch of his house, chewing the stone with an expression half tender, half petulant. When he slept he merely enjoyed a muscular suspension: his nerves were still up and around, adjusting the bed clothes, tossing and turning.

He permitted people to throw the stone for him and people would. But if the stone lodged somewhere he couldn't get to he raised such

an uproar that it was absolutely necessary that the stone be returned, for the public peace. His absorption was so great it brought
wrinkles to his face, and he grew old before his time. I think he used
to worry that somebody was going to pitch the stone into a lake or
a bog, where it would be irretrievable. He wore off every tooth in
his jaw, wore them right down to the gums, and they became mere
brown vestigial bumps. His breath was awful (he panted night and
day) and his eyes were alight with an unearthly zeal. He died in a
fight with another dog. I have always suspected it was because he
tried to hold the stone in his mouth all through the battle. The Camel
people will just have to take my word for it: that dog was a living
denial of the whole theory of relaxation. He was a paragon of nervous
tension, from the moment he first laid eyes on his slimy little stone
till the hour of his death.

The advertisement speaks of the way humans "prod" themselves
to endeavor—so that they keep on and on working, long after they
should quit. The inference is that a dog never does that. But I have
a dog right now that can prod himself harder and drive himself
longer than any human I ever saw. This animal is a dachshund, and
I shall spare you the long dull inanities of his innumerable obsessions.
His particular study (or mania) at the moment is a black-and-white
kitten that my wife gave me for Christmas, thinking that what my
life needed was something else that could move quickly from one
place in the room to another. The dachshund began his research on
Christmas eve when the kitten arrived "secretly" in the cellar, and
now, five months later, is taking his Ph.D., still working late at night
on it, every night. If he could write a book about that cat, it would
make *Middletown* look like the work of a backward child.

I'll be glad to have the Camel people study this animal in one of
his relaxed moods, but they will have to bring their own seismograph.
Even curled up cozily in a chair, dreaming of his cat, he quivers like
an aspen.

The Care and Training of a Dog

E. B. WHITE

THERE is a book out called *Dog Training Made Easy* and it was sent to me the other day by the publisher, who rightly guessed that it would catch my eye. I like to read books on dog training. Being the owner of dachshunds, to me a book on dog discipline becomes a volume of inspired humor. Every sentence is a riot. Some day, if I ever get a chance, I shall write a book, or warning, on the character and temperament of the dachshund and why he can't be trained and shouldn't be. I would rather train a striped zebra to balance an Indian club than induce a dachshund to heed my slightest command. For a number of years past I have been agreeably encumbered by a very large and dissolute dachshund named Fred. Of all the dogs whom I have served I've never known one who understood so much of what I say or held it in such deep contempt. When I address Fred I never have to raise either my voice or my hopes. He even disobeys me when I instruct him in something that he wants to do. And when I answer his peremptory scratch at the door and hold the door open for him to walk through, he stops in the middle and lights a cigarette, just to hold me up.

"Shopping for a puppy presents a number of problems," writes Mr. Wm. Cary Duncan, author of *Dog Training Made Easy*. Well, shopping for a puppy has never presented many problems for me, as most of the puppies and dogs that have entered my life (and there have been scores of them) were not the result of a shopping trip but of an act of God. The first puppy I owned, when I was about nine

176

years old, was not shopped for—it was born to the collie bitch of the postman of my older sister, who sent it to me by express from Washington, D.C., in a little crate containing, in addition to the puppy, a bar of Peters' chocolate and a ripe frankfurter. And the puppy I own now was not shopped for but was won in a raffle. Between these two extremes there have been many puppies, mostly unshopped for. It is not so much that I acquire dogs as it is that dogs acquire me. Maybe they even shop for me, I don't know. If they do I assume they have many problems, because they certainly always arrive with plenty, which they then turn over to me.

The possession of a dog to-day is a different thing from the possession of a dog at the turn of the century, when one's dog was fed on mashed potato and brown gravy and lived in a doghouse with an arched portal. To-day a dog is fed on scraped beef and Vitamin B_1 and lives in bed with you.

An awful lot of nonsense has been written about dogs by persons who don't know them very well, and the attempt to elevate the pure-bred to a position of national elegance has been, in the main, a success. Dogs used to mate with other dogs rather casually in my day, and the results were discouraging to the American Kennel Club but entirely satisfactory to small boys who liked puppies. In my suburban town, "respectable" people didn't keep she-dogs. One's washer-woman might keep a bitch, or one's lawn cutter, but not one's next-door neighbor.

The prejudice against females made a deep impression on me, and I grew up thinking that there was something indecent and unclean about she-things in general. The word bitch of course was never used in polite families. One day a little mutt followed me home from school, and after much talk I persuaded my parents to let me keep it— at least until the owner turned up or advertised for it. It dwelt among us only one night. Next morning my father took me aside and in a low voice said: "My son, I don't know whether you realize it, but that dog is a female. It'll have to go."

"But why does it have to?" I asked.

"They're a nuisance," he replied, embarrassed. "We'd have all the other dogs in the neighborhood around here all the time."

That sounded like an idyllic arrangement to me, but I could tell from my father's voice that the stray dog was doomed. We turned her out and she went off toward the more liberal section of town. This sort of incident must have been happening to thousands of American youngsters in those days, and we grew up to find that it had been permanently added to the record by Dorothy Parker in her short story "Mr. Durant."

On our block, in the days of my innocence, there were in addition to my collie, a pug dog, a dachshund named Bruno, a fox terrier named Sunny who spent many years studying one croquet ball, a red setter, and a St. Bernard who carried his mistress's handbag, shuffling along in a stately fashion with the drool running out both sides of his jaws. I was scared of this St. Bernard because of his size, and never passed his house without dread. The dachshund was old, surly, and disagreeable, and was endlessly burying bones in the flower border of the DeVries's yard. I should very much doubt if any of those animals ever had its temperature taken rectally, ever was fed raw meat or tomato juice, ever was given distemper inoculations, or ever saw the whites of a veterinary's eyes. They were brought up on chicken bones and gravy and left-over cereal, and were all fine dogs. Most of them never saw the inside of their owner's houses—they knew their place.

The "problem" of caring for a dog has been unnecessarily complicated. Take the matter of housebreaking. In the suburbia of those lovely post-Victorian days of which I write the question of housebreaking a puppy was met with the simple bold courage characteristic of our forefathers. You simply kept the house away from the puppy. This was not only the simplest way, it was the only practical way, just as it is to-day. Our parents were in possession of a vital secret—a secret which has been all but lost to the world: the knowledge that a puppy will live and thrive without ever crossing the threshold of a dwelling house, at least till he's big enough so he doesn't wet the rug.

Although our fathers and mothers very sensibly never permitted a puppy to come into the house, they made up for this indignity by always calling the puppy "Sir." In those days a dog didn't expect anything very elaborate in the way of food or medical care, but he did expect to be addressed civilly.

Mr. Duncan discusses housebreaking at some length and assumes, as do all writers of dog books, that the owner of a puppy has little else to do except own the puppy. It is Mr. Duncan's theory that puppies have a sense of modesty and don't like to be stared at when they are doing something. When you are walking the dog, he says, you must "appear utterly uninterested" as you approach some favorite spot. This, as any city dweller knows, is a big order. Anybody who has ever tried to synchronize a puppy's bowels with a rigid office schedule knows that one's interest in the small phenomena of early morning sometimes reaches fever pitch. A dog owner may feign disinterest, but his masque will not suffice. Nothing is more comical than the look on the face of a person at the upper end of a dog leash, pretending not to know what is going on at the lower.

A really companionable and indispensable dog is an accident of nature. You can't get it by breeding for it, and you can't buy it with money. It just happens along. Out of the vast sea of assorted dogs that I have had dealings with, by far the noblest, the best, and the most important was the first, the one my sister sent me in a crate. He was an old-style collie, beautifully marked, with a blunt nose, and great natural gentleness and intelligence. When I got him he was what I badly needed. I think probably all these other dogs of mine have been just a groping toward that old dream. I've never dared get another collie for fear the comparison would be too uncomfortable. I can still see my first dog in all the moods and situations that memory has filed him away in, but I think of him oftenest as he used to be right after breakfast on the back porch, listlessly eating up a dish of petrified oatmeal rather than hurt my feelings. For six years he met me at the same place after school and convoyed me home—a service he thought up himself. A boy doesn't forget that sort of association. It is a monstrous trick of fate that now, settled in the country and with sheep to take care of, I am obliged to do my shepherding with the grotesque and sometimes underhanded assistance of two dachshunds and a wire-haired fox terrier.

Obituary

BY

E. B. WHITE

Daisy ("Black Watch Debatable") died December 22, 1931, when she was hit by a Yellow Cab in University Place. At the moment of her death she was smelling the front of a florist's shop. It was a wet day, and the cab skidded up over the curb—just the sort of excitement that would have amused her, had she been at a safer distance. She is survived by her mother, Jeannie; a brother, Abner; her father, whom she never knew; and two sisters, whom she never liked. She was three years old.

Daisy was born at 65 West Eleventh Street in a clothes closet at two o'clock of a December morning in 1928. She came, as did her sisters and brothers, as an unqualified surprise to her mother, who had for several days previously looked with a low-grade suspicion on the box of bedding that had been set out for the delivery, and who had gone into the clothes closet merely because she had felt funny and wanted a dark, awkward place to feel funny in. Daisy was the smallest of the litter of seven, and the oddest.

Her life was full of incident but not of accomplishment. Persons who knew her only slightly regarded her as an opinionated little bitch, and said so; but she had a small circle of friends who saw through her, cost what it did. At Speyer Hospital, where she used to go when she was indisposed, she was known as "Whitey," because, the man told me, she was black. All her life she was subject to moods, and her feeling about horses laid her sanity open to question. Once she slipped her leash and chased a horse for three blocks through heavy traffic, in the carking belief that she was an effective agent against horses. Drivers of teams, seeing her only in the moments of her delirium, invariably leaned far out of their seats and gave tongue, mocking her; and thus made themselves even more ridiculous, for the moment, than Daisy.

She had a stoical nature, and spent the latter part of her life an invalid, owing to an injury to her right hind leg. Like many invalids, she developed a rather objectionable cheerfulness, as though to deny that she had cause for rancor. She also developed, without instruction or encouragement, a curious habit of holding people firmly by the ankle without actually biting them—a habit that gave her an immense personal advantage and won her many enemies. As far as I know, she never even broke the thread of a sock, so delicate was her grasp (like a retriever's), but her point of view was questionable, and her attitude was beyond explaining to the person whose ankle was at stake. For my own amusement, I often tried to diagnose this quirkish temper, and I think I understand it: she suffered from a chronic perplexity, and it relieved her to take hold of something.

She was arrested once, by Patrolman Porko. She enjoyed practically everything in life except motoring, an exigency to which she submitted silently, without joy, and without nausea. She never took pains to discover, conclusively, the things that might have diminished her curiosity and spoiled her taste. She died sniffing life, and enjoying it.

Our Friend, the Dog

BY

MAURICE MAETERLINCK

I

I HAVE lost, within these last few days, a little bull-dog. He had just completed the sixth month of his brief existence. He had no history. His intelligent eyes opened to look out upon the world, to love mankind, then closed again on the cruel secrets of death.

The friend who presented me with him had given him, perhaps by antiphrasis, the startling name of Pelléas. Why rechristen him? For how can a poor dog, loving, devoted, faithful, disgrace the name of a man or an imaginary hero?

Pelléas had a great bulging, powerful forehead, like that of Socrates or Verlaine; and, under a little black nose, blunt as a churlish assent, a pair of large hanging and symmetrical chops, which made his head a sort of massive, obstinate, pensive and three-cornered menace. He was beautiful after the manner of a beautiful, natural monster that has complied strictly with the laws of its species. And what a smile of attentive obligingness, of incorruptible innocence, of affectionate submission, of boundless gratitude and total self-abandonment lit up, at the least caress, that adorable mask of ugliness! Whence exactly did that smile emanate? From the ingenuous and melting eyes? From the ears pricked up to catch the words of man? From the forehead that unwrinkled to appreciate and love, or from the stump of a tail that wriggled at the other end to testify to the intimate and impassioned joy that filled his small being, happy once more to encounter the hand or the glance of the god to whom he surrendered himself?

Pelléas was born in Paris, and I had taken him to the country. His

182

bonny fat paws, shapeless and not yet stiffened, carried slackly through the unexplored pathways of his new existence his huge and serious head, flat-nosed and, as it were, rendered heavy with thought.

For this thankless and rather sad head, like that of an overworked child, was beginning the overwhelming work that oppresses every brain at the start of life. He had, in less than five or six weeks, to get into his mind, taking shape within it, an image and a satisfactory conception of the universe. Man, aided by all the knowledge of his own elders and his brothers, takes thirty or forty years to outline that conception, but the humble dog has to unravel it for himself in a few days: and yet, in the eyes of a god, who should know all things, would it not have the same weight and the same value as our own?

It was a question, then, of studying the ground, which can be scratched and dug up and which sometimes reveals surprising things; of casting at the sky, which is uninteresting, for there is nothing there to eat, one glance that does away with it for good and all; of discovering the grass, the admirable and green grass, the springy and cool grass, a field for races and sports, a friendly and boundless bed, in which lies hidden the good and wholesome couch-grass. It was a question, also, of taking promiscuously a thousand urgent and curious observations. It was necessary, for instance, with no other guide than pain, to learn to calculate the height of objects from the top of which you can jump into space; to convince yourself that it is vain to pursue birds who fly away and that you are unable to clamber up trees after the cats who defy you there; to distinguish between the sunny spots where it is delicious to sleep and the patches of shade in which you shiver; to remark with stupefaction that the rain does not fall inside the houses, that water is cold, uninhabitable and dangerous, while fire is beneficent at a distance, but terrible when you come too near; to observe that the meadows, the farm-yards and sometimes the roads are haunted by giant creatures with threatening horns, creatures good-natured, perhaps, and, at any rate, silent, creatures who allow you to sniff at them a little curiously without taking offence, but who keep their real thoughts to themselves. It was necessary to learn, as the result of painful and humiliating experiment, that you are not at liberty to obey all nature's laws without distinction in the dwelling of the gods; to recognize that the kitchen is the privileged and most agreeable spot in that divine dwelling, although you are hardly allowed to abide in it because of the cook, who is a considerable, but jealous power; to learn that doors are important and capricious volitions, which sometimes lead to felicity, but which most often, hermetically closed, mute and stern, haughty and heartless, remain deaf to all entreaties; to admit, once and for all, that the essential good things of life, the indisputable blessings, generally imprisoned in pots and stewpans, are almost always inaccessible; to know how to look at them with laboriously-acquired indifference and to practice to take no notice of them, saying to yourself that here are objects which are probably sacred, since merely to skim them with the tip of a respectful tongue is enough to let loose the unanimous anger of all the gods of the house.

And then, what is one to think of the table on which so many things happen that cannot be guessed; of the derisive chairs on which one is forbidden to sleep; of the plates and dishes that are empty by the time that one can get at them; of the lamp that drives away the dark? . . . How many orders, dangers, prohibitions, problems, enigmas has one not to classify in one's overburdened memory! . . . And how to reconcile all this with other laws, other enigmas, wider and more imperious, which one bears within one's self, within one's instinct, which spring up and develop from one hour to the other, which come from the depths of time and the race, invade the blood, the muscles and the nerves and suddenly assert themselves more irresistibly and more powerfully than pain, the word of the master himself, or the fear of death?

Thus, for instance, to quote only one example, when the hour of sleep has struck for men, you have retired to your hole, surrounded by the darkness, the silence and the formidable solitude of the night. All is sleep in the master's house. You feel yourself very small and weak in the presence of the mystery. You know that the gloom is peopled with foes who hover and lie in wait. You suspect the trees, the passing wind and the moonbeams. You would like to hide, to suppress yourself by holding your breath. But still the watch must be kept; you must, at the least sound, issue from your retreat, face the invisible and bluntly disturb the imposing silence of the earth, at the risk of bringing down the whispering evil or crime upon yourself alone. Whoever the enemy be, even if he be man, that is to say, the very brother of the god whom it is your business to defend, you must attack him blindly, fly at his throat, fasten your perhaps sacrilegious teeth into human flesh, disregard the spell of a hand and voice similar to those of your master, never be silent, never attempt to escape, never allow yourself to be tempted or bribed and, lost in the night without help, prolong the heroic alarm to your last breath.

There is the great ancestral duty, the essential duty, stronger than death, which not even man's will and anger are able to check. All our humble history, linked with that of the dog in our first struggles against every breathing thing, tends to prevent his forgetting it. And when, in our safer dwelling-places of to-day, we happen to punish him for his untimely zeal, he throws us a glance of astonished reproach, as though to point out to us that we are in the wrong and that, if we lose sight of the main clause in the treaty of alliance which he made with us at the time when we lived in caves, forests and fens, he continues faithful to it in spite of us and remains nearer to the eternal truth of life, which is full of snares and hostile forces.

But how much care and study are needed to succeed in fulfilling this duty! And how complicated it has become since the days of the silent caverns and the great deserted lakes! It was all so simple, then, so easy and so clear. The lonely hollow opened upon the side of the hill, and all that approached, all that moved on the horizon of the plains or woods, was the unmistakable enemy. . . . But to-day you can no longer tell. . . . You have to acquaint yourself with a civilization of which you disapprove, to appear to understand a thousand incomprehensible things. . . . Thus, it seems evident that henceforth the whole world no longer belongs to the master, that his property conforms to unintelligible limits. . . . It becomes necessary, therefore, first of all to know exactly where the sacred domain begins and ends. Whom are you to suffer, whom to stop? . . . There is the road by which every one, even the poor, has the right to pass. Why? You do not know; it is a fact which you deplore, but which you are bound to accept. Fortunately, on the other hand, here is the fair path which none may tread. This path is faithful to the sound traditions; it is not to be lost sight of; for by it enter into your daily existence the difficult problems of life.

Would you have an example? You are sleeping peacefully in a ray
of the sun that covers the threshold of the kitchen with pearls. The
earthenware pots are amusing themselves by elbowing and nudging
one another on the edge of the shelves trimmed with paper lace-
work. The copper stew-pans play at scattering spots of light over
the smooth white walls. The motherly stove hums a soft tune and
dandles three saucepans blissfully dancing; and, from the little hole
that lights up its inside, defies the good dog who cannot approach,
by constantly putting out at him its fiery tongue. The clock, bored
in its oak case, before striking the august hour of meal time, swings
its great gilt navel to and fro; and the cunning flies tease your ears.
On the glittering table lie a chicken, a hare, three partridges, besides
other things which are called fruits—peaches, melons, grapes—and
which are all good for nothing. The cook guts a big silver fish and
throws the entrails (instead of giving them to you!) into the dust-
bin. Ah, the dust-bin! Inexhaustible treasury, receptacle of windfalls,
the jewel of the house! You shall have your share of it, an exquisite
and surreptitious share; but it does not do to seem to know where
it is. You are strictly forbidden to rummage in it. Man in this way
prohibits many pleasant things, and life would be dull indeed and
your days empty if you had to obey all the orders of the pantry, the
cellar and the dining-room. Luckily, he is absent-minded and does
not long remember the instructions which he lavishes. He is easily
deceived. You achieve your ends and do as you please, provided you
have the patience to await the hour. You are subject to man, and he
is the one god; but you none the less have your own personal, exact
and imperturbable morality, which proclaims aloud that illicit acts
become most lawful through the very fact that they are performed
without the master's knowledge. Therefore, let us close the watchful
eye that has seen. Let us pretend to sleep and to dream of the
moon. . . .

Hark! A gentle tapping at the blue window that looks out on the
garden! What is it? Nothing; a bough of hawthorn that has come to
see what we are doing in the cool kitchen. Trees are inquisitive and
often excited; but they do not count, one has nothing to say to them,
they are irresponsible, they obey the wind, which has no principles.
. . . But what is that? I hear steps! . . . Up, ears open; nose on

the alert! . . . . It is the baker coming up to the rails, while the post-man is opening a little gate in the hedge of lime-trees. They are friends; it is well; they bring something; you can greet them and wag your tail discreetly twice or thrice, with a patronizing smile. . . .

Another alarm! What is it now? A carriage pulls up in front of the steps. The problem is a complex one. Before all, it is of consequence to heap copious insults on the horses, great, proud beasts, who make no reply. Meantime, you examine out of the corner of your eye the persons alighting. They are well-clad and seem full of confidence. They are probably going to sit at the table of the gods. The proper thing is to bark without acrimony, with a shade of respect, so as to show that you are doing your duty, but that you are doing it with intelligence. Nevertheless, you cherish a lurking suspicion and, be-hind the guests' backs, stealthily, you sniff the air persistently and in a knowing way, in order to discern any hidden intentions.

But halting footsteps resound outside the kitchen. This time it is the poor man dragging his crutch, the unmistakable enemy, the hereditary enemy, the direct descendant of him who roamed outside the bone-cramped cave which you suddenly see again in your racial memory. Drunk with indignation, your bark broken, your teeth multiplied with hatred and rage, you are about to seize their recon-cilable adversary by the breeches, when the cook, armed with her broom, the ancillary and forsworn sceptre, comes to protect the traitor, and you are obliged to go back to your hole, where, with eyes filled with impotent and slanting flames, you growl out fright-ful, but futile curses, thinking within yourself that this is the end of all things, and that the human species has lost its notion of justice and injustice. . . .

Is that all? Not yet; for the smallest life is made up of innumerable duties, and it is a long work to organize a happy existence upon the borderland of two such different worlds as the world of beasts and the world of men. How should we fare if we had to serve, while remaining within our own sphere, a divinity, not an imaginary one, like to ourselves, because the offspring of our own brain, but a god actually visible, ever present, ever active and as foreign, as superior to our being as we are to the dog?

We now, to return to Pelléas, know pretty well what to do and how to behave on the master's premises. But the world does not end at the house-door, and, beyond the walls and beyond the hedge, there is a universe of which one has not the custody, where one is no longer at home, where relations are changed. How are we to stand in the street, in the fields, in the market-place, in the shops? In consequence of difficult and delicate observations, we understand that we must take no notice of passers-by; obey no calls but the master's; be polite, with indifference, to strangers who pet us. Next, we must conscientiously fulfil certain obligations of mysterious courtesy toward our brothers the other dogs; respect chickens and ducks; not appear to remark the cakes at the pastry-cooks, which spread themselves insolently within reach of the tongue; show to the cats, who, on the steps of the houses, provoke us by hideous grimaces, a silent contempt, but one that will not forget; and remember that it is lawful and even commendable to chase and strangle mice, rats, wild rabbits and, generally speaking, all animals (we learn to know them by secret marks) that have not yet made their peace with mankind.

All this and so much more! . . . Was it surprising that Pelléas often appeared pensive in the face of those numberless problems, and that his humble and gentle look was often so profound and grave, laden with cares and full of unreadable questions?

Alas, he did not have time to finish the long and heavy task which nature lays upon the instinct that rises in order to approach a brighter region. . . . An ill of a mysterious character, which seems specially to punish the only animal that succeeds in leaving the circle in which it is born; an indefinite ill that carries off hundreds of intelligent little dogs, came to put an end to the destiny and the happy education of Pelléas. And now all those efforts to achieve a little more light; all that ardor in loving, that courage in understanding; all that affectionate gaiety and innocent fawning; all those kind and devoted looks, which turned to man to ask for his assistance against unjust death; all those flickering gleams which came from the profound abyss of a world that is no longer ours; all those nearly human little habits lie sadly in the cold ground, under a flowering elder-tree, in a corner of the garden.

II

Man loves the dog, but how much more ought he to love it if he considered, in the inflexible harmony of the laws of nature, the sole exception, which is that love of a being that succeeds in piercing, in order to draw closer to us, the partitions, ever elsewhere impermeable, that separate the species! We are alone, absolutely alone on this chance planet; and amid all the forms of life that surround us, not one, excepting the dog, has made an alliance with us. A few creatures fear us, most are unaware of us, and not one loves us. In the world of plants, we have dumb and motionless slaves; but they serve us in spite of themselves. They simply endure our laws and our yoke. They are impotent prisoners, victims incapable of escaping, but silently rebellious; and, so soon as we lose sight of them, they hasten to betray us and return to their former wild and mischievous liberty. The rose and the corn, had they wings, would fly at our approach like the birds.

Among the animals, we number a few servants who have submitted only through indifference, cowardice or stupidity: the uncertain and craven horse, who responds only to pain and is attached to nothing; the passive and dejected ass, who stays with us only because he knows not what to do nor where to go, but who nevertheless, under the cudgel and the pack-saddle, retains the idea that lurks behind his ears; the cow and the ox, happy so long as they are eating, and docile because, for centuries, they have not had a thought of their own; the affrighted sheep, who knows no other master than terror; the hen, who is faithful to the poultry-yard because she finds more maize and wheat there than in the neighboring forest. I do not speak of the cat, to whom we are nothing more than a too large and uneatable prey: the ferocious cat, whose sidelong contempt tolerates us only as encumbering parasites in our own homes. She, at least, curses us in her mysterious heart; but all the others live beside us as they might live beside a rock or a tree. They do not love us, do not know us, scarcely notice us. They are unaware of our life, our death, our departure, our return, our sadness, our joy, our smile. They do not even hear the sound of our voice, so soon as it no longer threatens them; and, when they look at us, it is with the distrustful bewilderment of the horse, in whose eye still hovers the infatuation of the elk or gazelle that sees us for the first time, or with the dull stupor of the ruminants, who look upon us as a momentary and useless accident of the pasture.

For thousands of years, they have been living at our side, as foreign to our thoughts, our affections, our habits as though the least fraternal of the stars had dropped them but yesterday on our globe. In the boundless interval that separates man from all the other creatures, we have succeeded only, by dint of patience, in making them take two or three illusory steps. And, if, to-morrow, leaving their feelings toward us untouched, nature were to give them the intelligence and the weapons wherewith to conquer us, I confess that I should distrust the hasty vengeance of the horse, the obstinate reprisals of the ass and the maddened meekness of the sheep. I should shun the cat as I should shun the tiger; and even the good cow, solemn and somnolent, would inspire me with but a wary confidence. As for the hen, with her round, quick eye, as when discovering a slug or a worm, I am sure that she would devour me without a thought.

III

Now, in this indifference and this total want of comprehension in which everything that surrounds us lives; in this incommunicable world, where everything has its object hermetically contained within itself, where every destiny is self-circumscribed, where there exist among the creatures no other relations than those of executioners and victims, eaters and eaten, where nothing is able to leave its steel-bound sphere, where death alone establishes cruel relations of cause and effect between neighboring lives, where not the smallest sympathy has ever made a conscious leap from one species to another, one animal alone, among all that breathes upon the earth, has succeeded in breaking through the prophetic circle, in escaping from itself to come bounding toward us, definitely to cross the enormous zone of darkness, ice and silence that isolates each category of existence in nature's unintelligible plan. This animal, our good familiar dog, simple and unsurprising as may to-day appear to us what he has done, in thus perceptibly drawing nearer to a world in which he was not

born and for which he was not destined, has nevertheless performed
one of the most unusual and improbable acts that we can find in the
general history of life. When was this recognition of man by beast,
this extraordinary passage from darkness to light, effected? Did we
seek out the poodle, the collie, or the mastiff from among the wolves
and the jackals, or did he come spontaneously to us? We cannot tell.
So far as our human annals stretch, he is at our side, as at present;
but what are human annals in comparison with the times of which
we have no witness? The fact remains that he is there in our houses,
as ancient, as rightly placed, as perfectly adapted to our habits as
though he had appeared on this earth, such as he now is, at the same
time as ourselves. We have not to gain his confidence or his friendship: he is born our friend; while his eyes are still closed, already he
believes in us: even before his birth, he has given himself to man.
But the word "friend" does not exactly depict his affectionate worship. He loves us and reveres us as though we had drawn him out of
nothing. He is, before all, our creature full of gratitude and more
devoted than the apple of our eye. He is our intimate and impassioned
slave, whom nothing discourages, whom nothing repels, whose ardent trust and love nothing can impair. He has solved, in an admirable and touching manner, the terrifying problem which human
wisdom would have to solve if a divine race came to occupy our
globe. He has loyally, religiously, irrevocably recognized man's
superiority and has surrendered himself to him body and soul, without after-thought, without any intention to go back, reserving of
his independence, his instinct and his character only the small part
indispensable to the continuation of the life prescribed by nature.
With an unquestioning certainty, an unconstraint and a simplicity
that surprise us a little, deeming us better and more powerful than all
that exists, he betrays, for our benefit, the whole of the animal kingdom to which he belongs and, without scruple, denies his race, his
kin, his mother and his young.

But he loves us not only in his consciousness and his intelligence:
the very instinct of his race, the entire unconsciousness of his specie,
it appears, think only of us, dream only of being useful to us. To
serve us better, to adapt himself better to our different needs, he has
adopted every shape and been able infinitely to vary the faculties,

the aptitudes which he places at our disposal. Is he to aid us in the pursuit of game in the plains? His legs lengthen inordinately, his muzzle tapers, his lungs widen, he becomes swifter than the deer. Does our prey hide under wood? The docile genius of the species, forestalling our desires, presents us with the basset, a sort of almost footless serpent, which steals into the closest thickets. Do we ask that he should drive our flocks? The same compliant genius grants him the requisite size, intelligence, energy and vigilance. Do we intend him to watch and defend our house? His head becomes round and monstrous, in order that his jaws may be more powerful, more formidable and more tenacious. Are we taking him to the south? His hair grows shorter and lighter, so that he may faithfully accompany us under the rays of a hotter sun. Are we going up to the north? His feet grow larger, the better to tread the snow; his fur thickens, in order that the cold may not compel him to abandon us. Is he intended only for us to play with, to amuse the leisure of our eyes, to adorn or enliven the home? He clothes himself in a sovereign grace and elegance, he makes himself smaller than a doll to sleep on our knees by the fireside, or even consents, should our fancy demand it, to appear a little ridiculous to please us.

You shall not find, in nature's immense crucible, a single living being that has shown a like suppleness, a similar abundance of forms, the same prodigious faculty of accommodation to our wishes. This is because, in the world which we know, among the different and primitive geniuses that preside over the evolution of the several species, there exists not one, excepting that of the dog, that ever gave a thought to the presence of man.

It will, perhaps, be said that we have been able to transform almost as profoundly some of our domestic animals: our hens, our pigeons, our ducks, our cats, our horses, our rabbits, for instance. Yes, perhaps; although such transformations are not comparable with those undergone by the dog and although the kind of service which these animals render us remains, so to speak, invariable. In any case, whether this impression be purely imaginary or correspond with a reality, it does not appear that we feel in these transformations the same unfailing and preventing good will, the same sagacious and exclusive love. For the rest, it is quite possible that the dog, or rather the inaccessible genius of his race, troubles scarcely at all about us and that we have merely known how to make use of various aptitudes offered by the abundant chances of life. It matters not: as we know nothing of the substance of things, we must needs cling to appearances; and it is sweet to establish that, at least in appearance, there is on the planet where, like unacknowledged kings, we live in solitary state, a being that loves us.

However the case may stand with these appearances, it is none the less certain that, in the aggregate of intelligent creatures that have rights, duties, a mission and a destiny, the dog is a really privileged animal. He occupies in this world a pre-eminent position enviable among all. He is the only living being that has found and recognizes an indubitable, tangible, unexceptionable and definite god. He knows to what to devote the best part of himself. He knows to whom above him to give himself. He has not to seek for a perfect, superior and infinite power in the darkness, amid successive lies, hypotheses and dreams. That power is there, before him, and he moves in its light. He knows the supreme duties which we all do not know. He has a morality which surpasses all that he is able to discover in himself and which he can practice without scruple and without fear. He possesses truth in its fulness. He has a certain and infinite ideal.

IV

And it was thus that, the other day, before his illness, I saw my little Pelléas sitting at the foot of my writing-table, his tail carefully folded under his paws, his head a little on one side, the better to question me, at once attentive and tranquil, as a saint should be in the presence of God. He was happy with the happiness which we, perhaps, shall never know, since it sprang from the smile and the approval of a life incomparably higher than his own. He was there, studying, drinking in all my looks; and he replied to them gravely, as from equal to equal, to inform me, no doubt, that, at least through the eyes the most immaterial organ that transformed into affectionate intelligence the light which we enjoyed, he knew that he was saying to me all that love should say. And, when I saw him thus, young, ardent and believing, bringing me, in some wise, from the depths of

unwearied nature, quite fresh news of life and trusting and wonder-
struck, as though he had been the first of his race that came to in-
augurate the earth and as though we were still in the first days of
the world's existence, I envied the gladness of his certainty, compared it with the destiny of man, still plunging on every side into
darkness, and said to myself that the dog who meets with a good
master is the happier of the two.

The Biscuit Eater

BY

JAMES STREET

LONNIE set the greasy bag of table scraps on a hummock of wire grass and leaned over the branch, burying his face in the cool water. He wiped his mouth with the back of his hand. Hundreds of black, frisky water bugs, aroused at his invasion of their playground, scooted to the middle of the stream, swerved as though playing follow-the-leader, and scooted back to the bank.

The boy laughed at their capers. Slowly, he stooped over the water. His hand darted as a cottonmouth strikes and he snatched one of the bugs and smelled it. There was a sharp, sugary odor on the bug.

"A sweet stinker, sure as my name is Lonnie McNeil," the boy muttered. If you caught a sweet stinker among water bugs, it meant good luck, maybe. Everybody knew that. Lonnie held the bug behind him, closed his eyes, tilted his head and whispered, to the pine trees, the branch, the wire grass and anything else in the silence that wanted to hear him and would never tell his wish: "I hope Moreover is always a good dog."

Then Lonnie put the bug back in the branch. It darted in circles for a second and skedaddled across the creek, making a beeline for the other bugs. There were tiny ripples in its wake. The boy grinned. He was in for some good luck. If the sweet stinker had changed its course, it would have broken the charm.

He picked up his bag of scraps, crossed the branch on a log and moseyed to the edge of the woods where the cleared land began. He pursed his lower lip and whistled the call of the catbird, watching the cabin in the field where Text lived with his mother, Aunt Charity, and her brood. Old Charity had a heap of young'uns, but Text was the last. She had listened to her preacher for days during protracted meetings, seeking a fit'n name for her man-child. And because the evangelist took text from this and text from that, she named him Text and reckoned it was a name that God approved. Or else the preacher wouldn't have used it so much.

Lonnie saw Text run to the rickety front gallery of the cabin and listen. He whistled again. Text answered and ran around the house, and a minute later he was racing across the field with a big, brooding dog at his heels. The white boy opened his arms and the dog ran to him and tried to lick his face.

Text said, "Hydee, Lon. Ol' Moreover is glad to see you. Me and him both."

Lonnie said, "Hi, Text. He looks slick as el-lem sap, don't he? Been working him?"

"A heap and whole lot," said Text. "Turned him loose in the wire grass yestiddy and he pointed two coveys 'fore I could say, 'Law 'a' mercy.' He's a prime superfine bird dawg, Lon. He ain't no no-'count biscuit eater."

Lonnie, the son of Harve McNeil, and Text had been friends long before they had got the dog on a mine-and-yours basis, but now they were inseparable. Moreover, the dog, was community property between them, and their community was the piney woods of South Alabama, where Lonnie's father trained fine bird dogs for Mr. Ames. The dog had wiped away all class and race barriers between the two.

Moreover's mother had run in the Grand National trials up at Grand Junction, Tennessee—the world series for bird dogs. Then Mr. Ames had sold her. Moreover's father was a good dog until he killed one of Mr. Eben's sheep, and was shot, according to the code of the piney woods. Harve knew the pup, the outcast of the litter, had a bad streak in him, but had tried to train him only because Lonnie loved the pup. And Lonnie loved him only because nobody else did.

Harve never had been able to get close to the dog's affections. There had been no feeling between them, no understanding. The pup had cowered at Lonnie's feet when Harve had ordered him into the fields to hunt. And when Harve had caught him sucking eggs, he had given him away to a Negro across the ridge.

"He's a suck-egg biscuit eater," Harve had told the Negro. A biscuit eater was an ornery dog. Everybody knew that. A biscuit eater wouldn't hunt anything except his biscuits and wasn't worth the salt in his feed.

The Negro had accepted the dog because he knew he could swap him. That night the dog had stolen eggs from the Negro's henhouse and the Negro had beaten him and called him a low-life biscuit eater. The dog had run under the cabin and sulked.

When Lonnie learned what his father had done with the outcast, he went to Text, and together they went over the ridge to bargain for the dog.

The Negro man was wily. He sensed a good bargain and was trader enough to know that if he low-rated the dog, the boys would want him more than ever. The dog had a cotton rope around his neck and the rope was fastened to a block, and when the dog walked, his head was pulled sideways as he tugged the block. The dog walked to Lonnie and rubbed against his legs. The boy ignored him. He mustn't let the Negro man know he really wanted the dog. The man grabbed the rope and jerked the dog away.

"He's a biscuit eater!" The Negro nudged the dog with his foot. The animal looked sideways at his master and slunk away. "He ain't worth much."

"He's a suck-egg biscuit eater, ain't he?" Lonnie asked. The dog watched him, and when the boy said "biscuit eater," the dog ran under the cabin, pulling the block behind him. "He's scared," Lonnie said. "You been beating him. And ever' time you jump him and you call him 'biscuit eater.' That's how come he's scared. Whatcha take for him?"

The man said, "Whatcha gimme?"

"I'll give you my frog-sticker." Lonnie showed his knife. "And I got a pretty good automobile tire. Ain't but one patch in it. It'd make a prime superfine swing for your young'uns."

The Negro asked Text, "What'll you chip in to boot?"

Text said, "You done cussed out the dawg so far I don't want no share of him. You done low-rated him too much. If he sucks eggs at my house, my maw'll bust me in two halves. Whatcha want to boot?"

"Whatcha got?"

"Nothin'," said Text, "cep'n two big hands what can tote a heap of wood. Tote your shed full of light'r knots for boot."

"What else?"

Text thought for a minute, weighing the deal. "Lon wants that dawg. I know where there's a pas'l of May haws and a honeybee tree."

The Negro man said, "It's a deal, boys, if'n you pick me a lard bucket full of May haws and show me the bee tree."

Lonnie took the block from the dog and led him across the field. Then Text led him awhile. Out of sight of the Negro's shack, the boys stopped and examined their possession.

Text ran his hand over the dog, smoothing the fur. "He's a good dawg, ain't he, Lon? Look at them big ol' eyes, and them big ol' feet, and that big ol' long tail. Bet he can point birds from here to yonder. Betcha if he tries, he can point partridges on light bread. What we gonna name him, Lon?"

Lonnie said, "Dunno, Text. But listen, don't ever call him——" He looked at the dog, then at Text. "You know." He held his fingers in the shape of a biscuit and pantomimed as though he were eating. The dog didn't understand. Neither did Text. So Lonnie whispered, "You know, 'biscuit eater.' Don't ever call him that. That's what's the matter with him. He expects a beating when he hears it."

"It's a go," Text whispered. "Let's name him Moreover. It's in the Bible."

"Where'bouts?"

"I heard the preacher say so. He said, 'Moreover, the dog,' and he was reading from the Bible."

Lonnie held the dog's chin with one hand and stroked his chest with the other. "He's Moreover then. He's a good dog, Text. And he's ours. You keep him and I'll furnish the rations. I can snitch 'em from papa. Will Aunt Charity raise Cain if you keep him?"

"Naw," said Text. "I 'member the time that big ol' brother of mine, ol' First-and-Second-Thessalonians, fetched a goat home, and maw didn't low-rate him. She just said she had so many young'uns, she didn't mind a goat. I spects she feels the same way 'bout a dawg, if'n he's got a Bible name."

"I reckon so too," said Lonnie, and ran home and told his father about the deal.

Harve told his son, "It's all right for you and Text to keep the dog, but keep him away from over here. I don't want him running around my good dogs."

Lonnie said, "He's a good dog, papa. He just ain't had no chance."

Harve looked at his son. The boy was growing, and the man was proud. "I'm going to work Silver Belle in the south forty," he said. "Want to come along?"

Lonnie shook his head. Harve knew then how much the boy loved his new dog; for, ordinarily, Lonnie would have surrendered any pleasure to accompany his father when he worked Silver Belle. She was the finest pointer in the Ames kennels and Harve had trained her since puppyhood. Already, she had won the Grand National twice. A third win would give his employer permanent possession of the Grand National trophy, and Harve wanted to win the prize for Mr. Ames more than he wanted anything in the world. He pampered Silver Belle. She was a small pointer—so small she had to wear a silver bell when hunting in the tall sage.

After his father and Silver Belle were gone, Lonnie collected the table scraps and went across the branch to Text's.

"Let's work him across the ridge today," Lonnie said. "Papa's got Silver Belle in the south forty and he won't want us and Moreover around."

Text said, "It's a go, Lon. I'll snitch ol' First-and-Second-Thessalonians' shotgun and meet you 'cross the ridge. But that there lan' over there is pow'ful close to Mr. Eben's place. I don't want no truck with that man."

"I ain't afraid of Mr. Eben," said Lonnie.

"Well, I am. And so are you! And so is your paw!"

"Papa is not afraid of anything, and I'll bust you in two halves if you say so."

"Then how come he didn't whip Mr. Eben when Mr. Eben kicked his dawg about two years ago?"

Negroes heard everything and forgot nothing. Everybody in the county had wondered why Harve McNeil hadn't thrashed Eben, when the farmer kicked one of the McNeil dogs without cause.

Lonnie was ashamed. He said, "Papa didn't whip Mr. Eben 'cause mother asked him not to, that's why."

"Lady folks sho' are buttinskies," Text said. "All time trying to keep men folks from whupping each other. Lady folks sho are scutters. All 'cept your maw and my maw, huh, Lon?"

Lonnie said, "Mr. Eben is just a crotchety man. Mother said so. He don't mean no harm."

"That's what you say," Text said. "But he's a scutter from way back. Maw says when he kills beeves he drinks the blood, and Ise popeyed scared of him. His lan' say, 'Posted. Keep Off. Law.' And I ain't messin' around over there."

Lonnie often had worked dogs with his father and had seen the best run at field trials. He began training Moreover by inspiring confidence in him. The big dog was clumsy, but Lonnie never upbraided him. When Moreover showed a streak of good traits, Lonnie and Text patted him. When he erred, they simply ignored him. The dog had a marvelous range, and moved through the saw grass at an easy gait, never tiring. He was not spectacular, but constant. He ran with a sort of awkward lope, twisting his head as though he still were tugging a block. But he covered ground. Day after day he trained and worked until the boys panted and stretched on the ground. Then he stood over them.

He had strange point. He would cock his long head in the air, then turn it slowly toward Lonnie as he came to a point. His tail was like a ramrod. The first time Text shot over him, he cowered. The boys showed their displeasure by ignoring him. He soon was no longer gun-shy and he worked for the sheer joy of working.

"He sho is a good dawg," Text said.

They were working him that day across the ridge near Eben's farm and Moreover, trailing a huge covey, raced through the stubble and disappeared in the sage. When the boys found him he was frozen on a point far inside Farmer Eben's posted land. And watching Moreover from a pine thicket was Eben, a shotgun held loosely in the crook of his arm.

Text was terror-stricken and gaped at Eben as though the stubble-faced man was an ogre. Lonnie took one look at his dog, then at the man, and walked to the thicket. Text was in his shadow. "Please don't shoot him, Mr. Eben," Lonnie said.

The farmer said, "Huh?"

"Naw, suh, please don't shoot him." Text found his courage. "He couldn't read yo' posted sign."

Eben scowled. "I don't aim to shoot him. That is, less'n he gets round my sheep. I was watching his point. Right pretty, ain't it?"

Lonnie said, "Mighty pretty. He's a good dog, Mr. Eben. If ever you want a mess of birds, I'll give you the loan of him."

"Nothing shaking," Eben said. "He's that biscuit eater your paw gave that niggah over the ridge."

Text protested. "Don't go calling him biscuit eater, please, suh. He don't like it."

"He can't read my posted sign, but he can understand English, huh?" Eben laughed. "Well, get him off'n my land or I'll sprinkle him with bird shot."

Lonnie whistled and Moreover broke the point and followed him.

At supper, Lonnie asked his father, "How come you didn't whip Mr. Eben that time he kicked your dog?"

Harve said, "I've had my share of fighting, son. I don't fight for such foolishness any more. How come you ask?"

"Just 'cause," Lonnie said, and Harve knew his son wasn't satisfied with the reply. He frowned and glanced at his wife. He hadn't punished Eben simply because he didn't think the crime of kicking a dog justified a beating. There had been a time when he thought differently. But he was older now, and respected. He wondered if Lonnie thought he was afraid of Eben, and the thought bothered him.

"I wish we had the papers on Moreover," Lonnie changed the subject. "I want to register him."

Harve said, "I've got the papers, son. You can have 'em. What you gonna do, run your dog against my Belle in the county-seat trials?" He was joshing the boy.

"That's what I aim to do," Lonnie said.

The father laughed loudly, and his laughter trailed off into a chuckle. Lonnie enjoyed hearing his father laugh that way. "It's a great idea, son. So you have trained that biscuit eater for the trials! Where you going to get your entry fee?"

"He ain't no biscuit eater!" Lonnie said defiantly.

His mother was startled at his impudence to his father. But Harve shook his head at his wife and said, " 'Course he ain't, son. I'm sorry. And just to show that me and Belle ain't scared of you and Moreover, I'll give you and Text the job of painting around the kennels. You can earn your entry fee. Is it a go?"

"Yes-siree, bob." Lonnie stuffed food in his mouth and hurried through his meal. "I'm going to high-tail it over and tell Text and Moreover."

Harve walked down the front path with his son. The boy reached to his shoulders. It was nice to walk down the path with his son. The father said simply and in man's talk, "Maybe I'm batty to stake you and your dog to your entry fee. You might whip me and Belle, and Mr. Ames might give you my job of training his dogs."

Lonnie didn't reply. But at the gate he paused and faced his father. "Papa, you ain't scared of Mr. Eben, are you?"

The trainer leaned against the gate and lit his pipe. "Son," he said, "I ain't scared of nothing but God. But don't tell your mother."

Mr. Ames, the Philadelphia sportsman, sat on the steps of the gun-club lodge and laughed when he saw his truck coming up the drive-way. His cronies, who had come to the county seat for the trials—a sort of a minor-league series—laughed too. Harve was driving. Silver Belle was beside him. Lonnie and Text were on the truck bed with dogs all around them, and behind the truck, tied with a cotton rope, loped Moreover. Mr. Ames shook hands with his trainer and met the boys.

"We got competition," Harve said, and nodded toward Moreover.

Ames studied the big dog. "By Joe, Harve! That used to be my dog. Is that the old bis——"

"Sh-h-h!" Harve commanded. "Don't say it. It hurts the dog's feelings. Or so the boys say."

Ames understood. He had a son at home. He walked around More-over and looked at him. "Mighty fine dog, boys. . . . If he beats

Belle, I might hire you, Lonnie, and fire your father." He winked at Harve, but the boys didn't see him.

They took Moreover to the kennels. They had fetched their own feed. Text ran to the kitchen of the lodge, and soon had a job doing kitchen chores. Moreover's rations were assured, and the best. Lonnie bedded his dog down carefully and combed him and tried to make him look spruce. But Moreover would not be spruce. There was a quizzical look in his eyes. The other dogs took attention as though they expected it, but Moreover rubbed his head along the ground and scratched his ears against the kennel box and mussed himself up as fast as Lonnie cleaned him. But he seemed to know that Lonnie expected something of him. All the other dogs were yelping and were nervous. But Moreover just flopped on his side and licked Lonnie's hands.

Inside the lodge, Ames asked Harve, "How's Belle?"

"Tiptop," said Harve. "She'll win hands down here, and I'm laying that she'll take the Grand National later. I'm gonna keep my boy with me, Mr. Ames. Text can stay with the help."

"What do those kids expect to do with that biscuit eater?" Ames laughed.

"You know how boys are. I'll bet this is the first time in history a colored boy and a white boy ever had a joint entry in a field trial. They get riled if anybody calls him a biscuit eater."

"Can't blame them, Harve," Ames said. "I get mad if anybody makes fun of my dogs. We are all alike, men and boys."

"You said it. Since the first, I reckon, boys have got mad if a fellow said anything against their mothers or dogs."

"Or fathers?" Ames suggested.

"Depends on the father," said Harve. "Wish Lonnie could take his dog to the quarter finals, or thereabouts. Do the boy a heap of good."

They were having a drink by the big fireplace. Ames said, "I hope that big brute is not in a brace with Belle. She's a sensitive dog." Then he laughed. "Be funny, Harve, if that dog whipped us. I'd run you bowlegged."

All the men laughed, but when the waiter told the pantry maid the story, he neglected to say that the threat was a jest. The pantry maid told the barkeeper. The barkeeper told the cook, and by the time the story was circulated around the kitchen, the servants were whispering that rich Mr. Ames had threatened to fire poor Mr. Harve because his son had fetched a biscuit eater to the field trials.

The morning of the first run, Text met Lonnie at the kennels, and together they fed Moreover. "Let's put some good ol' gunpowder in his vittles," Text said. "Make him hunt better."

"Aw, that's superstition," said Lonnie.

"I don't care what it is, it helps," said Text.

Lonnie couldn't see any need of tempting luck, so Moreover was fed a sprinkling of gunpowder.

Text said, "I got my lucky buckeye along. We bound to have luck, Lon."

Lonnie was getting too big for such foolishness, but then he remembered. "I caught a sweet stinker not so long ago," he whispered. "And he swum the right way."

"A good ol' sweet-stinking mellow bug?" asked Text eagerly. "Lon, good luck gonna bust us in two halves."

Harve took Silver Belle out with an early brace and the pointer completely outclassed her rival. Her trainer sent her back to her kennel and went into the fields with Ames to watch Moreover in his first brace. He was braced with a rangy setter. Even the judges smiled at the two boys and their dog. Text, in keeping with rules of the sport, gave not an order. Lonnie put Moreover down on the edge of a clover field and the big dog rolled over, then jumped up and loped around the boy, leaping on him and licking his face. Lonnie and Text walked into the field, and Moreover followed. Lonnie whistled shrilly. The big dog jerked up his head, cocked it and began casting. He ranged to the edge of the field and worked in. He loped past a patch of saw grass, wheeled and pointed, his head cocked toward Lonnie, his right leg poised and his tail stiff as a poker.

Lonnie kept his dog on the point until the judges nodded, then whistled him off of it. He called Moreover to the far edge of the field and set him ranging again. He was on a point in a flash.

Ames looked at Harve. "That's a good dog, McNeil. He's trained beautifully. He'll go to the finals with us, sure as shooting."

Harve was beaming with pride. "It proves what I've always

preached," Harve said, "that a bird dog will work for a man, if the man understands him. I couldn't do anything with that dog, but he will go to hell and back for my boy and Text."

Silver Belle and Moreover swept through the quarter and semi-finals, and news that father and son would be matched in the finals, with the famous Belle and a biscuit eater, brought sportsmen and sports writers swarming to the county seat. Harve and Lonnie slept and ate together, but the man didn't discuss the contest with his son. He didn't want to make him nervous. He treated Lonnie as he would any other trainer. He knew that boys hate condescension from their fathers. He knew boys could sense condescension if adults eased up in games and that boys never want their fathers to make things too easy for them.

Harve took Silver Belle to the edge of a field of stubble, and she stood motionless as he snapped a tiny silver bell around her neck. He arose from his knees, patted her fondly and whispered, "Go get 'em, girl."

The little pointer dashed into the stubble and soon was out of sight. Moreover rubbed against Lonnie's legs and watched her for a minute, then trotted along her path. There was no order between Lonnie and his dog, only understanding.

The men listened for the tinkling of the silver bell that told them the champion still was casting. Through the brush the men sauntered, their senses alert. Suddenly the bell hushed.

Belle was on a point. The delicate little animal was rigid. Her trim body was thrown forward a bit, her nose, perfectly tilted, was aimed toward a clump of sage. She didn't fleck a muscle. She might have been made of marble.

The judge nodded approval. Harve motioned to Belle. She took two steps, stopped, then two more. A roar of wings, a whistle of flight, and the covey of partridge was away like feathered lightning. Guns thundered. Belle didn't bat an eye as the salvo cracked over her. When the echoes died, she began fetching, and when the last bird was laid at Harve's feet, she dashed into the sage again, seeking the singles.

Lonnie had held Moreover while Belle worked. Now he turned the big dog loose. Moreover swung along through the sage at an easy gait. He cast a bit to the right, stuck his nose almost to the ground and found the trail Belle had just made. Then he broke into an easy trot. He never depended on ground scents, but on body scents, and kept his nose high enough to catch any smells the wind blew his way.

About a hundred yards back up Belle's trail, Moreover suddenly broke his trot and eased his nose higher in the air. Then he jerked his head toward Lonnie and froze to a point. His right leg came up slowly, deliberately. He cocked his head in that strange fashion, and the quizzical, comical look came in his eyes. Moreover was a still hunter. He never waited for orders. He held the birds until Lonnie clicked the safety off of his gun. When Moreover heard the click, he began creeping toward the covey. He didn't budge as Lonnie began dropping the birds, and then, without orders, he fetched the dead birds and began casting for singles.

The judges whistled softly. "Most beautiful dog work I ever saw," whispered one. Ames' face took on a worried look. So did Harve's. The big dog had picked up a covey right under Belle's nose.

Belle settled down to hunt. She seemed everywhere. She dashed to a point on the fringe of a cornfield, then held another covey while Harve weeded out the first. She raced over the ridge, her nose picking up scents in almost impossible places. Moreover just loped along, but every time Belle got a covey, he would cast for a few minutes, point, fetch and wait for her to set the pace. She was hunting because she was bred to hunt. He was hunting from habit and because Lonnie expected him to.

It was exasperating. Belle tried every trick of her training, but her skill was no match for his stamina. Her heart was pumping rapidly and she was tired when the men knocked off for lunch. Text ran back to the lodge to help fetch food to the field. He strutted into the kitchen and told the servants that Moreover was running Silver Belle ragged.

The servants shook their heads, and one told him that Mr. Ames would fire Harve if Moreover beat Belle. Text couldn't swallow his food. He waited around the fringe of hunters until he caught Lonnie's eye, and motioned to him. "That Mr. Ames sho is a scutter," said Text, after he told his story. "He's worse'n Mr. Eben. What we goin' do, Lon?"

Lonnie said, "He's half your dog, Text. What you say?"

"We can't let yo' paw get in no trouble on account of us, Lon. He got to have a job."

Lonnie nodded and bit his lip. He noticed that his father's face was drawn as the contest was renewed. Ames was nervous. The two men had worked for years to get Belle to perfection, and win the Grand National for the third time. And here an outcast dog was hunting her heart out at a minor meet. Lonnie thought his father was worried about his job and that Ames was angry.

His mind was made up. He watched Moreover leap across a creek, then race into a field of clover. He and Text were right behind him. Moreover came to his point, jerked his head toward his master and waited.

Lonnie cupped his hands and said hoarsely, "Hep!" It was an order Moreover never had heard. He turned and faced Lonnie. The judges gasped when the big dog left his point. Harve was puzzled.

Ames whispered, "He's breaking. That good-for-nothing streak is cropping out."

"Hep!" Lonnie said it again. The judges didn't hear. Moreover deserted the covey and walked to Lonnie and looked up. Lonnie shouted, "Back to your point, you low-life biscuit eater!"

Moreover tucked his tail between his legs and ran to the lodge and hid under it. Lonnie and Text followed him, without a word to the judges.

Ames looked at Harve for an explanation, and Harve said, "I don't get it. My son called his dog off. He quit."

It took Lonnie and Text a long time to coax Moreover from under the lodge. The dog crawled to Lonnie's feet and rolled over. Lonnie patted him, but Moreover didn't lick his face. The boys were with their dog in the kennel when the prize was awarded to Harve and Silver Belle.

"His feelings are hurt," Lonnie told Text as Moreover lay down and thumped his tail. . . . "I'm sorry I said it, Moreover. I had to."

Text said, "We sorry, puppy dawg. But us had to, didn't we, Lon?"

They loaded the truck, and Harve had his boy sit on the front seat by him. They said good-by and rolled away.

Harve said to Lonnie, "How come you did that, son?"

Lonnie didn't reply and the father didn't press the point. Finally, he said, "Don't ever quit, son, if you are winning or losing. It ain't fair to the dog."

"My dog is mad at me," Lonnie said.

"We'll give him a beef heart when we get home. His feelings are hurt because you threw him down. But he'll be all right. Dogs are not like folks. They'll forgive a fellow." He knew Lonnie had a reason for what he had done, and he knew that if his son wanted him to know the reason, he would tell him.

Back home, Lonnie cooked a beef heart for Moreover and took the plate to the back gallery where the dog was tied.

Harve said, "Untie him, son. You can let him run free over here. You don't ever have to keep him over at Text's house, unless you want to."

He untied his dog and put the food before him. Moreover sniffed the food and toyed with it. He never had had such good food before. Lonnie and his father went back into the house.

After supper, Lonnie went to see about his dog. The meat hadn't been touched and Moreover was gone.

Harve said, "He's probably gone back to Text's house."

Lonnie said, "I'm going after him."

"I'll go with you," said Harve, and got a lantern.

Text hadn't seen the dog. He joined the search and the three hunted through the woods for an hour or so, Lonnie whistling for Moreover, and Text calling him, "Heah, heah, fellow. Heah."

Harve sat on a stump, put the lantern down and called the boys to him. He had seen only a few dogs that would refuse to eat beef heart as Moreover had done.

"Text," he said sharply, "did Moreover ever suck eggs at your place?"

Text rolled his eyes and looked at Lonnie. "Yas, suh." He was afraid to lie to Harve. "But I didn't tell Lon. I didn't want to hurt his feelings. Moreover was a suck-egger, good and proper."

Harve said, "Go on, tell us about it."

"Maw put hot pepper in a raw egg, but it didn't break him. My ol' brother, ol' First-and-Second-Thessalonians, reckoned he'd kill

Moreover less'n he quit suck-egging. So I got to snitching two eggs ever' night and feeding him with 'em. He sho did like eggs, Mr. Harve, and we had plenty of eggs."

Lonnie said sharply, "You hadn't ought to have done that, Text."

Harve said, "Did you feed him eggs tonight?"

"Naw, suh," said Text. "I reckoned he had vittles at yo' house. We had done gathered all the eggs and maw had counted them by nightfall."

Harve got up. "I'm worried. Let's walk up the branch. . . . Text, you take the left side. . . . Lonnie, you take the right side. I'll walk up the bank."

Lonnie found Moreover's body, still warm, only a few feet from the water. He stooped over his dog, put the lantern by his head, and opened his mouth. The dog had been poisoned. Lonnie straightened. He didn't cry. His emotions welled up within him, and, having no outlet, hurt him.

"I'm sorry I called him a biscuit eater," he said simply.

Text said, "He was trying to get to water. I sho hate to think of him dying, wanting just one swallow of good ol' water."

"Who killed him, papa?" Lonnie turned to his father.

The man picked up the lantern and walked away, the boys at his heels. They walked over the ridge to Eben's house, and Harve pounded on the front gallery until the farmer appeared.

"My boy's dog is dead," Harve said. "Reckoned you might know something about it."

Eben said, "If he was poisoned, I do. He's a suck-egg dog. I put poison in some eggs and left them in the field. Seems he mout have committed suicide, McNeil."

"Seems you made it powerful easy for him to get those poisoned eggs," Harve said.

"Ain't no room round here for suck-egg dogs. His daddy was a sheep killer too. It's good riddance. You ain't got no cause to jump me, Harve McNeil."

Harve said, "He's right, boys. A man's got a right to poison eggs on his own land, and if a dog sucks 'em and dies, the dog's to blame."

Eben said, "Reckon you young'uns want to bury that dog. Buzzards will be thick tomorrow. You can have the loan of my shovel."

Lonnie looked at the man a long time. He bit his lip so he couldn't cry. "Me and Text will dig a hole with a stick," he said, and turned away.

"You boys go bury him," Harve said. "I'll be home in a few minutes."

Lonnie and Text walked silently into the woods. Text said, "He sho was a good dog, huh, Lon? You ain't mad at me 'cause I fed him eggs, are you, Lon?"

"No, Text. Let's wait up here and watch papa. He can't see us."

Back at Eben's gallery, Harve said, "I would have paid you for all the eggs the dog took, Eben. My boy loved that dog a heap."

"Looka heah!" Eben said. "I know my rights."

"I know mine," Harve said. "I always pay my debts, Eben. And I always collect them. I ain't got no cause to get riled because that dog stole poisoned eggs. You were mighty low life to plant 'em, though. But two years ago you kicked one of my dogs."

"He barked at me and scared my team on the road," Eben said.

"A dog has a right to bark," Harve said, and reached up and grabbed Eben by the collar.

"I'll law you!" Eben shouted.

Harve didn't reply. He slapped the man with his open palm, and when Eben squared off to fight, Harve knocked him down.

In the shadows of the woods, Lonnie whispered to Text, "What did I tell you? My papa ain't scared of nothing cep'n God."

They buried their dog near the branch. Text poured water in the grave. "I can't stand to think of him wanting water when there's a heap of water so close. Reckon if he could have got to the ol' branch he could have washed out that poison? Reckon, Lon?"

"Maybe so."

They were walking to Lonnie's house. "My ol' buckeye and your sweet-stinking mellow bug ain't helped us much, eh, Lon? Luck is plumb mad at us, ain't it, Lon?"

Lonnie waited at the gate until his father arrived. "Me and Text saw the fight," he said. "I won't tell mother. Women are scutters, ain't they, papa? Always trying to keep men folks from fighting."

"I'll give you boys another dog, son," Harve said. He peered into the darkness and saw a car parked behind his house, then hurried inside. Mr. Ames was warming himself by the fire and talking with Mrs. McNeil. She went to the kitchen to brew coffee, and left the men alone, after calling for Lonnie and Text to follow her.

Ames said, "I heard why your boy called his dog off. Call him and that little colored boy in here. I can't go back East with those boys thinking what they do of me."

Lonnie and Text stood by the fire and Ames said, "That story you heard about me isn't so. I wouldn't have fired this man if your dog had won. We were joking about it and the servants got the story all wrong. I just wanted you boys to know that."

Harve said, "Yes. But even if Mr. Ames would have fired me, it wouldn't have made any difference. You did what you thought was right, but you were wrong. Don't ever quit a race, once you start it."

Lonnie told Mr. Ames, "My dog is dead. I'm sorry I called him a biscuit eater. He wasn't. I just want you to know that."

Ames lit his pipe and passed his tobacco pouch to Harve. He saw Harve's bloody hand as the trainer accepted the tobacco.

"Ran into some briers," Harve said.

"Lot of them around here." Ames' eyes twinkled. "Just been thinking, Harve. I got some fine pups coming along. You need help down here. Better hire a couple of good men. Know where you can get two good hands? They got to be men who can lose without grumbling and win without crowing."

Harve looked at Lonnie and Text, and smiled. "I know where I can get a couple of good men."

"All right," said Ames, and shook hands all around. "I've got to be going. Good night, men."

Rex

BY

D. H. LAWRENCE

SINCE every family has its black sheep, it almost follows that every man must have a sooty uncle. Lucky if he hasn't two. However, it is only with my mother's brother that we are concerned. She had loved him dearly when he was a little blond boy. When he grew up black, she was always vowing she would never speak to him again. Yet when he put in an appearance, after years of absence, she invariably received him in a festive mood, and was even flirty with him.

He rolled up one day in a dog-cart, when I was a small boy. He was large and bullet-headed and blustering, and this time, sporty. Sometimes he was rather literary, sometimes colored with business. But this time he was in checks, and was sporty. We viewed him from a distance.

The upshot was, would we rear a pup for him. Now my mother detested animals about the house. She could not bear the mix-up of human with animal life. Yet she consented to bring up the pup.

My uncle had taken a large, vulgar public-house in a large and vulgar town. It came to pass that I must fetch the pup. Strange for me, a member of the Band of Hope, to enter the big, noisy, smelly, plate-glass and mahogany public-house. It was called The Good Omen. Strange to have my uncle towering over me in the passage, shouting, "Hello, Johnny, what d'yer want?" He didn't know me. Strange to think he was my mother's brother, and that he had his bouts when he read Browning aloud with emotion and éclat.

I was given tea in a narrow, uncomfortable sort of living-room, half

212

kitchen. Curious that such a palatial pub should show such miserable private accommodations, but so it was. There was I, unhappy, and glad to escape with the soft fat pup. It was winter-time, and I wore a big-flapped black overcoat, half cloak. Under the cloak-sleeves I hid the puppy, who trembled. It was Saturday, and the train was crowded, and he whimpered under my coat. I sat in mortal fear of being hauled out for traveling without a dog-ticket. However, we arrived, and my torments were for nothing.

The others were wildly excited over the puppy. He was small and fat and white, with a brown-and-black head: a fox terrier. My father said he had a lemon head—some such mysterious technical phraseology. It wasn't lemon at all, but colored like a field bee. And he had a black spot at the root of his spine.

It was Saturday night—bath-night. He crawled on the hearth-rug like a fat white tea-cup, and licked the bare toes that had just been bathed.

"He ought to be called Spot," said one. But that was too ordinary. It was a great question, what to call him.

"Call him Rex—the King," said my mother, looking down on the fat, animated little tea-cup, who was chewing my sister's little toe and making her squeal with joy and tickles. We took the name in all seriousness.

"Rex—the King!" We thought it was just right. Not for years did I realize that it was a sarcasm on my mother's part. She must have wasted some twenty years or more of irony, on our incurable naïveté.

It wasn't a successful name, really. Because my father, and all the people in the street, failed completely to pronounce the monosyllable Rex. They all said Rax. And it always distressed me. It always suggested to me seaweed, and rack-and-ruin. Poor Rex!

We loved him dearly. The first night we woke to hear him weeping and whining in loneliness at the foot of the stairs. When it could be borne no more, I slipped down for him, and he slept under the sheets.

"I won't have that little beast in the beds. Beds are not for dogs," declared my mother callously.

"He's as good as we are!" we cried, injured.

"Whether he is or not, he's not going in the beds."

I think now, my mother scorned us for our lack of pride. We were a little infra dig., we children.

The second night, however, Rex wept the same and in the same way was comforted. The third night we heard our father plod downstairs, heard several slaps administered to the yelping, dismayed puppy, and heard the amiable, but to us heartless voice saying, "Shut it then! Shut thy noise, 'st hear? Stop in thy basket, stop there!"

"It's a shame!" we shouted, in muffled rebellion, from the sheets.

"I'll give you shame, if you don't hold your noise and go to sleep," called our mother from her room. Whereupon we shed angry tears and went to sleep. But there was a tension.

"Such a houseful of idiots would make me detest the little beast, even if he was better than he is," said my mother.

But as a matter of fact she did not detest Rexie at all. She only had to pretend to do so, to balance our adoration. And in truth, she did not care for close contact with animals. She was too fastidious. My father, however, would take on a real dog's voice, talking to the puppy: a funny, high, sing-song falsetto which he seemed to produce at the top of his head. " 'S a pretty little dog! 's a pretty little doggy! —ay!—yes!—Wag thy strunt, then! Wag thy strunt, Raxie!—Ha-ha! Nay, tha munna—" This last as the puppy, wild with excitement at the strange falsetto voice, licked my father's nostrils and bit my father's nose with his sharp little teeth.

" 'E makes blood come," said my father.

"Serves you right for being so silly with him," said my mother. It was odd to see her as she watched the man, my father, crouching and talking to the little dog and laughing strangely when the little creature bit his nose and tousled his beard. What does a woman think of her husband at such a moment?

My mother amused herself over the names we called him.

"He's an angel—he's a little butterfly—Rexie, my sweet!"

"Sweet! A dirty little object!" interpolated my mother. She and he had a feud from the first. Of course he chewed boots and worried our stockings and swallowed our garters. The moment we took off our stockings he would dart away with one, we after him. Then as he hung, growling vociferously, at one end of the stocking, we at the other, we would cry:

"Look at him, mother! He'll make holes in it again." Whereupon my mother darted at him and spanked him sharply.

"Let go, Sir, you destructive little fiend!"

But he didn't let go. He began to growl with real rage, and hung on viciously. Mite as he was, he defied her with a manly fury. He did not hate her, nor she him. But they had one long battle with one another.

"I'll teach you, my Jockey! Do you think I'm going to spend my life darning after your destructive little teeth! I'll show you if I will!"

But Rexie only growled more viciously. They both became really angry, whilst we children expostulated earnestly with both. He would not let her take the stocking from him.

"You should tell him properly, mother. He won't be driven," we said.

"I'll drive him further than he bargains for. I'll drive him out of my sight forever, that I will," declared my mother, truly angry. He would put her into a real temper, with his tiny, growling defiance.

"He's sweet! A Rexie, a little Rexie!"

"A filthy little nuisance! Don't think I'll put up with him."

And to tell the truth, he was dirty at first. How could he be otherwise, so young! But my mother hated him for it. For he lived in the house with us. He would wrinkle his nose and show his tiny dagger-teeth in fury when he was thwarted, and his growls of real battle-rage against my mother rejoiced us as much as they angered her. But at last she caught him in flagrante. She pounced on him, rubbed his nose in the mess, and flung him out into the yard. He yelped with shame and disgust and indignation. I shall never forget the sight of him as he rolled over, then tried to turn his head away from the disgust of his own muzzle, shaking his little snout with a sort of horror, and trying to sneeze it off. My sister gave a yell of despair, and dashed out with a rag and a pan of water, weeping wildly. She sat in the middle of the yard with the befouled puppy, and shedding bitter tears she wiped him and washed him clean. Loudly she reproached my mother. "Look how much bigger you are than he is. It's a shame, it's a shame!"

"You ridiculous little lunatic, you've undone all the good it would do him, with your soft ways. Why is my life made a curse with animals! Haven't I enough as it is—"

There was subdued tension afterwards. Rex was a little white chasm between us and our parent.

He became clean. But then another tragedy loomed. He must be docked. His floating puppy-tail must be docked short. This time my father was the enemy. My mother agreed with us that it was an unnecessary cruelty. But my father was adamant. "The dog'll look a fool all his life, if he's not docked." And there was no getting away from it. To add to the horror, poor Rex's tail must be *bitten* off. Why bitten? we asked aghast. We were assured that biting was the only way. A man would take the little tail and just nip it through with his teeth at a certain point. My father lifted his lips and bared his incisors, to suit the description. We shuddered. But we were in the hands of fate.

Rex was carried away, and a man called Rowbotham bit off the superfluity of his tail in the Nags Head, for a quart of best and bitter. We lamented our poor diminished puppy, but agreed to find him more manly and *comme il faut*. We should always have been ashamed of his little whip of a tail, if it had not been shortened. My father said it had made a man out of him.

Perhaps it had. For now his true nature came out. And his true nature, like so much else, was dual. First he was a fierce, canine little beast, a beast of rapine and blood. He longed to hunt, savagely. He lusted to set his teeth in his prey. It was no joke with him. The old canine Adam stood first in him, the dog with fangs and glaring eyes. He flew at us when we annoyed him. He flew at all intruders, particularly the postman. He was almost a peril to the neighborhood. But not quite. Because close second in his nature stood that fatal need to love, the *besoin d'aimer* which at last makes an end of liberty. He had a terrible, terrible necessity to love, and this trammelled the native, savage hunting beast which he was. He was torn between two great impulses: the native impulse to hunt and kill, and the strange, secondary, supervening impulse to love and obey. If he had been left to my father and mother, he would have run wild and got himself shot.

As it was, he loved us children with a fierce, joyous love. And we loved him.

When we came home from school we would see him standing at the end of the entry, cocking his head wistfully at the open country in front of him, and meditating whether to be off or not: a white, inquiring little figure, with green savage freedom in front of him. A cry from a far distance from one of us, and like a bullet he hurled himself down the road, in a mad game. Seeing him coming, my sister invariably turned and fled, shrieking with delighted terror. And he would leap straight up her back, and bite her and tear her clothes. But it was only an ecstasy of savage love, and she knew it. She didn't care if he tore her pinafores. But my mother did.

My mother was maddened by him. He was a little demon. At the least provocation, he flew. You had only to sweep the floor, and he bristled and sprang at the broom. Nor would he let go. With his scruff erect and his nostrils snorting rage, he would turn up the whites of his eyes at my mother, as she wrestled at the other end of the broom: "Leave go, Sir; leave go!" She wrestled and stamped her foot, and he answered with horrid growls. In the end it was she who had to let go. Then she flew at him, and he flew at her. All the time we had him he was within a hair's-breadth of savagely biting her. And she knew it. Yet he always kept sufficient self-control.

We children loved his temper. We would drag the bones from his mouth, and put him into such paroxysms of rage that he would twist his head right over and lay it on the ground upside-down, because he didn't know what to do with himself, the savage was so strong in him and he must fly at us. "He'll fly at your throat one of these days," said my father. Neither he nor my mother dared have touched Rex's bone. It was enough to see him bristle and roll the whites of his eyes when they came near. How near he must have been to driving his teeth right into us cannot be told. He was a horrid sight, snarling and crouching at us. But we only laughed and rebuked him. And he would whimper in the sheer torment of his need to attack us.

He never did hurt us. He never hurt anybody, though the neighborhood was terrified of him. But he took to hunting. To my mother's disgust, he would bring large dead bleeding rats and lay them on the hearth-rug, and she had to take them up on a shovel. For he would not remove them. Occasionally he brought a mangled rabbit, and sometimes, alas, fragmentary poultry. We were in terror of prosecution. Once he came home bloody and feathery and rather sheepish-looking. We cleaned him and questioned him and abused him. Next day we heard of six dead ducks. Thank heaven no one had seen him.

But he was disobedient. If he saw a hen he was off, and calling would not bring him back. He was worst of all with my father, who would take him walks on Sunday morning. My mother would not walk a yard with him. Once, walking with my father, he rushed off at some sheep, and meant business. My father crawled through the hedge, and was upon him in time. And now the man was in a paroxysm of rage. He dragged the little beast into the road and thrashed him with a walking stick.

"Do you know you're thrashing that dog unmercifully?" said a passerby.

"Ay, an' mean to," shouted my father.

The curious thing was that Rex did not respect my father any the more for the beatings he had from him. He took much more heed of us children, always.

But he let us down also. One fatal Saturday he disappeared. We hunted and called, but no Rex. We were bathed, and it was bedtime, but we would not go to bed. Instead we sat in a row in our night-dresses on the sofa, and wept without stopping. This drove our mother mad.

"Am I going to put up with it? Am I? And for all that hateful little beast of a dog! He shall go! If he's not gone now, he shall go."

Our father came in late, looking rather queer, with his hat over his eye. But in his staccato tippled fashion he tried to be consoling.

"Never mind, my duckie, I s'll look for him in the morning."

Sunday came—oh, such a Sunday. We cried, and didn't eat. We scoured the land, and for the first time realized how empty and wide the earth is, when you're looking for something. My father walked for many miles—all in vain. Sunday dinner, with rhubarb pudding, I remember, and an atmosphere of abject misery that was unbearable.

"Never," said my mother, "never shall an animal set foot in this house again while I live. I knew what it would be! I knew."

The day wore on, and it was the black gloom of bed-time when we heard a scratch and an impudent little whine at the door. In trotted Rex, mud-black, disreputable, and impudent. His air of off-hand "how d'ye do!" was indescribable. He trotted round with suffisance, wagging his tail as if to say, "Yes, I've come back. But I didn't need to. I can carry on remarkably well by myself." Then he walked into his water, and drank noisily and ostentatiously. It was rather a slap in the eye for us.

He disappeared once or twice in this fashion. We never knew where he went. And we began to feel that his heart was not so golden as we had imagined it.

But one fatal day reappeared my uncle and the dog-cart. He whistled to Rex, and Rex trotted up. But when he wanted to examine the lusty, sturdy dog, Rex became suddenly still, then sprang free. Quite jauntily he trotted round—but out of reach of my uncle. He leaped up, licking our faces, and trying to make us play.

"Why what ha' you done wi' the dog—you've made a fool of him. He's softer than grease. You've ruined him. You've made a damned fool of him," shouted my uncle.

Rex was captured and hauled off to the dog-cart and tied to the seat. He was in a frenzy. He yelped and shrieked and struggled, and was hit on the head, hard, with the butt-end of my uncle's whip, which only made him struggle more frantically. So we saw him driven away, our beloved Rex, frantically, madly fighting to get to us from the high dog-cart, and being knocked down, whilst we stood in the street in mute despair.

After which, black tears, and a little wound which is still alive in our hearts.

I saw Rex only once again, when I had to call just once at The Good Omen. He must have heard my voice, for he was upon me in the passage before I knew where I was. And in the instant I knew how he loved us. He really loved us. And in the same instant there was my uncle with a whip, beating and kicking him back, and Rex cowering, bristling, snarling.

My uncle swore many oaths, how we had ruined the dog for ever, made him vicious, spoiled him for showing purposes, and been altogether a pack of mard-soft fools not fit to be trusted with any dog but a gutter-mongrel.

Poor Rex! We heard his temper was incurably vicious, and he had to be shot.

And it was our fault. We had loved him too much, and he had loved us too much. We never had another pet.

It is a strange thing, love. Nothing but love has made the dog lose his wild freedom, to become the servant of man. And this very servility or completeness of love makes a term of deepest contempt.— "You dog!"

We should not have loved Rex so much, and he should not have loved us. There should have been a measure. We tended, all of us, to overstep the limits of our own natures. He should have stayed outside human limits; we should have stayed outside canine. Nothing is more fatal than the disaster of too much love. My uncle was right, we had ruined the dog.

My uncle was a fool, for all that.

My Talks with Dean Spanley

BY

LORD DUNSANY

Preface

THAT there are passages in Dean Spanley's conversation that have
sometimes jarred on me, the reader will readily credit. But the
more that his expressions have been removed from what one might
have expected of a man in his position, or indeed any member of my
Club, the more they seemed to me to guarantee his sincerity. It would
have been easy enough for him to have acted the part that it is his
duty to play; but difficult, and I think impossible, to have invented in
such meticulous detail the strange story he told me. And for what
reason? Upon the authenticity of Dean Spanley's experience I stake
my reputation as a scientific writer. If he has deluded me in any particular, let scientific bodies reject not only these researches, but any
others that I may make hereafter. So sure am I of Dean Spanley's perfect veracity.

Should doubt be expressed of a single page of these talks, and the
case against it be made with any plausibility, it is probable that I shall
abandon not only this line of research, but that my Investigations
into the Origins of the Mentality of Certain Serious Persons, the
product of years of observation, may never even be published.

Chapter 1

Were I to tell how I came to know that Dean Spanley had a secret, I
should have to start this tale at a point many weeks earlier. For the

knowledge came to me gradually; and it would be of little interest to my readers were I to record the hints and guesses by which it grew to a certainty. Stray conversations gradually revealed it, at first partly overheard from a little group in a corner of a room at the Olympus Club, and later addressed directly to myself. And the odd thing is that almost always it was what Dean Spanley did not say, rather than any word he uttered, a checking of speech that occurred suddenly on the top of speculations of others, that taught me he must be possessed of some such secret as nobody else, at any rate outside Asia, appears to have any inkling of. If anyone in Europe has studied the question so far, I gladly offer him the material I was able to glean from Dean Spanley, to compare and check with his own work. In the East, of course, what I have gathered will not be regarded as having originality.

I will start my story then, on the day on which I became so sure of some astonishing knowledge which Dean Spanley kept to himself, that I decided to act upon my conviction. I had of course cross-examined him before, so far as one can cross-examine an older man in brief conversation in a rather solemn club, but on this occasion I asked him to dine with me. I should perhaps at this point record the three things that I had found out about Dean Spanley: the first two were an interest in transmigration, though only shown as a listener, greater than you might expect in a clergyman; and an interest in dogs. Both these interests were curiously stressed by his almost emphatic silences, just when it seemed his turn to speak upon either of these subjects. And the third thing I chanced to find was that the dean, though at the club a meager drinker of wine, was a connoisseur of old port. And it was this third interest of the dean's that is really the key to the strange information that I am now able to lay before the public. Well then, after many days, during which my suspicions had at first astonished me, and then excitedly ripened, I said to Dean Spanley in the reading-room of the Club, "Of course the difficulty about transmigration is that nobody ever yet remembered having lived a former life."

"H'm," said the dean.

And there and then I asked him if he would dine with me, giving as my reason what I knew to be the only one that would have any

chance of bringing him, my wish to have his advice upon some
vintage port that had been left me by an aunt, and which had been
given to her by Count Donetschau a little before 1880. The port was
as good as I had been able to buy, but I doubt if he would have drunk
it on that account without any name or history, any more than he
would have spoken to a man who was dressed well enough, but who
had not been introduced to him.

"Count Donetschau?" he said a little vaguely.

"Count Shevenitz-Donetschau," I answered.

And he accepted my invitation.

It was a failure, that dinner. I discovered, what I should have
known without any experience, that one cannot make a rather abstemious dean go past the point at which the wit stands sentry over the
tongue's utterance, merely by giving him port that he likes. He liked
the port well enough, but nothing that I could say made him take a
drop too much of it. Luckily I had not given myself away, had not
said a word to let him see what I was after. And in a month I tried
again. I said I found some port of a different vintage, hidden among
the rest, and would value his opinion as to which was the better. And
he accepted; and this time I had my plan.

Dinner was light, and as good as my cook could make it. Then
came the vintage port, three glasses the same as last time and no more,
except for half a glass of the old kind for sake of comparison, and
after his three and a half glasses came my plan.

"I have a bottle of Imperial Tokay in the cellar," I said.

"Imperial what!" said the dean.

"Imperial Tokay," I said.

"Imperial Tokay," he repeated.

"Yes," I said. For I had been able to get the loan of one from a
friend who in some way had become possessed of half a dozen of this
rare wine, that until a little while ago was only uncorked by command of Emperors of Austria. When I say the loan of a bottle, I
mean that I had told my friend, who was totally unscientific, that
there was something I wanted to draw out of this dean, and that I
saw no other way of doing it than to offer him a wine, when he had
come to his ordinary limit of drinking, so exciting that he would go
further from that point, and that anything left in the bottle, "after

you have made your dean drunk," as he put it, would be returned to him. I really think that the only reason he gave me the priceless bottle was for a certain unholy joy that his words implied. I doubt if my researches, which without that Imperial Tokay would have been impossible, will be of any interest to him.

Well the Imperial Tokay was brought in, and I poured out a glass for Dean Spanley. He drank it off at once. I don't know if a dean has a different idea of Heaven, some clearer vision of it, than the rest of us. I shall never know. I can only guess from what I saw in the eyes of Dean Spanley as that Imperial Tokay went down.

"Will you have another glass?" I asked.

"I never take more than three glasses usually," he replied.

"Oh, port doesn't count," I answered.

He had now had four and a half glasses that evening, and had just come to a point at which such remarks as my last, however silly it may seem here, appear to have wisdom. And, as I spoke, I poured into his glass that curious shining wine that has somewhat the taste of sherry strangely enchanted. It was now beside him, and we spoke of other things. But when he sipped the Tokay I said to him rather haltingly, "I want to ask you about a future life."

I said it haltingly, because, when two people are speaking, if one of them lacks confidence the other is the more apt to assume it. Certainly Spanley did. He replied, "Heaven. Undoubtedly Heaven."

"Yes, ultimately of course," I said. "But if there were anything in the theories one sometimes hears, transmigration and all that, I was wondering if that might work first."

There was a certain look of caution yet on his face, and so I went rambling on, rather than leave a silence in which he would have to answer, and by the answer commit himself to concealment of all I wanted to know. "I mean," I said, "going to other lives after this one, animals and all that, and working upwards or downwards in each incarnation, according to whether or not; you know what I mean."

And then he drained the glass and I poured out another; and, sipping that almost absently, the look of caution went, and I saw instead so beautiful a contentment reigning there in its place, flickering as it seemed with the passage of old reminiscences, that I felt that my opportunity must be come, and there and then I said to him: "You see I've been rather fond of dogs; and, if one chanced to be one of them in another incarnation, I wonder if there are any hints you could give me."

And I seem to have caught the right memory as it floated by on waves of that wonderful wine, for he answered at once: "Always go out of a room first: get to the door the moment it's opened. You may not get another chance for a long time."

Then he seemed rather worried or puzzled by what he had said, and cleared his throat and searched, I think, for another topic; but before he had time to find one I broke in with my thanks, speaking quickly and somewhat loudly, so as to frighten his thoughts away from any new topic, and the thoughts seemed easily guided.

"Thank you very much," I said, "very much indeed. I will say that over and over again to myself. I will get it into my very; you know, my ego. And so I shall hope to remember it. A hint like that will be invaluable. Is there anything more you could tell me, in case?"

And at the same time, while I spoke to him and held his attention, I refilled his glass with a hand that strayed outside the focus of the immediate view of either of us.

"Well," he said, "there's always fleas."

"Yes, that of course would be rather a drawback," I said.

"I wouldn't say that," he answered. "I rather like a few fleas; they indicate just where one's coat needs licking."

And a sudden look came over his face again, as though his thoughts would have strayed where I did not want them, back to strict sobriety and the duller problems of this life. To keep him to the subject that so profoundly interested me I hastily asked his advice, an act which in itself helps to hold the attention of any man.

"How can one best ingratiate oneself, and keep in with the Masters?"

"Ah, the Masters," he muttered, "the great ones. What benevolence! What wisdom! What power! And there was one incomparably greater and wiser than all of them. I remember how, if he went away for a day, it used to alter the appearance of the whole world; it affected the sunlight; there was less brightness in it, less warmth. I remember how, when he came back, I used to mix myself a good stiff whiskey and soda and. . . ."

"But dogs," I said, "dogs don't drink whiskey."

I learned afterwards never to interrupt him, but I couldn't help it now, and I wanted to get the truth, and thought he was talking mere nonsense; and yet it wasn't quite.

"Er, er, no," said Dean Spanley, and fumbled awhile with his memories, till I was afraid I had lost touch with the mystery that I had planned so long to explore. I sat saying never a word. And then he resumed once more.

"I got the effect," he said, "by racing round and round on the lawn, a most stimulating effect; it seems to send the blood to the head in a very exhilarating manner. What am I saying? Dear me, what *am* I saying?"

And I pretended not to have heard him. But I got no more that night. The curtain that cuts us off from all such knowledge had fallen. Would it ever lift again?

Chapter 2

A few nights later I met the dean at the Club. He was clearly vague about what we had talked of when he had dined with me, but just a little uneasy. I asked him then for his exact opinion about my port, until I had established it in his mind that that was my principal interest in the evening we spent together and he felt that nothing unusual could have occurred. Many people would have practiced that much deception merely to conceal from a friend that he had drunk a little more wine than he should have, but at any rate I felt justified in doing it now when so stupendous a piece of knowledge seemed waiting just within reach. For I had not got it yet. He had said nothing as yet that had about it those unmistakable signs of truth with which words sometimes clothe themselves. I dined at the next table to him. He offered me the wine-list after he had ordered his port, but I waved it away as I thanked him, and somehow succeeded in conveying to him that I never drank ordinary wines like those. Soon after I asked him if he would care to dine again with me; and he accepted, as I felt sure, for the sake of the Tokay. And I had no Tokay. I had returned the bottle to my friend, and I could not ask him for any of that wine from him again. Now I chanced to have met a Maharajah at a party, and fixing an appointment by telephoning to his secretary, I went to see him at his hotel. To put it briefly, I explained to him that the proof of the creed of the Hindus was within my grasp, and that the key to it was Imperial Tokay. If he cared to put up the money that would purchase the Imperial Tokay he would receive nothing less than the proof of an important part of his creed. He seemed not so keen as I thought he would be, though whether because his creed had no need of proof, or whether because he had doubts of it, I never discovered. If it were the latter, he concealed it in the end by agreeing to do what I wished; though, as for the money, he said: "But why not the Tokay?" And it turned out that he had in his cellars a little vault that was full of it. "A dozen bottles shall be here in a fortnight," he said.

A dozen bottles! I felt that with that I could unlock Dean Spanley's heart, and give to the Maharajah a strange secret that perhaps he knew already, and to much of the human race a revelation that they had only guessed.

I had not yet fixed the date of my dinner with Dean Spanley, so I rang him up and fixed it with him a fortnight later and one day to spare.

And sure enough, on the day the Maharajah had promised, there arrived at his hotel a box from India containing a dozen of that wonderful wine. He telephoned to me when it arrived, and I went at once to see him. He received me with the greatest amiability, and yet he strangely depressed me; for while to me the curtain that was lifting revealed a stupendous discovery, to him, it was only too clear, the thing was almost a commonplace, and beyond it more to learn than I had any chance of discovering. I recovered my spirits somewhat when I got back to my house with that dozen of rare wine that should be sufficient for twenty-four revelations, for unlocking twenty-four times that door that stands between us and the past, and that one had supposed to be locked for ever.

The day came and, at the appointed hour, Dean Spanley arrived at my house. I had champagne for him and no Tokay, and noticed a wistful expression upon his face that increased all through dinner, until by the time that the sweet was served, and still there was no Tokay, his inquiring dissatisfied glances, though barely perceptible, reminded me, whenever I did perceive them, of those little whines

that a dog will sometimes utter when gravely dissatisfied, perhaps because there is another dog in the room, or because for any other
reason adequate notice is not being taken of himself. And yet I do not
wish to convey that there was ever anything whatever about Dean
Spanley that in the least suggested a dog; it was only in my own
mind, preoccupied as it was with the tremendous discovery to the
verge of which I had strayed, that I made the comparison. I did not
offer Dean Spanley any Tokay during dinner, because I knew that
it was totally impossible to break down the barrier between him and
his strange memories even with Tokay, my own hope being to bring
him not so far from that point by ordinary methods, I mean by port
and champagne, and then to offer him the Tokay, and I naturally
noted the precise amount required with the exactitude of a scientist;
my whole investigations depended on that. And then the moment
came when I could no longer persuade the dean to take another drop
of wine; of any ordinary wine, I mean; and I put the Tokay before
him. A look of surprise came into his face, surprise that a man in possession of Tokay should let so much of the evening waste away before bringing it out. "Really," he said, "I hardly want any more
wine, but . . ."

"It's a better vintage than the other one," I said, making a guess
that turned out to be right.

And it certainly was a glorious wine. I took some myself, because
with that great bundle of keys to the mysterious past that the Maharajah's dozen bottles had given me I felt I could afford this indulgence. A reminiscent look came over Dean Spanley's face, and
deepened, until it seemed to be peering over the boundaries that shut
in this life. I waited a while and then I said: "I was wondering about
rabbits."

"Among the worst of Man's enemies," said the dean. And I knew
at once from his vehemence that his memory was back again on the
other side of that veil that shuts off so much from the rest of us. "They
lurk in the woods and plot, and give Man no proper allegiance. They
should be hunted whenever met."

He said it with so much intensity that I felt sure the rabbits had
often eluded him in that other life; and I saw that to take his side
against them as much as possible would be the best way to keep his

memory where it was, on the other side of the veil; so I abused rabbits. With evident agreement the dean listened, until, to round off
my attack on them, I added: "And over-rated animals even to eat.
There's no taste in them."

"Oh, I wouldn't say that," said the dean. "A good hot rabbit that
has been run across a big field has certainly an, an element of . . ."
And he did not complete his sentence; but there was a greedy look in
his eyes.

I was very careful about refilling the dean's glass; I gave him no
more for some while. It seemed to me that the spiritual level from
which he had this amazing view, back over the ages, was a very narrow one; like a ridge at the top of a steep, which gives barely a resting place to the mountaineer. Too little Tokay and he would lapse
back to orthodoxy; too much, and I feared he would roll just as
swiftly down to the present day. It was the ridge from which I
feared I had pushed him last time. This time I must watch the mood
that Tokay had brought, and neither intensify it nor let it fade, for
as long as I could hold it with exactly the right hospitality. He looked
wistfully at the Tokay, but I gave him no more yet.

"Rabbits," I said to remind him.

"Yes, their guts are very good," he said. "And their fur is good
for one. As for their bones, if they cause one any irritation, one can
always bring them up. In fact, when in doubt, always bring anything
up: it's easily done.

"But there is one bit of advice I would give to you. Out-of-doors.
It's always best out-of-doors. There are what it is not for us to call
prejudices: let us rather say preferences. But while these preferences
exist amongst those who hold them, it is much best out-of-doors. You
will remember that?"

"Certainly," I said. "Certainly."

And as I spoke I carefully watched his eyes, to see if he was still on
that narrow ledge that I spoke of, that spiritual plane from which a
man could gaze out on past ages. And he was. A hand strayed tentatively toward the Tokay, but I moved it out of his reach.

"Rats!" I said. And he stirred slightly, but did not seem greatly
interested.

And then, without any further suggestion from me, he began to talk of the home life of a dog, somewhere in England in the days long before motors.

"I used to see off all the carts that drove up to the back-door every day. Whenever I heard them coming I ran round; I was always there in time; and then I used to see them off. I saw them off as far as a tree that there was a little way down the drive. Always about a hundred barks, and then I used to stop. Some were friends of mine, but I used to see them off the same as the rest. It showed them the house was well guarded. People that didn't know me used to hit at me with the whip, until they found out that they were too slow to catch me. If one of them ever had hit me I should have seen him off the whole way down the drive. It was always pleasant to trot back to the house from one of these little trips. I have had criticism for this; angry words, that is to say; but I knew from the tone of the voices that they were proud of me. I think it best to see them off like that, because, because . . ."

I hastily said: "Because otherwise they might think that the house wasn't properly guarded."

And the answer satisfied him. But I filled the dean's glass with Tokay as fast as I could. He drank it and remained at that strange altitude from which he could see the past.

"Then sooner or later," he continued, "the moon comes over the hill. Of course you can take your own line about that. Personally, I never trusted it. It's the look of it I didn't like, and the sly way it moves. If anything comes by at night I like it to come on footsteps, and I like it to have a smell. Then you know where you are."

"I quite agree," I said, for the dean had paused.

"You can hear footsteps," he went on, "and you can follow a smell, and you can tell the sort of person you have to deal with, by the kind of smell he has. But folk without any smell have no right to be going about among those that have. That's what I didn't like about the moon. And I didn't like the way he stared one in the face. And there was a look in his stare as though everything was odd and the house not properly guarded. The house was perfectly well guarded, and so I said at the time.

"But he wouldn't stop that queer look. Many's the time I've told him to go away and not to look at me in that odd manner; and he pretended not to hear me. But he knew all right, he knew he was odd and strange and in league with magic, and he knew what honest folks thought of him: I've told him many a time."

"I should stand no nonsense from him," I said.

"Entirely my view," said the dean.

There was a silence then such as you sometimes see among well-satisfied diners.

"I expect he was afraid of you," I said; and only just in time, for the dean came back as it were with a jerk to the subject.

"Ah, the moon," he said. "Yes, he never came any nearer. But there's no saying what he'd have done if I hadn't been there. There was a lot of strangeness about him, and if he'd come any nearer everything might have been stranger. They had only me to look after them.

"Only me to look after them," he added reflectively. "You know, I've known them talk to a man that ought at least to be growled at, stand at the front door and talk to him. And for what was strange or magical they never had any sense; no foreboding I mean. Why, there were sounds and smells that would make my hair rise on my shoulders before I had thought of the matter, while they would not even stir. That was why they so much needed guarding. That of course was our *raison d'être*, if I may put it in that way. The French often have a way of turning a phrase, that seems somehow more deft than anything that we islanders do. Not that our literature cannot hold its own."

"Quite so," I said to check this line of thought, for he was wandering far away from where I wanted him. "Our literature is very vivid. You have probably many vivid experiences in your own memory, if you cast your mind back. If you cast your mind back you would probably find material worthy of the best of our literature."

And he did. He cast his mind back as I told him. "My vividest memory," he said, "is a memory of the most dreadful words that the ear can hear, 'Dirty dog.' Those unforgettable words; how clear they ring in my memory. The dreadful anger with which they were always uttered, the emphasis, the miraculous meaning! They are certainly the most, the most prominent words of all I have ever heard. They stand by themselves. Do you not agree?"

"Undoubtedly," I said. And I made a very careful mental note that, whenever he wandered away from the subject that so much enthralled me, those might be the very words that would call him back.

"Yes, dirty dog," he went on. "Those words were never uttered lightly."

"What used to provoke them?" I asked. For the dean had paused, and I feared lest at any moment he should find a new subject.

"Nothing," he said. "They came as though inspired, but from no cause. I remember once coming into the drawing-room on a lovely bright morning, from a very pleasant heap that there was behind the stable yard, where I sometimes used to go to make my toilet; it gave a very nice tang to my skin, that lasted some days; a mere roll was sufficient, if done in the right place; I came in very carefully smoothed and scented and was about to lie down in a lovely patch of sunlight, when these dreadful words broke out. They used to come like lightning, like thunder and lightning together. There was no cause for them; they were just inspired."

He was silent, reflecting sadly. And before his reflections could change I said, "What did you do?"

"I just slunk out," he said. "There was nothing else to do. I slunk out and rolled in ordinary grass and humbled myself and came back later with my fur all rough and untidy and that lovely aroma gone, just a common dog. I came back and knocked at the door and put my head in, when the door was opened at last, and kept it very low, and my tail low too, and I came in very slowly, and they looked at me holding their anger back by the collar, and I went slower still, and they stood over me and stooped, and then in the end they did not let their anger loose, and I hid in a corner I knew of. Dirty dog. Yes, yes. There are few words more terrible."

The dean fell then into a reverie, till presently there came the same look of confusion, and even alarm, on his face that I had noticed once before when he had suddenly cried out, "What am I talking about?" And to forestall any such uncomfortable perplexity I began to talk myself. "The lightning, the upkeep and the culinary problems," I said, "are on the one hand. On the other, the Committee should so manage the Club that its amenities are available to all, or even more so. You, no doubt, agree there."

"Eh?" he said. "Oh yes, yes."

I tried no more that night, and the rest of our conversation was of this world, and of this immediate sojourn.

Chapter 3

"I was the hell of a dog," said the dean, when next I was able to tempt him with the Tokay to that eminence of the mind from which he had this remarkable view down the ages, but it was not easily done; in fact it took me several weeks. "A hell of a dog. I had often to growl so as to warn people. I used to wag my tail at the same time, so as to let them know that I was only meaning to warn them, and they should not think I was angry.

"Sometimes I used to scratch up the earth, merely to feel my strength and to know that I was stronger than the earth, but I never went on long enough to harm it. Other dogs never dared do more than threaten me; I never had to bite them, my growl was enough, and a certain look that I had on my face and teeth, and my magnificent size, which increased when I was angry, so that they could see how large I really was.

"They were lucky to have me to guard them. It was an inestimable privilege to serve them; they had unearthly wisdom; but . . ."

"But they needed guarding," I said. For I remembered this mood of his. And my words kept him to it.

"They needed it," he said. "One night I remember a fox came quite near to the house and barked at them. Came out of the woods and on to our lawn and barked. You can't have that sort of thing. There's no greater enemy of man than the fox. They didn't know that. They hunted him now and then for sport; but they never knew what an enemy he was. I knew. They never knew that he has no reverence for man, and no respect for his chickens. I knew. They never knew of his plots. And here he was on the lawn barking at men. I was unfortunately in the drawing-room, and the doors were shut, or my vengeance would have been frightful. I should have gone out and leapt on him, probably in one single bound from the hall door, and I should have torn him up into four or five pieces and eaten every one of them. And that is just what I told him, holding back nothing. And then I told him all over again. Somebody had to tell him.

"Then one of the wise ones came and told me not to make so much noise; and out of respect to him I stopped. But when he went away the fox was still within hearing, so I told him about it again. It was better to tell him again, so as to make quite sure. And so I guarded the house against all manner of dangers and insults, of which their miraculous wisdom had never taken account."

"What other dangers?" I asked. For the dean was looking rather observantly at objects on the table, peering at them from under his thick eyebrows, so that in a few moments his consciousness would have been definitely in the world of the outer eye, and far away from the age that has gone from us.

"Dangers?" he said.

"Yes," I replied.

"The dark of the woods," he answered, "and the mystery of night. There lurked things there of which man himself knew nothing, and even I could only guess."

"How did you guess?" I asked him.

"By smells and little sounds," said the dean.

It was this remark about the woods and the night, and the eager way in which he spoke of the smells and the sounds, that first made me sure that the dean was speaking from knowledge, and that he really had known another life in a strangely different body. Why these words made me sure I cannot say; I can only say that it is oddly often the case that some quite trivial remark in a man's conversation will suddenly make you sure that he knows what he is talking about. A man will be talking perhaps about pictures, and all at once he will make you feel that Raphael, for instance, is real to him, and that he is not merely making conversation. In the same way I felt, I can hardly say why, that the woods were real to the dean, and the work of a dog no less to him than an avocation. I do not think I have explained how I came to be sure of this, but from that moment any scientific interest in what my Tokay was revealing was surpassed by a private anxiety to gather what hints I could for my own ends. I did not like to be adrift as I was in a world in which transmigration must be recognized as a fact, without the faintest idea of the kind of problems with which one would have to deal, if one should suddenly find oneself a dog in what was very likely an English rectory. That possibility came on me with more suddenness than it probably does to my reader, to whom I am breaking it perhaps more gently. From now on I was no longer probing a man's eccentric experience, so much as looking to him for advice. Whether it is possible to carry any such advice forward to the time one might need it is doubtful, but I mean to try my best by committing it carefully to memory, and all that I gleaned from the dean is of course at my reader's disposal. I asked him first about the simple things: food, water and sleep. I remember particularly his advice about sleep, probably because it confused me and so made me think; but, whatever the cause, it is particularly clear in my memory. "You should always pull up your blanket over your lips," he said. "It insures warm air when you sleep, and is very important."

It was some time since he had had a glass of Tokay, and to have questioned him as to his meaning would at once have induced in him a logical, or reasonable, frame of mind. We boast so much of our reason, but what can it see compared to that view down the ages that was now being laid before me? It is blind, compared to the dean.

Luckily I did not have to question him, for by a little flash of memory I recalled a dog sleeping, a certain spaniel I knew; and I remembered how he always tucked the feathery end of his tail over his nostrils in preparation for going to sleep: he belonged to an ignorant man who had neglected to have his tail cut off as a puppy. It was a tail that the dean meant, not a blanket.

Clear though the meaning was to me the moment I thought of the spaniel, I saw that the confusion of the dean's remark could only mean that a mist was beginning to gather over his view of time, and I hastily filled his glass. I watched anxiously till he drank it; it must have been his third or fourth; and soon I saw from the clearness of his phrases, and a greater strength in all his utterances, that he was safely back again looking out over clear years.

"The wise ones, the great ones," he went on meditatively, "they give you straw. But they do not, of course, make your bed for you. I trust one can do that. One does it, you know, by walking round several times, the oftener the better. The more you walk around, the better your bed fits you."

I could see from the way he spoke that the dean was speaking the truth. After all, I had made no new discovery. *In vino veritas;* that was all. Though the boundaries of this adage had been extended by my talks with Dean Spanley, beyond, I suppose, any limits previously known to man; at any rate this side of Asia.

"Clean straw is bad," continued the dean, "because there is no flavor to it at all. No."

He was meditating again, and I let him meditate, leaving him to bring up out of that strange past whatever he would for me.

"If you find anything good, hide it," he continued. "The world is full of others; and they all seem to get to know if you have found anything good. It is best therefore to bury it. And to bury it when no one is looking on. And to smooth everything over it. Anything good always improves with keeping a few days. And you know it's always there when you want it. I have sometimes smoothed things over it so carefully that I have been unable to find it when requiring it, but the feeling that it's there always remains. It is a very pleasant feeling, hard to describe. Those buryings represent wealth, which of course is a feeling denied to those greedy fellows who eat every bone they find, the moment they find it. I have even buried a bone when I've been hungry, for the pleasure of knowing that it was there. What am I saying! Oh Heavens, what am I saying!"

So sudden, so unexpected was this rush back down the ages, and just when I thought that he had had ample Tokay, that I scarcely knew what to do. But, whatever I did, it had to be done instantly; and at all costs I had to preserve from the dean the secret that through his babblings I was tapping a source of knowledge that was new to this side of the world, for I knew instinctively that he would have put a stop to it. He had uttered once before in my hearing a similar exclamation, but not with anything like the shocked intensity with which he was now vibrating, and his agitation seemed even about to increase. I had, as I say, to act instantly. What I did made a certain coolness between me and the dean, that lasted unfortunately for several weeks, but at least I preserved the secret. I fell forward over the table and lay unconscious, as though overcome by Tokay.

Chapter 4

There was one advantage in the awkwardness that I felt when I next saw the dean at the Club, and that was that my obvious embarrassment attracted his attention away from the direction in which a single wandering thought might have ruined everything. It was of vital importance to my researches that any question about over-indulgence in a rare wine should be directed solely at me. My embarrassment was not feigned, but there was no need to conceal it. I passed him by one day rather sheepishly, as I crossed the main hall of the Club and saw him standing there looking rather large. I knew he would not give me away to the other members, nor quite condone my lapse. And then one day I very humbly apologized to him in the reading-room.

"That Tokay," I said. "I am afraid it may have been a little bit stronger than I thought."

"Not at all," said the dean.

And I think we both felt better after that; I for having made my apology, he for the generosity with which his few kind words had bestowed forgiveness. But it was some while before I felt that I could quite ask him to dine with me. Much roundabout talk about the different dates and vintages of Imperial Tokay took place before I could bring myself to do that; but in the end I did, and so Dean Spanley and I sat down to dinner again.

Now I don't want to take credit for things that I have not done, and I will not claim that I maneuvered my guest to take up a certain attitude; I think it was merely due to a mood of the dean. But certainly what happened was that the dean took up a broad and tolerant line and drank his Tokay like a man, with the implication made clear, in spite of his silence, that there was no harm in Tokay, but only in not knowing where to stop. The result was that the dean arrived without any difficulty, and far more quickly than I had hoped, at that point at which the truth that there is in wine unlocked his tongue to speak of that clear vision that the Tokay gave him once more. No chemist conducting experiments in his laboratory is likely to have mixed his ingredients with more care than I poured out the Tokay from now on. I mean, of course, for the dean. I knew now how very narrow was the ridge on which his intellect perched to peer into the past; and I tended his glass with Tokay with the utmost care.

"We were talking, last time, about bones," I said. And if it had turned out to be the wrong thing to say I should have turned the discussion aside onto grilled bones. But no, there was nothing wrong with it. I had got him back to just the very point at which we left off last time.

"Ah, bones," said the dean. "One should always bury them. Then they are there when you want them. It is something to know that, behind all the noise and panting that you may make, there is a good solid store of bones, perhaps with a bit of meat on them, put away where others can't find it. That is always a satisfaction. And then, however hungry one may feel, one knows that the meat is improving all the time. Meat has no taste until it has been hidden awhile. It is always best to bury it. Very often, when I had nothing special to do, I would tear up a hole in the ground. I will tell you why I did that: it attracted attention. Then, if eavesdropping suspicious busybodies wanted to get your bone, they probably looked in the wrong place. It is all part of the scheme of a well-planned life: those that do not take these little precautions seldom get bones. Perhaps they may pick up a dry one now and again, but that is about all. Yes, always bury your bones."

I noticed the dawn of what seemed a faint surprise in his face, as though something in his words had struck him as strange, and I hastily filled his glass and placed it near his hand, which throughout the talks that I had with him had a certain wandering tendency reminiscent to me of a butterfly in a garden; it hovered now over that golden wine, then lifted the glass, and at once he was back where his own words seemed perfectly natural to him; as indeed they did to me, for I knew that he drew them straight from the well of Truth, that well whose buckets are so often delicate glasses such as I had on my table, and which were bringing up to me now these astonishing secrets. So often I find myself referring to this Tokay, that, borrowed though it was, it may be thought I am overproud of my cellar; but I cannot sufficiently emphasize that the whole scientific basis of my researches was the one maxim, *in vino veritas;* without that the dean might have exaggerated or misinterpreted, or even have in-

vented the whole of his story. What the law of gravity is to astro-
nomical study, so is this Latin maxim to those investigations that I
offer now to the public.

"Yes, bury your bone," said the dean. "The earth is often flavor-
less; yet, if you choose with discrimination, in farms, beside roads, or
in gardens, you hit on a delightful variety of flavors that greatly add
to your bone. I remember a favorite place of mine, just at the edge of
a pig-sty, which well bore out my contention that, by a careful
choice of earth, there is hardly any limit to the flavoring that may
improve a buried bone or a bit of meat. For pigs themselves I have
nothing at all but contempt. Their claim to be one of us is grossly
exaggerated. Always chase them. Chase cows too; not that I have
anything particular against them: my only reason for giving you
this advice is that by this means you have their horns pointing the
right way. Horns are dangerous things and, unless you chase them,
they are always pointing the wrong way, which, as I need hardly
say, is towards you. There is very likely some scientific reason for it,
but whenever you see cows they are always coming toward you;
that is to say, until you chase them. Whatever the reason is, I do not
think I have ever known an exception to this natural law. Horses one
should chase too: I do not exactly know why, but that is the way I
feel about it. I leave them alone on a road, but if I find them in a
field or on paths I always chase them. It always makes a bit of a stir
when horses come by; and if you don't chase them, the idea gets
about that it is they that are making the stir and not you. That leads
to conceit among horses, and all kinds of undesirable things. That's
the way I feel about it. There's just one thing to remember and that
is that, unlike cows, their dangerous end is towards you when you
chase them; but no one that has ever heard the jolly sound of their
hooves while being really well chased will ever think twice about
that. While standing still they can kick with considerable precision,
but one is not there on those occasions. While galloping their kicking
is often merely silly; and, besides that, one is moving so fast oneself
that one can dodge them with the utmost facility. Nothing is more
exhilarating than chasing a horse. Chasing anything is good as a
general rule; it keeps them moving, and you don't want things
hanging around, if you will excuse the modern expression."

The phrase made me a little uneasy, but I needn't have been, for he went straight on. "And that brings us," said the dean, "to the subject of cats. They are sometimes amusing to chase, but on the whole they are so unreliable that chasing cats can hardly be called a sport, and must be regarded merely as a duty. Their habit of going up trees is entirely contemptible. I never object to a bird going into a tree, if I happen to have chased it off the lawn, so as to keep the lawn tidy. A tree is the natural refuge of a bird. And, besides, one can always get it out of the tree by barking. But to see a four-footed animal in a tree is a sight so revolting and disgusting that I have no words in which to describe it. Many a time I have said what I thought about that, clearly and unmistakably, and yet I have never felt that I have finally dealt with the subject. One of these days perhaps my words will be attended to, and cats may leave trees for good. Till then, till then. . . ."

And I took the opportunity of his hesitation to attempt to turn the talk in a direction that might be more useful to me, if ever the time should come when this, that I call I, should be what Dean Spanley had evidently been once.

Chapter 5

There was a matter that seemed to me of vital importance if one could only get it fixed so firm in the core of one's memory that it would have a chance of survival, of surviving in fact the memory itself. This was the matter of wholesome food and water. How could one be sure of obtaining it? Sitting over a tidy table, with a clean tablecloth on it, and clean knives and forks, one may have exaggerated the importance of cleanliness; though I still feel that in the case of water such exaggeration is hardly possible. And then again I exaggerated the probability of finding oneself one day in the position I contemplated. But the vividness and sheer assurance of the dean's memories were most conducive to this. Add to that vividness and assurance a glass or two of Tokay, and I hardly know who would have held out against the belief that such a change was quite likely. And so I said to him, "I should object, as much as anything, to drinking bad water."

And the dean said: "There is no such thing as bad water. There is water with different flavors, and giving off different smells. There is interesting water and uninteresting water. But you cannot say there is bad water."

"But if there are really great impurities in it," I said.

"It makes it all the more interesting," said the dean. "If the impurities are so thick that it is solid, then it ceases to be water. But while it is water it is always good."

I may have looked a trifle sick; for the dean looked up and said to me reassuringly, "No, no, never trouble yourself about that."

I said no more for a while: it seemed hardly worth the trouble to drive and drive into one's memory, till they became almost part of one's character, little pieces of information that might perhaps survive the great change, if the information was no better than this. Of food I had heard his views already; the whole thing seemed disgusting; but I decided that in the interests of science it was my duty to get all the facts I could from the dean. So I threw in a word to keep him to the subject, and sat back and listened.

"It is the same with meat," he went on. "When meat can no longer be eaten, it is no longer there. It disappears. Bones remain always, but meat disappears. It has a lovely smell before it goes; and then fades away like a dream."

"I am not hungry," I said. And indeed truer word was never spoken, for my appetite was entirely lost. "Shall we talk of something else for a bit? If you don't mind. What about sport? Rats for instance."

"Our wainscot was not well stocked with game," said the dean, "either rats or mice. I have hunted rats, but not often. There is only one thing to remember at this sport: shake the rat. To shake the rat is essential.

"I need hardly tell you how to do that, because I think everybody is born to it. It is not merely a method of killing the rat, but it prevents him from biting you. He must be shaken until he is dead. Mice of course are small game."

"What is the largest game you have ever hunted?" I asked. For he had stopped talking, and it was essential to the interests of these researches that he should be kept to the same mood.

"A traction-engine," replied the dean.

That dated him within fifty years or so; and I decided that that incarnation of his was probably some time during the reign of Queen Victoria.

"The thing came snorting along our road, and I saw at once that it had to be chased. I couldn't allow a thing of that sort on our flower-beds, and very likely coming into the house. A thing like that might have done anything, if not properly chased at once. So I ran round and chased it. It shouted and threw black stones at me. But I chased it until it was well past our gate. It was very hard to the teeth, very big, very noisy and slow. They can't turn round on you like rats. They are made for defense rather than for attack. Much smaller game is often more dangerous than traction-engines."

So clearly did I picture the traction-engine on that Victorian road, with a dog yapping at the back wheels, that I wondered more and more what kind of a dog, in order to complete the mental picture. And that was the question I began to ask the dean. "What kind of a dog . . . ?" I began. But the question was much harder to ask than it may appear. My guest looked somehow so diaconal that the words froze on my lips; and, try as I would, I could not frame the sentence: what kind of a dog were you?

It seems silly, I know, to say that it was impossible merely to say seven words; and yet I found it so. I cannot explain it. I can only suggest to any that cannot credit this incapacity, that they should address those words themselves to any senior dignitary of the church, and see whether they do not themselves feel any slight hesitancy. I turned my question aside, and only lamely asked, "What kind of a dog used they to keep?"

He asked me who I meant. And I answered: "The people that you were talking about."

Thus sometimes conversations dwindle to trivial ends.

Many minutes passed before I gathered again the lost threads of that conversation. For nearly ten minutes I dared hardly speak, so near he seemed to the light of today, so ready to turn away from the shadows he saw so clearly moving in past years. I poured out for him more Tokay, and he absently drank it, and only gradually returned to that reminiscent mood that had been so gravely disturbed by the clumsiness of my question. Had I asked the dean straight out, "What kind of a dog were you?" I believe he would have answered satisfactorily. But the very hesitancy of my question had awaked suspicion at once, as though the question had been a guilty thing. I was not sure that he was safely back in the past again until he made a petulant remark about another engine, a remark so obviously un-true that it may not seem worth recording; I only repeat it here as it showed that the dean had returned to his outlook over the reaches of time and that he seems to have been contemporary with the threshing machine. "Traction-engines!" he said with evident loath-ing. "I saw one scratching itself at the back of a haystack. I thor-oughly barked at it."

"They should be barked at," I said, as politely as I could.

"Most certainly," said the dean. "If things like that got to think they could go where they liked without any kind of a protest, we should very soon have them everywhere."

And there was so much truth in that that I was able to agree with the dean in all sincerity.

"And then where should we all be?" the dean asked.

And that is a question unfortunately so vital to all of us that I think it is sufficient to show by itself that the dean was not merely wandering. It seemed to me that the bright mind of a dog had seen, perhaps in the seventies of the last century, a menace to which the bulk of men must have been blind; or we should never be over-run by machines as we are, in every sense of the word. He was talking sense here. Was it not therefore fair to suppose he was speaking the truth, even where his words were surprising? If I had faintly felt that I was doing something a little undignified in lowering myself to the level of what, for the greater part of these conversations, was practically the mind of a dog, I no longer had that feeling after this observation the dean had uttered about machinery. Henceforth I felt that he was at least my equal; even when turning, as he soon did, from philosophical speculation, he returned to talk of the chase.

"To chase anything slow," he said, "is always wearisome. You are continually bumping into what you are chasing. There is nothing so good as a ball. A ball goes so fast that it draws out your utmost speed, in a very exhilarating manner, and it can jump about as far as one can oneself, and before one can begin to be tired it always slows down. And then it takes a long time to eat; so that, one way and another, there is more entertainment in a ball than perhaps anything else one can chase. If one could throw it oneself, like the masters, I cannot imagine any completer life than throwing a ball and chasing it all day long."

My aim was purely scientific; I desired to reveal to Europeans a lore taught throughout Asia, but neglected, so far as I knew, by all our investigators; I desired to serve science only. Had it been otherwise, the momentary temptation that came to me as the dean spoke now might possibly have prevailed; I might possibly have hurried on some slight excuse from the room and come back with an old tennis ball, and perhaps have suddenly thrown it, and so have gratified that sense of the ridiculous that is unfortunately in all of us, at the expense of more solid study.

Chapter 6

The temptation to which I referred in the last chapter was far too trivial a thing to have its place in this record, or indeed in any summary of investigations that may claim to be of value to science. It should certainly have never arisen. And yet, having arisen, it enforces its place amongst my notes; for, my researches being of necessity conversational, whatever turned the current of the conversation between the dean and myself becomes of scientific importance. And that this unfortunately frivolous fancy, that came so inopportunely, did actually affect the current of our conversation is regrettably only too true. For about five minutes I was unable to shake it off, and during all that time, knowing well how inexcusable such action would be, I dared scarcely move or speak. Dean Spanley therefore continued his reminiscences unguided by me, and sometimes wandered quite away from the subject. I might indeed have lost him altogether; I mean to say, as a scientific collaborator; for during that five minutes I never even filled his glass. Luckily I pulled myself together in time, banished from my mind entirely that foolish and trivial fancy, and resumed the serious thread of my researches by saying to the dean: "What about ticks?"

"It is not for us to deal with them," said the dean. "The wise ones, the masters, can get them out. Nobody else can. It is of no use therefore to scratch. One's best policy towards a tick is summed up in the words, 'Live and let live.' That is to say, when the tick has once taken up his abode. When the tick is still wild it is a good thing to avoid him, by keeping away from the grasses in which they live, mostly in marshy places, unless led there by anything exciting, in which case it is of course impossible to think of ticks."

This fatalistic attitude to a tick, when once it had burrowed in, so strangely different from the view that we take ourselves, did as much as anything else in these strange experiences to decide me that the dean was actually remembering clearly where the rest of us forget almost totally; standing, as it were, a solitary traveler near one bank of the river of Lethe, and hearing his memories calling shrill through the mist that conceals the opposite shore. From now on I must say that I considered the whole thing proved, and only concerned myself to gather as many facts as possible for the benefit of science, a benefit that I considered it only fair that I should share myself, to the extent of obtaining any useful hints that I could for use in any other sojourn, in the event of my ever meeting with an experience similar to Dean Spanley's and being able to preserve the memory of what I had learned from him. Now that I considered his former sojourn proved (though of course I do not claim to be the sole judge of that) I questioned Dean Spanley about what seems to many of us one of the most mysterious things in the animal world, the matter of scent. To the dean there seemed nothing odd in it, and I suppose the mystery lies largely in the comparative weakness of that sense among us.

"How long would you be able to follow a man," I said, "after he had gone by?"

"That depends on the weather," said the dean. "Scent is never the same two days running. One might be able to follow after he had gone half an hour. But there is one thing that one should bear in mind, and that is that, if any of the masters in their superb generosity should chance to give one cheese, one cannot, for some while after that, follow with any certainty. The question of scent is of course a very subtle one, and cannot be settled lightly. The view that the archbishop takes, er, er, is . . ."

The moment had come for which I had been watching all the evening, the moment when the dean was waking up from the dream, or falling asleep from the reality, whichever way one should put it, the moment at which any words of his own describing his other sojourn would upon penetrating those diaconal ears, cause the most painful surprise. Twice before it had happened; and I felt that if it happened again I might no more be able to get the dean to dine with me. Science might go no further in this direction, in Europe. So I said, "Excuse me a moment. The telephone, I think." And rushed out of the room.

When I came back our conversation was not, I trust, without interest; but as it was solely concerned with the new lift that it is proposed to install in the club to which Dean Spanley and I belong, not many of my readers would easily follow the plans, were I to describe them here, or understand the importance of the new lift.

I pass over the next few weeks. The dean dined with me once more, but I was not able to persuade him to take sufficient Tokay to enable him to have that wonderful view of his that looked back down the ages, or indeed to see anything of any interest at all. He talked to me, but told me nothing that any reasonably well-educated reader could not find out for himself in almost any library. He was far far short of the point to which I had hoped my Tokay would bring him. I felt a renegade to science. There are those who will understand my difficulties; he was naturally an abstemious man; he was a dean; and he was by now entirely familiar with the exact strength of Tokay; it was not so easy to persuade him by any means whatever to go so far with that wine as he had gone three times already, three lapses that he must have at least suspected, if he did not even know exactly all about them. There are those who will understand all this. But there are others who in view of what was at stake will be absolutely ruthless; scientists who, in the study of some new or rare disease, would not hesitate to inoculate themselves with it, were it necessary to study it so, men who would never spare themselves while working for Science, and who will not withhold criticism from me. What prevented me, they will ask, from forcing upon

Dean Spanley, by any means whatever, sufficient alcohol for these important researches? For such a revelation as was awaiting a few more glasses of wine, any means would have been justified. It is easy to argue thus. But a broader mind will appreciate that you cannot ask a man to dine with you, let alone a dean, and then by trickery or violence, or whatever it is that some may lightly recommend, reduce him to a state that is far beyond any that he would willingly cultivate. All the permissible arts of a host I had already exercised. Beyond that I would not go. Meanwhile what was I to do? I felt like Keats' watcher of the skies when some new planet swims into his ken, and when almost immediately afterwards some trivial obstacle intervenes; a blind is drawn down, a fog comes up, or perhaps a small cloud; and the wonder one knows to be there is invisible. Much I had learned already, and I trust that what I have written has scientific value, but I wanted the whole story. I was no more content than a man would be who had obtained twenty or thirty pages of an ancient codex, if he knew that there were hundreds of pages of it. And what I sought seemed so near, and yet out of my grasp, removed from me by perhaps two small glasses. I never lost my temper with the dean, and when I found that I could no more question him stimulated, I questioned him sober. This was perhaps the most enraging experience of all; for not only was Dean Spanley extremely reticent, but he did not really know anything. An intense understanding of dogs, a sympathy for their more reputable emotions, and a guess that a strange truth may have been revealed to Hindus, was about all he had to tell. I have said already that I knew he had a secret; and this knowledge was what started me on my researches; but this secret of his amounted to no more knowledge, as a scientist uses the word, than a few exotic shells bought in some old shop on a trip to the seaside can supply a knowledge of seafaring. Between the dean sober at the Olympus Club, and the same dean after his fourth glass of Tokay, was all the difference between some such tripper as I have indicated and a wanderer familiar with the surf of the boundaries of the very furthest seas. It was annoying, but it was so. And then it seemed to me that perhaps where I had just failed alone I might be able to succeed with the help of example, if I asked one or two others to meet the dean. I was thinking in the form of a metaphor particularly unsuited to Tokay, "You may lead a horse to water, but you cannot make him drink." And from thinking of horses I got the idea of a lead out hunting, and so the idea of a little company at dinner easily came to me, one or two of the right kind who could be trusted to give a lead.

And I found the very man, and the moment I found him I decided that no more were necessary; just he and I and the dean would make a perfect dinner-party, from which I hoped that so much was to be revealed. I found him sitting next to me at a public dinner, a man of the most charming address, and with an appreciation of good wine that was evidently the foremost of all his accomplishments. He was so much a contrast to the man on the other side of me that I turned to Wrather (that was his name) quite early in the dinner and talked to him for the rest of the evening. The man on the other side of me was not only a teetotaller, which anybody may be, but one that wanted to convert his neighbors, and he started on me as soon as the sherry came round; so that it was a pleasure to hear from Wrather what was almost his first remark to me: "Never trust a teetotaller, or a man that wears elastic-sided boots." The idea struck me at once that he might be the man I wanted; and when I saw how well he was guided by the spirit of that saying, both in dress and in habits, I decided that he actually was. Later in that evening he put an arm round my shoulders and said: "You're younger than me; not with the whole of your life before you, but some of it; and this advice may be useful to you: Never trust a teetotaller or a man that wears elastic-sided boots."

One doesn't see elastic-sided boots as much now as one used to, and I fancied that he had evolved his saying early in life, or perhaps it was handed down to him.

We made great friends, and as we went out from the dinner together I tried to help him into his coat. He could not find the arm-hole, and said, "Never mind. I shall never find it. Throw the damned thing over my shoulders."

Which I did. And he added, "But for all that, never trust a tee-totaller, or a man that wears elastic-sided boots."

We shared a taxi and, in the darkness of it, he talked as delightfully as he had in the bright hall where we had dined; until, suddenly seeing a policeman, he stopped the cab and leaned out and shouted, "Bobby! There's something I want to tell you; and it's worth all you've ever learnt in Scotland Yard."

The constable came up slowly.

"Look here," said Wrather. "It's this. Never trust a teetotaller, or a man that wears elastic-sided boots."

"We've been dining with the Woolgatherers," I said through a chink beside Wrather.

And the constable nodded his head and walked slowly away.

"Sort of thing that will set him up," said Wrather, "if only he can remember it."

Chapter 7

I called on Wrather the very next day and told him about the dinner with the dean. I did not talk science or philosophy with Wrather, because he was not interested in science, and as far as I could gather from the talk of a single evening the tenets of transmigration did not appeal to him. But I told him that the dean kept a dog, and knew a great deal about dogs, and that when he had had a few glasses he thought he *was* a dog, and told dog-stories that were amusing and instructive. I told Wrather straight out that the dean went very slow with wine, and that to get any amusement out of him he must be encouraged to take his whack like a reasonable sportsman. Wrather said very little, but there was a twinkle in his eye that showed me I could rely on him whenever I should be able to get the dean. And I think that there may have been also in Wrather's mind, like a dim memory, the idea that I had helped him with a policeman, and he felt grateful. I watched next for the dean at the Club, and soon found him, and said that I hoped he would dine with me one day again, as I particularly wanted to ask him about the Greek strategy at Troy, a subject that I had found out he was keen on. He may have been a little afraid of that Tokay; on the other hand it attracted him. A man of the dean's degree of refinement could hardly fail to have been attracted by the Tokay, if he knew anything about wine at all; and Dean Spanley certainly did. He was not unpleased to be consulted by me about the Greek strategy; no man is entirely unmoved by being asked for information upon his particular subject; and he was very anxious to tell me about it. The final touch that may have decided him to accept my invitation was that he had beaten my Tokay last time, and so may well have thought that his fear of it was ungrounded. But an estimate of the dean's motives in accepting my invitation to dinner may not be without an element of speculation; the bare fact remains that he did accept it. It was to be for the Wednesday of the following week, and I hurried round to Wrather again and got him to promise to come on that day. I told him now still more about the dean: I said that I was a writer, and wanted to get some of the dean's stories; but there are many different kinds of writers, and I was far from telling Wrather what kind I was, for I knew that, had I told him I was a scientist, I should merely have bored him; I let him therefore suppose that I wanted the dean's dog-stories only for what might be humorous in them, and he never at any time had an inkling of the value of what I sought, the Golconda of knowledge that was lying so close to me. I told him that Tokay was the key to what I was after, and that the dean was rather difficult. "Did I ever tell you," asked Wrather, "a maxim that my old father taught me? Never trust a teetotaller, or a man who wears elastic-sided boots."

"Yes, I think you did," I answered. "But Dean Spanley is not a teetotaller. Only goes a bit slow, you know."

"We'll shove him along," said Wrather.

And I saw from a look in his eye that Wrather would do his best.

And certainly Wrather did do his best when the night came. To begin with he appreciated the Tokay for its own sake. But there was a certain whimsical charm about him that almost compelled you to take a glass with him when he urged you to do so in the way that he had. I know that what I am telling you is very silly. Why should a man take a glass of wine for himself because another man is taking one for *him*self? And yet it is one of those ways of the world that I have not been able to check. Some abler man than I may one day alter it. We did not come to the Tokay at once; we began on champagne. And certainly Dean Spanley went very slow with it, as I saw from a certain humorous and mournful look on the face of Wrather, as much as I did by watching the glass of the dean. And in the end we came to the Tokay; and Wrather goaded the dean to it.

"I don't suppose that a dean drinks Tokay," said Wrather, gazing thoughtfully at his own glass.

"And why not?" asked the dean.

"They are so sure of Heaven hereafter," said Wrather, "that they don't have to grab a little of it wherever they can, like us poor devils."

"Ahem," said the dean, and looked at the glass that I had poured out for him, the merits of which he knew just as well as Wrather.

"And then they're probably afraid of doing anything that people like me do, thinking we're all bound for Hell, and that their names might get mixed up by mistake with ours at the Day of Judgment, if they kept company with us too much."

"Oh, I wouldn't say that," said the dean.

I tried to stop Wrather after a while, thinking he went too far; but he wouldn't leave Dean Spanley alone: I had set Wrather onto him, and now I found that I could not call him off. At any rate the dean drank his Tokay. "Well, what more do you want?" Wrather seemed to say to me with a single glance of his expressive eyes, knowing perfectly well that I was trying to stop him. It was then that I asked the dean about the Greek strategy at Troy. Dean Spanley put down his third glass of Tokay and began to tell me about it, and a look came over Wrather's face that was altogether pro-Trojan, or at any rate against everything to do with the Greeks. As the dean talked on I poured out another glass of Tokay for him and watched him, and Wrather watched too. He was getting near to that point at which the curious change took place: I knew that by little signs that I had noted before. Wrather sat now quite silent, seeming to know as much as I did of the effect of the Tokay on the dean, though he had not ever seen him drink it before. But he was not there yet. I need not say what a thousand writers have said, that alcohol dulls the memory; I need not say what has been said for three thousand years, that wine sharpens the wit: both of these things are true; and both were to be observed in the same dean. Some minds are more easily affected than others; when forgetfulness came to the dean it came suddenly and very completely; had it not done so he would never have spoken out as he did. And right on top of the forgetfulness came this other phenomenon, the intense brightening of another part of the mind, a part of the mind that others of us may not possess, but far more likely, I think, a part that in most of us has never happened to be illuminated. It was, as I have said before, on only a narrow ridge that this occurred even with the dean, only for a short while, only after that precise glass, that exact number of drops of Tokay, that makes the rest of us think, upon careful reflection long after, that we may have perhaps taken a drop more than was strictly advisable. This ridge, this moment, this drop, was now approaching the dean, and Wrather and I sat watching.

"If we compare the siege of Troy with more modern sieges," said the dean, "or the siege of Ilion, as I prefer to call it, one finds among obvious differences a similarity of general principle."

Only he did not say the word principle; his tongue bungled it, went back and tried it again, tripped over it and fell downstairs. An effort that he made to retrieve the situation showed me the moment had come.

"Good dog," I said.

A momentary surprise flickered on Wrather's face, but with the dean bright memory shone on the heels of forgetfulness.

"Eh?" he said. "Wag was my name. Though not my only one. On rare occasions, very precious to me, I have been called 'Little Devil.'"

The surprise cleared from Wrather's face, and a look of mild interest succeeded it, as when a connoisseur notes a new manifestation.

Any difficulty the dean had had with his tongue had entirely disappeared.

"Ah, those days," he said. "I used to spend a whole morning at it."

"At what?" I asked.

"At hunting," said the dean, as though that should have been understood. "Ah, I can taste to this day, all the various tastes of digging out a rabbit. How fresh they were."

"What tastes?" I asked. For however tedious exactitude may be to some, it is bread and jam to a scientist.

"The brown earth," he said. "And sometimes chalk when one got down deeper, a totally different taste, not so pleasant, not quite so meaty. And then the sharp taste of the juicy roots of trees that almost always have to be bitten in two while digging out a rabbit. And little unexpected tastes, dead leaves, and even a slug. They are innumerable, and all delightful. And all the while, you know, there is that full ample scent of the rabbit, growing deeper and deeper as you get further in, till it is almost food to breathe it. The scent grows deeper, the air grows warmer, the home of the rabbit grows darker, and his feet when he moves sound like thunder; and all the while one's own magnificent scratchings sweep towards him. Winds blowing in past one's shoulders with scents from outside are forgotten. And at the end of it all is one's rabbit. That is indeed a moment."

"Some dean," muttered Wrather. An interruption such as no student of science would welcome at such a time. But I forgave him, for he had served science already far better than he could know, and I hushed him with a look, and the dean went on.

"It may be," said the dean, "though I cannot analyze it, but it may be that the actual eating of one's rabbit is no more thrilling than that gradual approach as one gnaws one's way through the earth. What would you say?"

"I should say it was equal," I answered.

"And you, Mr. Wrather?" said the dean.

"Not very good at definitions, you know," said Wrather. "But I will say one thing: one should never trust a teetotaller, or a man that wears elastic-sided boots."

And I could see that he was warming towards the dean; so that, trivial though such a thought is for a scientist to entertain in the middle of such researches, I saw that my little dinner-party would at any rate go well, as the saying is.

"There is one thing to bear in mind on those occasions," said the dean, fingering his collar with a touch of uneasiness, "and that is getting back again. When one's dinner is over one wants to get back. And if the root of a tree, that one has perhaps bitten through, or a thin flint pointing the wrong way, should get under one's collar, it may produce a very difficult situation."

His face reddened a little over his wide white collar even at the thought. And it is not a situation to laugh at.

"Where your head and shoulders have gone they can get back

again," the dean continued, "were it not for the collar. That is the danger. One does not think of that while eating one's rabbit, but it is always a risk, especially where there are roots of trees. There have been cases in which that very thing has happened; caught by the collar. I knew of a case myself. Someone was lost, and men were looking for him in our woods. Of course they could not smell. But I happened to be out for a walk, and I noticed a trail leading straight to a rabbit-hole, a very old trail indeed, but when one puts one's nose to the hole the dog was undoubtedly down there and had been there a long time. He must have been caught. I expect by the collar."

"And what did you do for him?" I couldn't help blurting out.

"He was nobody I knew," said the dean.

Chapter 8

Wrather turned his face slowly round and looked at me; and I could see that the feeling of friendship that he had had for the dean when he found he was not a teetotaller had suddenly all veered away. For myself I cared nothing for the dean, one way or the other, except as the only link that Europe is known to have between the twentieth century and lives that roamed other ages. As such he was of inestimable value, so that the callousness that was so repulsive to Wrather had no more effect upon me than a distorted bone has on a surgeon; it was just one manifestation of a strange case.

"Are you sure he hasn't elastic-sided boots?" murmured Wrather to me. An absurd question about any member of the Olympus Club. And I treated it with silence accordingly. And out of that silence arose Dean Spanley's voice, with a touch of the monotony that is sometimes heard in the voice of a man who is deep in reminiscences, far away from those he addresses.

"It's a grand life, a dog's life," he said.

"If one thinks one's a dog," muttered Wrather to me, "one should think one is a decent kind of a dog."

Dean Spanley never heard him, and rambled on: "It is undoubtedly the most perfect form of enjoyment that can be known. Where else shall we find those hourly opportunities for sport, romance and adventure combined with a place on the rugs of the wisest and greatest? And then the boundless facilities for an ample social life. One has only to sniff at the wheel of a cart to have news of what is going on, sometimes as much as five miles away. I remember once sniffing at a wheel myself and I found that there was a fellow who had been doing the same at a distance of nearly ten miles. And in the end I got to know him. He came one day with the cart, and I recognized him at once. We had a bit of a fight at first; on my part because I had to show him that the house was properly guarded and that it could not allow strangers, and he in order to show that that wheel was his. We fought on a patch of grass that there was near the back door. There was a grip that I used to be fond of; the ear. The throat-grip is of course final, but as nobody ever lets you in at it, or hardly ever, I used to think that it was waste of time to try for it, and I concentrated upon an ear. The ear was my specialty. Well, I got him by one of the ears and he shouted: 'I am a poor dog! I am being most dreadfully maltreated! I am far away from home and I am being killed in a cruel country! I am the favorite dog of very great and magnificent people! They would weep to see me killed like this. They brought me up very nicely! I am a poor dog! Oh! Oh! Oh! All is over with me now! It is the end! I was a poor good dog. But now I am quite dead.' I remember his words to this day. And then a lady came out from the kitchen with a bucket; and she had always a very high opinion of me, a very high opinion indeed, and treated me with the utmost consideration; but today she must have had some disappointment, for she acted with the bucket in a way quite unlike herself. Indeed I will not even say what she did with the bucket. It was a hasty act, and quite spoiled the fight. She did it without reflection. The other fellow licked the side of his paw and smoothed down his ear with it. 'Very powerful and angry people you have here,' he said.

" 'Not at all,' I said. 'She's never like that as a rule. She must have had some disappointment.'

" 'Never mind,' he said, 'it was a good fight as far as it went.'

" 'But I can't understand her spoiling it,' I said. 'I don't know what disappointed her.'

" 'Oh, they're the same everywhere,' he said. 'I have seen people act just as hastily with a broom.'

"We sat and talked like that: how clearly it all comes back to me. And from that we came to talking about sport. And I said that our woods held a lot of very big game. And we arranged a little party of him and me, and set out to hunt the woods there and then. And the very first thing we came to was a great big smell of an enormous animal, and a great enemy of man, and much too near the house, a fox. And we sat down and said should we hunt him? He was somewhere quite close, the smell was lying on the ground in great heaps and stretched as high up as you could jump. And we sat and thought for a while as to whether we ought to hunt him. And in the end the other fellow decided. I remember his words to this day. 'Perhaps not,' he said. So we went on then after rabbits. The woods were on a slope, and near the top there were brambles. I put him into the brambles and ran along the outside a little ahead of him at the edge of the trees. There were rabbits in those brambles that didn't properly belong to our wood at all: they came in there from the open land, to keep warm. So when my friend put one out, he ran to the open country that he had come from, over the top of the hill; and I gave a shout or two and we both went after him, and it was just the country for a hunt, no bushes or brambles where the rabbit could play tricks, good short grass very nice for the feet, and fine air for shouting in.

"The rabbit, as you know, has been given a white tail to guide us, so that we did not need to take any trouble to keep him in sight. He went over the top of the hill, smooth grass all the way, with nothing else but a few ant-heaps, and down the side of a valley: his home was a long way off, and it would have been a lovely hunt had he not resorted to trickery. We came to a thick hedge, full of trees, and he went in and hopped about the thorns and round the trunks of the trees in a silly sort of way, and in and out among brambles; in fact the whole thing got so stupid that after a while we decided to have no more to do with the silly thing. I said, 'Let's hunt something more sensible.'

"And he said, 'Let's.'

"I don't waste my time on folk that fool about among brambles. Well, we got back to the wood, and we went along taking observations in the air. Winds, you know, blew down paths and between trees, and we noted what was at the other end of the wind. And we hadn't gone far when there was a very strange scent indeed, quite close, and there was a big hole in the chalk and the scent coming pouring out of it. 'You have big game in your woods,' said my friend.

" 'Very big game indeed,' I said.

"And we went up to the hole. There was a badger at home down there and he seemed to be asleep. So we decided to wake him up. We just put our mouths right into the hole and barked at him. He was a long way down, but he must have heard us. We barked at him for ten minutes. It was the greatest fun. Then we went out on through the wood and presently what should we see but a very showy young rabbit who was out on a long walk, no doubt for social reasons. So we chased the young fellow all through the wood and back to his own house. It was a very populous neighborhood, and we didn't stop and dig: too many passages, you know, running in all directions. So I said: 'Let's come and hunt a large bad animal.'

"It was a pig that I meant, but that's how one puts it. You know the sniff beside the other fellow's face, and the beckoning of the head, that means that?"

I merely nodded: I was not going to interrupt the dean just now with a request for explanations. And I looked at Wrather, in case he was going to do so; but Wrather sat silent and interested.

"He said, 'Let's.' And I said, 'I know where there is one.' And I ran on in front.

"So we came to the pig's house and looked in through his door at him and shouted 'Pig.' He didn't like that. He looked just like a pig; he was a pig; and he knew it. He came towards his door saying silly surly things in a deep voice. You know the kind of talk. And we just shouted, 'Pig. Pig. Pig.' Both of us, for nearly half an hour. It was perfectly splendid and we enjoyed it immensely."

"What did he say?" asked Wrather.

"What could he say?" said the dean. "He knew he was a pig. But he didn't like being told about it. I've seldom enjoyed myself more. It made up for that fool of a rabbit that was so silly in the hedge on the hill.

"Then we went to the back of the stables and rolled in something nice, till our coats were smooth and we both had a beautiful scent. Then we killed a hen for the fun of it. It was a lovely evening.

"It was getting all dark and late now. In fact, if I stayed any longer, there would be terrible beatings. So I said: 'What about your cart?'

"And he said: 'It's a long way to go. I can catch that up when I like. We live three overs away.'"

"Overs?" I said.

"Dips over the hills," said the dean.

And I did not like to question him further for fear that it would bring him back to our day. But what I think he meant was a distance of three horizons.

"I said, 'Very well, old fellow, then we'll have a bit more sport.'

"'What shall it be?' he said.

"And even as he spoke a thing I had been suspecting happened on top of the hill. There'd been a suspicious light there for some time; not the right kind of light; a touch too much of magic in it to my liking; a thing to be watched. And sure enough the moon rose. It was of course my job to guard the house when the moon came large and sudden over that hill, as I have known it do before, but now that I had my friend with me I said, 'Shall we hunt it?' And he said, 'Oh, let's.' And we went up that hill quicker than we went after the rabbit; and when we got to the top we barked at the moon. And lucky for the moon he didn't stay where he was. And the longer we stayed the stranger the shadows got. Soon it was magic all round us, and more than one dog could bark at. Very magic indeed. When we had hunted the moon enough we came back through the wood; and we both of us growled as we came to the trees so as to warn whatever there was in the darkness, in case it should try to threaten us. There were lots of things in the wood that were hand-in-glove with the moon, queer things that did not bark or move or smell, and one could not see them, but one knew they were there. We came back down the hill with our mouths wide open, so as to breathe in all the pleasantness of that day: we had hunted a badger, two rabbits, a hen, a pig and the moon, and very nearly a fox; and I had a feeling I have not often had, that it was almost enough. And my friend said, 'I must go after my cart now, or the man will be thinking he's lost.' And I said, 'Let me know how you are, next time your cart is coming this way.' And he promised he would. And I promised to let him know how I was, whenever the cart came."

"He thinks he is one, all right," said Wrather to me.

"I beg your pardon?" said the dean.

"Nothing," said Wrather. "Something we were talking about the other day. I've let the Tokay stop in front of me. I *beg* your pardon." And he passed it on to the dean. We watched Dean Spanley, thus encouraged, pour out another glass. He drank a little, and Wrather continued, "But you were telling me about a very interesting evening."

"Yes, it was interesting," said the dean. "I remember coming back to the house and it was late and the door was unfortunately shut. And I knocked, but nobody came to it. And I had to shout, 'I am out in the cold.' 'I am out in the cold,' I shouted, 'and the moon is after me. It is a terrible terrible night and I shall die in the cold, and my ghost will haunt this house. My ghost will wail in the house when the cold and the moon have killed me. I am a poor dog out in the dark.'

"Those were my very words, and they came and opened the door; the wise ones, the great ones. And then they beat me with a stick. And of course I said, 'I am only a poor dog; a poor destitute dog overcome with profound shame, who will never sin again.' And, when the beating stopped, everything was very very beautiful.

"I went into the kitchen then and said to them there: 'I have had a splendid beating, and I am not at all the dog that I was before, but am utterly purged of sin, and I am wise now and good and never shall sin again, but I am very hungry.' I am telling you the exact words that I used, because they happen to be very clear in my memory. I don't know if my reminiscences interest you."

"Profoundly," said Wrather. "But I hope you aren't expecting me to drink all the Tokay by myself, and then perhaps going to laugh at me afterwards."

"Not at all," said the dean.

And he took a little more, though not much, and went on with his reminiscences, while I applauded Wrather as far as one can by a look. "They gave me a very beautiful dinner. They were good women of great wisdom. And when I had finished what they had given me, and I had cleaned the plate as one should, I was fortunate enough to find a good deal of bacon-rind, which was kept in a treasury that I knew of, and which by a great piece of luck was well mixed with some jam and some pieces of cheese, and a good deal of broom-sweepings with several different flavors, and one sausage, which happened to be old enough to give a distinct taste to the whole dish. It was a lovely dinner; and I knew that the moon would not dare to come back again after all I and the other fellow had said to him, so there was really no more to be done when they took me to bed. And I walked round eight or nine times on the straw, till my bed was just right, and I lay down and the night went away, and all the world was awake again."

Chapter 9

"When all the world woke up," the dean went rambling on, "there were the voices of a great many things that had come too close, impudent folk like birds, that had to be chased. So I shouted, asking to be let out at once. For a long while no one came, and then I heard a voice saying something about all this noise, which was just what I had been calling his attention to; and he let me out, but I think he had been worried overnight by the moon or one of those prowling things, for he did not look glad. And I ran out and chased everything that needed chasing. And so another day started."

"You must have been the hell of a dog," said Wrather suddenly.

That spoiled everything. To begin with, talk of any sort was rather liable to bring him back to the present day; and, besides that, it was not the way to address a dean. That he had once used similar words himself did not excuse Wrather.

In any case Dean Spanley, so far as I had observed him, never stayed for very long with his mind's eye open upon that strange past and shut to this age of ours. He started slightly now, and I indicated the bottle of Tokay, nearly empty, and then glanced towards Wrather, to account for, if not to excuse, the unfortunate words.

"When I was up at Oxford," said the dean, "I was certainly a young man of some, shall I say, considerable activity. But a dog in any sense of the word, let alone one qualified by the word you used, would be a much exaggerated way of describing me."

"Certainly. Quite so," I said.

And the incident passed off, while we both turned somewhat pitying eyes upon Wrather.

"You know, you're a bit overcome," I said to Wrather.

And Wrather understood me.

"I expect that's it," he said. And he took the line that I indicated.

It is curious that, of all the amazing things said in that room, the words that made far the most stir were the almost innocent remark of Wrather. And I am sure that Dean Spanley believed that this remark was the strangest that had been made there that evening. This was as it should be; but, while it left the way open for another dinner, it certainly made it difficult to get the dean to meet Wrather.

Our little dinner-party soon broke up; the dean was a trifle shocked at Wrather's lapse with the Tokay; Wrather was a bit ashamed of himself for having spoiled the sport, as he put it afterwards; and I had no longer any scientific interest in the dinner, as I realized that the dean would not go back through the years any more that night. I merely remained an ordinary host. I do not think it was any hardship on Wrather to have been suspected of drunkenness, for he had brought it all on himself; incidentally he had had an enormous amount of Tokay, but only incidentally, for it had no real effect on Wrather. We all went downstairs, and I called a taxi, into which I put the dean. Then Wrather came back into the house with me. Going upstairs he apologized for having "undogged the dean," and then we came to a room in which I sit and smoke a good deal, and we sat in front of the fire in armchairs and talked of Dean Spanley. And Wrather, with the air of a man who has been slightly cheated, said: "Have you noticed that he told us nothing of any love-affair?"

"No," I said. "He didn't. I wonder why."

"Too much dean still left in him," said Wrather. "You must get him deeper."

"Deeper?" I said.

"More Tokay," said Wrather.

It was all very well for Wrather to say that, but it couldn't be done. Besides which, I was by no means certain how wide that ridge was from which the dean saw the past: at a certain number of glasses he arrived there; might not two extra glasses topple him down beyond it, and, if so, where? Then Wrather, though he had no idea how much was at stake scientifically, was distinctly helpful. "I think he is there all the time; in his dog-kennel, you know," he said. "Only, in the glare of today, he can't see it. That Tokay of yours is just like pulling down a blind on the glare, and then the old dog can see. Keep him full of it and you should have some sport with him."

The flippancy of these remarks is obvious. But I give them to my reader for the element of truth that I think they contained, for flashes of truth may often appear to an insight even as unscientific as Wrather's. Moreover, Wrather's view bore out the idea that I had long ago formed, that Dean Spanley in broad daylight at his club knew something veiled from the rest of us, though too little to be of any real value, until he was entirely removed from unfavorable conditions. And this removal my Tokay seemed to accomplish.

"It's all very well," I said rather crossly, "for you to say keep him full of Tokay. But he won't drink it for me, not to any extent. He would for you somehow; but you've spoiled it all by calling him a dog, which is a thing no dean would stand."

"I'm sorry," said Wrather. "Let's think what we can do. You know I'm as keen as you are to hear the old dog talk."

That this was not the way to speak of Dean Spanley will be clear to my readers, but I said nothing of that then, and instead of touching on any such delicate matter we hatched a somewhat childish plot between us.

The plot went like this, and it was mainly Wrather's idea: the dean would not want to meet a drunken fellow like Wrather again; no dignitary of the church, no member of an important club, would. But represent Wrather as a man needing guidance, represent him as something much worse than what he had appeared to Dean Spanley, or anything he had ever been, a man about to be wrecked on the rocks of Tokay (if a liquid may be compared to a rock), and Wrather argued and I came to agree, and we hatched the thing out together, the dean would come to save an almost hopeless case; and, if he got a few glasses of the finest Tokay while he was doing it, who would deserve them more?

"Tell him it's no case for the pledge," said Wrather. "Tell him I'm past all that. And there's a certain amount of truth in that too. Say that I didn't drink fair. *He* didn't as a matter of fact: he wouldn't keep up. But say it was me. And say that I must be watched, and taught to drink at the same pace as other men, reasonable men like the dean, I mean; or otherwise the black fellow will get me. And I shouldn't be surprised if he did in any case, but that's neither here nor there. You get him drinking level with me, and we'll soon bring out the dog in him, and we'll have a whale of an evening."

It wasn't quite the way to talk, but I agreed. And I would have agreed to odder arrangements than that in the interests of science.

A few days later I had a talk with the dean in the Club, on the lines that Wrather and I had arranged.

"I am a good deal worried about that man Wrather," I said.

"He is a bit crude, somewhat uncouth, somewhat perhaps. . . ." said Dean Spanley.

And while he pondered some exacter word, I broke in with, "It's worse than that. The man of course will never be a teetotaller, but he does not notice what other men drink, reasonable men, I mean. His only chance would be to learn how much wine can be taken in safety."

"That's not always so easy to teach, in a case like that," said the dean.

"No," I said, "and I have come to you for advice about it, for I shouldn't like to see Wrather, or any man, utterly ruined, as he soon must be if he goes on like that. What I thought was that if he could be guided by some sensible man, he might learn what was good for him and limit himself to that."

"How do you mean?" said the dean.

"Well, drinking glass for glass," I said. "I would see that the wine was passed round continually, and that each man had only his share."

"H'm," said the dean.

"It's a rare wine, you see, and he's unfamiliar with it, and he'd learn, that way, how much he could take in safety. It might save him altogether."

But still the dean seemed suspicious, or at any rate not quite satisfied. "I take it you can do that yourself," he said.

It was then that I played, if I may say so, my master-stroke.

"I'm afraid not," I said.

"Eh?" said the dean.

"I am afraid," I said, "where so much is at stake for Wrather, I could not select myself as the perfect mentor."

"I see," said the dean.

He remembered the occasion when I had given way to Tokay, a surrender by no means enforced on me, but still a surrender.

"Of course if you think he can be checked and brought round in that way," said the dean, "and I dare say it may not be impossible —then of course you should be very careful how it is done."

"That is why I have come to you," I said.

"To me, eh?"

"Yes."

Things hung in the balance then, while the dean pondered.

"I don't see how giving him more wine can teach him to take less," he said, but there was doubt in his voice.

"If one tried to stop a case like that from taking any wine at all, one would lose the last vestige of influence over him, and he would be utterly lost. It's worth trying."

"Oh, I suppose so," said the dean, and without enthusiasm, for Wrather had been distinctly rude to him.

And then I flashed out on him the ace of trumps. "You suppose so! Can you doubt, Mr. Dean, that any soul is worth saving?"

The ace of trumps at his own game, and it had to take the trick.

"I will certainly be glad to try," he said.

So I arranged what at one time I had thought to have been impossible, another dinner at my house, at which Dean Spanley was to meet Wrather.

Then I went off to tell Wrather what I had done, and to book him for the date. And at the same time I tried, as tactfully as I could, to check in advance any levity in remarks he might make to the dean.

"You've got to damned well save my soul," said Wrather. "Never you mind about anything else."

"You'll bring him right back with a jerk," I said, "if you talk like that when he's there. The split infinitive alone would be almost enough to do it."

But all Wrather said was: "We'll have him so far under, that nothing will bring him back."

It is almost inconceivable to me, looking back on it, that such talk should have been the preliminary of a research of the first importance.

Chapter 10

It was exactly as Wrather had said, when the dinner came off; he did lead the dean to the point which we both of us, for very different reasons, desired: and today with all its trappings—sights, noises and points of view—fell away from him with the sudden completeness of snow on a southern slope, when the spring sun charms it thence and the sleeping grass is laid bare. At a certain stage of our dinner, and evidently just the right one, I had referred to his reminiscences. And at that moment I had addressed him not as Mr. Dean but by his earlier name of Wag. Just plain Wag.

"As soon as they brought me round from my own house," said the dean, "I used to have breakfast. And after that I used to run round to look for some food, in various places I knew of. There was the pigsty for one. A very greedy devil, the pig, and a lot of good stuff was brought to him; and, if one knew just where to look, there was always a lot of it to be found that had slopped over into the mud; and even when one found nothing to get one's teeth into, there was always a very meaty taste in the water of all the puddles around there. And then there was a heap near the stables where a lot of good things were put. Various places, you know. On a lucky day I would sometimes eat till dinner-time, then have dinner, and go out to look for a bit more. That is one way of eating, and a very satisfying way. Another way is to hunt your own game and eat it nice and hot. They say it gives one an appetite, which of course it does; but there is no need for that; one always has an appetite. Still, life would not be complete without hunting. Hunting and dog-fighting should be one's main pursuits, as guarding is a duty, and eating a pastime.

"I shouldn't like you to go away with the idea, by the way, that I would eat anything. That was not so. One had a certain position to keep up, and a certain (shall I say?) dignity to preserve; and to preserve it I made a point of never eating bread. There were those that offered it to me, until they got to know me, but I always had to leave it on the carpet. There is no harm in bread, yet it has not only no flavor, but is one of those things that do not develop a flavor even when buried for a long time, so that it can never become interesting.

"To be a bread-eater is to my mind to be lacking in refinement or self-respect. I do not of course refer to soft toast, on which perhaps a snipe has been lying, all saturated with gravy: such things may be very precious.

"And cake of course is never to be confused with bread; it has a similar taste and the same disabilities, but is a far more important food, so that there can never be any loss of dignity in eating a piece of cake. The wise ones eat cake by itself, but to bread they always add something before eating it, which shows the unimportance of bread. And from this I come to table manners. One should catch one's food as neatly as possible. By fixing one's eyes on the wise ones before they throw it is almost impossible to miss."

Wrather moved slowly nearer to me, sideways.

I knew what he was going to say.

"Do you think," he whispered, "that the old dog would catch anything now?"

I could not explain to Wrather at this time what in any case I had led him to believe was not the case, that this was research work on my part, not mere amusement. So all I said to him was, "Don't whisper," a rudeness that he forgave me at once with a twinkling eye.

"Eh? What?" said the dean. "I was saying that one should fix one's eyes on the wise ones. There are those that do not appreciate intense devotion at meal-times. But it is not for us to withhold our devotion on that account. It is born in all of us, and increased by beatings. A few sharp words should not diminish it. And sometimes it brings us abundant bones."

"I say," said Wrather, "the old dog wants bucking up a bit."

"Don't!" I said in an undertone. "You'll bring him round."

"No, I shan't," said Wrather. And to the dean he said, "Did you never have any more exciting experiences?"

"Exciting?" replied the dean. "Life is full of excitement, except while one is sleeping."

"Anything specially thrilling, I mean," said Wrather.

I couldn't stop him. But Dean Spanley, far from being brought back by him to our own time, leaned forward and looked at Wrather, and said: "I was out once for a walk by myself, and I saw a nursery-maid and two children and a dog coming my way, and a strange new smell ran past me, and I glanced up and saw the look in the eyes of the dog. And I ran. I started just in time and he never came after me. It was rabies. And the nursery-maid and the children came quietly on, walking as they do on a Sunday."

"Rabies!" said Wrather, all hushed. "How did you know?"

"How did I know?" said the dean. "I saw his eyes, and the look was there."

"And you couldn't have been mistaken?" I asked.

"It was glaring," replied the dean.

And that was one thing I learned from him.

Wrather drank off a whole glass of Tokay, and said: "Tell us something more cheerful."

I was afraid every moment that Wrather would bring him back.

"Down," I said to Wrather, who understood what I meant, and the sharp command helped, I think, to keep the dean where he was among his old memories. Nevertheless, he answered Wrather, and seemed to do what he asked.

"I remembered the hounds coming once to our house; professional hunters, you know. I should have liked to have asked them whether they had been permitted to come there by the wise master, and whether their intentions were entirely correct, and indeed a great many other things; and, if their answers had been satisfactory, I should have liked to have told them all about our woods and all about who lived in them. I could have helped them in hundreds of ways. But unfortunately I was shut up. I shouted a good deal to them from my house; but I should have liked to have gone with them and showed them the way; I should have liked to have gone round and seen that they were all quite well. And I should have liked to have chased the horses so that they should not think, on account of their size, that they were more important than me. But there it was, I was shut up.

"I had an enormous amount to do when they left. I had to go and find out who they all were, and where they had come from and if they were all quite well. Every tuft of grass had news of them. There were the scents of the hounds themselves, and scents from the roads they had come by, and tracks and scents of the horses: the field in front of our house was nothing less than a history; and it took me a long time to go through it. I was a bit behindhand owing to having been shut up, but scents that had gone from lawns and paths still hung in the taller grasses, and I was able to gather all the information that I required."

"What for?" blurted out Wrather, before I could stop him.

"To guard the house," said the dean. "It was my duty to guard it. And I had to know who had come near it, and what their business was. Our house was sacred, and we couldn't have people coming near it unless we knew what they had come for: there might have been an enemy among them. You will not suggest, I trust, that anybody and everybody should be allowed without enquiry, and without the most careful enquiry, near a sacred house."

"Not at all," said Wrather.

And I felt it necessary to add: "Of course not."

"Ours was a particularly sacred house," said the dean, still somewhat nettled. "Even the butcher's cart had to be barked at, though at many houses such a cart as that would be allowed to drive up without question. I certainly could not have all those people coming without enquiring into their motives and, as a matter of general interest, their state of health. So I naturally had a very busy morning. They went visiting in our wood while I was still shut up, and I heard them leave the wood hunting. They all shouted out that they were after a fox, and quite right too, but I could not allow them merely on that account to come near a house such as ours without proper investigations.

"And there were two or three light carriages that had come to our stables and that were fortunately still there when I was let out. So I sniffed at the wheels to get news of what was going on in the world, and I left a message with all of them to say that I was quite well."

Chapter 11

One more story we got from the dean that night; he had met his friend again, the one that lived three overs away; he had come to the house we had heard of, running behind his cart. The dean had gone up to him at once, or Wag, I should say, no doubt putting his nose right up to the other dog's, and flicking it away and trotting off, and the other dog had followed.

"I invited him to come hunting," said the dean, "and he said he would like to, and we went off at once."

"What was your friend's name?" put in Wrather.

"Lion-hunter," replied the dean.

"Did he hunt lions?" asked Wrather.

"No," said the dean, "but he was always ready to; he was always expecting a lion in his garden, and he thought of himself as Lion-hunter, therefore it was his name."

"Did you think of yourself as Wag?" asked Wrather, not in any way critically, but only, I think, to get the details right.

"No," said the dean, "I answered to it. I came to them when the great ones called that name. I thought of myself as Moon-chaser. I had often hunted the moon."

"I see," said Wrather.

And he had spoken so suavely that he never brought the dean around, as I feared a jarring note might have done.

"When we came to the wood," continued the dean, "we examined several rabbit-holes; and when we came to a suitable one, a house with only two doors to it, and the rabbit at home, I set Lion-hunter to dig, and stood myself at the back-door. He did all the barking, while I waited for the rabbit to come out. Had the rabbit come out I should have leaped on him and torn him to pieces, and eaten up every bit, not allowing Lion-hunter or anyone in the world to have a taste of it. When my blood is up no one can take anything from me, or even touch it. I should have caught it with one leap, and killed it with one bite, and eaten even the fur. Unfortunately the rabbit lived deeper down than we thought.

"But it was not long before a very strange and beautiful scent blew through the wood, on a wind that happened to come that way from the downs outside. We both lifted our noses, and sure enough it was a hare. We ran out of the wood, and we very soon saw him; he was running over the downs on three legs, in that indolent affected manner that hares have. He stopped and sat up and looked at us, as though he hadn't expected to meet two great hunters. Then he went on again. We raced to a point ahead of him, so as to meet him when he got there, and we soon made him put down that other hind leg. Unfortunately before he got to the point that we aimed at, he turned. This happened to leave us straight behind him. We shouted out that we were hunting him, and that we were great hunters, Lion-hunter and I, and that nothing ever escaped from us, and that nothing ever would. This so alarmed him that he went further. When he came to a ridge of the downs he slanted to his left, and we slanted more, so as to cut him off, but when we got over the ridge he had turned again. We shouted to him to stop, as it was useless to try to escape from us, but the tiresome animal was by now some way ahead. He had of course the white tail that is meant to guide us, the same as the rabbit has; and we kept him in sight for a long while. When he was no longer in sight we followed the scent, which Lion-hunter could do very well, though he was not as fast as I; and it led us to places to which I had never been before, over a great many valleys. We puzzled out the scent and followed on and on, and we did not give up the hunt until all the scent had gone, and nothing remained except the smell of the grass, and the air that blew from the sheep. Night came on rather sooner than usual, and we did not know where we were, so we turned for home."

"How did you do that," asked Wrather, "if you did not know where you were?"

"By turning towards it," replied the dean. "I turned first, and then Lion-hunter turned the same way."

"But how did you know which way to turn?" persisted Wrather.

"I turned towards home," said the dean.

There was something here that neither Wrather nor I ever quite understood, though we talked it over afterwards, and I was never able to get it from the dean. My own impression is that there was something concerned which we should not have understood in any case, however it had been explained. My only contribution to any investigation that there may be on these lines is merely that the queer thing is there: what it is I have failed to elucidate.

"We turned towards home," the dean went on, "and that led us past a lot of places I never had seen before. We passed a farm where strange people barked at us, and we met a new animal with a beard and a very fine smell. The question arose as to whether we should hunt him, but he lowered his horns at us, and jumped round so quickly that the horns were always pointing the wrong way. So we decided we would not hunt him, and told him we would come and hunt him some other day, when it was not so late and we had more time; and we went on towards home. Presently we saw a window shining at us, and it did not look right. It was a small house and all shut up, and it looked as though bad people might be hiding in it. I asked Lion-hunter if we should go up to the house and bark at them; but he thought that they might be asleep, and that it was better to let bad people go on sleeping. So we went by the lighted window, but it looked very bad in the night. Then the moon came over a ridge of the downs, but not large enough to be barked at. And then we came to a wood, and it turned out to be our own wood. And we ran down the hill and came to my house and barked under the window. And Lion-hunter said that he thought he would go back to his own house now, in case our door should open and anyone come out of it angry. And I said that might be best. And the door opened, and a great one appeared. And I said that I had been hunting and that I never would hunt again, and that I had stayed out much much too late, and that the shame of my sin was so great that I could not enter the house, and would only just crawl into it. So I crawled in and had a beating, and shook myself, and it was a splendid evening. I lay down in front of the fire and enjoyed the warmth of it, and turned over the memory of our hunt slowly in my mind; and the fire and my memories and the whole of the night seemed brightened by my beating. How beautiful the fire was! Warmer than the sun, warmer than eating can make you, or running or good straw, or even beatings, it is the most mysterious and splendid of all the powers of man. For man makes fire with his own hand. There is no completer life than lying and watching the fire. Other occupations may be as complete, but with none of them do the glow, the warmth and the satisfaction that there are in a fire come to one without any effort of one's own. Before a fire these things come merely by gazing. They are placed in the fire by man, in order to warm dogs, and to replenish his own magical powers. Wherever there is a fire there is man, even out of doors. It is his greatest wonder. On the day that he gives to dogs that secret, as he one day will, dogs and men shall be equal. But that day is not yet. I stray a little, perhaps, from my reminiscences. These things are taught, and are known to be true, but they are not of course any part of my personal observations."

"Who discovered that?" said Wrather before I could stop him.

"We do not know," said the dean.

"Then how do you know it's true?" asked Wrather.

"They shall be equal one day, and on that day," said the dean.

"What day?" asked Wrather.

"Why, the day on which man tells dogs the secret of fire," I said to end the discussion.

"Exactly," said the dean.

I frowned at Wrather, for we were getting near something very strange; and though Wrather's interruption did not bring the dean back, as I feared every moment it might, we heard no more of that strange belief from him. He talked of common things, the ordinary experiences of a dog on a rug at the fireside, things that one might have guessed, nothing that it needed a spiritual traveler to come from a past age to tell us.

Chapter 12

I pass over many weeks, weeks that brought no success to my investigations. A feeling that I had sometimes come very near to strange discoveries only increased my disappointment. It seemed to me that a dog had some such knowledge of the whereabouts of his home as the mariner has of the North Pole: the mariner knows by his compass: how does the dog know? And then I had gathered from the dean that a dog can detect rabies in another dog, before any signs of it appear to the eyes of men. How was that done? What a valuable discovery that might be, if only I could follow it up. But I had no more than a hint of it. And then the strange faith of which the dean had said only one or two sentences. All the rest that I had got was no more than what an observant man taking notes might have found out or guessed about dogs; but these three things beckoned to me, promising something far more, like three patches of gold on far peaks in some El Dorado of knowledge. The lure of them never left me. I had long talks with Wrather. I let him see that it was more to me than a mere matter of amusement; and he stuck to me and promised to do what he could. He and the dean and I dined together again, and Wrather and I did our utmost; but I began to see that, in spite of those lapses, induced partly by the rarity of the wine and mainly by the perseverance of deliberate efforts to lure him away from sobriety, the dean was an abstemious man. Only at the end of our dinner for three or four minutes he stepped back into that mid-Victorian age that he seemed able to enter in memory when the glare of today was dimmed for him; and the things that he said were trivial, and far from the secrets I sought. Nor were they the sort of things that one much cared to hear: there are many habits and tricks we forgive to dogs on account of their boundless affection, which somehow jar when heard from the lips of a dean.

Once more we dined together, and at that dinner the dean said nothing that would have surprised the timidest of any flock that he had ever tended. And the next day Wrather told me definitely that he could do no more with the dean.

"I won't say he's a teetotaller," said Wrather, "because I wouldn't say that lightly of any man and I know he is not; but he has a damned strong tendency that way. We have got him over it once or twice, but he'll develop it yet. I can do no more with him."

Not the way to talk; but never mind that: so much was at stake.

"What's to be done?" I said desperately.

"I'll help you all I can," said Wrather, "but it's only fair to tell you when I can do no more. He's not the right sort of fellow. He may have taken his whack once or twice like a sportsman, but it wasn't because he wanted to. It was just by accident because he didn't know the strength of the booze. There are not many people that do. You want to be an emperor of Austria to gauge the strength of Tokay to a nicety."

"Then I shall never find out what I'm after," I said in despair.

"I wouldn't say that," said Wrather. "I'm not the only sportsman in the world. You want to find someone who takes a stiffer whack than I do, and takes it in a brighter way. There are men you can't help taking a glass with."

For a moment I feared that such a quest was hopeless, till I suddenly thought of the Maharajah. It was said of him that champagne was to him what Vichy water is to some people; and, if a sportsman were needed, it was said too that even India had scarcely a score who might claim to be greater sportsmen. Moreover, he knew so much of the situation already that nothing would have to be explained to him. He was the very man.

"What about the Maharajah of Haikwar?" I said.

"He's a good sportsman," said Wrather.

"You know him?" I asked.

"No," said Wrather, "but of course I've heard of him. And he might do."

"I don't want stuff about lying in front of the fire," I said. "I want to find out how dogs can find their way home, by a new route and from a strange country. And I want to know how they can detect rabies long before we can; and one or two other things."

"You'll have to get him deeper, for all that," said Wrather, "deeper than I've been able to get him. It's all very well for a dull old dog like the dean to lay down the exact number of glasses at which one ought to stop; and he's been doing a good deal of stopping just lately; but the fact remains that when you have a real bright sportsman like the Maharajah of Haikwar taking a glass or two of wine with a man, he does follow along a bit. He'll get him further than I ever got him."

"Do you think so?" I said.

"I'm sure of it," said Wrather. "It's like horses out hunting. There's no horse living that would stand perfectly still and watch the field galloping away from him, however dull and slow he was.

"You'll see when the Maharajah comes. Ask me too and I'll do my bit, and we'll drag the dean along yet."

"Further than he's been hitherto?" I asked.

"The man's human, after all," said Wrather.

And somehow, from the way he spoke, I hoped again.

The next thing was to get the Maharajah. I called on his secretary, Captain Haram Bhaj, to ask if he and the Maharajah would come and dine with me. "The fact is," I said, "that the proof of one of the principal tenets of his religion, and yours, is at stake. A friend of mine has a memory of a former incarnation. I will get him to come to the dinner. And if we can get him to speak, we may have inestimable revelations that may be of the utmost value to all of your faith."

"Of course what His Highness is really interested in," said Captain Haram Bhaj, "is his handicap."

"His handicap," I lamely repeated.

"At polo," said Haram Bhaj.

"But surely," I said, "his religion must mean something to him."

"Oh yes," said Haram Bhaj. "Only, polo is His Highness's first interest."

And then I thought of Wrather.

"I have a friend," I said, "who used to play a good deal of polo once. It would be a great pleasure to him to meet the Maharajah sahib, if His Highness will come and dine with me."

Wrather had not actually spoken to me of polo, but I had a kind of feeling about him, which turned out to be right, that he had been a polo-player. When Captain Haram Bhaj saw that polo was likely to be the topic at dinner he said that he thought the Maharajah would come. And as it turned out, he did. I warned Wrather about the polo, and a few nights later we were all gathered at my table, the Maharajah of Haikwar, Captain Haram Bhaj, Wrather and I and the dean; the first four of these resolved to rob the fifth of a secret that might justify the hope of the East and astound Europe.

Chapter 13

Dean Spanley was asking the Maharajah of Haikwar about ancient customs in India, about Indian music, Indian dress and the tribes that live in the jungle. Wrather was talking to the Maharajah upon his other side, whenever he got an opportunity, about polo. And Haram Bhaj was watching.

Wrather had contributed to our efforts with one splendid remark that he had made to the dean before the Indians arrived. "In the East they think it a discourtesy if all the guests at a party do not drink glass for glass."

The remark created the perfect atmosphere in which the Maharajah's efforts and mine would have the best chance of thriving. The dean had drawn me aside and said: "Is this good for Mr. Wrather?"

And I had said: "Yes, it is ideal for him. The Maharajah never goes one drop beyond what a man should."

So now the plot was in progress with every chance of success. A base plot, some may say. Perhaps all plots are base. But look what there was at stake: a secret to which champagne and Tokay were the only keys. And what a secret! I felt that the world was waiting expectant outside the door.

We were all drinking champagne. Tokay was to come at the end as a coup de grâce. I flatter myself that the champagne was a good vintage, and the evening progressed to a point at which the Maharajah laid bare his heart and told Wrather the ambition of his life. I do not think that with an Oriental you always get a clear sight of his innermost feelings, but I think that it was so with the Maharajah of Haikwar. His ambition was to have a handicap of eight at polo. At present he was only seven. And as yet the dean had not spoken at all of anything nearer himself than the customs of Indian villages.

There was no servant in the room; my butler had gone to bed; and we passed round the champagne among ourselves. Haram Bhaj was particularly helpful. And the dean was holding back all the time. Yet that force was present that is sometimes found at the pastime of table turning, when everybody combines to pull the same way; and though Dean Spanley set himself against this force, he gradually went with it. More and more I felt that the world was hushed and waiting. And then with the first glass of the Tokay he spoke, spoke from that other century and sojourn. The Maharajah looked interested. But as yet nothing came that was stranger than what we had already heard, nothing that is not known or could not be guessed among those that have carefully studied the ways of dogs. I passed round more Tokay, and the Maharajah and Haram Bhaj and Wrather helped me. The dean was telling a story about a dog-fight, not greatly different from the one that I have already given my reader. As in the former one he went for the ear, and succeeded in getting the grip, and brought that tale to a close with a good deal of boasting. It was without doubt a dog that was speaking to us, but a dog with nothing to tell us we did not know. I tried yet more Tokay, and every one helped me. We got a little idyll then of a spring morning some decades back into the century that is gone, not very interesting except for the shining eyes of the dean as he told it, and not very seemly. The stock of Tokay was running low but was equal to one grand effort: we were all drinking it now in claret glasses. And suddenly I felt that the moment was hovering when what I waited for would be revealed, something that Man could not know unless told like this; and I knew that Dean Spanley's secrets were about to be laid bare.

I knew that the Maharajah cared more for his handicap than for those religious tenets that he mainly left to the Brahmins, and that the interest he had shown already was little more than the interest that he took as a sportsman in dogfights, but now that the moment was coming for which I had waited so long I held up my hand to hush them, and as a sign that the mystery of which I had spoken was going to be shown to us now. And so it was. And so it was.

Everything I had sought was laid bare with open hands. I learned the faith of the dog; I knew how they see rabies in the eyes of another long before men guess it; I knew how dogs go home. I knew more about scent than all the Masters of Hounds in England have ever guessed with all their speculations added together. I knew the wonderful secrets of transmigration. For half an hour that evening I might have spoken with Brahmins, and they would at least have listened to what I had to say without that quiet scorn lying under a faint smile, with which they listen to all else that we may say. For half an hour I knew things that they know. Of this I am sure. And now my readers will wish to hear them too. Be not too hard on me, reader. It is no easy thing to make a dean drunk. For a cause less stupendous I should not have attempted it. I attempted it for a secret unknown to Europe; and with the help of the Maharajah and the two others, drinking glass for glass, I accomplished it. All that I remember. What Dean Spanley said after his tale of the dog-fight and his little love-affair, I do not remember. I know that he held the key to some strange mysteries, and that he told us all. I remember the warm room and the lighted candles, and light shining in the champagne and in the Tokay, and people talking, and the words "Never trust a teetotaller or a man who wears elastic-sided boots." Then I noticed that a window was open, and some of the candles were out and all the rest were low, and everybody seemed to have gone. I went to the window then and leaned out to refresh myself, and when I came back to my chair, I kicked against a body on the floor and found that Wrather was still there, partly under the table, the Maharajah and Haram Bhaj and the dean were gone.

And I propped up Wrather against the legs of a chair, and after a while he spoke. And he said: "For God's sake give me a whiskey and soda. No more Tokay. For God's sake a whiskey and soda."

And I gave him a whiskey and soda, and that brought him round, and I took a little myself. And his first words after that were: "Well, we got the old dog to talk."

"Yes," I said. "What did he say?"

"That's what I can't remember," he said.

And that was my trouble too.

I gave Wrather a bed, and I went to bed myself, and in the morning our memories were no clearer.

Knowing the enormous importance of what was said I went round after a light breakfast to see Haram Bhaj.

He had been to Vine Street and stayed the night there, and they had let him go in the morning; and the only clue he had to what he had heard overnight was that he had told the inspector at Vine Street that he, Haram Bhaj, was a black and grey spaniel and could get home by himself.

"Now why did I say that?" he said.

But there was not enough in that to be of any use whatever; and later in the day I called on the Maharajah.

"It was a very jolly evening," he said; and he was evidently grateful to me. But after a while I saw that I should lose his attention unless I talked of polo. Either he remembered nothing, or the secrets of transmigration, if they were secrets from him, scarcely attracted his interest and he left all such things to the Brahmins.

It only remained to try Dean Spanley again, and this I shall never do now. For very soon after that dinner the dean was promoted to bishop. He still knows me, still greets me, whenever we meet at the Club. But I shall never get his secret. One of the shrewdest observers of the last century, the lady after whom the greater part of that hundred years was named, stated in one of her letters that she had never known a man who became a bishop to be quite the same as he was before. It was so with Dean Spanley. I can remember no act or word of his that ever showed it, and yet I have sufficiently felt the change never to trouble him with invitations to dine with me any more.

Wrather and I often dined together and, I trust, will often again. We feel like travellers who once, for a short while, have seen something very strange; and neither of us can remember what it was.

Memoirs of a Yellow Dog

BY

O. HENRY

I don't suppose it will knock any of you people off your perch to read a contribution from an animal. Mr. Kipling and a good many others have demonstrated the fact that animals can express themselves in remunerative English, and no magazine goes to press nowadays without an animal story in it, except the old-style monthlies that are still running pictures of Bryan and the Mont Pelée horror.

But you needn't look for any stuck-up literature in my piece, such as Bearoo, the bear, and Snakoo, the snake, and Tammanoo, the tiger, talk in the jungle books. A yellow dog that's spent most of his life in a cheap New York flat, sleeping in a corner on an old sateen underskirt (the one she spilled port wine on at the Lady 'Longshoremen's banquet), mustn't be expected to perform any tricks with the art of speech.

I was born a yellow pup; date, locality, pedigree, and weight unknown. The first thing I can recollect, an old woman had me in a basket at Broadway and Twenty-third trying to sell me to a fat lady. Old Mother Hubbard was boosting me to beat the band as a genuine Pomeranian-Hambletonian-Red-Irish-Cochin-China-Stoke-Pogis fox terrier. The fat lady chased a V around among the samples of gros grain flannelette in her shopping bag till she cornered it, and gave up. From that moment I was a pet—a mamma's own wootsey squidlums. Say, gentle reader, did you ever have a 200-pound woman breathing a flavour of Camembert cheese and Peau d'Espagne pick you up and wallop her nose all over you, remarking all the time in an Emma Eames tone of voice: "Oh, oo's um oodlum, doodlum, woodlum, toodlum, bitsy-witsy skoodlums?"

From a pedigreed yellow pup I grew up to be an anonymous yellow cur looking like a cross between an Angora cat and a box of lemons. But my mistress never tumbled. She thought that the two primeval pups that Noah chased into the ark were but a collateral branch of my ancestors. It took two policemen to keep her from entering me at the Madison Square Garden for the Siberian blood-hound prize.

I'll tell you about that flat. The house was the ordinary thing in New York, paved with Parian marble in the entrance hall and cob-blestones above the first floor. Our flat was three fl—well, not flights —climbs up. My mistress rented it unfurnished, and put in the reg-ular things—1903 antique upholstered parlour set, oil chromo of geishas in a Harlem tea house, rubber plant and husband.

By Sirius! there was a biped I felt sorry for. He was a little man with sandy hair and whiskers a good deal like mine. Henpecked?— well, toucans and flamingoes and pelicans all had their bills in him. He wiped the dishes and listened to my mistress tell about the cheap, ragged things the lady with the squirrel-skin coat on the second floor hung out on her line to dry. And every evening while she was get-ting supper she made him take me out on the end of a string for a walk.

If men knew how women pass the time when they are alone they'd never marry. Laura Jean Libbey, peanut brittle, a little almond cream on the neck muscles, dishes unwashed, half an hour's talk with the iceman, reading a package of old letters, a couple of pickles and two bottles of malt extract, one hour peeking through a hole in the win-dow shade into the flat across the air-shaft—that's about all there is to it. Twenty minutes before time for him to come home from work she straightens up the house, fixes her rat so it won't show, and gets out a lot of sewing for a ten-minute bluff.

I led a dog's life in that flat. 'Most all day I lay there in my corner watching that fat woman kill time. I slept sometimes and had pipe dreams about being out chasing cats into basements and growling at old ladies with black mittens, as a dog was intended to do. Then she would pounce upon me with a lot of that drivelling poodle palaver and kiss me on the nose—but what could I do? A dog can't chew cloves.

I began to feel sorry for Hubby, dog my cats if I didn't. We looked so much alike that people noticed it when we went out; so we shook the streets that Morgan's cab drives down, and took to climbing the piles of last December's snow on the streets where cheap people live.

One evening when we were thus promenading, and I was trying to look like a prize St. Bernard, and the old man was trying to look like he wouldn't have murdered the first organ-grinder he heard play Mendelssohn's wedding-march, I looked up at him and said, in my way:

"What are you looking so sour about, you oakum trimmed lobster? She don't kiss you. You don't have to sit on her lap and listen to talk that would make the book of a musical comedy sound like the maxims of Epictetus. You ought to be thankful you're not a dog. Brace up, Benedick, and bid the blues begone."

The matrimonial mishap looked down at me with almost canine intelligence in his face.

"Why, doggie," says he, "good doggie. You almost look like you could speak. What is it, doggie—Cats?"

Cats! Could speak!

But, of course, he couldn't understand. Humans were denied the speech of animals. The only common ground of communication upon which dogs and men can get together is in fiction.

In the flat across the hall from us lived a lady with a black-and-tan terrier. Her husband strung it and took it out every evening, but he always came home cheerful and whistling. One day I touched noses with the black-and-tan in the hall, and I struck him for an elucidation.

"See here, Wiggle-and-Skip," I says, "you know that it ain't the nature of a real man to play dry nurse to a dog in public. I never saw one leashed to a bow-wow yet that didn't look like he'd like to lick every other man that looked at him. But your boss comes in every day as perky and set up as an amateur prestidigitator doing the egg trick. How does he do it? Don't tell me he likes it."

"Him?" says the black-and-tan. "Why, he uses Nature's Own Remedy. He gets spifflicated. At first when we go out he's as shy as the man on the steamer who would rather play pedro when they make 'em all jackpots. By the time we've been in eight saloons he don't care whether the thing on the end of his line is a dog or a catfish. I've lost two inches of my tail trying to sidestep those swinging doors."

The pointer I got from that terrier—vaudeville please copy—set me to thinking.

One evening about 6 o'clock my mistress ordered him to get busy and do the ozone act for Lovey. I have concealed it until now, but that is what she called me. The black-and-tan was called "Tweetness." I consider that I have the bulge on him as far as you could chase a rabbit. Still "Lovey" is something of a nomenclatural tin can on the tail of one's self-respect.

At a quiet place on a safe street I tightened the line of my custodian in front of an attractive, refined saloon. I made a dead-ahead scramble for the doors, whining like a dog in the press despatches that lets the family know that little Alice is bogged while gathering lilies in the brook.

"Why, darn my eyes," says the old man, with a grin; "darn my eyes if the saffron-colored son of a seltzer lemonade ain't asking me in to take a drink. Lemme see—how long's it been since I saved shoe leather by keeping one foot on the foot-rest? I believe I'll——"

I knew I had him. Hot Scotches he took, sitting at a table. For an hour he kept the Campbells coming. I sat by his side rapping for the waiter with my tail, and eating free lunch such as mamma in her flat never equalled with her homemade truck bought at a delicatessen store eight minutes before papa comes home.

When the products of Scotland were all exhausted except the rye bread the old man unwound me from the table leg and played me outside like a fisherman plays a salmon. Out there he took off my collar and threw it into the street.

"Poor doggie," says he; "good doggie. She shan't kiss you any more. 'Sa darned shame. Good doggie, go away and get run over by a street car and be happy."

I refused to leave. I leaped and frisked around the old man's legs happy as a pug on a rug.

"You old flea-headed woodchuck-chaser," I said to him—"you

moon-baying, rabbit-pointing, egg-stealing old beagle, can't you see that I don't want to leave you? Can't you see that we're both Pups in the Wood and the missis is the cruel uncle after you with the dish towel and me with the flea liniment and a pink bow to tie on my tail. Why not cut that all out and be pards forever more?"

Maybe you'll say he didn't understand—maybe he didn't. But he kind of got a grip on the Hot Scotches, and stood still for a minute, thinking.

"Doggie," says he, finally, "we don't live more than a dozen lives on this earth, and very few of us live to be more than 300. If I ever see that flat any more I'm a flat, and if you do you're flatter; and that's no flattery. I'm offering 60 to 1 that Westward Ho wins out by the length of a dachshund."

There was no string, but I frolicked along with my master to the Twenty-third Street ferry. And the cats on the route saw reason to give thanks that prehensile claws had been given them.

On the Jersey side my master said to a stranger who stood eating a currant bun:

"Me and my doggie, we are bound for the Rocky Mountains."

But what pleased me most was when my old man pulled both of my ears until I howled, and said:

"You common, monkey-headed, rat-tailed, sulphur-colored son of a door mat, do you know what I'm going to call you?"

I thought of "Lovey," and I whined dolefully.

"I'm going to call you 'Pete,'" says my master; and if I'd had five tails I couldn't have done enough wagging to do justice to the occasion.

From Pillar to Post

or

How to Raise a Dog

BY

JACK ALAN

DOG OWNERS, arise! Too long has the actual head of your family not even paid an income tax. Too long have you tried to conceal from your dog the fact that he really owns you. Too long have you searched in vain for the counsel you so sorely need when, panting and tongue hanging out, you fall back into the nearest chair and finally admit to yourself that the lively little fellow isn't going to sit up and beg, hasn't the slightest intention of leaving that frayed end of the tapestry alone, and is unshakeably convinced that the mathematical center of the living-room rug is the Comfort Station Supreme.

You can expect no help from dog books or dog doctors. In this all-important emergency, all they do is back away, muttering incoherent statements about Training and Psychology. And you are left holding the bag, one end of which has already been chewed away, like everything else you own.

I am no expert. I might as well tell you right now that I generally go to sleep with a large, greasy bone under my pillow because I have failed to sway my dog in his opinion that there isn't a better spot in town for bone hiding. My house is thoroughly dog-broken. But I do not intend to leave my fellow man with his dog having the upper paw in the household.

I believe my predicament to be an average one, a valuable case history. I will show you how I deal with my dog. Maybe you will be able to discover where along the line something went terribly, terribly wrong.

Things started badly when I bought him. I didn't select him, he selected me. When I went to the kennel, I had decided definitely against buying four or five puppies, as I wanted to do. Phyllis claims that this is too many for a small apartment. Cunningly, however, I planned to get around this by getting as much dog as possible for my money—a great Dane.

I looked critically at the batch of puppies, which, while only three months old, were the size of Airedales. Then one detached himself from the mob. He had a lot of filling out to do. He took, I noticed, several steps before his skin started moving along with him. He galloped over, sat down heavily on my feet, and looked me over carefully. I couldn't move, so I had to look at him, too. He was obviously admiring me. His next step was to take my trouser leg in his mouth and shake it, possibly to test the quality of the material. Then he gave several pleased body wiggles, attempted to climb up on me, and washed my hand thoroughly with a salmon-pink tongue. Then he sat down again on my feet and admired me some more.

I had been chosen.

Several months have passed, and we have learned much about each other. Neither of us regrets his choice, although my training methods seem to lack something.

I have found that the very first step must be to Gain His Confidence. To accomplish this, I sit on the floor next to him and say, "*Good* little dog!" This is a flat lie and he knows it, being well aware that he is neither little nor good. He backs away several feet, presses himself close to the floor, and turns up his eyes at me with a wary "You-are-up-to-something-tricky-and-I'm-not-going-to-like-it" expression.

I reach out reassuringly and pat his nearest paw. He withdraws the paw and licks it off fastidiously.

I attempt now to get his attention by cupping both hands and saying coyly: "Guess what I've got here?"

Showing signs of interest, he nuzzles into my hands. I am caught flat-footed with nothing in them. I run to get a dog biscuit to absolve myself. Meanwhile he stalks off bitterly to a corner of the room, tenses his forelegs, digs a hole in the carpet, and lies down in it.

I now change my approach, deciding to try the Great Big Playmate tactic. Crouching on all fours, I advance on him, barking several times with mock ferocity. He decides to humor me by pretending he thinks I'm a huge, dangerous dog. With a happy yelp, he flashes around a chair and dashes upon me from behind. Since he weighs roughly eighty-two pounds at the moment, I am now flat on the floor with him on top of me. He wants to pretend he is shaking me by the neck. This is too difficult unless he actually does shake me by the back of the neck. So he does.

I get up and brush myself off. I brush him off me, too, several times. I have now succeeded in gaining his confidence and showing him that I am a regular fellow who doesn't mind a good, clean romp, so I am through. But he isn't. He likes it too well to quit. He gets my tie in his teeth and hangs from it. It is some time before I get my breath.

He still refuses to stop. It is therefore time for me to Punish Him. I decide to lock him in the bathroom. This consists of the following steps:

1. He instantly senses my purpose and scrambles into the bedroom and under the bed.
2. I rush after him and say, "Come out from under there this minute!"
3. He doesn't.
4. I get down on the floor and look under the bed. We face each other silently for a moment, each trying to outstare the other. I blink, which gives him the round.
5. I mutter several dire threats. So does he.
6. I hold out my handkerchief, hoping he will grab it and pull, thereby enabling me to drag him out.
7. He grabs it and pulls.
8. We are now both under the bed.
9. I seize him firmly and wriggle out.
10. A head bumps severely against the box spring. It is not his.
11. I shove and pull him into the bathroom and back out, closing the door.
12. I stop closing the door to avoid catching his nose in it.
13. I shove him back and close the door, catching my hand in it.
14. We both howl simultaneously.

Returning to the living room, tired but victorious (look up Pyrrhic in any good encyclopedia), I now proceed to describe my dog to you. He is still a puppy, seven months old. He is a good dog to have for a case history because, although a thoroughbred, he has a character which is practically a cross section of that of America's dogs.

Although large and getting larger, it is his opinion that he is a lap dog and as such entitled to climb on my chair whether I am in it or not. When I can catch him to give him a bath, he emerges as a dull gold in color with a mouth fringed with black. This mouth is already large enough to contain my arm and, when I am giving him a bath, does. Like all his breed, he has a short coat, but he sheds it with the success of the collie. He has a way of searching out tidbits in his food which probably reveals that in spite of his pedigree he contains a trace of ant-eater. He has a beery sort of baritone. And he is very democratic in his ideas about love.

When I first got him I called him Gilbert, the name I still introduce him by. The only word he will always answer to, however, is Food, so I generally call him that.

Food, or Gilbert, is still in the bathroom, you will recall. This is my golden opportunity to get something to eat unbeknownst to him. Let me explain.

Since I have known Gilbert, I have had few square meals at home. This is because Gilbert is an adept at a quiet, effective sort of bullying. When I am eating, he is too wily to use strong-arm tactics, realizing that force will be answered with force. He therefore just looks at me tragically. He keeps looking at me. He meditates on man's inhumanity to dog. He sighs. Beginning to feel like a heartless gourmand, I transfer my little morsel of food to my mouth. His glance never wavers. He drools slowly.

As a result, I spend a large part of my time at my dinner table chewing things up a little for Gilbert. Then I give them to him, cursing.

But now that Gilbert is in the bathroom, I turn on the radio full blast and enter the kitchen singing loudly, hoping that both noises will distract him.

It is a losing game. Gilbert, who would sleep soundly through a collision with another planet, easily detects the noiseless opening of the electric icebox. No sooner do I reach a guilty hand to a roast-beef bone than Gilbert utters a series of agonized cries, giving the entire neighborhood the impression that I am murdering him by inches. In self-defense I rush to the bathroom to make him stop.

He is very happy as I open the door, particularly since a well-timed move enables him to snatch the beef bone from my hand and rush back to the bathroom.

I am about to follow him to get back my bone when the doorbell rings.

It is Mrs. Garble, a middle-aged woman I do not like. She is the president of Phyllis' club. She is also a cat lover. She expresses relief at being able to come in for once and not have that great brute of a dog jumping all over her. Looking around nervously, she asks where he is. I tell her.

"What in the world is he doing in the bathroom?" she says.

"Well, really, Mrs. Garble," I reply primly, "he *said* he wanted to wash his hands."

This keeps her quiet for a moment. It then develops that she wants to see Phyllis, who isn't home. She looks at the carpet, which has no more than a normal amount of Gilbert's hair on it.

"Goodness gracious!" she says, clucking, "I don't see *how* you can keep a great Dane in a city apartment! Why, I'd just as soon keep a horse in one!"

I bristle and stifle a desire to say, "Oh, so you don't think I ought to keep my horse, either?"

Gilbert chooses this moment to enter. And not, to my surprise, with his usual attitude, which practically says, "Oh my chin and whiskers! What wonderful things have I been missing!" Instead, he comes in with measured dignity. He casts a sedate glance at Mrs. Garble.

"He seems to be getting much better manners," she says grudgingly. "You certainly are training him to behave like a gentleman!"

I decide that Mrs. Garble, too, seems to be getting better manners. I warm toward her, as I do to all types of characters who have a kind word to say for Gilbert. I even toy with the idea of giving her a drink.

I watch with paternal pride as Gilbert walks slowly over to her. He sniffs at her leg in a genteel way. I beam reassuringly. Mrs. Garble smiles back uncertainly. Gilbert seems about to walk past her. He doesn't. He stops. Trained to observe such matters, I suddenly notice an uncertain attitude, a slight quivering of the muscles of Gilbert's left hind leg.

"GILBERT!" I cry, in the nick of time.

There is no need to go into the next five minutes. It will serve no purpose for me to repeat my weak explanation to the outraged Mrs. Garble that Gilbert, being still in the experimental stage, was merely about to test out a comparatively new idea. And that there was no personal malice or intended criticism involved.

Gilbert and I are alone again—and it is definitely time for me to Take Him Out.

Gilbert *loves* to go out. Five, seven times a day he responds with mad joy to the rattle of his chain, dances with impatience as I attach his collar, and, in a series of chamoislike bounds, precipitates me to our apartment elevator, permitting me to touch the corridor with my feet only intermittently on the way.

If Gilbert is in luck, there will be another passenger in the elevator. This is a stout, very short gentleman with a red face who lives on the floor above us. He is generally on his way to some formal affair. There is something about his frock coats and silk hats which brings out Gilbert's warmest feelings of affection.

It takes Gilbert no time at all to place both his paws on the little man's carefully groomed shoulders. Gilbert's tongue then quickly and deftly leaves a long moist streak from chin to forehead, as Gilbert's body deposits large amounts of hair on the faultless apparel.

The little man's face now becomes even redder, because he does not Understand Dogs. I know he doesn't, because the very first time this occurred, I said to him reassuringly, "It's all right, he is friendly."

To which he replied: "I'm not."

Since then all we say to each other is "Look out!"

Once we have left the elevator and passed through the lobby—a passage too swift for the average vision—Gilbert and I find ourselves outside. It is now that my problems begin and Gilbert's end. This is because we spend a lot of time standing by trees, lampposts, and pillars. It is not the fact that Gilbert is generally standing on one more leg than I am which makes my position more difficult than his. It is rather that I am far more conscious than he of the famous girls' finishing school on our block. Since its dismissal times seem to coincide with our airings, it bothers me to feel that there are hundreds of pretty young girls in the world who believe I spend my entire time standing by upright columns.

It is therefore frequently necessary for me to pretend that I do not know Gilbert. This is difficult, because of the stout chain which connects us. There are various attitudes, however, which I assume:

1. That I happened to be out with a chain and a careless dog got caught in it.
2. That a dog happened to be out with a chain and *I* got caught in it.
3. That a chain happened to be out and the dog and I both got caught in it.

Between lampposts, Gilbert and I walk along with dignity. With as much dignity as possible, that is, considering that we are walking in the gutter.

Sometimes we pause in the gutter and turn around rapidly many times. Then one of us reads a newspaper, while the finishing school, which we are directly in front of, conducts a fire drill.

I could go on interminably. Maybe you think I have already. But anyway, we are agreed that my dog-handling methods are not ideal. Now let me give you some information which is really practical in case you plan to have a dog. Let us examine Gilbert's habits, his point of view, his psychology. I know all about them and it does me no good, but it may forewarn you about your own dog.

I have observed many of Gilbert's moods. They are, I believe, fairly common to his race. Here are a few of them:

1. *The Hooray-Hooray-a-New-Day's-Dawning! Mood.* This manifests itself twice a day. Once at six in the morning, at which time Gilbert lands heavily on my stomach, knocking both breath and sleep out of me. And a second time at a few moments past midnight, just after he has been bedded down, at which time he insists that I throw his rubber bone for him, or take him out with my coat over my pajamas. There must be some way to stop this.

2. *The Aren't-I-Supposed-to-Have-Any-Normal-Instincts-at-All? Mood.* This is caused simply by the fact that Gilbert is devoid of a sense of shame and I am not. It often results in our not speaking to each other and also in other people not speaking to me. There is no way to avoid this.

3. *The I-Was-Asleep-and-Some-Bad-Man-Must-Have-Come-in-*

and-Torn-that-Blue-Bedspread-to-Bits Attitude. This is accompanied by a brazen, hypocritical simulation of overweening joy at my entrance and is unconvincing because of the large piece of blue cloth which Gilbert is unconsciously carrying on his dewlap. One method of avoiding this is always to leave your bed bare to the springs until retiring.

All right. Now that I have revealed my relationship to my dog in all its squalor, the curious may inquire why I have a dog at all. The curious may, but not the wise.

The answer, of course, is simple. In Gilbert I have found a being to whom I am superior in many ways, in spite of the fact that Phyllis insists that a lot more people stop to admire him than me on the street. Gilbert cannot drive a car. I can. Gilbert cannot wash dishes, pour drinks for people, run errands, or do dozens of other things around the house Phyllis considers necessary. Above all, Gilbert is a living, breathing answer to her contention that I am the most inefficient form of life yet devised.

He is also the finest dog in town, even if he did tear up the very best parts of this piece.

A Dark-Brown Dog

BY

STEPHEN CRANE

A CHILD was standing on a street-corner. He leaned with one shoulder against a high board fence and swayed the other to and fro, the while kicking carelessly at the gravel.

Sunshine beat upon the cobbles, and a lazy summer wind raised yellow dust which trailed in clouds down the avenue. Clattering trucks moved with indistinctness through it. The child stood dreamily gazing.

After a time, a little dark-brown dog came trotting with an intent air down the sidewalk. A short rope was dragging from his neck. Occasionally he trod upon the end of it and stumbled.

He stopped opposite the child, and the two regarded each other. The dog hesitated for a moment, but presently he made some little advances with his tail. The child put out his hand and called him. In an apologetic manner the dog came close, and the two had an interchange of friendly pattings and waggles. The dog became more enthusiastic with each moment of the interview, until with his gleeful caperings he threatened to overturn the child. Whereupon the child lifted his hand and struck the dog a blow upon the head.

This thing seemed to overpower and astonish the little dark-brown dog, and wounded him to the heart. He sank down in despair at the child's feet. When the blow was repeated, together with an admonition in childish sentences, he turned over upon his back, and held his paws in a peculiar manner. At the same time with his ears and his eyes he offered a small prayer to the child.

He looked so comical on his back, and holding his paws peculiarly, that the child was greatly amused and gave him little taps repeatedly, to keep him so. But the little dark-brown dog took this chastisement in the most serious way, and no doubt considered that he had committed some grave crime, for he wriggled contritely and showed his repentance in every way that was in his power. He pleaded with the child and petitioned him, and offered more prayers.

At last the child grew weary of this amusement and turned toward home. The dog was praying at the time. He lay on his back and turned his eyes upon the retreating form.

Presently he struggled to his feet and started after the child. The latter wandered in a perfunctory way toward his home, stopping at times to investigate various matters. During one of these pauses he discovered the little dark-brown dog who was following him with the air of a footpad.

The child beat his pursuer with a small stick he had found. The dog lay down and prayed until the child had finished, and resumed his journey. Then he scrambled erect and took up the pursuit again.

On the way to his home the child turned many times and beat the dog, proclaiming with childish gestures that he held him in contempt as an unimportant dog, with no value save for a moment. For being this quality of animal the dog apologized and eloquently expressed regret, but he continued stealthily to follow the child. His manner grew so very guilty that he slunk like an assassin.

When the child reached his doorstep, the dog was industriously ambling a few yards in the rear. He became so agitated with shame when he again confronted the child that he forgot the dragging rope. He tripped upon it and fell forward.

The child sat down on the step and the two had another interview. During it the dog greatly exerted himself to please the child. He performed a few gambols with such abandon that the child suddenly saw him to be a valuable thing. He made a swift, avaricious charge and seized the rope.

He dragged his captive into a hall and up many long stairways in a dark tenement. The dog made willing efforts, but he could not hobble very skillfully up the stairs because he was very small and soft, and at last the pace of the engrossed child grew so energetic that the dog became panic-stricken. In his mind he was being dragged toward a grim unknown. His eyes grew wild with the terror of it. He began to wiggle his head frantically and to brace his legs.

The child redoubled his exertions. They had a battle on the stairs. The child was victorious because he was completely absorbed in his purpose, and because the dog was very small. He dragged his acquirement to the door of his home, and finally with triumph across the threshold.

No one was in. The child sat down on the floor and made overtures to the dog. These the dog instantly accepted. He beamed with affection upon his new friend. In a short time they were firm and abiding comrades.

When the child's family appeared, they made a great row. The dog was examined and commented upon and called names. Scorn was leveled at him from all eyes, so that he became much embarrassed and drooped like a scorched plant. But the child went sturdily to the center of the floor, and, at the top of his voice, championed the dog. It happened that he was roaring protestations, with his arms clasped about the dog's neck, when the father of the family came in from work.

The parent demanded to know what the blazes they were making the kid howl for. It was explained in many words that the infernal kid wanted to introduce a disreputable dog into the family.

A family council was held. On this depended the dog's fate, but he in no way heeded, being busily engaged in chewing the end of the child's dress.

The affair was quickly ended. The father of the family, it appears, was in a particularly savage temper that evening, and when he perceived that it would amaze and anger everybody if such a dog were allowed to remain, he decided that it should be so. The child, crying softly, took his friend off to a retired part of the room to hobnob with him, while the father quelled a fierce rebellion of his wife. So it came to pass that the dog was a member of the household.

He and the child were associated together at all times save when the child slept. The child became a guardian and a friend. If the large folk kicked the dog and threw things at him, the child made loud and violent objections. Once when the child had run, protesting loudly, with tears raining down his face and his arms outstretched, to protect his friend, he had been struck in the head with a very large saucepan from the hand of his father, enraged at some seeming lack of courtesy in the dog. Ever after, the family were careful how they threw things at the dog. Moreover, the latter grew very skilful in avoiding missiles and feet. In a small room containing a stove, a table, a bureau and some chairs, he would display strategic ability of a high order, dodging, feinting and scuttling about among the furniture. He could force three or four people armed with brooms, sticks and handfuls of coal, to use all their ingenuity to get in a blow. And even when they did it, it was seldom that they could do him a serious injury or leave any imprint.

But when the child was present these scenes did not occur. It came to be recognized that if the dog was molested, the child would burst into sobs, and as the child, when started, was very riotous and practically unquenchable, the dog had therein a safeguard.

However, the child could not always be near. At night, when he was asleep, his dark-brown friend would raise from some black corner a wild, wailful cry, a song of infinite loneliness and despair, that would go shuddering and sobbing among the buildings of the block and cause people to swear. At these times the singer would often be chased all over the kitchen and hit with a great variety of articles.

Sometimes, too, the child himself used to beat the dog, although it is not known that he ever had what truly could be called a just cause. The dog always accepted these thrashings with an air of admitted guilt. He was too much of a dog to try to look to be a martyr or to plot revenge. He received the blows with deep humility, and furthermore he forgave his friend the moment the child had finished, and was ready to caress the child's hand with his little red tongue.

When misfortune came upon the child, and his troubles overwhelmed him, he would often crawl under the table and lay his small distressed head on the dog's back. The dog was ever sympathetic. It is not to be supposed that at such times he took occasion to refer to the unjust beatings his friend, when provoked, had administered to him.

He did not achieve any notable degree of intimacy with the other members of the family. He had no confidence in them, and the fear that he would express at their casual approach often exasperated them exceedingly. They used to gain a certain satisfaction in underfeeding him, but finally his friend the child grew to watch the matter with some care, and when he forgot it, the dog was often successful in secret for himself.

So the dog prospered. He developed a large bark, which came wondrously from such a small rug of a dog. He ceased to howl persistently at night. Sometimes, indeed, in his sleep, he would utter little yells, as from pain, but that occurred, no doubt, when in his dreams he encountered huge flaming dogs who threatened him direfully.

His devotion to the child grew until it was a sublime thing. He wagged at his approach; he sank down in despair at his departure. He could detect the sound of the child's step among all the noises of the neighborhood. It was like a calling voice to him.

The scene of their companionship was a kingdom governed by this terrible potentate, the child; but neither criticism nor rebellion ever lived for an instant in the heart of the one subject. Down in the mystic, hidden fields of his little dog-soul bloomed flowers of love and fidelity and perfect faith.

The child was in the habit of going on many expeditions to observe strange things in the vicinity. On these occasions his friend usually jogged aimfully along behind. Perhaps, though, he went ahead. This necessitated his turning around every quarter-minute to make sure the child was coming. He was filled with a large idea of the importance of these journeys. He would carry himself with such an air! He was proud to be the retainer of so great a monarch.

One day, however, the father of the family got quite exceptionally drunk. He came home and held carnival with the cooking utensils, the furniture and his wife. He was in the midst of this recreation when the child, followed by the dark-brown dog, entered the room. They were returning from their voyages.

The child's practised eye instantly noted his father's state. He dived under the table, where experience had taught him was a rather safe place. The dog, lacking skill in such matters, was, of course, unaware of the true condition of affairs. He looked with interested eyes at his friend's sudden dive. He interpreted it to mean: Joyous gambol. He started to patter across the floor to join him. He was the picture of a little dark-brown dog en route to a friend.

The head of the family saw him at this moment. He gave a huge howl of joy, and knocked the dog down with a heavy coffee-pot. The dog, yelling in supreme astonishment and fear, writhed to his feet and ran for cover. The man kicked out with a ponderous foot. It caused the dog to swerve as if caught in a tide. A second blow of the coffee-pot laid him upon the floor.

Here the child, uttering loud cries, came valiantly forth like a knight. The father of the family paid no attention to these calls of the child, but advanced with glee upon the dog. Upon being knocked down twice in swift succession, the latter apparently gave up all hope of escape. He rolled over on his back and held his paws in a peculiar manner. At the same time with his eyes and his ears he offered up a small prayer.

But the father was in a mood for having fun, and it occurred to him that it would be a fine thing to throw the dog out of the window. So he reached down and, grabbing the animal by a leg, lifted him, squirming, up. He swung him two or three times hilariously about his head, and then flung him with great accuracy through the window.

The soaring dog created a surprise in the block. A woman watering plants in an opposite window gave an involuntary shout and dropped a flower-pot. A man in another window leaned perilously out to watch the flight of the dog. A woman who had been hanging out clothes in a yard began to caper wildly. Her mouth was filled with clothes-pins, but her arms gave vent to a sort of exclamation. In appearance she was like a gagged prisoner. Children ran whooping.

The dark-brown body crashed in a heap on the roof of a shed five stories below. From thence it rolled to the pavement of an alley-way.

The child in the room far above burst into a long, dirge-like cry, and toddled hastily out of the room. It took him a long time to reach the alley, because his size compelled him to go downstairs backward, one step at a time, and holding with both hands to the step above.

When they came for him later, they found him seated by the body of his dark-brown friend.

Ruffled Paws

BY

BERTHA DAMON

Does a dog that marries into a family along with his mistress ever fit into the new picture easily and immediately, I wonder. Dogs suffer jealousy; the passion is not unknown in man. Are a husband, a wife and such a dog what is meant by the eternal triangle?

One might summon Elizabeth Barrett's cocker spaniel Flush from the spirit world and ask him. Or summon Elizabeth herself. She ought to know; she understood cockers. With her large-eyed sensitive face, framed in long curls, she even looked like one. (She herself recognized the likeness, and with pleasure.) It is biography that Flush bit the suitor who was Robert Browning. It is history that Josephine's dog, backed up by Josephine, insisted on sleeping with Napoleon in the imperial bed, greatly to Napoleon's annoyance. It is even rumored that the mighty conqueror was bitten by the dog in the argument.

It seems there are two schools of thought holding sharply conflicting theories as to just where dogs should sleep. I myself before I ever had a dog would have repudiated the idea that I would permit one to sleep on my bed, let alone want one to. And the day I brought home a small cocker puppy—still I had no intention of such an arrangement; it was the puppy's own idea, strongly held to. It has turned out through many years to be a good one. Wherever Mickey and I found ourselves, alone in some spooky house I was rebuilding, or in a strange hotel, or in a camping site in the wild Sierra, I had only to pat a place near my feet and say, "Lie down, Mickey; it's our home." And it was that for both of us.

From Stella Benson, who as Christopher Morley observed saw with extraordinary intuition the feelings and gestures of animals—and even of buildings and automobiles—I learned much of what goes on in the minds of dogs and in the minds of dog-lovers as well. She used to say that the real dog-lover is invariably someone who has been hurt by life and needs a better opinion of himself, and that there is something in the quality of a dog's admiration that gives this to him. From experience I learned the strange truth that a dog's faithful presence through the night and his approval of me in the morning does have the power to remove a feeling of inadequacy and to replace it with courage and a little inner grin; that the indifference of the vast universe and the insignificance of the self make a quite satisfactory union if the catalytic agent is a dog who loves you. Nevertheless, some there are who disapprove of dogs in bedrooms.

And in dining rooms, when it comes to that. Mickey in pre-New Hampshire days had been accustomed to be in the dining room with the other people. He didn't get in the way; for his own peace of mind he always stayed in the safety zone inside the stretchers of the serving table. A cat claws and miaows when you eat, draws itself up to be a thorny vine twining round you, but a dog who has not been spoiled lies down at some distance and looks tactfully away, pretending you are not eating so you will not be embarrassed by a sense of your selfishness. It was not the food that attracted Mickey, but the sociability. If man can be classified as a social animal, so can dogs. Mickey, even when asleep or seeming so, would dreamily thump his tail when happy laughter burst out. But notwithstanding these extenuating circumstances, his presence in the dining room was known to be unwelcome.

Also there was here a novel standard of instant obedience. Any cocker when summoned is likely to run gaily in the opposite direction with a merry backward glance, not that he is disobedient but that he thinks it will be fun to do the opposite of what he is told. When cockers are puppies they are so tender-hearted that if you speak to one not sternly but just seriously, he breaks as to the heart (accusative of specification), he turns over on his back, he prayerfully folds his fringed paws out of harm's way and says, "Here am I. Whip me if you must, if the strange madness has come upon you to whip

your faithful dog, whose only fault is in loving you too too well."
Which has the effect of relaxing discipline. Such fundamentals of
cocker psychology I understood; there were an influential few who
did not.

I thought and thought, and at last I conceived a bold plan.
("Grandma," I had said abruptly in one of those days when I was
poring over the Adam-and-Eve-in-the-Garden story, "Grandma,
what does conceive mean?"

"It—what are you reading there, Bertha? Oh. Well, conceive means
—means imagine."

"That doesn't make sense," I said, small forefinger on the text.
"It says here, 'And-Adam-knew-Eve-his-wife-and-she-conceived-
and-bare-Cain.' "

"Yes, it does make sense," said Grandma. "Adam knew Eve, that
is, got acquainted with her, and after that she conceived, that is,
imagined, she was going to have a baby. And she did. His name was
Cain. You go out to the woodpile right-away and bring in some
wood.")

Now, I imagined that if I got my husband a puppy, a very young
cocker puppy, for him to bring up, it would take his eye off my dog;
and I felt quite sure that no matter what he did with his cocker its
resultant behavior would not be so flawless that he could say anything about flaws in my dog's behavior—not consistently. And I
knew my husband to be a pearl of consistency. I thought the chosen
puppy had better be a female, all tenderness and worship.

By what seemed a remarkable coincidence, my next trip to Boston
took me by a kennel of cockers. I stopped, and selected a small three-
months-old bundle of curls and love and timidity. I brought her home
in my car—not without several *contretemps*—and in due season laid
her gently in my husband's lap.

"A present for your birthday next week," I said, looking harmless
as doves, "a present from me." (Was that a shadow on his face?)
"But you needn't keep her," I added quickly, "if she doesn't appeal
to you. I haven't paid for her. She is on approval and can be returned
within ten days."

Politely he touched her with a thumb almost as big as one of her
folded paws.

"It was good of you to think of it," he said, "but really this isn't the breed I prefer. We'll just take care of it until you can return it conveniently."

By and by I brought a little dish of chopped meat and a cup of warm milk, with the suggestion that he himself and none other should administer them. I left him alone with his puppy-on-approval. She had silky ears. All day I kept away at each feeding time; the kind man fed her and she was grateful to him. She began to follow him a little. She had long eyelashes. The first night he arranged for her, back of the kitchen stove, a warm nest of his second best flannel trousers, and that first night there she slept—or, rather, there she wept. The next day she followed him more. She was auburn-gold all over, except for the little cream-colored ruffles that hung down behind like a frilled petticoat. In fact, that second night she followed him to bed and she slept with him. I did not openly notice this development. The next day she followed him all the time.

At the end of a week I went into my husband's study where he sat at his desk jabbing away at a manuscript with a blue pencil, and the puppy sat adoring in the best upholstered chair, pulled near for her convenience.

"Come on, puppy," I said, picking her up casually, "back you go to Massachusetts. Too bad! You're not the breed the Master likes."

"Put my dog down!" said my husband. "That's *my* dog. Her name is Betsey, and you leave her alone." So from then on she was his, his Betsey the Beloved, Betsey the—the Witch.

All went well.

Betsey the Beloved was never once asked to sleep in the kitchen; she slept regularly in her "master's" bedroom; she slept on his bed; more than that, she slept in his bed with him, under the bedclothes. On his bare feet she slept, in an utter abnegation of comfort, and almost of respiration, in an ultimate expression of love, and desire deeper than life for nearness to her Beloved. There—except on the hottest of nights in July or August—across his naked feet she always slept, except occasionally when she had to heave up and emerge as a whale does for air. Betsey the Beloved. Betsey the—Witch.

"I notice Betsey doesn't sleep in the kitchen as dogs should," I just couldn't help saying to the master at last. "I notice she sleeps in bed with you."

"Well, yes, she does. I haven't changed my mind, I tell you. I still think that having a dog on one's bed is unsanitary, it's undisciplined, it's sentimental. I think"—he burst out—"I think it's disgraceful! But somehow—that's where she sleeps. I can't seem to keep her from doing so."

"Don't you like it that way?"

"Well—yes—er—in a way I do. But have you never heard," he added with a self-deprecating grin, "that the worst thing ever said about slavery was that the slave liked it?"

Usually our New Hampshire nights are cool. But on one of those hot still nights that sometimes lie oppressive, just as I had managed to fall into a restless sleep, I was wakened by my husband's voice from the adjoining room.

"It *is* hot, isn't it, you poor dear," he said.

I was sleepily rallying myself to make proper meteorological reply, but unencouraged he went right on.

"How you pant, darling," he said.

Goodness, had I been panting so loud as all that?

"Shall I get up and get you some water, sweetheart? . . ."

Maybe this was the hottest night that ever was and I had not realized it. Just as I was catching my breath to call out, "Yes, thanks ever so much," he concluded—

"Water, poor little Betsey?"

Huh!

The rule against dogs in dining rooms was blessedly lost sight of. Betsey was in the dining room every meal time, often close to her master's feet and often out in the runway obliging the hired girl to walk around on the wrong side. She would sit up and put out the most feminine of paws with dainty ruffled wrist and touch a guest ever so gently, reminding him courteously that his enjoyment of his victual was greedy, that he was negligent of the needs of a languishing lady cocker. The most selfish gourmet could not enjoy his food until he had fed Betsey. Her master fed her too, the best bits on his plate, if I was not looking. And I never was.

Very early Betsey went in for automobile-chasing as her chief sport, and the day came when her master told her clearly—in so many words—that if she chased another car he would thrash her, thrash her in sight of all the world. She listened docilely and so the very next time a car came down our grassy driveway she gave one glad yelp and dashed after it and around it in circles and straight at it—to make it stop. From the corner of her eye she saw her master rise with dignity from his seat among his guests on the porch. Down across the deep lawn and back again and around the house she encouraged him to chase her and then, precisely in front of all the audience on the porch, she permitted him to overtake her. Somewhere along the route he had grabbed a lily-stalk, and now he raised it high. Betsey neatly laid herself on her back at his feet, her ruffled paws uplifted, gazed tenderly at him through her long eye-lashes and said, "Strike me, oh beloved—if you can."

Even Betsey's back-seat driving was pleasing to her master— Betsey's was. She was a back-seat driver of the most apprehensive sort. She would look far ahead to spy out a mud hole or a rough spot in the road and begin to yelp, "How in the world are we ever going to get around that? Yip, yip! Careful, now! Yip, ow, wow! Oh, do take care! Ow, yip, yip, wow!" However long the trip, she never allowed herself one moment's relaxation in sleep. Occasionally she permitted herself the pleasure of leaning out to envy birds or butter-flies or to put some large he-dog in his place, but most of the time she looked as if she were clinging desperately to the mast.

It was well for all of us that Betsey was a part of our little world, and for Mickey not least. She brought out all that was chivalrous in him. Someone has said that a dog is the only animal who always con-sistently shows consideration for his female. Be that as it may, Mickey continually gave up to Betsey his own highly prized dinner—in the dish that said D O G on it—never trying to drive her away, even though she drove him away most petulantly. Sometimes the sight of Betsey the Beloved leaving her own dinner, which nevertheless she gave him to understand was by no means discarded, and gobbling his with rude bitchy growls, was almost too much for him to bear and he would come and find me and protest in plaintive tones of self-pity. But to the proud beauty herself he said never a word.

For Betsey's sake he broke a strict rule he had made, never to bite a porcupine again, never. A porcupine, sure of himself as he is, is the only animal that cordially offers to let an inexperienced dog bite his behind. Mickey had accepted the first offer, he had accepted the second, and each time he had come away with a torturing mouthful and beard of barbed quills. Thereafter his policy was *laissez faire, laissez aller*. But Betsey, out of sheer wantonness, loved to meet a hedgehog somewhere in the woods, to lead the villain on and then to flee, calling in hysterical maidenly barks for Mickey her hero to save her from a fate worse than death.

How sweet are looks that ladies bend on whom their favors fall; for them I battle to the end to save from shame and thrall—and so Mickey, forgetting the torturing quills, the bloody pliers jerking them out, or perhaps not forgetting but daring all again for Betsey's sake, would pitch into the spiky porcupine and wrestle with him, while she removed her beautiful self to a nearby place of safety from which she might watch the gratifying carnage.

Samuel always refers to a certain class of carefree bitches as "spaded," which sounds pretty darn thorough. Contrary to Uncle John's advice, we never had Betsey spaded, and so it came about that the best summer ever was that one when Mickey and Betsey were blessed with a family of five. At the beginning of our first call to inquire after Betsey and her babies, she was apologetic.

"Oh, dear, look at all this," she said deprecatingly, crawling forward and laying her head on her master's beloved foot, "look at all this. But I really couldn't help it."

We praised her until she was convinced that she had achieved something that surely no other bitch had ever been clever enough to achieve before, and her maternal pride bordered on arrogance.

Honesty compels me to admit that Betsey was never a model mother. Her one thought was for her master. While the puppies in their nursery in the barn would be wailing and yipeing for warmth and maternal counsel and above all for supper, she would come sauntering along from somewhere and hop up lightly on her master's bed, intending to spend the night there. Over and over again I would have to chase Betsey, catch her, carry her to the puppies, and feed her to them, by main force.

As soon as the little ones were big enough to leave the nursery, auburn waves rippled after me wherever I went, but I thought it best in general to encourage the puppies to spend more time outdoors than in. One discovers, while bringing up a litter of puppies, the long-sought fountain of youth which, like many other things, has had its value increased by legendary rumor and is not precisely what had been hoped for.

Betsey had always had a charming way of hunting butterflies which were, of course, where butterflies should be—hovering over the best blossoms. She would take off from anywhere on the porch or the lawn and come down smash! among the bright fragile poppies. She taught this to her puppies, all of them at once, and it was a pretty sight to see. Their golden tail-tips wagging among the plants looked like butterflies of a livelier sort. Well, yes, the puppies dug holes sometimes, and sometimes they rolled down a few plants. But what of it? When hail beats the garden flat, we accept it as an act of God. Well, puppies are an act of God, and one of his very pleasantest. I believe in a balanced universe: some poppies and some puppies. To miss the joy is to miss all.

In fact, I didn't mind when Uncle John's teeth were ravished. Of late he has become quite careless about his uppers and unders—isn't that the last infirmity of noble mind, and not what Milton said?— and one day he was making a great to-do because he wanted to dress for golf and couldn't lay hands on his teeth anywhere. He swore he had left them rolled in his handkerchief on a corner of the porch magazine rack. The entire household was pressed into the search, which spread all over the porch and into the house, upstairs and down. We had just come from dismantling the east bathroom and were all assembled on the porch explaining to Uncle John he couldn't have left his teeth on the magazine rack or they would be there now, teeth certainly don't walk off by themselves, when out of the corner of my eye I saw down near the apple tree an unusually gay and active knot of puppies. There was something suspicious in their excited competition for some obviously rare treasure.

I have learned never to leave a family group abruptly enough to cause inquiry, but just to melt out of it. I melted, obscurely, and was presently down where the puppies were tussling and garglingly growing and giggling. One of them turned toward me with a wide grin, being temporarily possessed of Uncle John's uppers. Two other puppies were disputing the honor of the unders. I detached these features of Uncle John's from the regretful infants, wiped them off, not as thoroughly as I could have wished and, the family by now being off on another tack in quest of hidden treasure, I sneaked them into the magazine rack.

A little later Uncle John salvaged them, pointing out that he had been right all the time, he *had* left them in the magazine rack. There they were all the time—his teeth, unquestionably his. He did not notice that the puppies had made some indentures.

All in all, it was Betsey the Witch who through our ever-circling years brought in an age of gold, when Discipline never raised its ugly head and everywhere was peace and good will to dogs. Once in a while, to be sure, Uncle John would look thoughtfully at Betsey snuggling hour after hour on her master's left arm while he with his right jabbed away as best he could at a manuscript—Uncle John would look at Betsey snuggling there, never turning her head, only rolling her brown amber eyes at any who might pass; and Uncle John would say that she ought to be pampered less in general and above all ought to be trained to obedience when outdoors. He explained how the latter could be done.

"What you ought to do, Lindsay, is to get a spike collar and put on her, and a long stout chain. Take her out walking. Call her to heel, and when she doesn't obey—and that young bitch is sure not to —you just jerk the chain sharply till the spikes jab her neck. She'll learn after a few experiences of that."

"No doubt," my husband would reply, gently stroking Betsey's velvet drooping ears, and quite forgetful that he himself had once suggested that very discipline for another person and another cocker to follow. "No doubt. By the way, Uncle John, don't you think this looks like a good day for golf?"

(Ah, sweet little Betsey of the dainty ruffled paws, the fringed bright eye and coquettish glance—where are you now? Sometimes in the night it rains and I wake from a dream and know you are not in our house and I think, "Oh, we have forgotten Betsey and left her outdoors in the night." Then, waking, I remember that in more Elysian fields than ours you chase bright butterflies.)

Bashan

FROM "A MAN AND HIS DOG" BY

THOMAS MANN

He Comes Round the Corner

WHEN spring, the fairest season of the year, does honour to its name, and when the trilling of the birds rouses me early because I have ended the day before at a seemly hour, I love to rise betimes and go for a half-hour's walk before breakfast. Strolling hatless in the broad avenue in front of my house, or through the parks beyond, I like to enjoy a few draughts of the young morning air and taste its blithe purity before I am claimed by the labours of the day. Standing on the front steps of my house, I give a whistle in two notes, tonic and lower fourth, like the beginning of the second phrase of Schubert's Unfinished Symphony; it might be considered the musical setting of a two-syllabled name. Next moment, and while I walk towards the garden gate, the faintest tinkle sounds from afar, at first scarcely audible, but growing rapidly louder and more distinct; such a sound as might be made by a metal licence-tag clicking against the trimmings of a leather collar. I face about, to see Bashan rounding the corner of the house at top speed and charging towards me as though he meant to knock me down. In the effort he is making he has dropped his lower lip, baring two white teeth that glitter in the morning sun.

He comes straight from his kennel, which stands at the back of the house, between the props of the veranda floor. Probably, until my two-toned call set him in this violent motion, he had been lying there snatching a nap after the adventures of the night. The kennel has curtains of sacking and is lined with straw; indeed, a straw or so may

308

be clinging to Bashan's sleep-rumpled coat or even sticking between his toes—a comic sight, which reminds me of a painstakingly imagined production of Schiller's *Die Räuber* that I once saw, in which old Count Moor came out of the Hunger Tower tricot-clad, with a straw sticking pathetically between his toes. Involuntarily I assume a defensive position to meet the charge, receiving it on my flank, for Bashan shows every sign of meaning to run between my legs and trip me up. However at the last minute, when a collision is imminent, he always puts on the brakes, executing a half-wheel which speaks for both his mental and his physical self-control. And then, without a sound—for he makes sparing use of his sonorous and expressive voice —he dances wildly round me by way of greeting, with immoderate plungings and waggings which are not confined to the appendage provided by nature for the purpose but bring his whole hind quarters as far as his ribs into play. He contracts his whole body into a curve, he hurtles into the air in a flying leap, he turns round and round on his own axis—and curiously enough, whichever way I turn, he always contrives to execute these manœuvres behind my back. But the moment I stoop down and put out my hand he jumps to my side and stands like a statue, with his shoulder against my shin, in a slantwise posture, his strong paws braced against the ground, his face turned upwards so that he looks at me upside-down. And his utter immobility, as I pat his shoulder and murmur encouragement, is as concentrated and fiercely passionate as the frenzy before it had been.

Bashan is a short-haired German pointer—speaking by and large, that is, and not too literally. For he is probably not quite orthodox, as a pure matter of points. In the first place, he is a little too small. He is, I repeat, definitely undersized for a proper pointer. And then his forelegs are not absolutely straight; they have just the suggestion of an outward curve—which also detracts from his qualifications as a blood-dog. And he has a tendency to a dewlap, those folds of hanging skin under the muzzle, which in Bashan's case are admirably becoming but again would be frowned on by your fanatic for pure breeding, as I understand that a pointer should have taut skin round the neck. Bashan's colouring is very fine. His coat is a rusty brown with black stripes and a good deal of white on chest, paws, and under side. The whole of his snub nose seems to have been dipped in black paint.

Over the broad top of his head and on his cool hanging ears the black and brown combine in a lovely velvety pattern. Quite the prettiest thing about him, however, is the whorl or stud or little tuft at the centre of the convolution of white hairs on his chest, which stands out like the boss on an ancient breastplate. Very likely even his splendid coloration is a little too marked and would be objected to by those who put the laws of breeding above the value of personality, for it would appear that the classic pointer type should have a coat of one colour or at most with spots of a different one, but never stripes. Worst of all, from the point of view of classification, is a hairy growth hanging from his muzzle and the corners of his mouth; it might with some justice be called a moustache and goatee, and when you concentrate on it, close at hand or even at a distance, you cannot help thinking of an airedale or a schnauzer.

But classifications aside, what a good and good-looking animal Bashan is, as he stands there straining against my knee, gazing up at me with all his devotion in his eyes! They are particularly fine eyes, too, both gentle and wise, if just a little too prominent and glassy. The iris is the same colour as his coat, a rusty brown; it is only a narrow rim, for the pupils are dilated into pools of blackness and the outer edge merges into the white of the eye wherein it swims. His whole head is expressive of honesty and intelligence, of manly qualities corresponding to his physical structure: his arched and swelling chest where the ribs stand out under the smooth and supple skin; the narrow haunches, the veined, sinewy legs, the strong, well-shaped paws. All these bespeak virility and a stout heart; they suggest hunting blood and peasant stock—yes, certainly the hunter and game dog do after all predominate in Bashan, he is genuine pointer, no matter if he does not owe his existence to a snobbish system of inbreeding. All this, probably, is what I am really telling him as I pat his shoulder-blade and address him with a few disjointed words of encouragement.

So he stands and looks and listens, gathering from what I say and the tone of it that I distinctly approve of his existence—the very thing which I am at pains to imply. And suddenly he thrusts out his head, opening and shutting his lips very fast, and makes a snap at my face as though he meant to bite off my nose. It is a gesture of response to my remarks, and it always makes me recoil with a laugh, as Bashan knows beforehand that it will. It is a kiss in the air, half caress, half teasing, a trick he has had since puppyhood, which I have never seen in any of his predecessors. And he immediately begs pardon for the liberty, crouching, wagging his tail, and behaving funnily embarrassed. So we go out through the garden gate and into the open.

We are encompassed with a roaring like that of the sea; for we live almost directly on the swift-flowing river that foams over shallow ledges at no great distance from the poplar avenue. In between lie a fenced-in grass plot planted with maples, and a raised pathway skirted with huge aspen trees, bizarre and willowlike of aspect. At the beginning of June their seedpods strew the ground far and wide with woolly snow. Upstream, in the direction of the city, construction troops are building a pontoon bridge. Shouts of command and the thump of heavy boots on the planks sound across the river; also, from the further bank, the noise of industrial activity, for there is a locomotive foundry a little way downstream. Its premises have been lately enlarged to meet increased demands, and light streams all night long from its lofty windows. Beautiful glittering new engines roll to and fro on trial runs; a steam whistle emits wailing head-tones from time to time; muffled thunderings of unspecified origin shatter the air, smoke pours out of the many chimneys to be caught up by the wind and borne away over the wooded country beyond the river, for it seldom or never blows over to our side. Thus in our half-suburban, half-rural seclusion the voice of nature mingles with that of man, and over all lies the bright-eyed freshness of the new day.

It might be about half past seven by official time when I set out; by sun-time, half past six. With my hands behind my back I stroll in the tender sunshine down the avenue, cross-hatched by the long shadows of the poplar trees. From where I am I cannot see the river, but I hear its broad and even flow. The trees whisper gently, songbirds fill the air with their penetrating chirps and warbles, twitters and trills; from the direction of the sunrise a plane is flying under the humid blue sky, a rigid, mechanical bird with a droning hum that rises and falls as it steers a free course above river and fields. And Bashan is delighting my eyes with the beautiful long leaps he is making across the low rail of the grass-plot on my left. Backwards and forwards he leaps—as a matter of fact he is doing it because he knows

I like it; for I have often urged him on by shouting and striking the railing, praising him when he fell in with my whim. So now he comes up to me after nearly every jump to hear how intrepidly and elegantly he jumps. He even springs up into my face and slavers all over the arm I put out to protect it. But the jumping is also to be conceived as a sort of morning exercise, and morning toilet as well, for it smooths his ruffled coat and rids it of old Moor's straws.

It is good to walk like this in the early morning, with senses rejuvenated and spirit cleansed by the night's long healing draught of Lethe. You look confidently forward to the day yet pleasantly hesitate to begin it, being master as you are of this little untroubled span of time between, which is your good reward for good behaviour. You indulge in the illusion that your life is habitually steady, simple, concentrated, and contemplative, that you belong entirely to yourself—and this illusion makes you quite happy. For a human being tends to believe that the mood of the moment, be it troubled or blithe, peaceful or stormy, is the true, native, and permanent tenor of his existence; and in particular he likes to exalt every happy chance into an inviolable rule and to regard it as the benign order of his life—whereas the truth is that he is condemned to improvisation and morally lives from hand to mouth all the time. So now, breathing the morning air, you stoutly believe that you are virtuous and free; while you ought to know—and at bottom do know—that the world is spreading its snares round your feet, and that most likely tomorrow you will be lying in your bed until nine, because you sought it at two in the morning hot and befogged with impassioned discussion. Never mind. Today you, a sober character, an early riser, you are the right master for that stout hunter who has just cleared the railings again out of sheer joy in the fact that today you apparently belong to him alone and not to the world.

We follow the avenue for about five minutes, to the point where it ceases to be an avenue and becomes a gravelly waste along the riverbank. From this we turn away to our right and strike into another covered with finer gravel, which has been laid out like the avenue and like it provided with a cycle-path, but is not yet built up. It runs between low-lying, wooded lots of land, towards the slope which is the eastern limit of our river neighbourhood and Bashan's theatre of action. On our way we cross another road, equally embryonic, running along between fields and meadows. Further up, however, where the tram stops, it is quite built up with flats. We descend by a gravel path into a well-laid-out, parklike valley, quite deserted, as indeed the whole region is at this hour. Paths are laid out in curves and rondels, there are benches to rest on, tidy playgrounds, and wide plots of lawn with fine old trees whose boughs nearly sweep the grass, covering all but a glimpse of trunk. They are elms, beeches, limes, and silvery willows, in well-disposed groups. I enjoy to the full the well-landscaped quality of the scene, where I may walk no more disturbed than if it belonged to me alone. Nothing has been forgotten—there are even cement gutters in the gravel paths that lead down the grassy slopes. And the abundant greenery discloses here and there a charming distant vista of one of the villas that bound the spot on two sides.

Here for a while I stroll along the paths, and Bashan revels in the freedom of unlimited level space, galloping across and across the lawns like mad with his body inclined in a centrifugal plane; sometimes, barking with mingled pleasure and exasperation, he pursues a bird which flutters as though spellbound, but perhaps on purpose to tease him, along the ground just in front of his nose. But if I sit down on a bench he is at my side at once and takes up a position on one of my feet. For it is a law of his being that he only runs about when I am in motion too; that when I settle down he follows suit. There seems no obvious reason for this practice; but Bashan never fails to conform to it.

I get an odd, intimate, and amusing sensation from having him sit on my foot and warm it with the blood-heat of his body. A pervasive feeling of sympathy and good cheer fills me, as almost invariably when in his company and looking at things from his angle. He has a rather rustic slouch when he sits down; his shoulder-blades stick out and his paws turn negligently in. He looks smaller and squatter than he really is, and the little white boss on his chest is advanced with comic effect. But all these faults are atoned for by the lofty and dignified carriage of the head, so full of concentration. All is quiet, and we two sit there absolutely still in our turn. The rushing of the water comes to us faint and subdued. And the senses become alert

for all the tiny, mysterious little sounds that nature makes: the lizard's
quick dart, the note of the bird, the burrowing of a mole in the earth.
Bashan pricks up his ears—in so far as the muscles of naturally drooping ears will allow them to be pricked. He cocks his head to hear the
better; and the nostrils of his moist black nose keep twitching sensi-
tively as he sniffs.

Then he lies down, but always in contact with my foot. I see him
in profile, in that age-old, conventionalized pose of the beast-god, the
sphinx: head and chest held high, forelegs close to the body, paws
extended in parallel lines. He has got overheated, so he opens his
mouth, and at once all the intelligence of his face gives way to the
merely animal, his eyes narrow and blink and his rosy tongue lolls
out between his strong white pointed teeth. . . .

Notes on Bashan's Character and Manner of Life

A man in the Isar valley had told me that this kind of dog can
become a nuisance, by always wanting to be with his master. Thus I
was forewarned against taking too personally Bashan's persistent
faithfulness to myself, and it was easier for me to discourage it a little
and protect myself at need. It is a deep-lying patriarchal instinct in
a dog which leads him—at least in the more manly, outdoor breeds—
to recognize and honour in the man of the house and head of the
family his absolute master and overlord, protector of the hearth; and
to find in the relation of vassalage to him the basis and value of his
own existence, whereas his attitude towards the rest of the family
is much more independent. Almost from the very first day Bashan
behaved in this spirit towards me, following me with his trustful eyes
that seemed to be begging me to order him about—which I was chary
of doing, for time soon showed that obedience was not one of his
strong points—and dogging my footsteps in the obvious conviction
that sticking to me was the natural order of things. In the family circle
he always sat at my feet, never by any chance at anyone else's. And
when we were walking, if I struck off on a path by myself, he invariably followed me and not the others. He insisted on being with me
when I worked; if the garden door was closed he would disconcert

me by jumping suddenly in at the window, bringing much gravel in his train and flinging himself down panting beneath my desk.

But the presence of any living thing—even a dog—is something of which we are very conscious; we attend to it in a way that is disturbing when we want to be alone. Thus Bashan could become a quite tangible nuisance. He would come up to me wagging his tail, look at me with devouring gaze, and prance provocatively. On the smallest encouragement he would put his forepaws on the arm of my chair, lean against me, and make me laugh with his kisses in the air. Then he would examine the things on my desk, obviously under the impression that they must be good to eat since he so often found me stooped above them; and so doing would smudge my freshly written page with his broad, hairy hunter's paws. I would sharply call him to order and he would lie down on the floor and go to sleep. But when he slept he dreamed, making running motions with all four paws and barking in a subterranean but perfectly audible sort of way. I quite comprehensibly found this distracting; in the first place the sound was uncannily ventriloquistic, in the second it gave me a guilty feeling. For this dream life was obviously an artificial substitute for real running, hunting, and open-air activity; it was supplied to him by his own nature because his life with me did not give him as much of it as his blood and his senses required. I felt touched; but since there was nothing for it, I was constrained in the name of my higher interests to throw off the incubus, telling myself that Bashan brought altogether too much mud into the room and also that he damaged the carpet with his claws.

So then the fiat went forth that he might not be with me or in the house when I was there—though of course there might be exceptions to the rule. He was quick to understand and submit to the unnatural prohibition, as being the inscrutable will of his lord and master. The separation from me—which in winter often lasted the greater part of the day—was in his mind only a separation, not a divorce or severance of connections. He may not be with me, because I have so ordained. But the not being with me is a kind of negative being-with-me, just in that it is carrying out my command. Hence we can hardly speak of an independent existence carried on by Bashan during the hours when he is not by my side. Through the glass door of my study

I can see him on the grass-plot in front of the house, playing with the children and putting on an absurd avuncular air. He repeatedly comes to the door and sniffs at the crack—he cannot see me through the muslin curtains—to assure himself of my presence within; then he sits down and mounts guard with his back to the door. Sometimes I see him from my window prosing along on the elevated path between the aspen trees; but this is only to pass the time, the excursion is void of all pride or joy in life; in fact, it is unthinkable that Bashan should devote himself to the pleasures of the chase on his own account, though there is nothing to prevent him from doing so and my presence, as will be seen, is not always an unmixed advantage.

Life for him begins when I issue from the house—though, alas, it does not always begin even then! For the question is, when I do go out, which way am I going to turn: to the right, down the avenue, the road towards the open and our hunting-ground, or towards the left and the place where the trams stop, to ride into town? Only in the first case is there any sense in accompanying me. At first he used to follow me even when I turned left; when the tram thundered up he would look at it with amazement and then, suppressing his fears, land with one blind and devoted leap among the crowd on the platform. Thence being dislodged by the popular indignation, he would gallop along on the ground behind the roaring vehicle which so little resembled the cart he once knew. He would keep up with it as long as he could, his breath getting shorter and shorter. But the city traffic bewildered his rustic brains; he got between people's legs, strange dogs fell on his flank, he was confused by a volume and variety of smells, the like of which he had never imagined, irresistibly distracted by house-corners impregnated with lingering ancient scents of old adventures. He would fall behind; sometimes he would overtake the tram again, sometimes not; sometimes he overtook the wrong one, which looked just the same, ran blindly in the wrong direction, further and further into a mad, strange world. Once he only came home after two days' absence, limping and starved to death, and, seeking the peace of the last house on the river-bank, found that his lord and master had been sensible enough to get there before him.

This happened two or three times. Then he gave it up and definitely declined to go with me when I turned to the left. He always knows instantly whether I have chosen the wild or the world, directly I get outside the door. He springs up from the mat in the entrance where he has been waiting for me and in that moment divines my intentions; my clothes betray me, the cane I carry, probably even my bearing: my cold and negligent glance or on the other hand the challenging eye I turn upon him. He understands. In the one case he tumbles over himself down the steps, he whirls round and round like a stone in a sling as in dumb rejoicing he runs before me to the gate. In the other he crouches, lays back his ears, the light goes out of his eyes, the fire I have kindled by my appearance dies down to ashes, and he puts on the guilty look which men and animals alike wear when they are unhappy.

Sometimes he cannot believe his eyes, even though they plainly tell him that there is no hope for the chase today. His yearning has been too strong. He refuses to see the signs, the urban walking-stick, the careful city clothes. He presses beside me through the gate, turns round like lightning, and tries to make me turn right, by running off at a gallop in that direction, twisting his head round, and ignoring the fatal negative which I oppose to his efforts. When I actually turn to the left he comes back and walks with me along the hedge, with little snorts and head-tones which seem to emerge from the high tension of his interior. He takes to jumping to and fro over the park railings, although they are rather high for comfort and he gives little moans as he leaps, being evidently afraid of hurting himself. He jumps with a sort of desperate gaiety which is bent on ignoring reality; also in the hope of beguiling me by his performance. For there is still a little—a very little—hope that I may still leave the high-road at the end of the park and turn left after all by the roundabout way past the pillar-box, as I do when I have letters to post. But I do that very seldom; so when that last hope has fled, then Bashan sits down and lets me go on my way.

There he sits, in that clumsy rustic posture of his, in the middle of the road and looks after me as far as he can see me. If I turn my head he pricks up his ears, but he does not follow; even if I whistled he would not, for he knows it would be useless. When I turn out of the avenue I can still see him sitting there, a small, dark, clumsy figure in the road, and it goes to my heart, I have pangs of conscience as I mount the tram. He has waited so long—and we all know what torture waiting can be! His whole life is a waiting—waiting for the next walk in the open, a waiting that begins as soon as he is rested from the last one. Even his night consists of waiting; for his sleep is distributed throughout the whole twenty-four hours of the day, with many a little nap on the grass in the garden, the sun shining down warm on his coat, or behind the curtains of his kennel, to break up and shorten the empty spaces of the day. Thus his night sleep is broken too, not continuous, and manifold instincts urge him abroad in the darkness; he dashes to and fro all over the garden—and he waits. He waits for the night watchman to come on his rounds with his lantern and when he hears the recurrent heavy tread heralds it, against his own better knowledge, with a terrific outburst of barking. He waits for the sky to grow pale, for the cocks to crow at the nursery-gardener's close by; for the morning breeze to rise among the treetops—and for the kitchen door to be opened, so that he may slip in and warm himself at the stove.

Still, the night-time martyrdom must be mild compared with what Bashan has to endure in the day. And particularly when the weather is fine, either winter or summer, when the sunshine lures one abroad and all the muscles twitch with the craving for violent motion—and the master, without whom it is impossible to conceive doing anything—simply will not leave his post behind the glass door. All that agile little body, feverishly alive with pulsating life, is rested through and through, is worn out with resting; sleep is not to be thought of. He comes up on the terrace outside my door, lets himself down with a sigh that seems to come from his very heart, and rests his head on his paws, rolling his eyes up patiently to heaven. That lasts but a few seconds, he cannot stand the position any more, he sickens of it. One other thing there is to do. He can go down again and lift his leg against one of the little formal arbor-vitæ trees that flank the rose-bed—it is the one to the right that suffers from his attentions, wasting away so that it has to be replanted every year. He does go down, then, and performs this action, not because he needs to, but just to pass the time. He stands there a long time, with very little to show for it, however—so long that the hind leg in the air begins to tremble and he has to give a little hop to regain his balance. On four legs once more he is no

better off than he was. He stares stupidly up into the boughs of the
ash trees, where two birds are flitting and chirping; watches them
dart off like arrows and turns away as though in contempt of such
lightheadedness. He stretches and stretches, fit to tear himself apart.
The stretching is very thorough; it is done in two sections, thus: first
the forelegs, lifting the hind ones into the air; second the rear quarters,
by sprawling them out on the ground; both actions being accompanied by tremendous yawning. Then that is over too, cannot be
spun out any longer, and if you have just finished an exhaustive
stretching you cannot do it over again just at once. He stands still
and looks gloomily at the ground. Then he begins to turn round on
himself, slowly and consideringly, as though he wanted to lie down,
yet was not quite certain of the best way to do it. Finally he decides
not to; he moves off sluggishly to the middle of the grass-plot, and
once there flings himself violently on his back and scrubs to and fro
as though to cool off on the shaven turf. Quite a blissful sensation, this,
it seems, for his paws jerk and he snaps in all directions in a delirium
of release and satisfaction. He drains this joy down to its vapid dregs,
aware that it is fleeting, that you cannot roll and tumble more than
ten seconds at most, and that no sound and soul-contenting weariness
will result from it, but only a flatness and returning boredom, such
as always follows when one tries to drug oneself. He lies there on his
side with his eyes rolled up, as though he were dead. Then he gets
up and shakes himself, shakes as only his like can shake without fearing concussion of the brain; shakes until everything rattles, until his
ears flop together under his chin and foam flies from his dazzling
white teeth. And then? He stands perfectly still in his tracks, rigid,
dead to the world, without the least idea what to do next. And then,
driven to extremes, he climbs the steps once more, comes up to the
glass door, lifts his paw and scratches—hesitantly, with his ears laid
back, the complete beggar. He scratches only once, quite faintly;
but this timidly lifted paw, his single, faint-hearted scratch, to which
he has come because he simply cannot think of anything else, are too
moving. I get up and open the door, though I know it can lead to no
good. And he begins to dance and jump, challenging me to be a man
and come abroad with him. He rumples the rugs, upsets the whole
room and makes an end of all my peace and quiet. But now judge for

yourself if, after I have seen Bashan wait like this, I can find it easy to go off in the tram and leave him, a pathetic little dot at the end of the poplar avenue!

In the long twilights of summer, things are not quite so bad: there is a good chance that I will take an evening walk in the open and thus even after long waiting he will come into his own and with good luck be able to start a hare. But in winter if I go off in the afternoon it is all over for the day, all hope must be buried for another four-and-twenty hours. For night will have fallen; if I go out again our hunting-grounds will lie in inaccessible darkness and I must bend my steps towards the traffic, the lighted streets, and city parks up the river—and this does not suit Bashan's simple soul. He came with me at first, but soon gave it up and stopped at home. Not only that space and freedom were lacking; he was afraid of the bright lights in the darkness, he shied at every bush, at every human form. A policeman's flapping cloak could make him swerve aside with a yelp or even lead him to attack the officer with a courage born of desperation; when the latter, frightened in his turn, would let loose a stream of abuse to our address. Unfortunate episodes mounted up when Bashan and I went out together in the dark and the damp. And speaking of policemen reminds me that there are three classes of human beings whom Bashan does especially abhor: policemen, monks, and chimney-sweeps. He cannot stand them, he assails them with a fury of barking wherever he sees them or when they chance to pass the house.

And winter is of course the time of year when freedom and sobriety are with most difficulty preserved against snares; when it is hardest to lead a regular, retired, and concentrated existence; when I may even seek the city a second time in the day. For the evening has its social claims, pursuing which I may come back at midnight, with the last tram, or losing that am driven to return on foot, my head in a whirl with ideas and wine and smoke, full of roseate views of the world and of course long past the point of normal fatigue. And then the embodiment of that other, truer, soberer life of mine, my own hearthstone, in person, as it were, may come to meet me; not wounded, not reproachful, but on the contrary giving me joyous welcome and bringing me back to my own. I mean, of course, Bashan. In pitchy darkness, the river roaring in my ears, I turn into the poplar avenue, and after the first few steps I am enveloped in a soundless storm of prancings and swishings; on the first occasion I did not know what was happening. "Bashan?" I inquired into the blackness. The prancings and swishings redouble—is this a dancing dervish or a Berserk warrior here on my path? But not a sound; and directly I stand still, I feel those honest, wet and muddy paws on the lapels of my raincoat, and a snapping and flapping in my face, which I draw back even as I stoop down to pat the lean shoulder, equally wet with snow or rain. Yes, the good soul has come to meet the tram. Well informed as always upon my comings and goings, he has got up at what he judged to be the right time, to fetch me from the station. He may have been waiting a long while, in snow or rain, yet his joy at my final appearance knows no resentment at my faithlessness, though I have neglected him all day and brought his hopes to naught. I pat and praise him, and as we go home together I tell him what a fine fellow he is and promise him (that is to say, not so much him as my-self) that tomorrow, no matter what the weather, we two will follow the chase together. And resolving thus, I feel my worldly preoccupa-tions melt away; sobriety returns; for the image I have conjured up of our hunting-ground and the charms of its solitude is linked in my mind with the call to higher, stranger, more obscure concerns of mine.

There are still other traits of Bashan's character which I should like to set down here, so that the gentle reader may get as lively and speak-ing an image of him as is anyway possible. Perhaps the best way would be for me to compare him with our deceased Percy; for a better-defined contrast than that between these two never existed within the same species. First and foremost we must remember that Bashan was entirely sound in mind, whereas Percy, as I have said, and as often happens among aristocratic canines, had always been mad, through and through, a perfectly typical specimen of frantic over-breeding. I have referred to this subject before, in a somewhat wider connection; here I only want, for purposes of comparison, to speak of Bashan's infinitely simpler, more ordinary mentality, expressed for instance in the way he would greet you, or in his behaviour on our walks. His manifestations were always within the bounds of a hearty and healthy common sense; they never even bordered on the hysterical, whereas Percy's on all such occasions overstepped them in a way that was at times quite shocking.

And even that does not quite cover the contrast between these two creatures; the truth is more complex and involved still. Bashan is coarser-fibred, true, like the lower classes; but like them also he is not above complaining. His noble predecessor, on the other hand, united more delicacy and a greater capacity for suffering, with an infinitely firmer and prouder spirit; despite all his foolishness he far excelled in self-discipline the powers of Bashan's peasant soul. In saying this I am not defending any aristocratic system of values. It is simply to do honour to truth and actuality that I want to bring out the mixture of softness and hardiness, delicacy and firmness in the two natures. Bashan, for instance, is quite able to spend the coldest winter night out of doors, behind the sacking curtains of his kennel. He has a weakness of the bladder which makes it impossible for him to remain seven hours shut up in a room; we have to fasten him out, even in the most inhospitable weather, and trust to his robust constitution. Sometimes after a particularly bitter and foggy winter night he comes into the house with his moustache and whiskers like delicately frosted wires; with a little cold, even, and coughing in the odd, one-syllabled way that dogs have. But in a few hours he has got all over it and takes no harm at all. Whereas we should never have dared to expose our silken-haired Percy to such rigours. Yet Bashan is afraid of the slightest pain, behaving so abjectly that one would feel disgusted if the plebeian simplicity of his behaviour did not make one laugh instead. When he goes stalking in the underbrush, I constantly hear him yelping because he has been scratched by a thorn or a branch has struck him in the face. If he hurts his foot or skins his belly a little, jumping over a fence, he sets up a cry like an antique hero in his death-agony; comes to me hobbling on three legs, howling and lamenting in an abandonment of self-pity—the more piercingly, the more sympathy he gets—and this although in fifteen minutes he will be running and jumping again as though nothing had happened.

With Percival it was otherwise; he clenched his jaws and was still. He was afraid of the dog-whip, as Bashan is too; and tasted it, alas, more often than the latter, for in his day I was younger and quicker-

tempered and his witlessness often assumed a vicious aspect which
cried out for chastisement and drove me on to administer it. When
I was quite beside myself and took down the lash from the nail
where it hung, Percy might crawl under a table or a bench. But not
a sound would escape him under punishment; even at a second flail-
ing he would give vent only to a fervent moan if it stung worse than
usual—whereas the base-born Bashan will howl abjectly if I so much
as raise my arm. In short, no sense of honour, no strictness with himself. And anyhow, it seldom comes to corporal punishment, for I
long ago ceased to make demands upon him contrary to his nature, of
a kind which would lead to conflict between us.

For example, I never ask him to learn tricks; it would be of no use.
He is not talented, no circus dog, no trained clown. He is a sound,
vigorous young hunter, not a professor. I believe I remarked that he
is a capital jumper. No obstacle too great, if the incentive be present:
if he cannot jump it he will scrabble up somehow and let himself fall
on the other side—at least, he conquers it one way or another. But it
must be a genuine obstacle, not to be jumped through or crawled
under; otherwise he would think it folly to jump. A wall, a ditch, a
fence, a thickset hedge, are genuine obstacles; a crosswise bar, a stick
held out, are not, and you cannot jump over them without going
contrary to reason and looking silly. Which Bashan refuses to do. He
refuses. Try to make him jump over some such unreal obstacle; in
the end you will be reduced to taking him by the scruff of the neck,
in your anger, and flinging him over, while he whimpers and yaps.
Once on the other side he acts as though he had done just what you
wanted and celebrates the event in a frenzy of barking and capering.
You may coax or you may punish; you cannot break down his reasonable resistance to performing a mere trick. He is not unaccommo-
dating, he sets store by his master's approval, he will jump over a
hedge at my will or my command, and not only when he feels like it
himself, and enjoys very much the praise I bestow. But over a bar or
a stick he will not jump, he will crawl underneath—if he were to die
for it. A hundred times he will beg for forgiveness, forbearance,
consideration; he fears pain, fears it to the point of being abject. But
no fear and no pain can make him capable of a performance which
in itself would be child's-play for him, but for which he obviously

lacks all mental equipment. When you confront him with it, the question is not whether he will jump or not; that is already settled, and the command means nothing to him but a beating. To demand of him what reason forbids him to understand and hence to do is simply in his eyes to seek a pretext for blows, strife, and disturbance of friendly relations—it is merely the first step towards all these things. Thus Bashan looks at it, so far as I can see, and I doubt whether one may properly charge him with obstinacy. Obstinacy may be broken down, in the last analysis it cries out to be broken down; but Bashan's resistance to performing a trick he would seal with his death.

Extraordinary creature! So close a friend and yet so remote; so different from us, in certain ways, that our language has not power to do justice to his canine logic. For instance, what is the meaning of that frightful circumstantiality—unnerving alike to the spectator and to the parties themselves—attendant on the meeting of dog and dog; or on their first acquaintance or even on their first sight of each other? My excursions with Bashan have made me witness to hundreds of such encounters, or, I might better say, forced me to be an embarrassed spectator at them. And every time, for the duration of the episode, my old familiar Bashan was a stranger to me, I found it impossible to enter into his feelings or behaviour or understand the tribal laws which governed them. Certainly the meeting in the open of two dogs, strangers to each other, is one of the most painful, thrilling, and pregnant of all conceivable encounters; it is surrounded by an atmosphere of the last uncanniness, presided over by a constraint for which I have no preciser name; they simply cannot pass each other, their mutual embarrassment is frightful to behold.

I am not speaking of the case where one of the parties is shut up behind a hedge or a fence. Even then it is not easy to interpret their feelings—but at least the situation is less acute. They sniff each other from far off, and Bashan suddenly seeks shelter in my neighbourhood, whining a little to give vent to a distress and oppression which simply no words can describe. At the same time the imprisoned stranger sets up a violent barking, ostensibly in his character as a good watch-dog, but passing over unconsciously into a whimpering much like Bashan's own, an unsatisfied, envious, distressful whine. We draw near. The strange dog is waiting for us, close to the hedge, grousing and be-

moaning his impotence; jumping at the barrier and giving every sign
—how seriously one cannot tell—of intending to tear Bashan to pieces
if only he could get at him. Bashan might easily stick close to me and
pass him by; but he goes up to the hedge. He has to, he would even
if I forbade him; to remain away would be to transgress a code older
and more inviolable than any prohibition of mine. He advances, then,
and with a modest and inscrutable bearing performs that rite which
he knows will soothe and appease the other—even if temporarily—
so long as the stranger performs it too, though whining and complaining in the act. Then they both chase wildly along the hedge, each on
his own side, as close as possible, neither making a sound. At the end
of the hedge they both face about and dash back again. But in full
career both suddenly halt and stand as though rooted to the spot;
they stand still, facing the hedge, and put their noses together through
it. For some space of time they stand thus, then resume their curious,
futile race shoulder to shoulder on either side of the barrier. But in
the end my dog avails himself of his freedom and moves off—a frightful moment for the prisoner! He cannot stand it, he finds it name-
lessly humiliating that the other should dream of simply going off
like that. He raves and slavers and contorts himself in his rage; runs
like one mad up and down his enclosure; threatens to jump the hedge
and have the faithless Bashan by the throat; he yells insults behind the
retreating back. Bashan hears it all, it distresses him, as his manner
shows. But he does not turn round, he jogs along beside me, while
the cursings in our rear die down into whinings and are still.

Such the procedure when one of the parties is shut up. Embarrass-
ments multiply when both of them are free. I do not relish describing the scene: it is one of the most painful and equivocal imaginable.
Bashan has been bounding light-heartedly beside me; he comes up
close, he fairly forces himself upon me, with a sniffling and whimpering that seem to come from his very depths. I still do not know what
moves his utterance, but I recognize it at once and gather that there
is a strange dog in the offing. I look about—yes, there he comes, and
even at this distance his strained and hesitating mien betrays that he
has already seen Bashan. I am scarcely less upset than they; I find the
meeting most undesirable. "Go away," I say to Bashan. "Why do you
glue yourself to my leg? Can't you go off and do your business by

yourselves?" I try to frighten him off with my cane. For if they start biting—which may easily happen, with reason or without—I shall find it most unpleasant to have them between my feet. "Go away!" I repeat, in a lower voice. But Bashan does not go away, he sticks in his distress the closer to me, making as brief a pause as he can at a tree-trunk to perform the accustomed rite; I can see the other dog doing the same. We are now within twenty paces, the suspense is frightful. The strange dog is crawling on his belly, like a cat, his head thrust out. In this posture he awaits Bashan's approach, poised to spring at the right moment for his throat. But he does not do it, nor does Bashan seem to expect that he will. Or at least he goes up to the crouching stranger, though plainly trembling and heavy-hearted; he would do this, he is obliged to do it, even though I were to act my-self and leave him to face the situation alone by striking into a side path. However painful the encounter, he has no choice, avoidance is not to be thought of. He is under a spell, he is bound to the other dog, they are bound to each other with some obscure and equivocal bond which may not be denied. We are now within two paces.

Then the other gets up, without a sound, as though he had never been behaving like a tiger, and stands there just as Bashan is standing, profoundly embarrassed, wretched, at a loss. They cannot pass each other. They probably want to, they turn away their heads, rolling their eyes sideways; evidently the same sense of guilt weighs on them both. They edge cautiously up to each other with a hang-dog air; they stop flank to flank and sniff under each other's tails. At this point the growling begins, and I speak to Bashan low-voiced and warn him, for now is the decisive moment, now we shall know whether it will come to biting or whether I shall be spared that rude shock. It does come to biting, I do not know how, still less why: quite suddenly they are nothing but a raging tumult and whirling coil out of which issue the frightful guttural noises that animals make when they engage. I may have to engage too, with my cane, to fore-stall a worse calamity; I may try to get Bashan by the neck or the collar and hold him up at arm's length in the air, the stranger dog hanging on by his teeth. Other horrors there are, too, which I may have to face—and feel them afterwards in all my limbs during the rest of our walk. But it may be, too, that after all the preliminaries the affair will pass tamely off and no harm done. At best it is hard to part the two; even if they are not clenched by the teeth, they are held by that inward bond. They may seem to have passed each other, they are no longer flank to flank, but in a straight line with their heads in opposite directions; they may not even turn their heads, but only be rolling their eyes backwards. There may even be a space between them—and yet the painful bond still holds. Neither knows if the right moment for release has come, they would both like to go, yet each seems to have conscientious scruples. Slowly, slowly, the bond loosens, snaps; Bashan bounds lightly away, with, as it were, a new lease on life.

I speak of these things only to show how under stress of circumstance the character of a near friend may reveal itself as strange and foreign. It is dark to me, it is mysterious; I observe it with head-shakings and can only dimly guess what it may mean. And in all other respects I understand Bashan so well, I feel such lively sympathy for all his manifestations! For example, how well I know that whining yawn of his when our walk has been disappointing, too short, or devoid of sporting interest; when I have begun the day late and only gone out for a quarter of an hour before dinner. At such times he walks beside me and yawns—an open, impudent yawn to the whole extent of his jaws, an animal, audible yawn insultingly expressive of his utter boredom. "A fine master I have!" it seems to say. "Far in the night last night I met him at the bridge and now he sits behind his glass door and I wait for him dying of boredom. And when he does go out he only does it to come back again before there is time to start any game. A fine master! Not a proper master at all—really a rotten master, if you ask me!"

Such was the meaning of his yawn, vulgarly plain beyond all misunderstanding. And I admit that he is right, that he has a just grievance, and I put out a hand to pat his shoulder consolingly or to stroke his head. But he is not, under such circumstances, grateful for caresses; he yawns again, if possible more rudely than before, and moves away from my hand, although by nature, in contrast to Percy and in harmony with his own plebeian sentimentality, he sets great store by caresses. He particularly likes having his throat scratched and has a funny way of guiding one's hand to the right place by energetic little jerks of his head. That he has no room just now for endearments is partly due to his disappointment, but also to the fact that when he is in motion—and that means that I also am—he does not care for them. His mood is too manly; but it changes directly I sit down. Then he is all for friendliness again and responds to it with clumsy enthusiasm.

When I sit reading in a corner of the garden wall, or on the lawn with my back to a favourite tree, I enjoy interrupting my intellectual preoccupations to talk and play with Bashan. And what do I say to him? Mostly his own name, the two syllables which are of the utmost personal interest because they refer to himself and have an electric effect upon his whole being. I rouse and stimulate his sense of his own ego by impressing upon him—varying my tone and emphasis— that he *is* Bashan and that Bashan is his name. By continuing this for a while I can actually produce in him a state of ecstasy, a sort of intoxication with his own identity, so that he begins to whirl round on himself and send up loud exultant barks to heaven out of the weight of dignity that lies on his chest. Or we amuse ourselves, I by tapping him on the nose, he by snapping at my hand as though it were a fly. It makes us both laugh, yes, Bashan has to laugh too; and as I laugh I marvel at the sight, to me the oddest and most touching thing in the world. It is moving to see how under my teasing his thin animal cheeks and the corners of his mouth will twitch, and over his dark animal mask will pass an expression like a human smile, or at least some ungainly, pathetic semblance of one. It gives way to a look of startled embarrassment, then transforms the face by appearing again. . . .

The Dog of Pompeii

BY

LOUIS UNTERMEYER

Tɪᴛᴏ and his dog Bimbo lived (if you could call it living) under
the wall where it joined the inner gate. They really didn't live
there; they just slept there. They lived anywhere. Pompeii was one
of the gayest of the old Latin towns, but although Tito was never
an unhappy boy, he was not exactly a merry one. The streets were
always lively with shining chariots and bright red trappings; the
open-air theatres rocked with laughing crowds; sham-battles and
athletic sports were free for the asking in the great stadium. Once a
year the Caesar visited the pleasure-city and the fire-works lasted for
days; the sacrifices in the Forum were better than a show. But Tito
saw none of these things. He was blind—had been blind from birth.
He was known to every one in the poorer quarters. But no one could
say how old he was, no one remembered his parents, no one could tell
where he came from. Bimbo was another mystery. As long as people
could remember seeing Tito—about twelve or thirteen years—they
had seen Bimbo. Bimbo had never left his side. He was not only dog,
but nurse, pillow, playmate, mother and father to Tito.

Did I say Bimbo never left his master? (Perhaps I had better say
comrade, for if any one was the master, it was Bimbo.) I was wrong.
Bimbo did trust Tito alone exactly three times a day. It was a fixed
routine, a custom understood between boy and dog since the beginning of their friendship, and the way it worked was this: Early in
the morning, shortly after dawn, while Tito was still dreaming,
Bimbo would disappear. When Tito awoke, Bimbo would be sitting

quietly at his side, his ears cocked, his stump of a tail tapping the ground, and a fresh-baked bread—more like a large round roll—at his feet. Tito would stretch himself; Bimbo would yawn; then they would breakfast. At noon, no matter where they happened to be, Bimbo would put his paw on Tito's knee and the two of them would return to the inner gate. Tito would curl up in the corner (almost like a dog) and go to sleep, while Bimbo, looking quite important (almost like a boy) would disappear again. In half an hour he'd be back with their lunch. Sometimes it would be a piece of fruit or a scrap of meat, often it was nothing but a dry crust. But sometimes there would be one of those flat rich cakes, sprinkled with raisins and sugar, that Tito liked so much. At supper-time the same thing happened, although there was a little less of everything, for things were hard to snatch in the evening with the streets full of people. Besides, Bimbo didn't approve of too much food before going to sleep. A heavy supper made boys too restless and dogs too stodgy— and it was the business of a dog to sleep lightly with one ear open and muscles ready for action.

But, whether there was much or little, hot or cold, fresh or dry, food was always there. Tito never asked where it came from and Bimbo never told him. There was plenty of rain-water in the hollows of soft stones; the old egg-woman at the corner sometimes gave him a cupful of strong goat's milk; in the grape-season the fat wine-maker let him have drippings of the mild juice. So there was no danger of going hungry or thirsty. There was plenty of everything in Pompeii—if you knew where to find it—and if you had a dog like Bimbo.

As I said before, Tito was not the merriest boy in Pompeii. He could not romp with the other youngsters and play Hare-and-Hounds and I-spy and Follow-your-Master and Ball-against-the-Building and Jack-stones and Kings-and-Robbers with them. But that did not make him sorry for himself. If he could not see the sights that delighted the lads of Pompeii he could hear and smell things they never noticed. He could really see more with his ears and nose than they could with their eyes. When he and Bimbo went out walking he knew just where they were going and exactly what was happening.

"Ah," he'd sniff and say, as they passed a handsome villa, "Glaucus Pansa is giving a grand dinner tonight. They're going to have three kinds of bread, and roast pigling, and stuffed goose, and a great stew— I think bear-stew—and a fig-pie." And Bimbo would note that this would be a good place to visit tomorrow.

Or, "H'm," Tito would murmur, half through his lips, half through his nostrils. "The wife of Marcus Lucretius is expecting her mother. She's shaking out every piece of goods in the house; she's going to use the best clothes—the ones she's been keeping in pine-needles and camphor—and there's an extra girl in the kitchen. Come, Bimbo, let's get out of the dust!"

Or, as they passed a small but elegant dwelling opposite the public-baths, "Too bad! The tragic poet is ill again. It must be a bad fever this time, for they're trying smoke-fumes instead of medicine. Whew! I'm glad I'm not a tragic poet!"

Or, as they neared the Forum, "Mm-m! What good things they have in the Macellum today!" (It really was a sort of butcher-grocer-market-place, but Tito didn't know any better. He called it the Macellum.) "Dates from Africa, and salt oysters from sea-caves, and cuttlefish, and new honey, and sweet onions, and—ugh!—water-buffalo steaks. Come, let's see what's what in the Forum." And Bimbo, just as curious as his comrade, hurried on. Being a dog, he trusted his ears and nose (like Tito) more than his eyes. And so the two of them entered the center of Pompeii.

The Forum was the part of the town to which everybody came at least once during each day. It was the Central Square and everything happened here. There were no private houses; all was public—the chief temples, the gold and red bazaars, the silk-shops, the town-hall, the booths belonging to the weavers and jewel-merchants, the wealthy woolen market, the shrine of the household gods. Everything glittered here. The buildings looked as if they were new—which, in a sense, they were. The earthquake of twelve years ago had brought down all the old structures and, since the citizens of Pompeii were ambitious to rival Naples and even Rome, they had seized the opportunity to rebuild the whole town. And they had done it all within a dozen years. There was scarcely a building that was older than Tito.

Tito had heard a great deal about the earthquake though, being about a year old at the time, he could scarcely remember it. This particular quake had been a light one—as earthquakes go. The weaker houses had been shaken down, parts of the out-worn wall had been wrecked; but there was little loss of life, and the brilliant new Pompeii had taken the place of the old. No one knew what caused these earthquakes. Records showed they had happened in the neighborhood since the beginning of time. Sailors said that it was to teach the lazy city-folk a lesson and make them appreciate those who risked the dangers of the sea to bring them luxuries and protect their town from invaders. The priests said that the gods took this way of showing their anger to those who refused to worship properly and who failed to bring enough sacrifices to the altars and (though they didn't say it in so many words) presents to the priests. The tradesmen said that the foreign merchants had corrupted the ground and it was no longer safe to traffic in imported goods that came from strange places and carried a curse with them. Every one had a different explanation —and every one's explanation was louder and sillier than his neighbor's.

They were talking about it this afternoon as Tito and Bimbo came out of the side-street into the public square. The Forum was the favorite promenade for rich and poor. What with the priests arguing with the politicians, servants doing the day's shopping, tradesmen crying their wares, women displaying the latest fashions from Greece and Egypt, children playing hide-and-seek among the marble columns, knots of soldiers, sailors, peasants from the provinces—to say nothing of those who merely came to lounge and look on—the square was crowded to its last inch. His ears even more than his nose guided Tito to the place where the talk was loudest. It was in front of the Shrine of the Household Gods that, naturally enough, the householders were arguing.

"I tell you," rumbled a voice which Tito recognized as bath-master Rufus's, "there won't be another earthquake in my lifetime or yours. There may be a tremble or two, but earthquakes, like lightnings, never strike twice in the same place."

"Do they not?" asked a thin voice Tito had never heard. It had a high, sharp ring to it and Tito knew it as the accent of a stranger.

"How about the two towns of Sicily that have been ruined three times within fifteen years by the eruptions of Mount Etna? And were they not warned? And does that column of smoke above Vesuvius mean nothing?"

"That?" Tito could hear the grunt with which one question answered another. "That's always there. We use it for our weather-guide. When the smoke stands up straight we know we'll have fair weather; when it flattens out it's sure to be foggy; when it drifts to the east—"

"Yes, yes," cut in the edged voice. "I've heard about your mountain barometer. But the column of smoke seems hundreds of feet higher than usual and it's thickening and spreading like a shadowy tree. They say in Naples—"

"Oh, Naples!" Tito knew this voice by the little squeak that went with it. It was Attilio, the cameo-cutter. "*They* talk while we suffer. Little help we got from them last time. Naples commits the crimes and Pompeii pays the price. It's become a proverb with us. Let them mind their own business."

"Yes," grumbled Rufus, "and others, too."

"Very well, my confident friends," responded the thin voice which now sounded curiously flat. "We also have a proverb—and it is this: Those who will not listen to men must be taught by the gods. I say no more. But I leave a last warning. Remember the holy ones. Look to your temples. And when the smoke-tree above Vesuvius grows to the shape of an umbrella-pine, look to your lives."

Tito could hear the air whistle as the speaker drew his toga about him and the quick shuffle of feet told him the stranger had gone.

"Now what," said the cameo-cutter, "did he mean by that?"

"I wonder," grunted Rufus, "I wonder."

Tito wondered, too. And Bimbo, his head at a thoughtful angle, looked as if he had been doing a heavy piece of pondering. By night-fall the argument had been forgotten. If the smoke had increased no one saw it in the dark. Besides, it was Caesar's birthday and the town was in holiday mood. Tito and Bimbo were among the merry-makers, dodging the charioteers who shouted at them. A dozen times they almost upset baskets of sweets and jars of Vesuvian wine, said to be as fiery as the streams inside the volcano, and a dozen times they were cursed and cuffed. But Tito never missed his footing. He was thankful for his keen ears and quick instinct—most thankful of all for Bimbo.

They visited the uncovered theatre and, though Tito could not see the faces of the actors, he could follow the play better than most of the audience, for their attention wandered—they were distracted by the scenery, the costumes, the by-play, even by themselves—while Tito's whole attention was centered in what he heard. Then to the city-walls, where the people of Pompeii watched a mock naval-battle in which the city was attacked by the sea and saved after thousands of flaming arrows had been exchanged and countless colored torches had been burned. Though the thrill of flaring ships and lighted skies was lost to Tito, the shouts and cheers excited him as much as any and he cried out with the loudest of them.

The next morning there were *two* of the beloved raisin and sugar cakes for his breakfast. Bimbo was unusually active and thumped his bit of a tail until Tito was afraid he would wear it out. The boy could not imagine whether Bimbo was urging him to some sort of game or was trying to tell something. After a while, he ceased to notice Bimbo. He felt drowsy. Last night's late hours had tired him. Besides, there was a heavy mist in the air—no, a thick fog rather than a mist— a fog that got into his throat and scraped it and made him cough. He walked as far as the marine gate to get a breath of the sea. But the blanket of haze had spread all over the bay and even the salt air seemed smoky.

He went to bed before dusk and slept. But he did not sleep well. He had too many dreams—dreams of ships lurching in the Forum, of losing his way in a screaming crowd, of armies marching across his chest, of being pulled over every rough pavement of Pompeii.

He woke early. Or, rather, he was pulled awake. Bimbo was doing the pulling. The dog had dragged Tito to his feet and was urging the boy along. Somewhere. Where, Tito did not know. His feet stumbled uncertainly; he was still half asleep. For a while he noticed nothing except the fact that it was hard to breathe. The air was hot. And heavy. So heavy that he could taste it. The air, it seemed, had turned to powder, a warm powder that stung his nostrils and burned his sightless eyes.

Then he began to hear sounds. Peculiar sounds. Like animals under the earth. Hissings and groanings and muffled cries that a dying creature might make dislodging the stones of his underground cave. There was no doubt of it now. The noises came from underneath. He not only heard them—he could feel them. The earth twitched; the twitching changed to an uneven shrugging of the soil. Then, as Bimbo half-pulled, half-coaxed him across, the ground jerked away from his feet and he was thrown against a stone-fountain.

The water—hot water—splashing in his face revived him. He got to his feet, Bimbo steadying him, helping him on again. The noises grew louder; they came closer. The cries were even more animal-like than before, but now they came from human throats. A few people, quicker of foot and more hurried by fear, began to rush by. A family or two—then a section—then, it seemed, an army broken out of bounds. Tito, bewildered though he was, could recognize Rufus as he bellowed past him, like a water-buffalo gone mad. Time was lost in a nightmare.

It was then the crashing began. First a sharp crackling, like a monstrous snapping of twigs; then a roar like the fall of a whole forest of trees; then an explosion that tore earth and sky. The heavens, though Tito could not see them, were shot through with continual flickerings of fire. Lightnings above were answered by thunders beneath. A house fell. Then another. By a miracle the two companions had escaped the dangerous side-streets and were in a more open space. It was the Forum. They rested here a while—how long he did not know.

Tito had no idea of the time of day. He could *feel* it was black—an unnatural blackness. Something inside—perhaps the lack of breakfast and lunch—told him it was past noon. But it didn't matter. Nothing seemed to matter. He was getting drowsy, too drowsy to walk. But walk he must. He knew it. And Bimbo knew it; the sharp tugs told him so. Nor was it a moment too soon. The sacred ground of the Forum was safe no longer. It was beginning to rock, then to pitch, then to split. As they stumbled out of the square, the earth wriggled like a caught snake and all the columns of the temple of Jupiter came down. It was the end of the world—or so it seemed. To walk was not enough now. They must run. Tito was too frightened to know what to do or where to go. He had lost all sense of direction. He started to go back to the inner gate; but Bimbo, straining his back to the last inch, almost pulled his clothes from him. What did the creature want? Had the dog gone mad?

Then, suddenly, he understood. Bimbo was telling him the way out—urging him there. The sea-gate of course. The sea-gate—and then the sea. Far from falling buildings, heaving ground. He turned, Bimbo guiding him across open pits and dangerous pools of bubbling mud, away from buildings that had caught fire and were dropping their burning beams. Tito could no longer tell whether the noises were made by the shrieking sky or the agonized people. He and Bimbo ran on—the only silent beings in a howling world.

New dangers threatened. All Pompeii seemed to be thronging toward the marine-gate and, squeezing among the crowds, there was the chance of being trampled to death. But the chance had to be taken. It was growing harder and harder to breathe. What air there was choked him. It was all dust now—dust and pebbles, pebbles as large as beans. They fell on his head, his hands—pumice-stones from the black heart of Vesuvius. The mountain was turning itself inside out. Tito remembered a phrase that the stranger had said in the Forum two days ago: "Those who will not listen to men must be taught by the gods." The people of Pompeii had refused to heed the warnings; they were being taught now—if it was not too late.

Suddenly it seemed too late for Tito. The red hot ashes blistered his skin, the stinging vapors tore his throat. He could not go on. He staggered toward a small tree at the side of the road and fell. In a moment Bimbo was beside him. He coaxed. But there was no answer. He licked Tito's hands, his feet, his face. The boy did not stir. Then Bimbo did the last thing he could—the last thing he wanted to do. He bit his comrade, bit him deep in the arm. With a cry of pain, Tito jumped to his feet, Bimbo after him. Tito was in despair, but Bimbo was determined. He drove the boy on, snapping at his heels, worrying his way through the crowd; barking, baring his teeth, heedless of kicks or falling stones. Sick with hunger, half-dead with fear and sulphur-fumes, Tito pounded on, pursued by Bimbo. How long he never knew. At last he staggered through the marine-gate and felt soft sand under him. Then Tito fainted. . . .

Some one was dashing sea-water over him. Some one was carrying him toward a boat.

"Bimbo," he called. And then louder, "Bimbo!" But Bimbo had disappeared.

Voices jarred against each other. "Hurry—hurry!" "To the boats!" "Can't you see the child's frightened and starving!" "He keeps calling for some one!" "Poor boy, he's out of his mind." "Here, child—take this!'

They tucked him in among them. The oar-locks creaked; the oars splashed; the boat rode over toppling waves. Tito was safe. But he wept continually.

"Bimbo!" he wailed. "Bimbo! Bimbo!"

He could not be comforted.

Eighteen hundred years passed. Scientists were restoring the ancient city; excavators were working their way through the stones and trash that had buried the entire town. Much had already been brought to light—statues, bronze instruments, bright mosaics, household articles; even delicate paintings had been preserved by the fall of ashes that had taken over two thousand lives. Columns were dug up and the Forum was beginning to emerge.

It was at a place where the ruins lay deepest that the Director paused.

"Come here," he called to his assistant. "I think we've discovered the remains of a building in good shape. Here are four huge mill-stones that were most likely turned by slaves or mules—and here is a whole wall standing with shelves inside it. Why! It must have been a bakery. And here's a curious thing. What do you think I found under this heap where the ashes were thickest? The skeleton of a dog!"

"Amazing!" gasped his assistant. "You'd think a dog would have had sense enough to run away at the time. And what is that flat thing he's holding between his teeth? It can't be a stone."

"No. It must have come from this bakery. You know it looks to me like some sort of cake hardened with the years. And, bless me, if those little black pebbles aren't raisins. A raisin-cake almost two thousand years old! I wonder what made him want it at such a moment?"

"I wonder," murmured the assistant.

Being a Public Character

DON MARQUIS

E VER since I bit a circus lion, believing him to be another dog like myself, only larger, I have been what Doc Watson calls a Public Character in our town.

Freckles, my boy, was a kind of Public Character, too. He went around bragging about my noble blood and bravery, and all the other boys and dogs in town sort of looked up to him and thought how lucky he was to belong to a dog like me. And he deserved whatever glory he got out of it, Freckles did. For, if I do say it myself, there's not a dog in town got a better boy than my boy Freckles, take him all in all. I'll back him against any dog's boy that is anywhere near his size, for fighting, swimming, climbing, foot-racing, or throwing stones farthest and straightest. Or I'll back him against any stray boy, either.

Well, some dogs may be born Public Characters, and like it. And some may be brought up to like it. I've seen dogs in those travelling Uncle Tom's Cabin shows that were so stuck on themselves they wouldn't hardly notice us town dogs. But with me, becoming a Public Character happened all in a flash, and it was sort of hard for me to get used to it. One day I was just a private kind of a dog, as you might say, eating my meals at the Watsons' back door, and pretending to hunt rats when requested, and not scratching off too many fleas in Doc Watson's drug store, and standing out from underfoot when told, and other unremarkable things like that. And the next day I had bit that lion and was a Public Character, and fame came so sudden I scarcely knew how to act.

Even drummers from big places like St. Louis and Chicago would come into the drug store and look at my teeth and toe nails, as if they must be different from other dogs' teeth and toe nails. And people would come tooting up to the store in their little cars, and get out and look me over and say:

"Well, Doc, what'll you take for him?" and Doc would wink, and say:

"He's Harold's dog. You ask Harold."

Which Harold is Freckles's other name. But any boy that calls him Harold outside of the schoolhouse has got a fight on his hands, if that boy is anywhere near Freckles's size. Harry goes, or Hal goes, but Harold is a fighting word with Freckles. Except, of course, with grown people. I heard him say one day to Tom Mulligan, his parents thought Harold was a name, or he guessed they wouldn't have given it to him; but it wasn't a name, it was a handicap.

Freckles would always say, "Spot ain't for sale."

And even Heinie Hassenyager, the butcher, got stuck on me after I got to be a Public Character. Heinie would come two blocks up Main Street with lumps of Hamburg steak, which is the kind some one has already chewed for you, and give them to me. Steak, mind you, not old grisly scraps. And before I became a Public Character Heinie even begrudged me the bones I would drag out of the box under his counter when he wasn't looking.

My daily hope was that I could live up to it all. I had always tried, before I happened to bite that lion, to be a friendly kind of a dog towards boys and humans and dogs, all three. I'd always been expected to do a certain amount of tail-wagging and be friendly. But as soon as I got to be a Public Character, I saw right away that I wasn't expected to be *too* friendly any more. So, every now and then, I'd growl a little, for no reason at all. A dog that has bit a lion is naturally expected to have fierce thoughts inside of him; I could see that. And you have got to act the way humans expect you to act if you want to slide along through the world without too much trouble.

So when Heinie would bring me the ready-chewed steak I'd growl at him a little bit. And then I'd bolt and gobble the steak like I didn't think so derned much of it, after all, and was doing Heinie a big

personal favor to eat it. And now and then I'd pretend I wasn't going
to eat a piece of it unless it was chewed finer for me, and growl at
him about that.

That way of acting made a big hit with Heinie, too. I could see
that he was honored and flattered because I didn't go any further
than just a growl. It gave him a chance to say he knew how to manage
animals. And the more I growled, the more steak he brought. Everybody in town fed me. I pretty near ate myself to death for a while
there, besides all the meat I buried back of Doc Watson's store to
dig up later.

But my natural disposition is to be friendly. I would rather be
loved than feared, which is what Bill Petterson, the village drunkard,
used to say. When they put him into the calaboose every Saturday
afternoon he used to look out between the bars on the back window
and talk to the boys and dogs that had gathered round and say that
he thanked them one and all for coming to an outcast's dungeon as
a testimonial of affection, and he would rather be loved than feared.
And my natural feelings are the same. I had to growl and keep dignified and go on being a Public Character, and often I would say to
myself that it was losing me all my real friends, too.

The worst of it was that people, after a week or so, began to expect
me to pull something else remarkable. Freckles, he got up a circus,
and charged pins and marbles, and cents, when he found any one
that had any, to get into it, and I was the principal part of that circus.
I was in a cage, and the sign over me read:

SPOT, THE DOG THAT LICKED A LION
TEN PINS ADMITION

To feed the lion-eater, one cent or two white
      chiney marbles extry but bring your own
      meat.
Pat him once on the head twinty pins, kids
      under five not allowed to.
For shaking hands with Spot the lion-eater
      girls not allowed, gents three white
      chinies, or one aggie marble.
Lead him two blocks down the street and
      back, one cent before starting, no
      marbles or pins taken for leading him.

> For sicking him on the cats three cents or one
> red cornelian marble if you furnish the cat.
> Five cents to use Watson's cat. Watson's biggest
> Tom-cat six cents must be paid before sicking. Small
> kids and girls not allowed to sick him on cats.

Well, we didn't take in any cat-sicking money. And it was just as well. You never can tell what a cat will do. But Freckles put it in because it sounded sort of fierce. I didn't care for being caged and circused that way myself. And it was right at that circus that considerable trouble started.

Seeing me in a cage like that, all famoused-up, with more meat poked through the slats than two dogs could eat, made Mutt Mulligan and some of my old friends jealous.

Mutt, he nosed by the cage and sniffed. I nosed a piece of meat out of the cage to him. Mutt grabbed it and gobbled it down, but he didn't thank me any. Mutt, he says:

"There's a new dog down town that says he blew in from Chicago. He says he used to be a Blind Man's Dog on a street corner there. He's a pretty wise dog, and he's a right ornery-looking dog, too. He's peeled considerably where he has been bit in fights."

"Well, Mutt," says I, "as far as that goes I'm peeled considerable myself where I've been in fights."

"I know you are, Spot," says Mutt. "You don't need to tell me that. I've peeled you some myself from time to time."

"Yes," I says, "you did peel me some, Mutt. And I've peeled you some, too. More'n that, I notice that right leg of yours is a little stiff yet where I got to it about three weeks ago."

"Well, then, Spot," says Mutt, "maybe you want to come down here and see what you can do to my other three legs. I never saw the day I wouldn't give you a free bite at one leg and still be able to lick you on the other three."

"You wouldn't talk that way if I was out of this cage," I says, getting riled.

"What did you ever let yourself be put into that fool cage for?" says Mutt. "You didn't have to. You got such a swell head on you the last week or so that you gotta be licked. You can fool boys and humans all you want to about that accidental old lion, but us dogs got your number, all right. What that Blind Man's Dog from Chicago would do to you would be a plenty!"

"Well, then," I says, "I'll be out of this cage along about supper time. Suppose you bring that Blind Man's Dog around here. And if he ain't got a spiked collar on to him, I'll fight him. I won't fight a spike-collared dog to please anybody."

And I wouldn't, neither, without I had one on myself. If you can't get a dog by the throat or the back of his neck, what's the use of fighting him? You might just as well try to eat a blacksmith shop as fight one of those spike-collared dogs.

"Hey, there!" Freckles yelled at Tom Mulligan, who is Mutt Mulligan's boy. "You get your fool dog away from the lion-eater's cage!"

Tom, he hissed Mutt away. But he says to Freckles, being jealous himself, "Don't be scared, Freck, I won't let my dog hurt yours any. Spot, he's safe. He's in a cage where Mutt can't get to him."

Freckles got riled. He says, "I ain't in any cage, Tom."

Tom, he didn't want to fight very bad. But all the other boys and dogs was looking on. And he'd sort of started it. He didn't figure that he could shut up that easy. And there was some girls there, too.

"If I was to make a pass at you," says Tom, "you'd wish you was in a cage."

Freckles, he didn't want to fight so bad, either. But he was running this circus, and he didn't feel he could afford to pass by what Tom said too easy. So he says:

"Maybe you think you're big enough to put me into a cage."

"If I was to make a pass at you," says Tom, "there wouldn't be enough left of you to put in a cage."

"Well, then," says Freckles, "why don't you make a pass at me?"

"Maybe you figure I don't dast to," says Tom.

"I didn't say you didn't dast to," says Freckles; "any one that says I said you didn't dast to is a link, link, liar, and so's his Aunt Mariar."

Tom, he says, "I ain't got any Aunt Mariar. And you're another and dasn't back it."

Then some of the other kids put chips on to their shoulders. And each dared the other to knock his chip off. And the other kids pushed, and jostled them into each other till both chips fell off, and they went at it then. Once they got started they got really mad and each did all he knew how.

And right in the midst of it Mutt run in and bit Freckles on the calf of his leg. Any dog will fight for his boy when his boy is getting the worst of it. But when Mutt did that I give a budge against the wooden slats on the cage and two of them came off, and I was on top of Mutt. The circus was in the barn, and the hens began to scream and the horses began to stomp, and all the boys yelled, "Sick 'im!" and "Go to it!" and danced around and hollered, and the little girls yelled, and all the other dogs began to bark, and it was a right lively and enjoyable time. But Mrs. Watson, Freckles's Mother, and the hired girl ran out from the house and broke the fight up.

Grown women are like that. They don't want to fight themselves, and they don't seem to want any one else to have fun. You got to be a hypocrite around a grown woman to get along with her at all. And then she'll feed you and make a lot of fuss over you. But the minute you start anything with real enjoyment in it she's surprised to see you acting that way. Nobody was licked satisfactory in that fight, or licked any one else satisfactory.

Well, that night after supper, along comes that Blind Man's Dog. Never did I see a Blind Man's Dog that was as tight-skinned. I ain't a dog that brags, myself, and I don't say I would have licked that heavy a dog right easy, even if he had been a loose-skinned dog. What I do say is that I had been used to fighting loose-skinned dogs that you can get some sort of a reasonable hold on to while you are working around for position. And running into a tight-skinned dog that way, all of a sudden and all unprepared for it, would make anybody nervous. How are you going to get a purchase on a tight-skinned dog when you've been fighting loose-skinned dogs for so long that your teeth and jaws just naturally set themselves for a loose-skinned dog without thinking of it?

Lots of dogs wouldn't have fought him at all when they realized how they had been fooled about him, and how tight-skinned he was. But I was a Public Character now, and I had to fight him. More than that, I ain't ready to say yet that that dog actually licked me. Freckles he hit him in the ribs with a lump of soft coal, and he got off of me and run away before I could get my second wind. There's no telling what I would have done to that Blind Man's Dog, tight-skinned as he was, if he hadn't run away before I got my second wind.

Well, there's some mighty peculiar dogs in this world, let alone boys and humans. The word got around town, in spite of his running away like that before I got my second wind, that that Blind Man's Dog, so called, had actually licked me! Many pretended to believe it. Every time Freckles and me went down the street some one would say:

"Well, the dog that licked the lion got licked himself, did he?"

And if it was a lady said it, Freckles would spit on the sidewalk through the place where his front teeth are out and pass on politely as if he hadn't heard, and say nothing. And if it was a man that said it Freckles would thumb his nose at him. And if it was a girl that said it he would rub a handful of sand into her hair. And if it was a boy anywhere near his size, there would be a fight. If it was too big a boy, Freckles would sling railroad iron at him.

For a week or so it looked like Freckles and I were fighting all the time. On the way to school, and all through recess-times, and after school, and every time we went on to the street. I got so chewed and he got so busted up that we didn't hardly enjoy life.

No matter how much you may like to fight, some of the time you would like to pick the fights yourself and not have other people picking them off of you. Kids began to fight Freckles that wouldn't have dast to stand up to him a month before. I was still a Public Character, but I was getting to be the kind you josh about instead of the kind you are proud to feed. I didn't care so awful much for myself, but I hated it for Freckles. For when they got us pretty well hacked, all the boys began to call him Harold again.

And after they had called him Harold for a week he must have begun to think of himself as Harold. For one Saturday afternoon when there wasn't any school, instead of going swimming with the other kids or playing baseball, or anything, he went and played with girls.

He must have been pretty well down-hearted and felt himself pretty much of an outcast, or he wouldn't have done that. I am an honest dog, and the truth must be told, the disgrace along with everything else, and the truth is that he played with girls of his own accord that day—not because he was sent to their house on an errand, not because it was a game got up with boys and girls together, not because it was cousins and he couldn't dodge them, but because he was an outcast. Any boy will play with girls when all the boys and girls are playing together, and some girls are nearly as good as boys; but no boy is going off alone to look up a bunch of girls and play with them without being coaxed unless he has had considerable of a downfall.

Right next to the side of our yard was the Wilkinses. They had a bigger house and a bigger yard than ours. Freckles was sitting on the top of the fence looking into their orchard when the three Wilkins girls came out to play. There was only two boys in the Wilkins family, and they was twins; but they were only year-old babies and didn't amount to anything. The two oldest Wilkins girls, the taffy-colored-haired one and the squint-eyed one, each had one of the twins, taking care of it. And the other Wilkins girl, the pretty one, she had one of those big dolls made as big as a baby. They were rolling those babies and the doll around the grass in a wheelbarrow, and the wheel came off, and that's how Freckles happened to go over.

"Up in the attic," says the taffy-colored-haired one, when he had fixed up the wheelbarrow, "there's a little old express wagon with one wheel off that would be better'n this wheelbarrow. Maybe you could fix that wheel on, too, Harold."

Freckles, he fell for it. After he got the wagon fixed, they got to playing charades and fool girl games like that. The hired girl was off for the afternoon, and pretty soon Mrs. Wilkins hollered up the stairs that she was going to be gone for an hour, and to take good care of the twins, and then we were alone in the place.

Well, it wasn't much fun for me. They played and they played, and I stuck to Freckles—though his name was called nothing but Harold all that afternoon, and for the first time I said to myself "Harold" seemed to fit. I stuck to him because a dog should stick to his boy, and a boy should stick to his dog, no matter what the disgrace. But after a while I got pretty tired and lay down on a rug, and a new kind of flea struck me. After I had chased him down and cracked him with my teeth I went to sleep.

I must have slept pretty sound and pretty long. All of a sudden

I waked up with a start, and almost choking, for the place was smoky. I barked and no one answered.

I ran out to the landing, and the whole house was full of smoke. The house was on fire, and it looked like I was alone in it. I went down the back stairway, which didn't seem so full of smoke, but the door that led out on to the first-floor landing was locked, and I had to go back up again.

By the time I got back up, the front stairway was a great deal fuller of smoke, and I could see glints of flame winking through it way down below. But it was my only way out of that place. On the top step I stumbled over a gray wool bunch of something or other, and I picked it up in my mouth. Think I, "That is Freckles's gray sweater, that he is so stuck on. I might as well take it down to him."

It wasn't so hard for a lively dog to get out of a place like that, I thought. But I got kind of confused and excited, too. And it struck me all of a sudden, by the time I was down to the second floor, that that sweater weighed an awful lot.

I dropped it on the second floor, and ran into one of the front bedrooms and looked out.

By Jings! The whole town was in the front yard and in the street.

And in the midst of the crowd was Mrs. Wilkins, carrying on like mad.

"My baby!" she yelled. "Save my baby. Let me loose! I'm going after my baby!"

I stood up on my hind legs, with my head just out of that bedroom window, and the flame and smoke licking up all around me, and barked.

"My doggie! My doggie!" yells Freckles, who was in the crowd. "I must save my doggie!" And he made a run for the house, but some one grabbed him and slung him back.

And Mrs. Wilkins made a run, but they held her, too. The front of the house was one sheet of flame. Old Pop Wilkins, Mrs. Wilkins's husband, was jumping up and down in front of Mrs. Wilkins yelling, here was her baby. He had a real baby in one arm and that big doll in the other, and was so excited he thought he had both babies. Later I heard what had happened. The kids had thought that they were getting out with both twins but one of them had saved the doll and left a twin behind. The squint-eyed girl and the taffy-colored-haired girl and the pretty girl was howling as loud as their mother. And every now and then some man would make a rush for the front door, but the fire would drive him back. And every one was yelling advice to every one else, except one man who was calling on the whole town to get him an axe. The volunteer fire engine was there, but there wasn't any water to squirt through it, and it had been backed up too near the house and had caught fire and was burning up.

Well, I thinks that baby will likely turn up in the crowd somewhere, after all, and I'd better get out of there myself while the getting was good. I ran out of the bedroom, and run into that bunched-up gray bundle again.

I ain't saying that I knew it was the missing twin in a gray shawl when I picked it up the second time. And I ain't saying that I didn't know it. But the fact is that I did pick it up. I don't make any brag that I would have risked my life to save Freckles's sweater. It may be I was so rattled I just picked it up because I had had it in my mouth before and didn't quite know was I was doing.

But the *record* is something you can't go behind, and the record is that I got out the back way and into the back yard with that bundle swinging from my mouth, and walked around into the front yard and laid that bundle down—*and it was the twin!*

I don't make any claim that I *knew* it was the twin till I got into the front yard, mind you. But you can't prove I *didn't* know it was.

And nobody tried to prove it. The gray bundle let out a squall.

"My baby!" yells Mrs. Wilkins. And she kissed me. I rubbed it off with my paw. And then the taffy-colored-haired one kissed me. But when I saw the squint-eyed one coming I got behind Freckles and barked.

"Three cheers for Spot!" yelled the whole town. And they give them.

And then I saw what the lay of the land was, so I wagged my tail and barked.

It called for that hero stuff, and I throwed my head up and looked noble—and pulled it.

An hour before Freckles and me had been outcasts. And now we was Public Characters again. We walked down Main Street and we

owned it. And we hadn't any more than got to Doc Watson's drug
store than in rushed Heinie Hassenyager with a lump of Hamburg
steak, and with tears in his eyes.

"It's got chicken livers mixed in it, too!" says Heinie.

I ate it. But while I ate it, I growled at him.

Moses

BY

WALTER D. EDMONDS

It was a long climb. The scent was cold, too; so faint that when he found it behind the barn he could hardly trust himself. He had just come back from Filmer's with a piece of meat, and he had sat down behind the barn and cracked it down; and a minute later he found that scent reaching off, faint as it was, right from the end of his nose as he lay.

He had had the devil of a time working it out at first, but up here it was simple enough except for the faintness of it. There didn't appear to be any way to stray off this path; there wasn't any brush, there wasn't any water. Only he had to make sure of it, when even for him it nearly faded out, with so many other stronger tracks overlaying it. His tail drooped, and he stumbled a couple of times, driving his nose into the dust. He looked gaunt when he reached the spot where the man had lain down to sleep.

The scent lay heavier there. He shuffled round over it, sifting the dust with an audible clapping of his nostrils to work out the pattern the man had made. It was hard to do, for the dust didn't take scent decently. It wasn't like any dust he had ever come across, either, being glittery, like mica, and silvery in his nose. But he could tell after a minute how the man had lain, on his back, with his hands under his head, and probably his hat over his eyes to shield them from the glare which was pretty dazzling bright up this high, with no trees handy.

His tail began to cut air. He felt better, and all of a sudden he lifted up his freckled nose and let out a couple of short yowps and then a good chest-swelled belling. Then he struck out up the steep going once more. His front legs may have elbowed a little, but his hind legs were full of spring, and his tail kept swinging.

That was how the old man by the town entrance saw him, way down below.

The old man had his chair in the shadow of the wall with a black and yellow parasol tied to the back of it as an extra insurance against the sun. He was reading the Arrivals in the newspaper, the only column that ever interested him; but he looked up sharply when he heard the two yowps and the deep chest notes that, from where he sat, had a mysterious floating quality. It was a little disturbing; but when he saw a dog was the cause he reached out with his foot and shoved the gate hard, so that it swung shut and latched with a sound like a gong. Only one dog had ever come here, and that sound had been enough to discourage him; he had hung round for a while, though, just on the edge, and made the old man nervous. He said to himself that he wasn't going to watch this one, anyway, and folded the paper in halves the way the subway commuter had showed him and went on with the Arrivals.

After a while, though, he heard the dog's panting coming close and the muffled padding of his feet on the marble gate stone. He shook the paper a little, licked his thumb, and turned over half a sheet and read on through the Arrivals into the report of the Committee on Admissions. But then, because he was a curious old man, and kind-hearted, noticing that the panting had stopped—and because he had never been quite up to keeping his resolves, except once—he looked out of the gate again.

The dog was sitting on the edge of the gate stone, upright, with his front feet close under him. He was a rusty-muzzled, blue-tick foxhound, with brown ears, and eyes outlined in black like an Egyptian's. He had his nose inside the bars and was working it at the old man.

"Go away," said the old man. "Go home."

At the sound of his voice the hound wrinkled his nose soberly and his tail whipped a couple of times on the gate stone, raising a little star dust.

"Go home," repeated the old man, remembering the dog that had hung around before.

He rattled the paper at him, but it didn't do any good. The dog just looked solemnly pleased at the attention, and a little hopeful, and allowed himself to pant a bit.

"This one's going to be worse than the other," the old man thought, groaning to himself as he got up. He didn't know much about dogs anyway. Back in Galilee there hadn't been dogs that looked like this one—just pariahs and shepherds and the occasional Persian greyhound of a rich man's son.

He slapped his paper along the bars; it made the dog suck in his tongue and move back obligingly. Peter unhooked his shepherd's staff from the middle crossbar, to use in case the dog tried to slip in past him, and let himself out. He could tell by the feeling of his bare ankles that there was a wind making up in the outer heavens and he wanted to get rid of the poor creature before it began really blowing round the walls. The dog backed off from him and sat down almost on the edge, still friendly, but wary of the shepherd's staff.

"Why can't the poor dumb animal read?" thought Peter, turning to look at the sign he had hung on the gatepost.

The sign read:—

TAKE NOTICE
NO
DOGS
SORCERERS
WHOREMONGERS
MURDERERS
IDOLATERS
LIARS
WILL BE
ADMITTED

When he put it up, he had thought it might save him a lot of trouble; but it certainly wasn't going to help in the case of this dog. He expected he would have to ask the Committee on Admissions to take the matter up; and he started to feel annoyed with them for not having got this animal on the list themselves. It was going to mean a lot of correspondence and probably the Committee would send a memorandum to the Central Office suggesting his retirement again, and Peter liked his place at the gate. It was quiet there, and it was pleasant for an old man to look through the bars and down the path, to reassure the frightened people, and, when there was nothing else to do, to hear the winds of outer heaven blowing by.

"Go away. Go home. Depart," he said, waving his staff; but the dog only backed down on to the path and lay on his wishbone with his nose between his paws.

II

Peter went inside and sat down and tried to figure the business out. There were two things he could do. He could notify the Committee of the dog's arrival, or he could give the information to the editor. The Committee would sit up and take notice for once if they found the editor had got ahead of them. It would please the editor, for there were few scoops in Heaven. And then, as luck would have it, the editor himself came down to the gate.

The editor wasn't Horace Greeley or anybody like that, with a reputation in the newspaper world. He had been editor of a little country weekly that nobody in New York, or London, or Paris had ever heard of. But he was good and bursting with ideas all the time. He was now.

"Say, Saint Peter," he said, "I've just had a swell idea about the Arrivals column. Instead of printing all the 'arrivals' on one side and then the 'expected guests' on the other, why not just have one column and put the names of the successful candidates in upper-case type? See?" He shoved a wet impression under Peter's nose and rubbed the back of his head nervously with his inkstained hand. "Simple, neat, dignified."

Peter looked at the galley and saw how simple it would be for him, too. He wouldn't have to read the names in lower case at all. It would make him feel a lot better not to know. Just check the upper-case names as they came to the gate.

He looked up at the flushed face of the editor and his white beard parted over his smile. He liked young, enthusiastic men, remembering how hard, once, they had been to find.

"It looks fine to me, Don," he said. "But the Committee won't like losing all that space in the paper, will they?"

"Probably not," the editor said ruefully. "But I thought you could pull a few wires with the Central Office for me."

Peter sighed.

"I'll try," he said. "But people don't pay attention to an old man, much, Don. Especially one who's been in service."

The editor flushed and muttered something about bums.

Peter said gently, "It doesn't bother me, Don. I'm not ashamed of the service I was in." He looked down to his sandals. He wondered whether there was any of the dust of that Roman road left on them after so long a time. Every man has his one great moment. He'd had two. He was glad he hadn't let the second one go. "I'll see what I can do, Don."

It was a still corner, by the gate; and, with both of them silently staring off up the avenue under the green trees to where the butterflies were fluttering in the shrubbery of the public gardens, the dog decided to take a chance and sneak up again.

He moved one foot at a time, the way he had learned to do behind the counter in the Hawkinsville store, when he went prospecting towards the candy counter. These men didn't hear him any more than the checker players in the store did, and he had time to sniff over the gatepost thoroughly. It puzzled him; and as the men didn't take any notice, he gumshoed over to the other post and went over that, too.

It was queer. He couldn't smell dog on either of them and they were the best-looking posts he had ever come across. It worried him some. His tail drooped and he came back to the gate stone and the very faint scent on it, leading beyond the gate, that he had been following so long. He sat down again and put his nose through the bars, and after a minute he whined.

It was a small sound, but Peter heard it.

"That dog," he said.

The editor whirled round, saying, "What dog?" and saw him.

"I was going to let you know about him, only I forgot," said Peter. "He came up a while ago, and I can't get rid of him. I don't know how he got here. The Committee didn't give me any warning and there's nothing about him in the paper."

"He wasn't on the bulletin," said the editor. "Must have been a slip-up somewhere."

"I don't think so," said Peter. "Dogs don't often come here. Only one other since I've been here, as a matter of fact. What kind of a dog is he anyway? I never saw anything like him." He sounded troubled and put out, and the editor grinned, knowing he didn't mean it.

"I never was much of a dog man," he said. "But that's a likely-looking foxhound. He must have followed somebody's scent up here. Hi, boy!" he said. "What's your name? Bob? Spot? Duke?"

The hound lowered his head a little, wrinkled his nose, and wagged his tail across the stone.

"Say," said the editor. "Why don't I put an ad in the Lost and Found? I've never had anything to put there before. But you better bring him in and keep him here till the owner claims him."

"I can't do that," said Peter. "It's against the Law."

"No dogs. Say, I always thought it was funny there were no dogs here. What happens to them?"

"They get removed," said Peter. "They just go."

"That don't seem right," the young editor said. He ruffled his black hair with his hand. "Say, Saint," he asked, "who made this law anyway?"

"It's in Revelations. John wasn't a dog man, as you call it. Back in Galilee we didn't think much of dogs, you see. They were mostly pariahs."

"I see," said the editor. His blue eyes sparkled. "But say! Why can't I put it in the news? And write an editorial? By golly, I haven't had anything to raise a cause on since I got here."

Peter shook his head dubiously.

"It's risky," he said.

"It's a free country," exclaimed the editor. "At least nobody's told me different. Now probably there's nothing would mean so much to the owner of that dog as finding him up here. You get a genuine dog man and this business of passing the love of women is just hooey to him."

"Hooey?" Peter asked quietly.

"It just means he likes dogs better than anything. And this is a good dog, I tell you. He's cold-tracked this fellow, whoever he is, Lord knows how. Besides, he's only one dog, and look at the way the rabbits have been getting into the manna in the public garden. I'm not a dog man, as I said before, but believe me, Saint, it's a pretty thing on a frosty morning to hear a good hound high-tailing a fox across the hills."

"We don't have frost here, Don."

"Well," said the editor, "frost or no frost, I'm going to do it. I'll have to work quick to get it in before the forms close. See you later."

"Wait," said Peter. "What's the weather report say?"

The editor gave a short laugh.

"What do you think? Fair, moderate winds, little change in temperature. Those twerps up in the bureau don't even bother to read the barometer any more. They just play pinochle all day, and the boy runs that report off on the mimeograph machine."

"*I* think there's a wind making up in the outer heavens," Peter said. "When we get a real one, it just about blows the gate stone away. That poor animal wouldn't last a minute."

The editor whistled. "We'll have to work fast." Then, suddenly his eye blazed. "All my life I wanted to get out an extra. I never had a chance, running a weekly. Now, by holy, I will."

He went off up the avenue on the dead run. Even Peter, watching him go, felt excited.

"Nice dog," he said to the hound; and the hound, at the deep gentle voice, gulped in his tongue and twitched his haunches. The whipping of his tail on the gate stone made a companionable sound for the old man. His beard folded on his chest and he nodded a little.

III

He was dozing quietly when the hound barked.

It was a deep, vibrant note that anyone who knew dogs would have expected the minute he saw the spring of those ribs; it was mellow, like honey in the throat. Peter woke up tingling with the sound of it and turned to see the hound swaying the whole hind half of himself with his tail.

Then a high loud voice shouted, "Mose, by Jeepers! What the hell you doing here, you poor dumb fool?"

Peter turned to see a stocky, short-legged man who stuck out more than was ordinary, both in front and behind. He had on a gray flannel shirt, and blue denim pants, and a pair of lumberman's rubber packs on his feet, with the tops laced only to the ankle. There was a hole in the front of his felt hat where the block had worn through. He wasn't, on the whole, what you might expect to see walking on that Avenue. But Peter had seen queer people come to Heaven and he said mildly, "Do you know this dog?"

"Sure," said the stout man. "I hunted with him round Hawkinsville for the last seven years. It's old Mose. Real smart dog. He'd hunt for anybody."

"Mose?" said Peter. "For Moses, I suppose."

"Maybe. He could track anything through hell and high water."

"Moses went through some pretty high water," said Peter. "What's your name?"

"Freem Brock. What's yours?"

Peter did not trouble to answer, for he was looking at the hound; and he was thinking he had seen some people come to Heaven's gate and look pleased, and some come and look shy, and some frightened, and some a little shamefaced, and some satisfied, and some sad (maybe with memories they couldn't leave on earth), and some jubilant, and a whole quartette still singing "Adeline" just the way they were when the hotel fell on their necks in the earthquake. But in all his career at the gate he had never seen anyone express such pure, unstifled joy as this rawboned hound.

"Was he your dog?" he asked Freeman Brock.

"Naw," said Freem. "He belonged to Pat Haskell." He leaned his shoulder against the gatepost and crossed one foot over the other. "Stop that yawping," he said to Mose, and Mose lay down, wagging. "Maybe you ain't never been in Hawkinsville," he said to Peter. "It's a real pretty village right over the Black River. Pat kept store there and he let anybody take Mose that wanted to. Pretty often I did. He liked coming with me because I let him run foxes. I'm kind of a fox hunter," he said, blowing out his breath. "Oh, I like rabbit hunting all right, but there's no money in it. . . . Say," he broke off, "you didn't tell me what your name was."

"Peter," said the old man.

"Well, Pete, two years ago was Mose's best season. Seventy-seven fox was shot ahead of him. I shot thirty-seven of them myself. Five crosses and two blacks in the lot. Yes, sir. I heard those black foxes had got away from the fur farm and I took Mose right over there. I made three hundred and fifty dollars out of them hides."

"He was a good dog, then?" asked Peter.

"Best foxhound in seven counties," said Freem Brock. He kicked the gate with his heel in front of Mose's nose and Mose let his ears droop. "He was a fool to hunt. I don't see no fox signs up here. Plenty rabbits in the Park. But there ain't nobody with a gun. I wish I'd brought my old Ithaca along."

"You can't kill things here," said Peter.

"That's funny. Why not?"

"They're already dead."

"Well, I know that. But it beats me how I got here. I never did nothing to get sent to this sort of place. Hell, I killed them farm foxes and I poached up the railroad in the *pre*-serve. But I never done anything bad."

"No," said St. Peter. "We know that."

"I got drunk, maybe. But there's other people done the same before me."

"Yes, Freem."

"Well, what the devil did I get sent here for, Pete?"

"Do you remember when the little girl was sick and the town doctor wouldn't come out at night on a town case, and you went over to town and made him come?"

"Said I'd knock his teeth out," said Freem, brightening.

"Yes. He came. And the girl was taken care of," said Peter.

"Aw," Freem said, "I didn't know what I was doing. I was just mad. Well, maybe I'd had a drink, but it was a cold night, see? I didn't knock his teeth out. He left them in the glass." He looked at the old man. "Jeepers," he said. "And they sent me here for that?"

Peter looked puzzled.

"Wasn't it a good reason?" he asked. "It's not such a bad place."

"Not so bad as I thought it was going to be. But people don't want to talk to me. I tried to talk to an old timber-beast named Boone down the road. But he asked me if I ever shot an Indian, and when I said no he went along. You're the only feller I've seen that was willing to talk to me," he said, turning to the old man. "I don't seem to miss likker up here, but there's nowhere I can get to buy some tobacco."

Peter said, "You don't have to buy things in Heaven."

"Heaven?" said Freeman Brock. "Say, is that what this is?" He looked frightened all at once. "That's what the matter is. I don't belong here. I ain't the kind to come here. There must have been a mistake somewhere." He took hold of Peter's arm. "Listen," he said urgently. "Do you know how to work that gate?"

"I do," said Peter. "But I can't let you out."

"I got to get out."

Peter's voice grew gentler.

"You'll like it here after a while, Freem."

"You let me out."

"You couldn't go anywhere outside," Peter said.

Freem looked through the bars at the outer heavens and watched a couple of stars like water lilies floating by below. He said slowly, "We'd go some place."

Peter said, "You mean you'd go out there with that dog?"

Freem flushed.

"I and Mose have had some good times," he said.

At the sound of his name, Mose's nose lifted.

Peter looked down at the ground. With the end of his shepherd's staff he thoughtfully made a cross and then another overlapping it and put an X in the upper left-hand corner. Freem looked down to see what he was doing.

"You couldn't let Mose in, could you, Pete?"

Peter sighed and rubbed out the pattern with his sandal.

"I'm sorry," he said. "The Committee don't allow dogs."

"What'll happen to the poor brute, Pete?"

Peter shook his head.

"If you ask me," Freem said loudly, "I think this is a hell of a place."

"What's that you said?"

Peter glanced up.

"Hello, Don," he said. "Meet Freem Brock. This is the editor of the paper," he said to Freem. "His name's Don."

"Hello," said Freem.

"What was that you said about Heaven being a hell of a place?" asked the editor.

Freem drew a long breath. He took a look at old Mose lying outside the gate with his big nose resting squashed up and sideways against the bottom crossbar; he looked at the outer heavens, and he looked at the editor.

"Listen," he said. "That hound followed me up here. Pete says he can't let him in. He says I can't go out to where Mose is. I only been in jail twice," he said, "but I liked it better than this."

The editor said, "You'd go out there?"

"Give me the chance."

"What a story!" said the editor. "I've got my extra on the Avenue now. The cherubs will be coming this way soon. It's all about the hound, but this stuff is the genuine goods. Guest prefers to leave Heaven. Affection for old hunting dog prime factor in his decision. It's human interest. I tell you it'll shake the Committee. By holy, I'll have an editorial in my next edition calling for a celestial referendum."

"Wait," said Peter. "What's the weather report?"

"What do you think? Fair, moderate winds, little change in temperature. But the Central Office is making up a hurricane for the South Pacific and it's due to go by pretty soon. We got to hurry, Saint."

He pounded away up the Avenue, leaving a little trail of star dust in his wake.

Freem Brock turned on Saint Peter.

"He called you something," he said.

Peter nodded.

"Saint."

"I remember about you now. Say, you're a big shot here. Why can't you let Mose in?"

Peter shook his head.

"I'm no big shot, Freem. If I was, maybe—"

His voice was drowned out by a shrieking up the Avenue.

"Extry! Extry! Special Edition. Read all about it. Dog outside Heaven's Gate. Dog outside . . ."

A couple of cherubs were coming down the thoroughfare, using their wings to make time. When he saw them, Freem Brock started. His shoulders began to itch self-consciously and he put a hand inside his shirt.

"My gracious," he said.

Peter, watching him, nodded.

"Everybody gets them. You'll get used to them after a while. They're handy, too, on a hot day."

"For the love of Pete," said Freem.

"Read all about it! Dog outside Heaven's Gate. Lost Dog waiting outside . . ."

"He ain't lost!" cried Freem. "He never got lost in his life."

" 'Committee at fault,' " read Peter. "Thomas Aquinas isn't going to like that," he said.

"It don't prove nothing," said Freem.

"Mister, please," said a feminine voice. "The editor sent me down. Would you answer some questions?"

"Naw," said Freem, turning to look at a young woman with red hair and a gold pencil in her hand. "Well, what do you want to know, lady?"

The young woman had melting brown eyes. She looked at the hound. "Isn't he cute?" she asked. "What's his name?"

"Mose," said Freem. "He's a cute hound all right."

"Best in seven counties," said Peter.

"May I quote you on that, Saint?"

"Yes," said Peter. "You can say I think the dog ought to be let in." His face was pink over his white beard. "You can say a hurricane is going to pass, and that before I see that animal blown off by it I'll go out there myself—I and my friend Freem. Some say I'm a has-been, but I've got some standing with the public yet."

The girl with red hair was writing furiously with a little gold glitter of her pencil. "Oh," she said.

"Say I'm going out too," said Freem. "I and Pete."

"Oh," she said. "What's your name?"

"Freeman Brock, Route 5, Boonville, New York, U. S. A."

"Thanks," she said breathlessly.

"How much longer before we got that hurricane coming?" asked Freem.

"I don't know," said the old man, anxiously. "I hope Don can work fast."

"Extry! Owner found. Saint Peter goes outside with hound, Moses. Committee bluff called. Read all about it."

"How does Don manage it so fast?" said Peter. "It's like a miracle."

"It's science," said Freem. "Hey!" he yelled at a cherub.

They took the wet sheet, unheeding of the gold ink that stuck to their fingers.

"They've got your picture here, Pete."

"Have they?" Peter asked. He sounded pleased. "Let's see."

It showed Peter standing at the gate.

"It ain't bad," said Freem. He was impressed. "You really mean it?" he asked. Peter nodded.

"By cripus," Freem said slowly, "you're a pal."

Saint Peter was silent for a moment. In all the time he had minded Heaven's Gate, no man had ever called him a pal before.

IV

Outside the gate, old Mose got up on his haunches. He was a weather-wise dog, and now he turned his nose outwards. The first puff of wind came like a slap in the face, pulling his ears back, and then it passed. He glanced over his shoulder and saw Freem and the old man staring at each other. Neither of them had noticed him at all. He pressed himself against the bars and lifted his nose and howled.

At his howl both men turned.

There was a clear gray point way off along the reach of the wall, and the whine in the sky took up where Mose's howl had ended.

Peter drew in his breath.

"Come on, Freem," he said, and opened the gate.

Freeman Brock hesitated. He was scared now. He could see that a real wind was coming, and the landing outside looked almighty small to him. But he was still mad, and he couldn't let an old man like Peter call his bluff.

"All right," he said. "Here goes."

He stepped out, and Mose jumped up on him, and licked his face.

"Get down, darn you," he said. "I never could break him of that trick," he explained shamefacedly to Peter. Peter smiled, closing the gate behind him with a firm hand. Its gong-like note echoed through Heaven just as the third edition burst upon the Avenue.

Freeman Brock was frightened. He glanced back through the bars, and Heaven looked good to him. Up the Avenue a crowd was gathering. A couple of lanky, brown-faced men were in front. They started towards the gate.

Then the wind took hold of him and he grasped the bars and looked outward. He could see the hurricane coming like an express train running through infinity. It had a noise like an express train. He understood suddenly just how the victim of a crossing accident must feel.

He glanced at Peter.

The old Saint was standing composedly, leaning on his staff with one hand, while with the other he drew Mose close between his legs. His white robe fluttered tight against his shanks and his beard bent sidewise like the hound's ears. He had faced lack of faith, in others; what was worse, he had faced it in himself; and a hurricane, after all, was not so much. He turned to smile at Freem. "Don't be afraid," he said.

"O.K.," said Freem, but he couldn't let go the gate.

Old Mose, shivering almost hard enough to rattle, reached up and licked Peter's hand.

One of the brown-faced men said, "That's a likely-looking hound. He the one I read about in the paper?"

"Yep," said Freem. He had to holler now.

Daniel Boone said, "Let us timber-beasts come out with you, Saint, will you?"

Peter smiled. He opened the gate with a wave of his hand, and ten or a dozen timber-beasts—Carson, Bridger, Nat Foster—all crowded through, and started shaking hands with him and Free-man Brock. With them was a thin, mild-eyed man.

"My name's Francis," he said to Freem when his turn came. "From Assisi."

"He's all right," Daniel Boone explained. "He wasn't much of a shot, but he knows critters. We better get holt of each other, boys."

It seemed queer to Freem. Here he was going to get blown to eternity and he didn't even know where it was, but all of a sudden he felt better than he ever had in his life. Then he felt a squirming round his legs and there was Mose, sitting on his feet, the way he would on his snowshoes in cold weather when they stopped for a sandwich on earth. He reached down and took hold of Mose's ears.

"Let her blow to blazes," he thought.

She blew.

The hurricane was on them. The nose of it went by, sweeping the wall silver. There was no more time for talk. No voices could live outside Heaven's gate. If a man had said a word, the next man to hear it would have been some poor heathen aborigine on an island in the Pacific Ocean, and he wouldn't have known what it meant.

The men on the gate stone were crammed against the bars. The wind dragged them bodily to the left, and for a minute it looked as if Jim Bridger were going, but they caught him back. There were a lot of the stoutest hands that ever swung an axe in that bunch hold-ing on to Heaven's gate, and they weren't letting go for any hurri-cane—not yet.

But Freem Brock could see it couldn't last that way. He didn't care, though. He was in good company, and that was what counted the most. He wasn't a praying man, but he felt his heart swell with gratitude, and he took hold hard of the collar of Mose and felt the license riveted on. A queer thing to think of, a New York State dog license up there. He managed to look down at it, and he saw that it had turned to gold, with the collar gold under it. The wind tore at him as he saw it. The heart of the hurricane was on him now like a million devils' fingers.

"Well, Mose," he thought.

And then in the blur of his thoughts a dazzling bright light came down and he felt the gate at his back opening and he and Peter and

Francis and Daniel and the boys were all drawn back into the peace of Heaven, and a quiet voice belonging to a quiet man said, "Let the dog come in."

V

They were sitting together, Freem and Peter, by the gate, reading the paper in the morning warmth, and Peter was having an easy time with the editor's new type arrangement. "Gridley," he was reading the upper-case names, "Griscome, Godolphin, Habblestick, Hafey, Hanlon, Hartwell, Haskell . . ."

"Haskell," said Freem. "Not Pat?"

"Yes," said Peter. "Late of Hawkinsville."

"Not in big type?"

"Yes."

"Well, I'll be . . . Well, that twerp. Think of that. Old Pat." Peter smiled.

"By holy," said Freem. "Ain't he going to be amazed when he finds Mose up here?"

"How's Mose doing?"

"He's all right now," said Freem. "He's been chasing the rabbits. I guess he's up there now. The dew's good."

"He didn't look so well, I thought," Peter said.

"Well, that was at first," said Freem. "You see, the rabbits just keep going up in the trees and he couldn't get a real run on any of them. There, he's got one started now."

Peter glanced up from the paper.

Old Mose was doing a slow bark, kind of low, working out the scent from the start. He picked up pace for a while, and then he seemed to strike a regular knot. His barks were deep and patient.

And then, all of a sudden, his voice broke out—that deep, ringing, honey-throated baying that Freem used to listen to in the late afternoon on the sand hills over the Black River. It went away through the public gardens and out beyond the city, the notes running together and fading and swelling and fading out.

"He's pushing him pretty fast," said Freem. "He's going to get pretty good on these rabbits."

The baying swelled again; it came back, ringing like bells. People in the gardens stopped to look up and smile. The sound of it gave Peter a warm tingling feeling.

Freem yawned.

"Might as well wait here till Pat Haskell comes in," he said.

It was pleasant by the gate, under the black and yellow parasol. It made a shade like a flower on the hot star dust. They didn't have to talk, beyond just, now and then, dropping a word between them as they sat.

After a while they heard a dog panting and saw old Mose tracking down the street. He came over to their corner and lay down at their feet, lolling a long tongue. He looked good, a little fat, but lazy and contented. After a minute, though, he got up to shift himself around, and paused as he sat down, and raised a hind leg, and scratched himself behind his wings.

The Soul of Caliban

BY

EMMA-LINDSAY SQUIER

F ROM French Louie I had this story, which you will accept as true or scout as impossible, according to your liking and knowledge of dogs. For myself, I think it is true, for he was not blessed— or cursed—with imagination.

French Louie is a curious mixture of savagery and simplicity. For many years he lived by trapping in the northern woods. And yet, despite his cruel occupation, he has always loved animals. Many a fox cub he has reared to adulthood when it came to grief in his traps. Many a tear has he shed—I can well believe it—when a dragged and bloody trap told the mute story of an animal's desperate gnawing of a foot or a leg as the price of freedom. One day when he heard a visitor to the menagerie remark that it was a pity that animals had no souls, he flew into a rage, fairly booted the visitor out of the place, and was still sputtering French and English when I dropped in upon him.

"No souls, they say!" he snorted, spreading his hands and puckering his lips in contemptuous mimicry. "Faugh! They give me the gran' pain! The only animal they ever have, I bet you, he is a canary bird that say 'Pretty Poll' all day long!"

"That's a parrot," I said mildly. But he only snorted.

"No soul, they say! Listen, I tell you somet'ing I bet you nobody believe, by Gar! Or they say, 'Oh, dat dog he obey hees instinct.' *Bien*, all I say ees, who know what ees instinct and what ees soul? And I bet you many a man he ain't got the soul that that dog got instinct—no, by Gar!"

366

It was in the sheep country of Alberta that Louie knew the dog, Caliban. Leon Suprenon was his owner, and Louie used to visit the sheep man at his ranch, far removed from civilization.

"Leon he was one fine educated man, by Gar," he told me. "Books —with pictures—he had many of them in hees 'ouse. Dat dog, Caliban, he name' heem from a pleh by Shakespeare—you have heard of heem?"

"Yes," I said, unsmiling.

"You know a pleh with a dog name' Caliban in eet?"

"Not a dog," I answered, "but a poor imprisoned monster, ugly, deformed, and very wicked, yet somehow very pitiful."

French Louie nodded vigorously.

"*C'est la même chose*," he assured me. "Dat dog, Caliban—oh, *mon Dieu*, he was ogly! Hees lip she always lifted up like zis—in a snar-rl—all the time dat lip! And hees eyes—leetle, mean-looking eyes, wid a frown between dem always, and teeth dat would snep together —*clop!* No tramps ever came near the place of Leon Suprenon. Dey know dat dog, Caliban; he was not a beast to be trifle' with."

"What kind of a dog was he?" I asked of Louie the Frenchman.

He shrugged his shoulders, spread out his hands and shook his head. No kind, and every kind, was what I gathered from his description—a big, shaggy dog, as large as a sheep dog, and much more stockily built. His hair had no silky smoothness to it. Rather it was like the rough, matted fur of a wolf—and Louie maintained that that Caliban had wolf blood in him. There was a strain of bulldog, too, that made his legs short and bowed a bit. His under jaw came out pugnaciously—always with that lifted lip which was no fault of his, but which gave his face a perpetually savage expression.

Ugly he must have been; yet useful, too. As a guard against tramps and the lawless characters who are to be found in any part of the country where civilization is at a distance, he was invaluable. As a sheep dog, too, he had not his equal in Alberta. Perhaps it is too much to say that he could count the sheep his master owned. But it is true that he would watch them, passing into the big corrals, his sharp, shaggy ears pointed, his small, close-set eyes never wavering in their intense regard, his whole body taut with concentration. And if any lingered or did not come, Caliban would need no word of command

to stir him to action. Like an arrow he would dart out, snapping at
the lagging heels, turning in a scatter-brained ewe, or dashing off
across the fields to find a sheep which he knew had strayed or had
fallen into the river.

A dog of strange, tumultuous jealousies, and incomprehensible
tenderness. So rough was he, when herding the sheep, that Leon
Suprenon was always shouting: "Caliban, you devil! Stop biting that
sheep or I'll beat your ugly brains out!"

Caliban would stop short, regard his master with a long, disdainful
stare, and then look back at the sheep, as if to say: "Those silly
things! What difference does it make whether I bite their heels or
not?"

And yet—that was the dog that, after seeing the sheep into the
corral one winter afternoon when a blizzard was threatening to blow
down from the north, did not come into the house to dream and
twitch under the kitchen stove as was his custom. When darkness
fell Leon noticed the dog's absence at first with unconcern, and then
with growing uneasiness. The rising wind flung itself viciously upon
doors and windows, the white snow whirled up against the panes
with sharp, sibilant flurries. Leon went to the door and called. The
blizzard drove his voice back in his throat; the wind hurled him
against the portals, and drove an icy blast of snow into the hall.

Leon Suprenon was not the man to be daunted by a storm. He remembered that after the gates were shut, Caliban had stood steadily
gazing away toward the dim fields, where the menacing curtain of
oncoming wind and snow was blotting out the contours of stream
and distant forest.

So he took a lantern and fought his way out into the terrible night,
out toward the sheep corrals, and then out toward the invisible fields
beyond the stream. A mile he went—perhaps more—fighting his way
against the fury of the storm. It was out by the cluster of pine trees
that marks the east line of the ranch that he met Caliban, coming
home.

The dim light of the lantern threw a weak golden circle against
the driving white mistiness of the snow. And into the nebulous ring
of light came Caliban, grim, staggering, a grotesque monster loom-
ing out of the white darkness, his mouth strangely misshapen by

something he was carrying—*a lamb*, newly born. Beside him, struggling weakly yet valiantly against the driving snow, came the mother sheep, which had given birth to her baby in the midst of the dreadful blizzard. Caliban was coming slowly, adapting his pace to hers, stopping when she would stop, yet with unmistakable signs that he expected her to struggle forward with him. And the lamb—the weak, bleating little thing that swung from his teeth as lightly as if it had been a puff of thistledown.

Now the dog Caliban never begged for caresses. He was not the sort of dog to leap and bark and wag his tail when the master came home. Between him and Leon Suprenon there was an understanding—a man's understanding of mutual respect and restraint. A word of commendation sufficed him, or sometimes a pat on the head. But never, as long as Leon had owned the dog, could he recall a time when Caliban had ever sought to ingratiate himself by being friendly and playful, as the other dogs would do.

Nevertheless, Caliban had his jealousies, fierce, deep and primitive. He killed a dog that Leon petted casually; he took it by the throat and crushed it with his great teeth, then flung the quivering body down and stared at it with those baleful, close-set eyes. There was blood on the perpetual snarl of his lifted lip.

Then fearlessly he awaited his punishment. Leon beat him cruelly. But Caliban never flinched or whimpered, just stood there hunching himself up and shutting his eyes, licking his lips a bit as the blows hurt him more and more. When it was over, he shook himself, stretched, then pricked up his ears and looked Leon in the face, as if to say: "Well, that's over. Now have you any orders?" If he had whimpered once—but he did not. Leon swore furiously, and had the dead dog buried in the meadow. He did not caress the other dogs after that. They were valuable to him—but Caliban was priceless. And Leon knew that the only way of breaking his stubborn spirit would be to kill him.

Caliban had one abiding hatred: cats. Whereas the other dogs chased them joyously, or ignored them as inferior creatures, Caliban loathed them, chased them savagely, killed them mercilessly. He had a short, brutal way of doing it; if he caught a luckless cat—and he would run like a yearling buck, that dog Caliban—he would give it one shake, like the crack of a whip, and then toss the cat into the air. It usually died with a broken neck and a broken back. And by the law of the survival of the fittest, the cats that escaped from Caliban's savage sallies were wise in their generation and kept out of his way.

But there was one small cat, not yet out of kittenhood, that had either come recently to the ranch, or else by an accident had not crossed Caliban's path—a gentle little cat, all gray, with a white paw which she was always licking as if proud of it.

One day she sat sunning herself on the porch before the house. Caliban came by that way, and saw her.

With the savage, deep-throated growl that all the other cats had learned to fear as the most deadly thing of life, he leaped at her, caught her, flung her up into the air.

Perhaps it was supreme ignorance of danger that saved her from death. For the gentle little cat had not tried to run from the oncoming whirlwind of teeth and gleaming eyes. She lay where Caliban had flung her, dazed, inert, staring at the terrible dog, with round, uncomprehending eyes. He saw that he had not killed her. He came nearer, ready to shake her with the peculiarly deadly twist that he knew so well. Still she did not move. She could not. She only mewed, a very small, pitiful mew, and her stunned body twitched a little.

Caliban hesitated, sniffed at her, turned away. After all, he seemed to tell himself, you could not kill a weak, helpless thing like that—a thing that could not run.

Leon Suprenon came out and found the little cat. He took her up very gently, and she tried to purr as he stroked her quivering, hurt body.

"Caliban," Leon said sternly, "that was not a sportsmanlike thing to do. I am ashamed of you!"

And to his great surprise, Caliban, the insolent, the ever-snarling, put his tail between his legs and slunk down the porch steps. He too was ashamed.

But Caliban, that ugly, misshapen dog with the perpetual snarl on his lifted lip, could make amends. And to the best of his ability he did. The gentle little cat did not die, but never did she fully recover the use of her limbs. She had a slow, halting way of walking, and running was an impossibility. She would have been an easy prey for the joyous, roistering dogs that chased cats, not from enmity, but because it was the proper thing to do. But Caliban stood between her and eager, sniffing dogs like a savage, sinister warrior. Too well did the other ranch dogs know the menace of those close-set eyes, the ugly, undershot jaw, and the snarl that showed the glitter of deadly, clamping teeth. They learned—through experience—that the little gray cat was not to be molested.

Not only did Caliban become the little gray cat's protector; he became her friend. She would sit on the fence and watch for the sheep dogs to come up to the house after the day's work was done. When the other dogs filed past her, she paid no attention, realizing perfectly that they dared not harm her. And when Caliban came, close at the heels of Leon Suprenon, she would yawn and stretch, purr loudly, and drop squarely and lightly on the big dog's back. He would carry her gravely into the kitchen, lie down while she got slowly off his back, and would lie under the stove, with the little cat purring and rubbing about his face. It was not in him to show affection. But he permitted her carefully to wash his face and ears, tug at burrs that matted his heavy coat, and to sleep between his forefeet.

Once another cat, emboldened by the gray cat's immunity from danger, went to sleep between Caliban's great paws. When he awoke and found the intruder peacefully purring against his chest, he gave one terrific growl, sprang to his feet, seized the strange cat and shook it. Savagely he flung it across the room. It was dead before ever it struck the floor.

Now it was at this time that Leon Suprenon married Amelie Morin, from Dubuiqui, and brought her to the ranch that was bounded by dark forests and deep, turbulent rivers. She chafed a little under the isolation of the place, and shivered when at night the wolves howled far back on the distant slopes. But she loved Leon Suprenon, and in time became reconciled to the loneliness of the ranch—still more reconciled when a baby was born to her, and was strong and healthy and beautiful.

Caliban had accepted the girl, Amelie, stoically, without apparent resentment. It was as if he knew that sooner or later his master would bring home a woman to share the lonely ranch house. But the baby —that was a different thing. He had not bargained on the small intruder who became at once the lord and tyrant of the household. When Leon took up the tiny baby in his arms, Caliban growled, and his eyes became a baleful red.

When Leon put the baby in its crib, and spoke to it foolishly, fondly, as all fathers do, Caliban came and stood beside him, looking down at the red-faced crinkly-eyed baby; and again the dog growled, deep in his throat.

One day when Leon caressed the child, Caliban sprang, trying to tear the infant out of his arms. Leon kicked the dog furiously aside, and beat him with a leather whip.

"Caliban, you devil!" he panted between the blows. "If you ever touch that baby, I'll kill you!"

And, as if the dog understood, he hunched himself and shut his eyes, licking his lips as the heavy lash fell again and again. Then he shook himself, stared at his master with somber, unwavering eyes, and went out of the house without once looking back.

For a whole week he did not return. One of the ranchmen reported that he had seen Caliban in the forest, that the dog had mated with a female wolf.

Leon Suprenon said that it was not true, and that Caliban would come back. But Amelie cried out:

"No, no! That dog, he is a monster! Never again would I feel that my baby was safe!"

"You misjudge him," Leon said soothingly, "he is a little jealous of the baby, it is true, but he will overcome that in time. An ugly-looking dog, I grant you, but he is very gentle, nevertheless."

"*Gentle*—that beast!" The girl shut her eyes and shuddered.

Caliban did come back. He appeared at the kitchen door one day when Leon was out looking after the sheep—sullen, defiant, his glittering, close-set eyes seeming to question whether or not he would not be welcomed. The perpetual snarl on his lifted lip and the misshapen ugliness of his powerful body made him ever more repellent to the girl Amelie, who snatched up her baby from where he was playing on the floor, ran with him to the bedroom, and closed and bolted the door. But a royal welcome he received from the little gray cat, that dragged herself toward him with purring sounds of joy. She mewed delightedly, rubbed against his bowed legs, and tried to lick his face. Caliban, for the first and last time, bent his ugly head, and licked the little gray cat, briefly and furtively.

The dog had learned his lesson as to the status of the baby. And whether or not his heart was seared with that savage, primitive jealousy which he had shown at first so plainly, no hint of it now appeared. At first he ignored the child, even when it crawled toward him as he lay under the kitchen stove. Later he would watch the round-faced baby with rigid, attentive eyes—eyes in which there were blue-green wolf gleams behind the honest brown. Sometimes he would sniff at the child questioningly, as if trying to ascertain for himself what charm such a helpless crawling little animal could possibly have for the man who was his master and his idol.

Little by little Amelie's distrust lessened, and she was willing that the baby should lie in his crib on the sunny porch, when Caliban was stretched out on the steps with the little gray cat sleeping between his paws.

Then one day, after a morning of housework within doors, she came out to take the baby—and he was gone. The crib was empty, the little blankets were rumpled into confusion. The dog Caliban still lay sleeping upon the porch, and the little gray cat purred drowsily against his furry chest.

Amelie screamed, and the men came running up from the sheep pens and barns, snatching up sticks of wood, or fumbling with guns. Leon came running with a face the color of chalk; and Amelie clung to him, screaming, sobbing, wild with hysterical fear. She was certain that some wild animal had snatched her baby out of his crib and devoured him.

"Nonsense!" said Leon Suprenon positively. "No wild animal could have come near the house with Caliban on guard."

After an hour of frantic searching, they found the child. Back of the ranch house where the garbage was dumped and burned, there they found the baby, playing happily with an old tin can, dirty and bedraggled, yet quite quite unhurt and unharmed.

In the first moment of acute relief, no one thought to question how the child had come so far. But afterward—

Leon stood in deep thought, staring down at Caliban, who returned his look steadily, unflinchingly, as was his wont. For the first time a doubt of the dog's integrity came into his mind. He knew Caliban's great strength, knew that the dog could have carried the baby as easily as he had carried the newborn lamb. And the garbage pile— there was a grim humor in that which pointed to Caliban's line of reasoning. Undesirable things were thrown out there; things put upon the garbage pile were never brought back into the house; therefore, if the baby were put out there, with the rest of the rubbish . . .

"Caliban, you devil!" said Leon Suprenon between clenched teeth. Yet he could not beat the dog. The evidence was only circumstantial.

Had the thing happened to any one else's child, he would have laughed heartily at the story. But to him it was not so funny. Anything might have happened to the child. The dog might have dropped it; or stray wolves might have come down out of the woods. The baby might have cut its hands terribly on broken glass or rusty tin cans.

"Caliban," said Leon Suprenon sternly, "you have spoiled my belief in you. I will never be able to trust you again."

The great ugly dog stared at him with those glittering, close-set eyes, then turned away abruptly and lay down. It was as if he accepted the defeat of his plans, the humiliation, the loss of his master's trust, with stoical resignation. It was almost as if he had shrugged his shoulders.

Now there came the winter time—a lean, terrible winter, when the wolves howled about the ranch, sometimes becoming so bold as to come close to the barns, and corrals, and the house.

The spring was late, and even when the snow began to melt, and the first warm breezes to come up from the south, still the howling of the wolf pack was heard on distant hills, and still tracks were found in the crusted snow about the barn and the sheep corrals.

One day in the spring an urgent message came to Amelie Suprenon, begging her to come to a neighboring ranch where a woman lay in child-birth.

She could only go on horseback—and the need for her help was imminent. She saddled her horse herself, for the men were out on the ranges. Then she hesitated as to leaving or taking the baby. But Leon had said he would return at noon, and the sun was then almost at the zenith. She scribbled a note for him, put the baby in the bedroom in the little pen which Leon had made for it, and shut the door.

Then she mounted her horse and rode hard and fast to the woman who was in need of her.

Leon Suprenon did not get the note. A hint of spring sickness had come upon some of the sheep, and he worked all through the morning and late into the afternoon with sheep dip and sprays. When he was about to return to the ranch house, one of the men told him that he had seen Amelie riding by, at noon, in the direction of the Pourers' ranch. Leon frowned at bit. He did not like to have Amelie ride alone, especially on the forest roads. He flung himself upon his horse, shouted to his men to go on with their work, and took a short cut across the fields to ride home with Amelie.

He met her just as she came out of the door, tired, but smiling.

"Such a sweet little baby boy!" she called to Leon as he rode nearer. Then her face suddenly clouded.

"The baby—our baby—" she said uncertainly. "You did not leave him alone?"

Leon stared back at her, his forehead wrinkled.

"The baby?" he repeated. "Why, surely, Amelie, he is with you?"

For an instant she did not reply. A slow fear was dawning in her heart that stretched her eyes wide and made them hard and glassy.

"No—no," she almost whispered. "I left a note—I thought you would come at noon. The baby then—he is there alone—perhaps with —Caliban—" Her voice died away, as if she were afraid of the name she had spoken.

Leon tried to laugh, to make light of her fears. But his lips were a bit stiff, and he breathed as he helped her into the saddle.

"Come, come, Amelie, you worry too much. The little one will be quite well—you shall see—only very hungry perhaps and exercising his small lungs terrifically. As for Caliban—"

Amelie slashed at her horse's flank with the whip. Her face was dead-white.

"Where was that dog—that terrible beast, when you came away?" she gasped as they galloped down the snowy road.

"I don't know," Leon jerked out grimly, as if thinking aloud. "I can't remember seeing him—yes, yes, he stood looking away toward the ranch house; I remember now that he barked once—then trotted away. I thought he was rounding up a sheep. I did not call him back. One of the men laughed and said that he was going to meet the lady—"

"*Wolf!*" the girl finished hoarsely. "O *grand Dieu*, guard my baby! He is in danger, I tell you, Leon; I feel it, I know it! That beast—that horrible beast who mates with bloodthirsty wolves—you would not believe it, Leon, but I tell you it is true—true! Oh, my baby, my little baby!"

She lashed her horse with frenzied, hysterical hands, and the startled animal reared and plunged forward. Fast, faster, the slender hoofs pounded through the snowy slush of the road, and Leon's horse followed, breathing hard and straining at the bit.

They did not speak again, the husband and wife, but rode, rode as if for the saving of a life.

It was Amelie who dismounted first, when at the end of that wild ride her horse came to a stop, panting and trembling. She dashed the unlocked door wide open, and an instant later a wild scream sent the blood ebbing from Leon's face and made his hands numb clods of flesh as they fumbled for the gun in his belt.

The scene he saw as he stumbled through the hallway turned him sick with a deadly nausea of horror and despair.

Amelie lay fainting in the open doorway of the bedroom. Beyond, an empty cradle, an open window, with muddy tracks on the window sill, told a dreadful story. But the thing that made him cry out, savagely, hoarsely, was the dog—Caliban. The snarling, misshapen beast stood in the doorway, staring at him with red, malevolent eyes —*and there was blood on the heavy jowls and the thick matted hair of the chest.*

"You—you devil!" Leon screamed like a madman—and fired.

The dog still stood there, just an instant. The small, close-set eyes blinked slightly, the ugly head jerked back once—and he fell in a silent, twitching heap.

"Oh, God! Oh, God!" Leon was sobbing, hardly knowing what he said or did. And then—he heard a baby crying.

Stunned, incredulous, almost believing himself in a tortured dream, the man went slowly forward. The baby lay behind the door, lay where it had been dragged to safety. It was crying with fright and hunger, beating the air vaguely with its pink little hands. And over by the dresser, in a pool of blood—lay a dead wolf.

"There is a grave on the ranch of Leon Suprenon," said French Louie solemnly, in the language of his people, "where the dog, Caliban, lies buried. And above it is a tombstone of marble—yes, the whitest of marble—with this inscription:

Here lies Caliban, a dog. He died as he lived, misjudged, maligned, yet unafraid. In life he never failed in duty, and in death he was faithful to his trust.

"And dat is why," said Louie, the Frenchman, lapsing into the argot of his daily life, "dat I get so mad inside of me when people say animals dey have no souls. Did not the dog, Caliban, have a soul? Oh, *mon Dieu!* I know dis: when he died dat day, and hees spirit went out of hees big, ogly body and rose up to the skies, the good Saint who guards the gates up dere he look out, and say: 'Why, Caliban, ees dat you? Come in, *mon brave.* I did not know you. How beautiful you have grown!' "

The Dark Gentleman

BY

G. B. STERN

Chapter 1

G OLDEN Toes lurched sideways with laughter, tripped over his ear, and tossed it back again inside out. His two friends, the Chows, were really excruciatingly funny; and their solemn, carved expressions helped to bring out the point of any story they might be telling him. Toes, after the fashion of spaniels, wished that he were a chow, Chinese, inscrutable . . .

"That was a good one!" he said, gasping, and wiping his eyes with the other ear. "I wish the others could have heard it."

The Chows said nothing, but a queer stiffening of their features indicated that this mention of "the others" had not passed unnoticed. Golden Toes, young, friendly, and open-hearted, was always thus wistfully trying to establish peace and good-will between the Chows, who lived in the house at the foot of the hill, and his own pals in the house on top of the hill. English and Chinese, living in Italy—surely fate had intended them for alliance? But so far his efforts had been futile and wasted. Baloo and Pekoe remained the enemies. A feud which had begun on instinct developed on events. It was, indeed, remarkable that Toes should ever have had enough initiative to charge through the standing barrier of hostility; or that Baloo and Pekoe should have consented to receive him on the further side of it. But so it was; they liked Toes; Toes liked them. Boris and Kim and Tessa shrugged their shoulders and wrinkled their noses with

378

distaste, but allowed him to amble to and fro as he pleased. As for Renny, who was Toe's mother, she said anxiously that she hoped those horrid Chows wouldn't teach him any nasty outlandish ways with chopsticks and opium . . . and that you never knew, with foreigners!

"I wish," said Toes, now, undaunted by his failures in the past, "I wish you fellows got on rather better with our fellows. You don't give them a chance, you know. They need *knowing*." At this moment they were trotting along the road past the end of our fellows' garden, Toes between Baloo and Pekoe, and the master of Baloo and Pekoe striding on ahead for his usual morning survey of the budding artichokes. "They'd *like* to know you better," Toes went on earnestly, hoping for the best. "Drop in to call in a friendly way, and—"

Boris, Tessa, and Kim had sighted the enemy. They all rushed forward on to the edge of the topmost terrace, hurling each other out of the way, lashing their tails, barking so that the very hills were shaken with the deep sinister howl which swelled from Boris's massive throat; with Tessa's yap, on a higher, more persistent pitch of anger; with the Irish terrier yelling: "I'll fight you—I'll fight you— I'll fight you!" "Get away—get away!" from Boris; "Go on, you beasts! Go on, you curs! Go on, you cowards!" screamed Tessa, dancing on the extreme edge of the terrace. And then, all together, on a note of noisy derision: "Soup! Soup!! Soup!!!" for they had heard a delicious rumour, that, among discriminating Orientals, the chow puppy was entirely bred and valued to be turned into broth.

Baloo and Pekoe stood still.

"Oh, *come* on!" pleaded Golden Toes.

Baloo and Pekoe, with wooden features, stared steadfastly upwards, measuring the distance. The big wolf-hound lifted his head high and lashed his tail from side to side. How dared the Chows pass along the road that looped their garden slope? The air was torn to shreds with the furious barking of the dogs at Casa Lucceola. You felt that the drifting splinters and fragments would never again form and be one large whole air. . . .

"—don't mean half they say. People never do," finished Golden Toes, rather disconcerted. The Chows had, after all, contented themselves with mere growling, but he could not help feeling that their growls held more certain menace than all the row kicked up by his troublesome pals.

For a few moments they continued their walk in silence. Toes, to hide embarrassment, affected to discover a new and rather cheery form of smell, and went burrowing after it into the scrub and wild peppermint of the hill-side beyond his own garden confines. When he returned to his companions, with a lot of earth on his nose and the split on his lower lip reopened, Pekoe said: "We t'ink Renny looking stlangely much beautiful, last night."

"Why, you didn't see her, did you? We were in the dining-room with the Legs."

"N-no. No see. But felt she looking beautiful. So did Baloo him t'ink, too."

Baloo blushed. He was suddenly glad that no low-minded and unworthy quadruped up at Casa Lucceola had a great ruff like his own; its shining pallor, he knew, set off his mouth and tongue like black enamel. He wondered whether Renny admired very fair dogs with black mouths. He thought he was handsomer than Pekoe, though the Honourable-Legs had said to a connoisseur in chows that Pekoe had cost him more.

"Toes, Toes, Toes, Toes, Toes!" The call was wafted, faint but undeniable, from the Legs-in-Authority at Casa Lucceola. Toes rolled on jauntily for a few more steps, then began to hang back and look around. He knew that the Legs-in-Authority was not at all keen on this morning walk with the alien chows, mainly for the reason that the Honourable-Legs was so liable afterwards to boast about his influence over a Lucceola spaniel.

"Toes, *Toes!*" More emphatic, the summons. The Legs-in-Authority had been calling before at random, but now he had actually caught sight of the long, clumsy shape of dark golden-brown just turning the corner where the path squiggled up among the olives towards a disused sheepcote with a red roof; near by, a great clump of cactus spikes was cruelly jabbing away a spreading wild-rose bush from the edge of a deep stone well.

"Toes!"

It was not etiquette to acknowledge that when the Legs called, sooner or later you had to obey. "I've just got to go and see a dog about a man," Toes remarked, in an offhand way, to the Chows, who understood the formula perfectly. "So long! Meet you to-morrow morning, usual place." And off he scuttered wildly, at what he imagined was a good spanking gallop, for home, ears flying wildly in all directions; fat, comfortable body tumbling sideways, hardly raised from the ground by those big spreading paws that had gained him his name, paws richly coloured as a wheat-field lit by the level sunrays of evening. And they were kind paws, too; you felt that the whole nature of Toes was somehow expressed by them: warm, reliable, friendly paws. The Legs-in-Authority bent to slap him pleasantly on his side, as Toes collapsed, gasping, near his feet. "Haven't much wind, have you?" he remarked; "you funny, fat old idiot!" And, grateful for the compliment, Toes turned up his amber eyes and licked whatever was handiest to lick. Toes was only a puppy still.

The Legs dismissed him, and he shambled off round to the back of the house, where he met Boris and Kim.

"Been keeping low company again?" said Boris reprovingly.

"Oh, don't bother me," answered Toes. "You're so insular, all of you. Had breakfast yet?"

Boris nodded. And then he said the most surprising thing: "Renny's looking so strangely beautiful this morning!"

"Renny?" repeated Toes, in amazement. It was old-fashioned to say "mother," although Poppit, his little sister, never addressed Renny otherwise than as "Mamma." "Renny *beautiful*? But how queer that you should have said that! Baloo and Pekoe said exactly the same thing to me, only a few minutes ago!"

. . . A sort of tremor passed down Boris's back, and Kim's tail went suddenly erect. "Did they?" grunted Boris. And *"Did* they?" muttered Kim.

"And anyway, *Renny—*" Toes began anew, in good-natured disparagement.

But at that moment she came towards them. She had been visiting the little grave at the end of the kidney-bean-bed, under the wall supporting that patch of garden which the home-sick Legs called Lower Peckham. It was Upper Peckham on which Boris, Tessa, Kim,

and Toes were now standing. Renny always went for a few minutes
every morning, or at least nearly every morning, to visit her poor,
dear, dead husband's grave; and to make sure that the Legs kept it
properly tended and watered. She was a little upset because they
grew nothing there except white stocks. Dr. Watson had so loved
a bit of colour. He had been a great deal older than herself, so that
she had entertained for him that sort of winsome respect which a
small shy, charming, Cocker spaniel would naturally feel for a sedate
and experienced Field spaniel. It had been a happy marriage, on the
whole. Watson was not good-looking, and he nearly always had a
wart or two on his melancholy nose, which used to spring into fresh
prominence whenever it had nearly healed, through his frequent
earth-burrowing in search of irresistible smells. Toes had inherited
this tendency, but fortunately his disfigurement was well under his
lower lip. He was a far handsomer dog than his father, more shining
and silky, recalling the grain, the light and shade, of a table-top in
polished old golden-walnut; and in temper he was not nearly so much
of a wet blanket. Kim and Boris, who could still remember the
elderly Watson, much preferred his grave to his company. But
Renny remained a faithful mourner:

"I had such reverence for the Doctor, my dears. He was most distinguished in his profession. Only a general practitioner, of course;
but sometimes, when they called him up at night, he used to go for
miles to see a puppy with spaghetti-sickness." For she was careful
never to mention worms, or anything the least bit crude, in front of
Poppit. "And so thrifty! I've seen him take his biscuit, and trot away
with it, and bury it where he'd already buried six or seven others,
without breaking off a bit, in case a rainy day should come when
he'd want them. Oh, he was a great loss to us, a very great loss. . . ."
But all this had happened over eight months ago. Toes and Poppit
could hardly remember their dad.

Renny was not strikingly lovely. She was a plain, serviceable dark-
brown, with quite good features—humble, sherry-coloured eyes,
seeking for ever some object at whom to languish and adore, two
longish ears, an acquiescent nose, four docile paws, a short and un-
critical tail, and a very obvious lack of burnish, either to her coat or
to her temperament. Unkind friends had called her well-meaning,

and the Legs said she was a good little thing and never gave any
trouble. She was reasonably well-born, but without a pedigree; she
spoke with a faintly Cocker accent, or not so much accent, perhaps,
as inflection. Kim, who really ought to have been the Hon. Aubrey
O'Hara, if he had not had a bar sinister across his escutcheon—Kim
had merely looked her all over once, and pronounced judgment, with
that command of foreign languages which gave him such an advantage over the others: "She'll just do for Watson. But I simply can't
imagine any other dog looking at her twice. She has neither chic nor
chien." Boris, who was standing by, very young and solemn at the
time, a mere chubby ball of fawn woolliness, asked innocently:
"What does that mean?" "It means," replied Kim, never at a loss,
"that she has neither chick nor child."

Well, Renny now had both; but she had not been a sparkling success in Lucceola circles for any except her more homely qualities.

Later on, Tessa appeared among them. Two of the legs coming out
of Italy from England had brought her along as a future wife for
Boris; and Tessa, having undeniable chic, had no difficulty whatever in acquiring chien.

Tessa had race quivering in every finely cut limb, in the high poise
of her head, the conical prick of her ears, her scornful attitude
towards all affection that was abundantly offered to her from the
Legs. Then, too, it expressed itself in her aptitude for giving trouble;
no one could give trouble to the extent that Tessa did. She was for
ever restless, on wires, demanding that doors should be opened for
her, darting impatiently away from embraces; for ever getting ill,
or chasing hens, or biting stray Legs that meandered too confidently
up the garden path. She arrived with that pitifully thin and adolescent
look about her which always causes anxiety, and for weeks had fussed
about her food in a way that almost drove the Legs crazy; despising
milk, lifting a coy and critical nose away from whatever was ordered
for her by the Veterinary-Legs; threatening to die at any moment.
. . . And then, just when her behaviour had been such that all the
Legs and all the other dogs had begun to feel that they would hardly
care if she did die as long as she hurried up about it—suddenly and
delicately, and with no apparent effort, she would begin to charm
them, put forth all her exquisite airs and graces, bestow swift and

unlooked-for caresses that were valued at fifty times their worth because of their rareness—"*Darling* Tessa! Isn't she *too* adorable?" ...

And Tessa, having gained her point, relapsed afresh into being a nuisance.

Of course Tessa despised Renny and Poppit from the first moment she saw them. Renny was humdrum; she told prosy anecdotes; if you listened to the beginning and the end, it never mattered whether or not you had heard the sagging middle. She was a widow, too, and what could be duller than that? reflected Tessa, youthful, slim, intolerant, and divinely conceited. She had imagined hitherto that all the dogs agreed with her; so that she was at a complete loss to understand their queer, entranced gaze as Renny came towards them from round the bed of daffodils tossing on Upper Peckham. . . .

"I should like to paint you like that," said Boris. "You know what I mean—all those waving yellow flowers, and then your glorious shining brown coat next to them. Oh, Renny, I *do* so love dark-brown, and ears that hang down!"

Tessa, taking this last remark to be a mere impertinence directed at herself, and not an honest expression of opinion—how could it be? —at once and vindictively bit all four of his legs, one after the other: "Take that, and that, and that, and *that!*" . . . But Boris did not even notice. Putting her aside, and with his handsome eyes still heavy with dreams, he followed Renny up the steep cobbled path towards the kennels.

She was going to have her Regular Morning Talk with Poppit. Very serious talks they were, for she believed in an old-fashioned upbringing. She did not want Poppit to grow like Tessa, for instance; and, indeed, there was very little danger of that. Tessa had this dreadful modern style about her. Poor little Poppit, as she was always called, was the youngest by eight hours of Renny's seven puppies, and so very much the smallest that you would hardly have said she and Toes could possibly be brother and sister. The Legs had said many times that Poppit was the runt, but Renny felt that "runt" was again not a very nice word, and did not like to hear it used in her presence. She had reprimanded Toes very sharply when once, in boisterous high spirits, he had cried: "Runt you are!" in answer to one of Poppit's timid requests; unquenched by reproof, he had gone shouting and swaggering and rolling down the hill, again and again tripping over his ears and calling out: "Runt-o! Runt you are! *Runt* you are!" in diminishing shouts of school-dog glee.

Tessa got up and, standing like a little silvery fawn, disdainfully watched Renny's progress up the path, with Boris lumbering devotedly in her wake. "Isn't Renny absurd?" she said turning to Kim. "She actually believes that Boris is following *her!* She gave him such a skittish little twirl of her tail just now. Fancy, that little frump! I expect he's been called away on business to the end of the garden."

But Kim failed to respond. . . . True, he did not like Tessa. He never had liked her. She was too twentieth-century in her style, too slim, unformed and insolent. But certainly he had never before extolled Renny either, except for her tractable qualities of wife and mother. His taste was for fine women, of the Edwardian period: "You should have seen Lillie Langtry!" he often said. Yet now, his long pointed nose and tan throat supine upon his crossed paws, his eyes two reticent slits, he drawled forth a contradictory: "I don't know. . . . Why shouldn't he be drawn by Renny? She's not a classic beauty, but there's a disturbing fascination about her. . . ."

"About *Renny?*" cried Tessa, incredulous. Surely Kim was mocking her? "Well, that just about takes the Melox!"

But he continued, as though he had not heard her sharp bark of amazement: "A disturbing fascination. . . . Better than beauty! Better, or worse! More destructive. . . . How did Troy fall? Are these walls any stronger? . . . Tantalizing little Renny. . . ."

He raised his head uneasily, and twisted it from side to side, as though an invisible net were descending upon him; the same net, perhaps, which had ensnared his great-grandfather, the first to betray the long line of an impeccable family by becoming too much aware of that lovely little Italian greyhound.

Kim sighed. It was from this great-grandmother that he had inherited his fleetness and his nervous grace; but she had broken the pedigree, and the O'Hara rakes could not boast any more. "It's a wise dog that knows his own great-grandmother," murmured Kim, softly mocking at that tenacious instinct which even in him, outcast, rake, mongrel—to use the bitterest word of all!—held it a sorrow to have belonged in his time to every exclusive club in London—except the Kennel Club. . . .

"But," Tessa argued, "only last week you said—"

"Tessa, my child, you'll never be successful with dogs if you remind them of what they said last week." And Kim added musingly: "It's her carriage that attracts me particularly. There's a *je ne sais quoi* about it; supple and yet gallant, as though she spurned the gravel."

Tessa was getting all hot and bothered. What *was* the matter with them? First Boris and then Kim! She looked at Toes, hoping to find an ally. But Toes was rolling on his back, rocking gently from side to side, his taut throat the hue of bright warm gingerbread when licked to a hotter colour by the reflection of fire flame.

. . . Tessa drew back on her haunches and crouched, with flattened ears, watchful of Toes. His fat, jolly, ungainly bulk was at all times an irresistible magnet to the primeval wolf in her. He was so warm, so silky, so luscious. . . . Fitful longings stirred and moved in the buried portions of her brain. She felt it would be nice—satisfying and *nice* to get all of Toes into her mouth at once; all of him, though he was bigger than she was—and crunch! Her eyes gleamed, and she sprang. . . .

Presently they were rolling over and over on the gravel, jaws snapping, teeth like the flash of white castanets; dirty, strong, gloriously happy. Tessa, uppermost for the moment, called over her shoulder to Kim: "Renny bustles when she walks! Yes, she does, she bustles! She waggles from side to side. She looks hideous from the front and worse from the back!" But now Toes was on top of her again and she had no breath left for further insults.

But she grew more and more bewildered as the long, hot day wore on, and still Renny seemed to be weaving spells round the befuddled judgments of Boris and Kim, and, according to Toes, of the Chows, shut up into their garden at the foot of the hill. Tessa was interested in the Chows, though she barked formidably at their approach, because she was a wolf, and on wolves depended the safety of the house, and the safety of the Legs, and the sanctity of every stone in the garden. Supposing you left that sort of thing to spaniels? Good heavens, *spaniels* . . .

But Pekoe and Baloo were without doubt handsome, and descendants of a fine old family; she had heard that the civilization of the Chinese, their art and their culture, were infinitely superior to those of the later European races; and Tessa, who accepted presents without any Victorian fuss, would gladly have become the possessor of a jade necklace—a lump of carved jade would add such allure, lying on the silver and black grizzle of her soft fur.

Renny would look awful in jade. . . .

It was at luncheon, the Legs' luncheon, to which the dogs were sometimes admitted, that Renny herself first became conscious of the unwonted sensation of being admired. At once she began to ripple, to hold her nose at a coyer angle, to flick back her ears, and even, with a daring glance, to take a bone from the very mouth of Boris, who sat back chivalrously, more than ever like the King of Cadonia, and paid her some ponderous compliment about the flavour of the marrow not being nearly so sweet as a lick from her adorable little tongue.

"Great Spratt!" groaned Tessa.

In consequence of this atmosphere of impending courtship, they did not pay so much attention as they wontedly did to the Legs, or to their chances of favours being dispensed from the table above into their imploring jaws. Usually they found the spectacle of the Legs at their meals full of interest and possibilities. The Legs behaved very oddly, of course. Why, for instance—and this was the subject of endless speculation—did each two of them remain stodgily seated in the same place, and eating off the same platter, instead of vehemently pushing their muzzles into another's platter and sampling if what was there might be better than in their own; jostling the platters along as they gobbled up the contents; dashing back again to their own places, for fear that what they had left might now have been lapped up by another two of the Legs? . . . *That* was the way to enjoy food. Their own banquets were boisterous, rollicking affairs, compared with these that happened four times a day in the dining-room of Casa Lucceola.

They each had their own methods of begging for scraps. The spaniels, frankly imploring, their whole shaggy bodies an upward yearning; their paws, impervious to snubs, planted on first one and then another pair of knees: "Oh, please, please, *plea-ea-ease!*" But Kim would thrust a long, cool, insidious nose on to a chosen knee and keep it there, his liquid eyes unwaveringly fixed, expectant, but not sycophantic, for even in the act of beggary Kim retained an imperial pride. And Tessa, whose personality was liker to Kim's than anybody's, would sit with her head thrown back, her ears pricked, her neck arched, her little chest thrust regally out, her fore-paws wide apart and slightly turned inwards, arrogant in the knowledge that her thin, bony little frame, rigid now with desire for that which the Legs might choose at any moment to bestow, was so exquisitely built that it would cause any artist to cry aloud for joy at its immature perfection.

"The trouble about Boris," she thought, flicking an impatient glance at her affianced husband, "is that he gives himself too easily. How does he expect the Legs to value his handshake if he's done it about forty-nine times a minute?" For Boris's established method with the Legs was to walk majestically up to two of them—Boris was noble and majestic in all his movements—and, deliberately raising his large white fore-paw, to present it with the air of one benignly conferring a favour, at the same time turning his magnificent head slightly in the opposite direction, blinking a little self-consciously as he did so. The Legs, especially if it were the Green-Silk-Legs, who adored him, dizzy at the flattery of his condescension, would shake him gratefully by the paw and then let it drop with a thud to the ground. A subtle inclination of Boris's head acknowledged that the ceremony had been quite in order. He would then sit for a few seconds, motionless. Thereafter might be observed another idea rising slowly from the depths of his being into its cerebral plateau as a bubble rises to the surface of the water. "I think"—thus the idea could be interpreted—"that I will give them my paw—*again*." When this performance had repeated itself—well, perhaps Tessa had exaggerated when she said forty-nine times a minute!—but about eighteen times, the recipient of the succession of paws would collapse into hysteria. . . .

"I think," said Boris—and the bubble rose—"that I'll give them my paw—*again!*" and with the stress of "*again*" came the flump of the paw on the knee!

Kim, on rare occasions, also presented his paw, but he presented it delicately, and it lay light and cool as a snow-flake in the palm with no weight behind the drop. Kim could control every movement of his lean, dapper body as though he were a little tan harlequin. When the Legs gave him a piece of meat he never snatched, as did Tessa and the spaniels; nor took it gently and clumsily like Boris, but with fastidious precision, as though a piece of velvet had just touched your fingers and withdrawn itself again, leaving no dabbled wetness of tongue nor dent of teeth behind it. It was easy to believe that Boris had had a Public School education—Winchester and Oxford, double blue, and rowed number five in his boat; but how astonishing that Kim should have been brought up anyhow, allowed to run wild over in Ireland, to pick up his schooling anywhere, to listen unchecked to the too cynical conversation of his brother, the elder O'Hara— Rake O'Hara they had called him. Kim's queer, grim heart had starved for affection when he was a puppy, and though he would never allow the Legs to guess it, he still craved to be made much of, even for occasional sloppiness. "Kim is so aloof and impersonal," complained the more sentimental among the Legs; but the Legs-in-Authority and the Shapely-Legs and the Nutritious-Legs understood him better—understood that a dog, a real dog, a terrier, simply could not allow himself to give way and become affectionate while there were spaniels about. After all, he had caste to keep up.

The Equestrian-Legs now presented Kim with something from his plate. "Carrots!" said Kim coldly. "Thank you. Have you ever seen me in a Eustace Miles restaurant by any chance? No? Well then . . ."

Tessa chimed in, sympathizing with him: "I could fancy a taste of *pâté de foie gras* to-day; just the merest morsel to tempt my appetite. One needs a change!" She lunged violently on to the gravy and scraps which had just been injudiciously put down on the floor for Tommy, the cat; and, with one voracious gobble, went straight through it and out at the other end. . . .

"Just the merest morsel!" scoffed Kim. "You're not a gourmet, Tessa, you're a gourmande. There's all the difference in the world between the two."

Tommy was looking dreadfully disappointed, but not vindictive.

He was never vindictive. From the day of his first arrival at Casa Lucceola, when shouts of admiration from the Italian-Retainer-Legs proclaimed the beauty of *il gatto inglese,* Tommy had always been in a good humour. He had sprung lightly from the basket and, purring loudly, made his tour of inspection of the house: "Well, dear me, this is a very nice dresser! I like this mahogany table. What a truly excellent fireplace!" Such had been Tommy's friendly, cheerful mood. And, finally: "Yes, these Legs will suit me very well," rubbing himself against them, his back arched like a croquet-hoop. There was a general idea among the Legs that Tommy, though popular, was inclined to be cheeky, *prepotente;* for not only was he pleased with the house, pleased with the Legs, pleased with the dogs, pleased with life—he was also mighty pleased with himself! Boris had a habit, when Tommy was still a kitten, of picking him up and carrying him about inside his mouth, so that it was no unusual sight to see Boris walking about with a long Persian-tabby tail waving gently from one corner of his jaw. Then, perhaps, he would yawn or open his mouth to catch a stone thrown him by the Legs . . . and Tommy would leap out, crumpled but serene, and still purring.

Gertie and Maudie were only San Goffredo cats, the one white, the other black; both very thin from underfeeding and inferiority complexes when they first strayed up to Casa Lucceola demanding to be taken in, kept, fed and cherished. They could not, of course, be compared for looks or charm with *il gatto inglese.* In fact, to Tommy they were objects of polite interest, because Tommy, by dint of living entirely among dogs, had come to fancy himself a dog. "What queer-looking creatures!" he would say, watching Gertie and Maudie skirmishing wildly up an olive tree. "Local fauna, I presume!" And then, with his bushy tail held very high and waving slightly at the tip, he would accompany the Legs on their country walks, answering their summons with as much confidence as Boris, Tessa, Kim, Renny, Poppit and Toes. "Here I am! Here I am!" was Tommy's cry, hurrying out, and, as he imagined, barking. . . . Tommy tried so hard to bark. He felt that if he could only bring it out once, just once, he'd be able to bark ever afterwards.

He was least popular at meals, when his needles would suddenly stab into a calf of the Legs, under the table, just by way of announcing that he was there—he, Tommy, *il gatto inglese*. The Green-Silk-Legs was frightfully funny in her behaviour to Tommy. She would jump up screaming and throw back her chair with a clatter, her hand to her heart, announcing that she couldn't—simply couldn't—sit in the same room with a *cat!*—she was made like that!—and would babble something in extenuation, about Lord Roberts. . . . Tommy regarded her horror of him as a curious phenomenon that might easily be overcome by politeness and perseverance on his part. "Let's be friends!" he used to say to the Green-Silk-Legs, running up to her and, with a light spring, arriving on her lap or shoulder. But by this time the table was in an uproar, and the Green-Silk-Legs had shot across the room yelling for help. "Funny!" remarked Tommy. "Funny. . . ."

"No, thank you," said Kim, courteously refusing for the second time a fragment proffered by the Legs from their lunch. It was not Kim's lucky day. "Apples? Thank you, no. I've never yet felt the need of keeping the doctor away." Then he broke off and chuckled reminiscently. "At least, only once. . . . Pretty little woman, she was!" Then his eye was drawn magnetically by Renny, and he added gallantly in a lower voice: "I'm beginning to think *all* doctors' wives are bewitching."

Boris, not to be outdone in courtship, brought a piece of chewed cheese-rind and dropped it from his mouth in silent homage near Renny's nose. "Cheese to the cheese," he said, not quite knowing what this meant, but having heard something very like it used in compliment the other day by the Equestrian-Legs to the Shapely-Legs when putting sugar in her coffee. A flicker of irony passed across Kim's wrinkled forehead, but he made no comment.

"Oh, you mustn't!" coquettishly from Renny. "I mean, it's so dear of you, but you mustn't say things like that to me. I'm afraid you're a sad Legs with the ladies!"

Tessa's sharp eyes darted jealously from one to the other of the Legs, wondering if they, too, had fallen into this sudden bewildering delusion about Renny's beauty. The flattering deference of Kim's attention, the awakening lovelight in Boris's mournful eyes, were now too conspicuous not to have been observed. The Legs were indeed talking about Renny. Tessa caught the name repeated several times, but she could not quite get the hang of their conversation. "I can understand them as long as they're simple and straightforward," the dogs always declared, "but all this euphuism and terminology, these reverberating inexactitudes, this confusion of archaic metaphor. . . ."

Lunch was over, and the animals made a rush after the Legs-in-Authority, who had opened the door into the garden. Boris, however, standing aside to let Renny pass through first, was intercepted and caught by the Green-Silk-Legs, who had a passion for him. "Bi-i-ig," she groaned in adoration—Boris and Tessa were sometimes hailed as Big Wolf and Little Wolf, or even Big and Little—"Bi-i-ig, my darling, I *must* hug you!" And hug him she did, both arms stranglingly clasped around his massive white throat. Boris stood patient and rock-like, his head looking over her shoulder and slightly turned away from her. He was too much of a gentleman not to endure such demonstrations without showing what he suffered from them; and, indeed, his expression was not altogether free from a touch of heroic complacence: "This little woman is, I'm afraid, getting rather too fond of me!"

"Bi-i-ig!" swooned the Green-Silk-Legs afresh, "the others don't love you a bit, darling. I'm the only one that cares for you. The others don't care a straw about you, really! They like Little better, but I won't let you be left out!"

"What was she talking about?" Boris queried a few minutes later, when the Legs had scattered to their various recreations or siestas, and the animals, idle, lordly creatures with nothing to do, and all the hours of the day to do it in, were basking luxuriously in the sun on the grassy terrace just beyond the veranda: "Do any of you know what she was talking about? The Legs *do* love me, and I'm not left out! I've never said that I was, have I?"

Kim, who really had excellent brains when he chose to exert them, began to explain the problem of the Green-Silk-Legs from the angle revealed by psychoanalysis: "I should say she had a slight inferiority complex and was seeking compensation, if you get me—" —he knew that Boris didn't!—"by this attempt to establish herself as your only protector and adorer. It's what's called the Freudian wish, if you get me—"—again, for he saw Renny's brown eyes watching him with respect, and her lips move. What she was really saying to herself was: "My poor, dear old husband used to talk like this!"—"—struggling for fulfilment, you see. She rejects the knowledge that you actually are popular and cared for, because it doesn't fit in with the Wish. I can't tell, of course, if the Jung School of Mental Science would interpret the case of the Green-Silk-Legs any differently," added Kim, with the merest hint of swagger.

Boris had listened to his explanation with conscientious attention. "Most interesting, *most* interesting!" he said heavily. "Science and all that. I always liked science; test-tubes and things. Of course, I never had very much time for it, what with sport and my duties to the tenants. . . ."

Renny's soft, admiring look liquidated from Kim to Boris. How noble he would look, so she thought, with frogs on his uniform! Such a chest as he had, and such a commanding presence! She could simply imagine him saying: "Left, right, left, right!"—or wasn't that what Field-Marshals said? She did hope her Poppit wouldn't fall a victim to his splendid dogly Boris!

She need not have bothered. All Poppit's tiny early-Victorian heart, shaped like a pincushion with "Mizpah" on it, was given to Kim; Kim, who was so clever and so sarcastic, and who had lived such a mysterious, dreadful, thrilling life; Kim, the philanderer and the rake; Kim, who never took any notice of nobody when he hadn't a mind to, though he always made a point of being specially nice and specially gentle to poor little Poppit, thus stuffing her with dreams that her mamma never suspected.

It was very pleasant dozing out there with the hot rays beating through your coat and on to your spine; stretched lazily on your back, or with your nose pushed down between your paws; and with the earth beneath you, a pattern of little running savours and flavours that you were too indolent to pursue. Very pleasant indeed—and the mysterious fascination that abode in Renny was as yet far-away and glamorous. . . . Boris and Kim felt lazily and it was harmoniously lapping around them without being too tormenting. . . . Sweet Renny, sweet little brown princess! . . . Good earth, nice hot sun, joyous smells—a great feeling of well-being over everything. Even restless Tessa had yielded to it. She twitched her nose voluptuously and crooned: "You may stroke me if you like. My temperament is not too exacting to-day," as the Shapely-Legs strolled across the lawn and paused beside her. But the Shapely-Legs, remembering previous snubs, was minded to speak a truth or two to Tessa: "I suppose you think you're the favourite dog here?" she addressed her sternly. "I suppose you think you top the list? Well, you don't. You'd be surprised if you knew what a long way down you come. About ninth, I should say!" and passed on into the house.

"About ninth?" repeated Boris, who was always being perplexed by something. "But how can Tessa be ninth on the list when there are only six of us? Ninth?—Sixth?—Six?—Nine?" He tried to work it out, thumping alternately with his fore-paw and his tail. "Four, five, six; one, three, nine; nine, six, one—"

Tessa had arisen, and with considerable dignity had walked away. She would get even, somehow, with the Shapely-Legs for humiliating her in front of the others, and especially in front of that dusty little prose-bag Renny!

. . . "Three, two, one—" Boris was still worrying.

"What's the matter with him?" Toes asked, dashing down the steps on to the lawn, very excited about some discovery he had made. Boris promptly boxed his ears, and Toes subsided, howling. But then Boris said to Kim in an undertone—for although he disapproved of Kim in several ways—"I can't always understand that fellow's code of honour . . ."—he had a profound veneration for the terrier's quicker intuitions: "What *did* she mean?"

"She meant," replied Kim dryly, "that they had just noticed something about the charming little lady who is going to be your wife."

"Ah, she's young, she's young," Boris said, tolerant whenever Tessa's tantrums were under discussion. "She'll improve by keeping, like wine, you know."

"Like rats," murmured Kim sleepily; and Boris was most earnest in agreeing with him that rats *did* improve by keeping, and told an anecdote of one that he had found behind the water-butt on Lower Peckham: "with a fine old ten-day vintage about it. I think Gertie must have left it there; I remember she was rather bothered at having mislaid a rat, about a fortnight ago."

"Talking of vintages," remarked Kim, who really was a good deal of a connoisseur, and could not resist the cue to show off, "I see the Legs have been laying down—"

"*Lying* down," corrected Boris gravely.

"—Some Brauneberger, 1922," Kim went on, without heeding the senseless interruption. "It ought to be worth drinking in time. A very delicate bouquet, Rheinwein—"

Boris, struggling to maintain the conversation at its sophisticated level, tried to tell about some very rare and excellent wine which he had once sampled: "The—er—velvet, you know . . . like velvet! it was green, I remember—"

"Green?—Oh, Chablis! Yes."

"Green. Hot and mellow and opaque. *Very* satisfying. I had two whole platefuls and begged for a third. That *was* a wine, if you like!"

"A real old Symington's pea vintage!" laughed Kim, suddenly enlightened.

"Look here, I say!" cried Toes, recovering from the singing head which Boris's blow had given him. "What *do* you think I found at the back of Kim's kennel? You know how he'll never tell us how old he is? Well—"

"May I ask," Kim interrupted, "what you were doing in my kennel?"

Toes tried to look inscrutable as the Chows.

"Oh, darling, don't pull those grimaces!" cried his mother, distressed. "And you know Kim doesn't like anyone in his kennel. Tell him at once what you were doing there and give him back what you found."

"Well, if you want to know," Toes replied, his eyes rolling in a puppish fashion, half fearfully and half joyfully, towards Kim, "I was making him an apple-pie bed!" He stood ready to dodge, if need be, a second punishment. "And then, stuck right down in a hole under the straw, I found these," and he flung Kim's war medals upon the grass.

Kim, not displeased that these concealed proofs of a truculent career should have been dragged out just now in front of Renny, murmured some gruff and confused statement to the effect that any other fellow would have done the same . . . and that Toes would surely come to a bad end. Boris, deeply interested, picked up the medals and examined them closely.

"So you were in the South African War? Lucky beggar! Wish I'd had the chance. I wasn't born then, and you can't have been much more than a boy."

"Is that where you get your limp?" asked Renny.

Kim nodded. "Spion Kop!" he said shortly.

"Oh!" gushed Renny, "I expect you were in the Royal Marines!" Nobody knew just why Renny expected that.

Kim, on being pressed, admitted to having raised a special company of Pow-wows' Wow-wows.

"What did you *do?*" breathed Poppit, admiringly, and Tessa, who had rejoined the group on the lawn, remarked with laconic pertness: "They rode about."

Kim gave her a dark look. "All bitches are women!" he muttered, but not so that Renny or Poppit could hear him.

"Oh!" the latter babbled, all her usual shyness quenched in enthusiasm, "you must have looked wonderful!" And Kim would have been rude if it had been anyone else but Poppit, who to him was so meek, so unattractive and Gawd-'elp-us, so wholly lacking in all sex allure, that, in that perverse and cantankerous spirit which characterized so many of his actions, he could not forbear from being amazingly tender and chivalrous to her. He even used to take her out to lunch sometimes; to very long lunches all alone with him, and tell her, between courses, very long and not poignantly interesting anecdotes with which he would never dare to bore any more exacting companion. Poppit vainly tried to delude herself that he *meant* something by these lunches, but she felt vaguely that some essential fire was lacking from them. "Kim will never marry," she used to say, sorrowfully; and the others, not knowing that she was suffering from unrequited affection and would shortly go into a decline, also frequently remarked with cheerful conviction: "Old Kim will never marry. Kim's not the marrying sort!"

Boris was different. Boris was essentially what might be described as a marrying dog. Even the Legs recognized that. That was why Tessa had been brought out from England. "A marriage has been arranged and will shortly take place. . . ."

Boris, when he saw Tessa, was heavily pleased at the prospect awaiting him in a year or two. "It's too soon to talk about anything yet. She's nothing but a child still," he would say indulgently, when anybody pitied him for Tessa's temperament, her airs and disdain, the consequential toss of her head—"but you can see that there's Breeding and Family there. . . ." Kim merely blinked at that Handsome Softy's reverence for Family. Kim knew well enough, and was cynically resigned to such knowledge, that the Legs would never go to the trouble and expense of importing an aristocratic mate for *him*. . . .

Tessa's impressions on first sight of Boris were not so wholly complacent. She had been pleased enough to go south at the beginning of a dreary winter: "I need the sun," she had said to her brothers and sisters. "I can't be Myself unless I feel the sun beating down on my back." But she had at least expected, on springing furiously from the basket in which she had travelled, an enraged and refractory captive, that her future husband would prick his ears at the sight of her, if indeed they were not pricked all the time, as a decent wolf-dog's should be. Tessa's own ears, at the time of her arrival, were in that piquant condition when one stood erect and pointed, and the other still flopped slightly, puppy-fashion, so that dogs noticed her queer, uneven, crooked charm and said they could not bear regular features. Gravely she surveyed Boris. He was big, yes; strong and muscular— why, yes; she liked his thick white throat, the splashes of white on his grizzled fawn-and-black coat, his deep-baying voice, like the King of Wolves summoning his pack to some valiant encounter; but his silky, fawn ears only rose a very little way before they fell on either side of his broad, his much too broad and benevolent forehead; and his clear brown eyes were so mournful. They gazed at you, even when you had done nothing, Tessa declared passionately, with such unutterably tender reproach from the tortoise-shell rims that encircled them with the effect of large and owlish spectacles.

"He's handsome enough," thought Tessa judicially, "but is he brilliant? Is he subtle? Will he understand anyone so difficult and so complex as Me? Will he appreciate me except just for my looks? Can he master me? Is he even intelligent? Does he care about books and pictures and music? What will he say when he knows that I want to be a dancer, that it's in my blood to dance, that on moonlight nights I go wild suddenly, and dance, and dance, and *dance?* . . ."

And little Tessa's worst fears were realized. Boris, like Gallio, cared for none of these things. Boris would be a good husband, but dull, and occasionally pompous. He would never encourage her individuality. Any other little Tessa would have done equally well for him. Often when Tessa woke in the morning her pillow was soaked with tears at thinking that she could not escape this humdrum fate in store for her.

It was just shortly after her betrothal, as Poppit winsomely called it, that the Legs began to build a row of new kennels up at the back of the garden; rather smart kennels, with sloping green roofs and red doors, and a concrete run outside them between wire netting. Up till now the dogs had always slept either in the house or in some of the barns and outhouses. Tessa watched the building operations breathlessly, her ears pricked—both of them by this time. The Legs wondered why she was so interested? why she kept on counting? . . . She was vigilant in her fear that she and Boris might have to share a double kennel—some of the Legs were so old-fashioned! "Oh, I know what it'll be!" Tessa thought, for she had read rather more than was good for her and seen too many modern plays, "I shan't be able to breathe!". . . And she had a vision of her future self going to sit by the window, unable to bear his snores, and he would grunt sleepily: "You'll catch cold, darling." "I hope to Dog I get pneumonia and *die!*" she could answer defiantly. . . . "And then," reflected Tessa, in the truly ironical modern style, "I'll probably catch a cold, and the Legs will give me a purga!" For that was the note on which life was interpreted nowadays.

Such was her state of mind at this period of watching and counting, that she went off and had cocktails with Kim while Boris was out, knowing that the latter would disapprove. Kim was rather exciting, for he showed so clearly that he disliked her. Indeed, he told her a few frank and brutal truths about herself and her vanity, and her egoism, and her poses, that thrilled Tessa . . . until he went on and told her a few more that were so super-true that they merely annoyed her.

Renny had watched them in shocked silence from afar, and when

Boris came home she went out to meet him and looked at him with melting, sympathetic, motherly eyes, and fussed around, offering him soup—till Boris began to suspect. He suspected for a long time without getting anywhere near a confirmation, until, tired of waiting about for the big melodramatic scene that her nerves craved in satisfaction, Tessa was forced to confess her own guilt.

"You don't understand!" Tessa declared passionately. "I need change now and then! You, with your notions of deportment—is that what you'd call it?—you're a—a washout! You only believe in two things, innocence or guilt, and what isn't one is the other. Kim —oh, I know you think he's my lover—" Boris didn't. Kim made no secret of what he felt about Tessa. What was upsetting Boris was that Tessa should drink cocktails. He was afraid they would hinder her growth; "Oh, Kim and I talk about—well, about books and pictures."

"You remind me," said Boris, thereby attempting at once to conciliate her and to fulfil her more exotic demands upon him, "you remind me of a picture in the What-d'you-call-it Gallery. When I first saw you, it was like a bit out of a—a book I'd been reading—"

"You!" scornfully, "you never read anything but the Sports column in the *Wolves' Gazette!*" And Boris growled and grumbled indignantly: "I do! I read a lot more. There are some very intellectual bits in the *Continental Daily Howl;* and they've got a Poet's Corner, too. What I object to is that Kim has loose ideas."

"That's better than having no ideas at all," laughed Tessa, and danced away, tantalizing him with her insouciance.

Renny, who had overheard part of the scene, confronted her indignantly. "Down on your knees," said Renny, "and thank Heaven, fasting, for a good dog's love."

"Poppit engaged yet?" asked Tessa, sweetly. And this was already a constant source of friction between Renny and Tessa the interloper. Tessa the beautiful, the audacious; for Poppit watched Tessa's jaunty passage through life with a sort of awed and fearful admiration; and Tessa, accepting this as her due, and lightly patronizing, would often say: "Come to lunch to-morrow, dear. We'll just be by ourselves. No males—I know you prefer that!" an assumption which Poppit's mother found particularly irritating. Why shouldn't her Poppit meet eligible males and be given chances? And she could not even console herself by imagining that Tessa was apprehensive of a rival.

But just on this hot, happy afternoon in March, Renny had ceased to be preoccupied with maternal busyness. She was in a mood both restless and elated. Had she been wasting her time all these years, a slave to domestic preoccupations, to humdrum moral precepts? Surely life could always henceforth be a gay and intoxicating affair, like to-day, for instance? especially for any spaniel so charming, so bewitching, so alluring as Renny. . . . For the attitude of Kim and Boris had mounted to her head, and causing her to feel a little giddy and light in the paw. Perhaps a stroll under the olives by herself might have a calming influence, especially with the benison of sunset slanting richly over shadowy valley and pulled like a tight gold cap over each rounded hill-top.

So Renny left her suitors and went mincing up the steep garden path, hardly pausing when Poppit's meek little head, with its long brown ringlets, was thrust round the aperture of her kennel: "Oh, pray, dear Mamma, my sampler is in a sad knot and tangle! If you could help me—?"

"Not now, my dear; some other time." Renny trotted on. Sampler, indeed!

Near the garden gate the Legs-in-Authority was picking out slugs from the lettuces. Seeing Renny, he took the pipe from his month and bent to pat her. "Good little thing!" he said, as the Legs always did, to Renny. But for once Renny did not fawn in gratitude for his cursory kindness, but wriggled rebelliously away. *Why* did they always call her a "good little thing"? Why "good"? Why "little"? Why "thing"? She *wasn't* a good little thing—not at all. Renny trotted on, under the wire fence that encircled the garden, and on to the path and the free world beyond.

. . . A small, furtive shape, dingy white blotched with grey, had, unobserved, been standing sentinel under the clump of olives just above the slope of Casa Lucceola. Now, seeing Renny, it slipped forward stealthily out into the open.

Suddenly Renny knew she was being pursued. Nothing tangible— just a warning instinct to run. In silence the pursuer streaked after her. The stony path writhed due west, straight into the hot splash of the sun. It swam before Renny in a dazzle. She was a little afraid, especially when she heard distant shouts from the Legs-in-Authority: "Renny! Renny! Renny!" Obey? *No!* But run. . . . This was adventure, gay and glorious. This was experience, still more glamorous than adventure, because it was fear-compelling. . . . She did not look over her shoulder, not once. . . . She had not known she could fly so fast.

Off the path now and down into the grass. That was better—soft, juicy grass for the pad of her paws. Above her head the longer weeds and flowers met, and above those were the giant crusty-grey trunks of the olives with their far-off drip of shining black and tarnished silver. And beyond even the olives, the luminous sky, too distant to care what might happen to a small brown spaniel. . . . The terraces were rushing backwards from her flight, wheeling away into the limbo of familiar ground, for Renny was up in the strange hills now, still aware of pursuit, still frightened, still glad. . . . She was young again, and nothing would ever make her old!

Dry tongue and pulsing throat. . . . The breeze whirled past her hot ears, cooling them, . . . eddied beneath her sensitive nose. . . . All the scents of early spring in the South were chasing backwards, too, madly in pursuit of the winds; thyme, wild mint, the crushed, sweet, fruity smell of myrtle. . . . What was that?—a patch of white and yellow narcissi, cutting with the sharpness of wet blades across the more voluptuous, swooning odours. . . . It was nearly unbearable to be so alive, so conscious. . . .

"Renny, Renny, *Renny!*"

. . . But she could not stop; she had to fly on, drunk with speed; drunk with the illusion that the earth had been arid before; and only now, as she passed like a goddess, the whole intricate web of little threads and runnels of smell just under the soil had pushed up and were actually bursting into blossom, into flame, as she ran. . . .

A goddess? Did old legends, old magic, come true again here on these pagan slopes? . . . Renny remembered the tale of how Diana had hunted across these very hills and terraces, Diana and her dogs and a flying stag, in a rippling frieze beside the sea. . . . Wherever she received a check, so the story was echoed down the centuries, a

mountain village was named after her. . . . Was that a legend? Or
was she herself Diana? or a dog of Diana? or the hunted stag? . . .
Was it all happening for the first time, or hundreds of years ago? as
many hundred years as the laurel, the vine, the olive and the wild
fig had grown and twisted into this dim, green-shaded plunge, down,
down into the valley, across the stream and up again. . . . The sunset was behind her now, and redder than before. . . . The sky was
on fire, and fire was in the meadow of wild crocuses, each single
bloom a frail and gleaming chalice. The little spaniel's heart was
thumping as she burst through this pale, lit purple. . . . Had she
indeed created it all? She, Renny, Renny—

"Renny, Renny, *Renny!*"

. . . She had travelled too far. Her trembling legs hardly seemed
hers to control any more. . . . But by a miracle the path grew
familiar. She recalled to a twig how that fig-tree grew, overhanging
the well. She had been driven, as dreams will loop and drive their
victims, in a tremendous circle, and now she was nearly home again.
And still—Renny was ecstatically aware of this!—still whatever was
pursuing her had not given up the chase; so lovely she was, so full
was her blossoming, and the unfurling of leaf and petal that licked
after her wherever she had run. Triumph rose to a pæan as, without
ever looking round, she sped under the wire and sank, with dark,
drenched coat and sobbing breast, on to the safe straw of her kennel
at last. . . .

Yes, she understood. It was nothing tangible that had thundered
and lightened in her wake. It was the Call of Life! It was Trans-
cendental Romance! It was Creation! It was the Essential Flowering!
It was Dog Itself—

—"It was that mangy little grey cur that's always hanging round,"
said the Legs-in-Authority, entering the dining-room and flinging
himself down, tired out, into the arm-chair. "I'm quite hoarse with
calling her. Well, I'll have to go into San Remo to-morrow, I suppose."

Chapter II

Kim had had a miserably unhappy childhood, but then, again, as
a young dog-about-town, he had been spoilt. The result was that his

sense of irony was over-developed, and—alas! as Poppit would say —what moral sense he owned could hardly be perceived with a powerful microscope. He had a positive talent for getting his own way; if Kim meant to enter a room and the door was closed, Kim quietly and persistently demanded to be admitted until he *was* admitted; he did not merely hurl himself against it for a time and howl a bit and then go away, as did Tessa or the spaniels. And if Kim meant to occupy an arm-chair already occupied by two of the Legs, his procedure was always successful: first of all he would eye the arm-chair; then he would eye the Legs. . . . "No," said whichever Legs was in possession, "*I'm* sitting here!" Kim, quite rightly, took no notice of this feeble argument. With dashing activity he sprang over the arm of the chair and curled up at the back of it wherever space might offer for his supple body. "All right," from the Legs, choosing to look upon this as flattery and affection from the usually offhand terrier: "All right, little fellow! We'll share it, shall we?" Kim merely grinned. . . . The O'Haras never shared if they could help it. Gradually and subtly Kim would occupy more and more of the arm-chair, the Legs less and less; eventually the Legs found himself, he never knew how, so uncomfortably perched on the outermost rim that he would get up and seek another seat. Then Kim, with a deep sigh of satisfaction, spread himself out and shamelessly enjoyed his ease. "I wonder why we stick it?" reflected the Legs. And, of course, from a spaniel they never did stick it. The spaniels, especially Renny, had only one art of occupation: Renny, on being peremptorily ordered off a chair or divan or bed, gazed back pleadingly, dumbly, stupidly—and then made herself heavy . . . a dead weight, so that she had to be ignominiously rolled off; and she was never intuitive enough to grasp that this plan of campaign irritated the Legs to a sadistic frenzy of action, instead of numbing them, as by Kim's technique, to amazed submission.

A strange, warped character was Kim: gambler, roué and scapegrace; fascinating without being handsome; aristocratic without the right to claim a lineage; expensive in his habits and not a brass cent of income or capital. Boris was comfortably off, but not so rich as Kim would have been if Kim were not so desperately poor. Kim, when a minor, had borrowed an enormous amount of money because

he would not have to repay it; though, later on, he had received—
and destroyed—many a missive beginning: "To account rendered,
£757, etc. With compliments." He was fastidious over his food and
drink; fastidious in his speech; fastidious about his personal appearance. . . . His caustic remarks, when the juvenile and exuberant
Toes had pleaded to be allowed to wear Oxford-Bags, represented
the whole of one generation's concentrated condemnation of the
next generation's callow taste.

He was a little old-fashioned, perhaps, in his deliberate selection
of books to read that were not quite *comme il faut;* thus, Gyp and
de Maupassant were the style of literature he preferred. His brain
was a cellar, dim and cobwebby and aromatic, of fine old vintage
anecdotes upheld in their own crust: "When I was digging in the
Albany . . ." He never remembered his digs in the Albany without
a sigh of regret; none of the other dogs had ever dug in the Albany.
For hours the Hon. Aubrey O'Hara would remain motionless and
upright in front of the dining-room fire of olive logs, squatting as
close as he could without scorching himself, for he felt the cold, and
his thin little light-brown shape sometimes shivered even while actually sitting there . . . shivered, perhaps, from memory of past days
that had been fireless. "What can Kim be thinking of?" the Legs
often remarked, watching him, calling him, stroking him. . . . Kim
blinked once or twice, and the vertical lines between his eyes deepened, but he did not move. . . .

"He looks like Buddha," said the Legs; or again: "Doesn't he look
like a jackal?"—a swift, slim, yellow jackal, indifferent and cruel.
. . . Yet Kim had queer decencies and a queer code of his own.
"Never display emotion" was the Alpha of it, and "Preserve class
distinctions at all costs" its Omega. And he had his kind impulses,
too. They broke out where you least expected them—in fact, where
they were most liable to disconcert those of his abusers who said
that he had no heart. For instance, he was extremely punctilious,
every holiday, not to miss taking out his late elder brother's children
—Rake O'Hara had not been married when he died! And he never
fobbed off a cheap tea-shop and a suburban pantomime on them,
either. No—very precisely he would select a revue that was not fit
for them to see and a frightfully swish restaurant where their ap-

preciation of food could be educated to a costly and useless degree
that might seriously demoralize their future lives. Naturally, they
adored him. Very stiffly he would inquire, at the end of the day's
treat, after their various mothers—"She was extremely good-looking
when I first met her. . . ." But then women had petted Kim ever
since he first learnt not to lick blacking. He had gone about a lot,
with Rake O'Hara; and when that *fin-de-siècle* masher had died, it
was Kim alone of his family who was present while the last messages
and legacies were taken down; while Rake, feebly, but with a vicious
gleam of humour under his wearily drooping eyelids, dictated: "Lady
So-and-So—fine, fair woman—she'll be upset about this!—lives in
Oxfordshire. . . . Hon. Mrs. Such-and-Such—poor Daffodil!—
never would learn to make up properly. . . . Melody Minx, of the
Old Gaiety—no, no, cross that out—might give the Duke a handle—
I'd rather not do him a good turn. Poor Melody, she'll think I've
forgotten her—and so I have. . . ." And so on, and so on. Kim
thought a lot of Rake's taste in women; he had sampled one or two
of them . . . but he didn't tell his brother that. Of the others' addresses he made a mental note.

. . . Such was the past over which Kim brooded, half-hypnotized,
swaying ever so slightly as he stared and stared into the flames . . .
his memory gone away, gone away among the cobwebs and the
shadows, sipping and sampling old wines, old sorrows, old loves, old
sins. . . . "Mistresses, with cold, smooth, marble limbs—" Repent-
ing, was he? . . . "Ah well, every Legs has his day, they say, and
it's not so different for us. We all come down to the Level Crossing
in the end!"

The Level Crossing at the foot of the hill on which stood Casa
Lucceola was, in a sense, the animals' red-light district. Outside one
or other of its neighbouring cluster of houses could nearly always
be glimpsed a motley queue of dogs. When Renny used to say to
Boris, shocked reproach in her voice, "I'm afraid Kim is going rapidly
downhill," Kim literally was doing so, rapid as a little streak of yellow
lightning, for fear the Legs might see him and call him back; not
that he ever bothered to obey, of course—not while that little so-
called Russian, Olga, of mysterious origin and fitful fascination, was
beckoning him. . . . But occasionally the Legs took more drastic

action and actually followed and caught him, lifted him up and carried him back, while Kim silently and determinedly tried to bite them, his upper lip raised in a snarl; if he chose to be a libertine, that was his own business. He was not going to be thwarted by a lot of Puritan Legs. . . .

Well, the Russian's lucky moon had waned; she ceased to draw the tide. The novelty was over: "Olga's rather *passée*, don't you think? Wonder what we ever saw in her?". . . The queue dropped away. Boris, always chivalrous and dogly, even in his desertions, remembered, indeed, after the episode was over, to call in at the florist's and send her flowers—an eminently stiff and correct bouquet which—not to hurt her feelings—differed neither in expense nor in clumsiness from the bouquet that he would inevitably send Tessa on the eve of their wedding. Kim merely stopped going down, without another word. And sentimental Toes, who had suffered from a school-dog infatuation for the alluring little pseudo-Russian, waggled down the hill after he had recovered, to sit with her, and said, tearfully: "How bee-*yoo*-tiful you were last week!" and begged her to sing that little ballad again, just once, because it reminded him of the time when he still loved her. . . .

Renny had been terribly distressed about his early emancipation: "But, Toes, my darling, she's not at all a *nice* creature! And I'm sure, if your poor dear father had been alive he would never have allowed you to go down to the Level Crossing—and your ears looking so disreputable! I'm sure she must have chewed them. I simply don't know why you can't stay at home for a healthy romp when Poppit invites her friends up to the kennels for tea and music—elegant, amiable little spaniels, whose mothers I could *know*. . . . What's that you're keeping from me?" She snatched at a crumpled flower, warm from where it had lain above Toes's pulsing heart. It was a leg-rose that Olga had given him. . . .

Olga, of course, was not the only attraction down at the Level Crossing, and she had lived a very secluded life lately and given her lesser rivals a chance. But now it was rumoured that she had had her drawing-room redecorated, and might—who knows?—be receiving visitors again. "Olga's not one to lie leggo for ever," remarked Kim. "Who told you, Toes? Pekoe? Ah, Slav and Mongolian. . . . Still, she was a witty little devil. One gets tired of claret, you know, and takes to Madeira; and then, satiated, one goes back to claret again. . . . I must call on Olga!"

A soft wind was wafted over the terraces, spicy with the returning spring. . . .

But the next day, the day after Renny's wild flight over the thyme at sunset, sirocco blew up. Sirocco is a wind that makes your ears hang down and your coat feel hot and sticky, with layers of grit wherever you can't get at them. It makes you feel uneasy, too; something might happen at any moment. . . . You don't want to stay indoors, and you don't want to stay out of doors, when sirocco is blowing. You lie quietly curled up, your nose between your paws, comfortable for a few moments—and then, suddenly galvanized, you spring up, and for no apparent reason pace to the other end of the lawn and lie down again in precisely the same position. You prowl about after food and then leave it irritably untouched. You scratch violently, sitting on the ground, your hind paw in furious operation behind the obliquely opposite ear—and even that fails to soothe your disquieted spirit. And oh! how stupid the Legs are—how infuriating and dense and stupid, on a day when sirocco blows!

And Renny was locked up.

They did not even shut her up in the kennels where you might leap over the top of the wire fencing or bite your way through it, or at least converse with her, sympathizing with her plight and comforted by the sight of her silky hair and eyes like melting toffee—the light kind. If she had been shut up in the kennels, Kim could have startled the pigeons for her amusement, scattering them in a whir of blue wings and plaintive cries from the roof of the hen-house. And Boris could have stood, his feet sturdily planted among the parsley, the rosemary bush rising in scented spikes behind him, while he skillfully caught stones thrown to him over and over again by the patient Green-Silk-Legs. It would have been just bearable, even on a day of sirocco, if they had imprisoned beautiful little Renny in the kennels.

But the Legs-in-Authority had given orders before he left for San Remo; and Renny was out of sight, though they could hear her crying from behind the door of what used to be the goat-shed, crying to be set free, to come out and play. She had not learnt yet that a princess of romance is always closely incarcerated in a Tower-room, where her suitors may not visit her; it is one of the oldest laws of fairy-tale. But Renny could not understand; she thought she was being punished for not obeying the call of the Legs-in-Authority the evening before; so she wept aloud, until, to quiet her, they let Poppit go in; and Poppit's was not in the least the companionship that Renny desired.

Kim, ever resourceful, tried to bite his way through and under the wood, where the walls of the shed rose from the ground; and he was getting on nicely, working away in true terrier style with his teeth and both his paws, swift, concentrated, silent, the earth and the wood-chips flying to the right and left of his assault, and Renny's soft, velvety nose, snuffling and twitching, so near, so hopeful, on the further side. . . .

But the Savoury-Legs, who worked about the garden, and was paid for it by the Legs-in-Authority, unfortunately took it into his head to plant potatoes in the bed close by the goat-shed that morning, and he saw what Kim was doing; and he told the Shapely-Legs, who told the Equestrian-Legs, who came out and thrashed Kim.

"Damn you!" muttered the terrier, twisting and writhing in the oppressor's grip, trying to get his teeth well into the knuckles of the hand which held the strap. "And don't you do it again, or you'll get another!" added the Equestrian-Legs, carrying Kim down the garden path, forcing him into the dining-room and then closing the door.

Doors!—these were always the purely mechanical advantage which the Legs wielded over the otherwise independent existences of the dogs; they could keep doors open and keep doors closed; they could shut dogs outside a room or let them in; they could separate them or herd them together; and all simply by this accidental power of being able to open and close doors. Doors!—who invented them? They were always inconvenient, but to-day they were more than inconvenient; they were sinister. Boris and Kim, who were both in love, had never before felt the ignominy of being so helpless, so dependent on the whims of these—these commissionaires. Doors!—Renny was withheld from them by a closed door, and Kim was thwarted of rescuing her by yet another door. And now the Legs chose to open a door and took them all out for a walk—and that was not so bad, though it was a difficult business driving them past the door behind which Renny wailed and whimpered, longing to join them in their first jostle and rush over the terraces. And . . . doors again! For, an hour later, the door of the goat-shed was opened, and Renny, too, was taken for a walk, on a lead, with Poppit trotting amenably beside her; and Tommy, as usual, with majestically waving tail, in the rear, barking: "Wait for me, wait for me, wait for mee-ee-a-ow!" But by now Kim and Boris were behind the door of the sun-room, hearing the distant scamper of Renny's feet, and howling with rage and disappointment; pounding with all their frustrated vitality against the panels, till the whole house shook. . . . Until, æons later, steps were heard approaching, and the Nutritious-Legs, performing the usual mysterious trick with the handle, threw open the door and released them. "There! Go along, my poor lambs!" Forth they rushed into the garden—at last! at last! But Renny, home from her walk, was shut up again in the goat-shed. Always a door closed between them. Vigilant and cunning the Legs moved about, brutal as gods, strong as giants. And Renny cried, and sirocco blew, and the day wore away, like a slow trickling of sand through a hole. . . .

At last, panting a little in the grey, sweaty sunless air, Boris and Kim abandoned the unequal contest with those who controlled their destinies, and flopped down on the little lawn beyond the veranda: Kim sulkily, with his back turned to the distant view of the goat-shed, their symbolical Tower-room; Boris facing the other way, his great white paws crossed, his mournful gaze dodging the string of washing which sagged, between him and Renny's prison, from olive-tree to olive-tree. Ah, if washing were the only barrier! how his teeth would rend the blue table-cloth and the yellow night-gown, and that nameless, shapeless garment flopping beside it!

"Darling little Renny, darling little Renny!" he groaned. Then answered, with a languid lick, the fervent embrace of the Green-Silk-Legs; who rewarded him by throwing at least a dozen small pebbles, one by one, into Boris's expectant jaws.

"I never let the Legs kiss me on the muzzle," said Kim, in an under-

tone to Tessa. "You never know where they've *been*. Boris allows
it, of course. He'll pick up something he doesn't like, one of these
days."

Tessa assented. "And Toes goes and rolls on the divan directly
after the Legs have been lying there. I simply don't know how he *can!*
Why, they might have fleas!"

Kim agreed, listlessly, that it was dreadful the way one picked up
fleas with all those Legs about the house. He might have enlarged
on this engrossing topic, but at that moment Tessa caught sight of
Toes making short, gambolling rushes at a frog hidden where the
grass was long, and at once the old perverse craving seized her to
crunch him. . . . She crouched, and her ears flattened; then she
sprang. . . .

"*Tessa!*" shouted the Shapely-Legs, warningly, from a window:
"Tessa, you little horror, leave Toes alone!"

—Toes rolled himself free, and Tessa retired, with her usual dignity, wondering what she could do next to cause a disturbance? She,
too, was feeling restless and hot; this weather did not agree with her;
it was not what she had expected, when she came to winter in the
South. The Veterinary-Legs had said she was a bundle of nerves;
yet the Legs showed no consideration for this, whatsoever; and made
very little difference between their treatment of her, delicately
strung as a violin, and that dingy little slap-cabbage, Renny. It made
her feel on edge now to hear Renny's constant wailing and yelping;
and then when she sought a little pleasant relaxation, she was scolded.
And Kim and Boris were behaving so ridiculously!

"If you were *dogs*," said Tessa, taunting their disconsolate submission, "you wouldn't give in to the Legs, and allow yourselves to
be shoved about here and there, just as the whim takes them! If you
really wanted to be with Renny—and I'm sure I don't know why anyone should!—then for Dog's sake, *do* something about it!"

Boris turned his sad, reproachful eyes in her direction.

"Do?" he echoed, deeply. "Why, what can we do?"

Tessa laughed and flung back her head. Her silvery ruff stiffened
and vibrated, as though her spirit were tingling down each separate
hair till every tip glistened. "Do?" she repeated, imitating the ac-

quiescent rumble of Boris's tones: "What can we *do?* You've got teeth, haven't you, and jaws? Why don't you rebel?"

. . . Kim lifted his sleek, narrow head.

And precisely at this moment, when Tessa was exploiting the already menacing atmosphere to stir up mischief—which was always fun, and always better than stagnation!—at precisely this moment a small brown shape wriggled and scuffled away, body pressed close to the ground, through the hole which Kim had partly dug under the boards of the goat-shed. . . . And Renny came dashing down the path to liberty, ears flying, eyes sparkling, stumpy tail wagging furiously. Oh, it was so lonely in there, and so dull, and so dark! And here were all the others on the lawn, and Kim and Boris rushing to meet her, Toes in their wake, all of them yelping and barking with excitement and greeting!

—But before even their noses could touch, destiny interfered again. The Nutritious-Legs, rushing from round an unexpected corner, grasped in a second what had happened. . . . She seized Renny, picked her up, struggling and twisting. . . . Shouted to the Equestrian-Legs and to the Savoury-Legs, who beat off the swarming, leaping pack. . . . And carried Renny back again to the goat-shed; back again to imprisonment, to the Tower-room.

. . . And for a while there was silence, except for the steady thud of a hammer on wood, as the Savoury-Legs, given brisk orders, nailed fresh boards across the hole through which Renny had escaped.

"Well?" said Tessa, with bright dark eyes dancing from Kim to Boris, from Boris to Kim again: "Well? . . . Are you going to put up with it?"

Kim said slowly: "I wonder *why* we've always submitted?— except now and then, of course, over little things that don't count. I wonder *why* we've allowed the Legs to become our masters? After all . . . we needn't!"

"It's because you're afraid of them," taunted Tessa.

But Boris spoke, and she was silent. "No, you're wrong. We're not afraid of them. Why should we be? We're stronger than they are. Our jaws are stronger; our teeth are stronger. If I really chose. . . ."

Golden Toes began to jig up and down. "Oh, *do* let's choose!" he cried eagerly; not really grasping quite what were the issues, but young and easily swayed.

Boris said again, and his voice was like thunder rising in the distant hills: "They've no right to keep me away from Renny. I love her."

"You!" Tessa shrilled, spitefully. "Much you care, or you'd have crashed a way through to her long ago. All you care about is catching stones, and stones, and *stones*. . . . There you stand, all day long looking stupid, panting, with your mouth wide open"—Tessa had often felt hysterical at the sight of Boris engaged in his favourite pastime—"and then you call it *sport!* By Dog, it's choking me!—this life kennelled up with all of you! And not one with the spirit of a lizard! If I loved an animal, and he couldn't bite his way through a few minor obstacles in order to win me, I'd never look at him again!"

"Oh, *let's* bite something!" shouted Toes, wagging his tail and rushing at a stray dandelion; "Oh, do let's bite something! Hurray! Let me help! Oh, I say, you will let me help, won't you, when you begin?"

A crisis was working up. Boris answered back angrily to Tessa's charge: "Yes, I do like catching stones. Why shouldn't I? It's hopeless to try and explain to you about the rules of sport—fielding, and bowling, and not allowing yourself to go out of bounds into the flower-beds; catching a stone when it's going to land behind you by flinging your head right back with a sort of paw-break on the off side. . . . Bah, what's the good? First you say I'm afraid of the Legs, and then you say I only care about catching stones!" He flumped disgustedly to the ground again.

"I catch stones, too," exclaimed Toes, picking one up, and throwing it to himself, and falling over his ears, and tumbling over the wall into the nasturtiums below, and charging back again. "It's a ripping game! I'm not much good at it yet, but Boris says I don't shape badly at all."

Tessa ignored this contribution. "Very well then, prove that you're not afraid, and prove that you care for love more than for catching stones. To-day's your chance. The Legs-in-Authority has gone away, and we don't know when he'll be back. If we could only break through the habit of years," she wheedled, enticing them to a Great Rebellion, "if we could all charge together, when they're not expecting it, and bite them, and throw them down. Oh, we needn't bite them hard! Just enough to teach them that we're the masters" —airily—"then we could crash against those few rotten pieces of wood, and set Renny free, and do whatever we liked for ever afterwards, and make the Legs open and shut doors as *we* pleased, not as *they* pleased, and go for walks, and go out on to the road, and go down the hill into the town, and jump on to the table and eat—not just have niggly bits of gristle thrown to us, but *really* eat—whole platefuls of meat. . . ."

"Wow, wow, *wow!*" from Toes, by now inarticulate with ecstasy. "Wa-a-aow!" in a crescendo of admiration at Tessa's initiative and daring.

—"And lie in arm-chairs," Tessa went on, "soft arm-chairs; let the Legs lie on the floor if they want to; we'd turn them out of the chairs. What's to prevent us? Nothing!" She darted a wary glance in Kim's direction. Though Boris's valour seemed the slowest to rise, yet she was most uncertain of Kim, and of his attitude towards her scheme. But Tessa had all the wiles of the instinctive agitator. She knew exactly when one note had been thumped often enough, and when it was wise to leave it and strike another. . . . "Poor Renny!" she said softly, still with an eye on Kim. "How glad, how gloriously glad, she was when she got through the hole that Kim had scrabbled for her. It was rather a shame of the Legs, wasn't it, to drag her back? After all, she hasn't done anything wrong. And now they're boarding up the hole. Listen!"

. . . Thud—thud—thud. The blows of the Savoury-Legs' hammer on the wood. Thud—thud—thud. Slow, ominous blows. The Legs meant to have their own way.

Still Kim said no word, but he got up, and stood tensely listening, his head raised, his eyes aslant.

Tessa went on: "She'll think us terribly disloyal if we don't do anything. Just imagine her, inside there, in the dark, listening, and wondering if Boris or Kim—"

"If we revolt now," said Kim, with such a matter-of-fact inflection that it came almost as a shock, contrasted with the melodramatic urgings of Tessa the Conspirator, and Boris's answering rant. And yet, somehow, you felt that Kim might be more dangerously in earnest than either of them: "If we revolt now, you know, it's for good."

"Why not?" whispered Tessa, hoping this would clinch it. "Why not?"

"Wa-a-aow . . ." from the concentrated pack-spirit which was Toes.

Boris, too, was standing erect, his ears for once pricked and alert. A low growl escaped his throat; it might have escaped him without his intent. His tail slowly lashed from side to side. . . .

Kim and Boris looked at one another. Sometimes, but rarely, they had been good friends; occasionally they had fought; oftenest they had been companions by accident of propinquity; but Kim had slightly mocked at Boris, and Boris had faintly disapproved of Kim. Now, however, and without further speech, a sudden understanding passed from one to the other. There was a trembling of the balance . . . and it dipped.

—"No," said Kim, abruptly, "I'm not going to rise against the Legs. The Legs are confounded nuisances, but I'm fond of them."

Boris heaved a great sigh of relief. "They're fond of us," he said.

And Toes chimed in with: "Good old Legs! Three cheers for the Legs! I *like* the Legs!"

. . . "And you call yourselves—dogs!" was Tessa's only comment. And with one quivering look of scorn she walked away and sat with her back to them, at the end of the wall, looking down the garden path towards the road.

Boris stirred uncomfortably. All his sensations that day had been uncomfortable. He was fatuously in love for the first time; his lady was being withheld from him by cruel guardians; and sirocco was chafing his coat and his soul equally. But even worse than all these had been the suggestion of rebellion, abhorrent to all the sane conservatism of his nature; rebellion, Bolshevism, seeing red. . . . Boris never saw red, without a further attachment of white and blue. And besides, he was devoted to the Legs, even when they closed doors in his very nose; even when they lifted up Renny, and carried her, struggling and panting, away from his yearning, mournful eyes. But if Kim had thrown his weight on to the side of rebellion, Boris felt that, out of knightly regard for Renny, he, too, would have had to throw in his lot with the soul's awakening of animal serfdom against

oppression. But now, thank Dog, thank Dog for it! Kim had elected
to stand loyally by his masters; and Boris felt more drawn to him
than ever in his life before. He shifted his noble bulk a little closer
to the terrier:

"When they come home," he said—but softly, for he did not wish
for any more pricked-ear stuff from young Tessa—"Whenever they
come home, and we rush out to meet them, it's rather jolly, don't
you think? to *have* somebody to rush out to meet who's so glad to
see us, and shouts our names, and rolls us over and over, and throws
stones. They really *are* glad—you can hear it in their voices! What I
mean is, we can always count on it, and it seems to mean a lot to
them."

"Yes," Kim assented, briefly; but for once not snubbing Boris
for the display of a few simple emotions.

"And," Boris continued, expanding genially, "they're decent, too,
when there's anything the matter with us—cut paw, or canker. They
take an awful lot of trouble, the Legs do; and I've noticed that when
we're down and out, or something's hurting us, it makes them really
miserable. In fact, what with one thing and another, I don't think,
Kim—do you?—that we could possibly have turned against the Legs
and bitten them. Do you know that they once refused to let this
house, at great financial advantage"—proceeded Boris, who always
talked very seriously about money, as a thing to be respected—"because they weren't quite sure that we'd be happy with the tenants?"

Again Kim nodded: "I know."

"So I do feel it's up to us to stand by them as long as they stand
by us. It's only playing the game. Tessa's nothing but a child still;
she hasn't really had time to get attached to them. But you and I are
the oldest dogs here except sweet little Renny!"—Kim was bearing
all this with remarkable fortitude. "My favourite virtue," concluded
Boris—and his soft, sherry-coloured eyes were a little misty—"is
loyalty; just as my favourite country is England." And he brought
his paw up to the salute.

Kim turned his head a little away from Boris. It might be that his
eyes, too, had filled with tears, but it is more likely that he was smiling—though for once kindly, not ironically.

"Yes, that's what I've said all along!" burst out Toes, unable any longer to keep silent. "One couldn't bite the Legs, you know. I mean, one couldn't, could one? I mean, it's blithering rot! I've got an old shoe, Boris, that belonged to one of the Legs. Would you like it? It hasn't been buried long. Would you like it?" And he leapt up eagerly to lick his hero, Boris, upon the nose.

Then, suddenly, his own nose became attentive. . . .

"I think I can smell—yes, cheers! that's his step coming up the road—just at the bend, where we can't see him. It's the Legs-in-Authority home again! Ooh, cheers!"

Boris and Kim also sprang to their paws, delighted, exultant, prepared to hurl themselves, barking a frenzied welcome, towards the returning traveller.

But then Tessa's voice, mocking their enthusiasm, and yet with a queer, elated thrill in it, held them back. From Tessa's point of vantage she could command a view of the road, before, at the last loop, it became invisible for fifty yards or so.

"I'd wait a moment, if I were you," she said. "Wait until you see them, anyway."

"*Them?*"

"Yes. The Legs-in-Authority isn't alone."

. . . They stood waiting, watching the road intently where it reappeared at the slope at the foot of the garden path. Some instinct, some foreknowledge, born, perhaps, of Tessa's triumphant poise upon the wall, prevented them from hurling themselves forward. . . .

And then they saw the Legs-in-Authority. He was not alone. He was leading another dog. A very handsome large black spaniel. A stranger.

The Legs-in-Authority looked anxiously around. He saw Boris, Kim, Tessa and Toes on the terrace facing west. He did not call to them as he usually did. Instead, he went round by the other side of the house, and reappeared again higher up the garden. He was still leading the strange dog.

Toes, always friendly, went scampering up the path after them. Kim, Boris, and Tessa remained motionless, but their eyes were turned now towards the goat-shed, where Renny was imprisoned. Could it be possible—?

The Legs-in-Authority and his captive walked straight along to the goat-shed. The Legs-in-Authority unlocked the door; then he slipped the lead off the black spaniel's collar and invited him to enter. After that he locked the door again and, attended by the gambolling Toes, returned to the house.

And a great strangled cry went up from the parched throats of Kim and Boris: "*Nous sommes trahis!*"

. . . Tessa sank down on to the edge of the wall, and thrust her nose deep, deep between her paws. A sensuous shiver rippled the silver and fawn and black of her fur. She did not want to jump about and pertly scoff "I told you so!" at the stricken pair of dogs; she did not want to talk, to see, to hear; only to remember the one fleeting vision that had been hers. Gone was all her hardness, all her pride. She had fallen in love. . . .

"Well?" said Boris to Kim, huskily.

Kim shrugged his shoulders . . . and went down to the Level Crossing.

But Boris lumbered slowly up the path as far as the goat-shed, and sat outside the door and leaned his head against the wood.

Chapter III

Sometimes the Savoury-Legs poured too much wine down his unslakable throat. Two and a half flasks a day was his usual self-allowance; handsome two-litre flasks, their bellies strapped in straw; flasks that rocked slightly where they stood, till vision rocked them the more. But on special nights the Savoury-Legs ramped gloriously past his allowance, and the number of litres that he poured down his unslakable throat ran into two figures. These special nights happened once a month, when he received his salary from the Legs-in-Authority; or twice a month if he begged half his salary in advance; also, roughly, on every Saint's Day, on Christmas Day, and Easter Day, and on the day when Santa Maria del Mare passes over the Mediterranean and pronounces it warm enough for bathing, and this is in mid-July; on his seven birthdays a year; and on national *festas*, which were innumerable and eccentric, including as a matter of course the day on which somebody-or-other marched to Rome, and the day on which somebody defeated somebody else who was marching on Rome, and the day that Romulus and Remus began to build Rome, and, more certainly, the day on which Garibaldi . . . and all those other days when Garibaldi . . . and Garibaldi's birthday, and United Italy Day; and once—but this was by accident—the Savoury-Legs celebrated Queen Alexandra's Rose Day. . . .

On the night of the arrival of the dark stranger at Casa Lucceola, or, rather, between the night and the dawn of the next day, the Savoury-Legs came singing up the hill. He always sang when he was drunk—no, he did not sing, he became the vehicle of song; song was released from its thrall of centuries, and poured through him, and rushed out, and went soaring up and up, striking the stars. He was bound by no fetters of tune, nor laws of harmony and notation; he proved, once and for all, that what a lusty man need do with his voice is to set it free—and then he will become as a god. Only in the subject of his song was he something less than cosmic; for he sang of the Savoury-Legs, and the wonder and the miracle of the Savoury-Legs, his soul and his being, and his capacity for holding liquor . . . and thus he sang the song that all creatures long to sing, but they are craven, and suppress it for fear of what the world will say; but Savoury-Legs recked nothing of the world; he opened his mouth, and he sang.

. . . Nearer and nearer to the house, and yet sometimes further, as his wayward course, following some ideal for ever unexpressed, took a great bend away from it; nearer and further, and round and round and round the house, drawing a magic ring about its walls. And sometimes he paused and cried "Yip!" very loudly, and the "Yip!" reverberated and swung over the hills, and he cried "Yip!" again, because he was so happy. Sometimes he stopped singing, and there was a pause, and eloquent silence . . . and then the sound of his voice became stationary as the Savoury-Legs delivered a discourse to a multitude that was not there; and his discourse was all of the Savoury-Legs, and the wonder and miracle of the Savoury-Legs, his soul and his being, and his capacity for holding liquor. And then again a pause, while his ears, perhaps, echoed the applause and thunders from his infatuated audience; or perhaps the Savoury-Legs needed no audience, was far above audiences, contemptuous of their approbation, and needed only himself, and himself, and himself, a world of Savoury-Legs, singing loudly and alone beneath the stars. . . .

Savoury-Legs dwelt in a one-roomed outlying hut, in the valley which swept west round the hill on which stood Casa Lucceola. But on a grand night like this, after wassail and carouse, he was not sure where he dwelt; but, vaguely, through spinning mists of silver and gold and vermilion—silver of the olives, and gold of the moon, and vermilion the gladness in his heart—he surmised that there was indeed a familiar floor on which he was wont to cast himself down at the end of the night's serenade and slumber contentedly without taking off his socks. He knew, too, that if he went round and round the house in ever widening circles, like a hound casting, he might presently fall over his home, and then he would know it was there, and that he was there, and all would be well.

So, still singing, the voice of the Savoury-Legs grew fainter and fainter, till with one last "Yip!" it died away. . . .

Tessa heard the drunken chant of the Savoury-Legs, not for what it was, but brokenly, through her dreams. She thought it was the Dark Spaniel serenading her, and she was ecstatic, forgetting Renny and reality. . . . She was assured and reassured that she was Tessa the Beautiful! Tessa the Seductive! Tessa the Unique! Tessa, who could at will command valour and song and a hundred royal lovers! . . . Hark . . . listen! He is drawing nearer: "Tessa, Tessa!" . . .

And she rolled a little in the straw, and flung out one voluptuous paw.

Boris heard the drunken chant of the Savoury-Legs, from where he slept, watch-dog, before the door of the bedroom of the Legs-in-Authority. He was wakeful; and his wakefulness(blurred by conjecture and sorrow, thought it a rapturous duet sung together by the lovers in the goat-shed. . . . And suddenly he could not bear it, but came loping across the floor to the bed-side of the Legs-in-Authority, and flumped down an imploring paw upon his master's chest. If only the inexorable decree could be relaxed; if only now, now, they would open all doors to him and let him rush, unchecked, into the goat-shed and kill that Dark Spaniel! Kill him! . . . For the moon hung low over the sea. . . . And Renny, sweet, soft-eyed, fascinating, was nearer than the moon, and nearer than the sea, and the Legs did not understand, and the song was maddening him. . . . If he were a wolf again, a free wolf in the forests of the mountains that rolled back behind the olive slopes, then he could show Renny who was the better fighter. But what could an animal do with the power of the Legs against him? . . . And now, at his hope of conflict by jaw and by fang, the serenade thrummed martially, or so his illusion heard it, and he stood up and threw out his chest and flung back his head and joined in with a great howl. . . . But the Legs-in-Authority only said: "Boris, lie down!" . . . and despairingly, he loped back to his post by the door and sank his head between his paws.

The song died away. Over his drowsy brain flickered a last image of Renny . . . moonlight. . . .

The Legs did not understand.

Poppit heard the drunken chant of the Savoury-Legs, and sat up, and shuddered a little, and thought that a good Poppit's influence might do much for those poor stumbling, misguided Legs. More clearly than any of the others at Casa Lucceola—for Toes slept heavily and all the rest were befuddled with love—did she realize exactly what had happened, and why to-night the hemisphere was tattered and slashed with melody. It was all so *wrong*, sighed Poppit; so wicked, such a pity. . . . Yet one must be quick to deplore, but slow to blame. What could be done? She would so like to talk to dear Mamma about him, but Mamma was not with her to-night—"Yip!" shouted the Savoury-Legs exultantly. . . . Poppit wondered uneasily what had come over dear Mamma the last day or two? They used to have such nice little talks together. . . .

Renny and the Dark Spaniel heard what seemed to them all Nature uplifted, rejoicing at the lordly fulfilment of their dreams. They were above song; but it was right and fitting, and no cause for wonder, that song should come and do homage round and round the Tower-room, round and round in ever widening circles. . . .

"There go the Savoury-Legs, at it again!" remarked Kim to Olga as the Bacchanalian hymn lurched over the Level Crossing.

Chapter IV

". . . But my poor dear husband, the late Dr. Watson that *was*, never agreed with that theory," said Renny, entertaining the Dark Spaniel on the morning after his amazing arrival. For one couldn't always be fondling and nose-licking, could one? and in *Kennel Chat* she had recently read a very winsome article on the art of never allowing your dog-folk to get bored—little dreaming that so soon an opportunity would arise to put the writer's dictums to the test. Besides, there was no harm in letting this thrilling stranger know that she had already had one devoted husband—though, of course, one does not want to be a widow all one's life—no, indeed!—but still, Boris and Kim had been showing her most marked attentions both yesterday and the day before . . . though now she had almost forgotten the very existence of Boris and Kim. . . . Dear good fellows, both of them—but how commonplace compared with this dark aristocrat now sitting beside her, entranced by her conversation, his arrogance subdued, his glorious eyes, limpid yet fiery, like clear marmalade shot through and through with sunshine.

"—No, he never agreed with the cranks, and, though he wasn't brilliant, he was *sound*, if you know what I mean? He went into things *thoroughly*." . . . The rain drummed on the tiled roof of the goat-shed, while her loyal voice drummed as persistently on the subject of Watson's virtues: " 'It's all fly-away nonsense,' he used to say to me. 'No meat in hot countries? And, pray, doesn't the system need toning up and nourishing as much in hot countries as in cold? More; because one is apt to get more exhausted and to lose more swe—perspiration' "—Renny corrected her inelegance just in time. "And he made such a fuss that at last my Poppit got her meat; and though she isn't what you would call *big* even now. . . ."

"You are like a wine-brown pansy," declared the Dark Spaniel dreamily; "your tongue is like rose-red plush. I could listen to you talking for ever. You have not told me your name—no, do not tell me; I have no wish to know. All the names I have known have faded and become wearisome. Yours will remain a mystery and a fragrance." For that was how he talked, the Dark Spaniel.

"You do say things!" whispered Renny.

The Dark Spaniel, seeing that he had made a hit, quivered with joy, and went on in the same high-barking strain: "Besides, though we meet for the first time, we have met before. Your tender voice, the silken waves of your hair—'They have been sung of, though I know not why; they have been fought for, though I know not where.' When I was first led in here I felt a shock, not only of rapture, but of awed recognition. 'Here she is!' I said to myself; 'yes, here—She is! . . .'"

"It *was* a surprise, I'm sure," Renny agreed, and slipped her little liver-coloured paw into his big black one. "And yet, you know, do you ever get a feeling that something's going to happen? I do. My poor dear dead husband, the late Dr. Watson that *was*, always said that I had premonitions. He said it was quite uncanny; and only last night—no, it wasn't last night, it can't have been, because it was last night you arrived, wasn't it?—one does get so mixed now that the days are drawing out!—but the night before, just about sunset it was —I was feeling I couldn't settle down to anything, and I went out for a walk. We've some pretty walks round about here; not too steep. Well, somehow I went further than I meant to, and suddenly I got frightened," continued Renny, suppressing details. "It came over me all of a sudden—terribly frightened I felt, and I turned round and I ran home just as fast as ever I could. And I assure you, when I reached my kennel, I was trembling from nose to tail! And I said to myself: 'You mark my words,' I said to myself, 'something's going to happen!'"

"You shall never be frightened again!" rumbled the Dark Spaniel. He bent down and reverently licked her paw. "You've found a protector now. You're so exquisitely sensitive and helpless, you must surely be the daughter of some Ancient Country Kennel."

The subtle flattery of those three words raised her at once to the rank of a heroine: "Daughter of an Ancient Country Kennel. . . ." Renny lifted her nose and, metaphorically, sniffed the partridges!

"Have you read *The Green Muzzle?*" she asked. "I'm sure you must have! It's so thrilling." Tessa had lent it to Poppit, but Renny, naturally, would not allow Poppit to read it—all the part about "that shameful, shameless spaniel"! Well!—but she had read it herself, her heart thumping, her tears trickling and splashing into the straw. Little did she think, dreaming over the pages, that her own tempestuous hour of love had been so near. He was wonderful, this stranger from far lands. Where had he been? What had he done? Whom had he loved?

"Tell me," pleaded Renny, "all about yourself. Who are your Legs, for instance?"

"They are exceedingly exclusive," said the Dark Spaniel; but he would not say more than that, eliminating all their kind and human qualities. Perhaps he believed a shadowy background to be the more impressive.

Renny chattered on, telling him about the Legs-in-Authority—"It was he that brought us together, you know." ("It was destiny that brought us together," corrected her lover sternly.) . . . And about the Green-Silk-Legs, who could not bear Tommy; and how the Italian-Retainer-Legs always respectfully prefixed her name, calling her "*La* Renny," which was as it should be, from them. They called Tessa "La Tessa," too, but Renny did not see why she need mention that—it pleased poor little Tessa, of course, because it made her think she was a dancer!—that child had her head stuffed full of extravagant notions. . . . Secure in the ardent admiration of the suitor lying at her feet, Renny hoped, benevolently, that poor little Tessa, in spite of her follies, might one day do well for herself.

. . . She chattered on, softly, crooningly—about Poppit, "my home-bird," who had been the favourite of her poor dear dead father, the late Dr. Watson that *was*. And how Golden Toes had the digestion of an ostrich, and had never given her an hour's anxiety in her life. And she told how Tessa was so spoilt, and had once deliberately ousted her from a cushion in front of the fire—"I'm afraid I'm too good-natured," in parentheses!—But how a spark had fallen from the fire on to the cushion, and nobody had noticed it smouldering hotter and hotter inside, until, at last, the Legs, usually so curiously insensitive to smells, had actually begun to sniff, and had discovered what was happening, and had turned Tessa off the cushion, which shortly afterwards burst into flames; but Tessa had been annoyed, because it was a cold night, and she had been unusually warm and cosy while it smouldered under her, and had remarked—

fancy, the little hussy!—that she thought the Legs ought to sacrifice a cushion to her every day!

. . . Renny chattered on and on . . . and the rain pattered on to the roof . . . and the Dark Spaniel lay beside her in the straw, fascinated. . . . Nobody came near them, and they were glad of it. They wanted no one but each other. . . . Once or twice, in the distance, they could hear the Legs calling: "Kim, Kim!" . . . And, with rising exasperation, "Kim, Kim, *Kim!*"

". . . A very good old Irish-terrier family," Renny related. "The O'Haras, you know!—but he's *wild*. There was a scandal about his grandmother—only gossip, of course—I never repeat gossip—but they say . . ."

"Kim, Kim, *Kim!*"

All day long they were calling him back, fetching him back, but Kim was in a lowering mood, and he had done with obedience to the Legs. It was his will against theirs. "Kim, Kim!" But he did not listen, only dashed faster down the hill, over the slippery cobbles shining in the rain. Kim hated cold and rain. He was shivering with a sort of ague all the time, but he continued to resist even the temptation of sleep by the dining-room fire. When they shut him up, he managed to elude them somehow; his lean tan body squeezed a defiant passage through incredibly narrow apertures. If for one second they relaxed their vigilance, he was off again, and no more to be seen until brought back, silently snarling, by the Legs-in-Authority, or the Savoury-Legs, or the Italian-Retainer-Legs.

Twice they shut him in the kennels, and he leapt over the wire fencing, neat as an acrobat; once he simulated repentance, and curled himself up into a slumber so indifferent to sin and temptation in the world outside that the Legs said: "Poor old Kim, he's quite done in," and forgot to close the door—and, like a streak, Kim was off again. Halfway down the garden he met the Shapely-Legs, picking scarlet and purple anemones. Before she had even noticed him, Kim determined on his tactics. He pretended that he was aimlessly nosing about, in the hope of having bits of stick thrown to him. Once he had made his way past her by this ruse, he turned round and looked at her. It was clearly evident in his eyes that he meditated another dash for liberty, and was mocking their lack of power to stop him. The Shapely-Legs gazed back at him. . . . "Shall I go now, or in five minutes?" questioned insolent Kim. "Well—now, I think!"

The Shapely-Legs, recovering from a state of hypnotized immobility, rushed forward. Kim laughed, bounded from the top of the wall on to the winding sash of the road below, and was gone like a streak.

And that time, when he was carried back, and after the usual thrashing, which he endured with his usual mute and bad-tempered courage, they attached him to the ring outside his kennel wall by collar and chain. Kim merely waited until the Legs had gone about their business, and then wriggled his slinky neck through the hole; and, politely leaving the collar and chain where they were, made a slight détour by the garden, and under the barbed wire, so as not to pain the Legs in the house by the sight of his swaggering freedom; and once more, by the upper path and across the river near the cemetery, returned to the Level Crossing. He hated water, but he was so wet already from the rain that it did not matter. Wet and cold and stubborn, that was Kim; and he had had no food that day.

. . . He limped back of his own accord in the late afternoon, conscious of the need, perhaps, for respite and for getting a little warmth into his chilled, slender bones; but he carefully chose a time when the Legs were not calling him, nor looking for him, so that they need not feel encouraged by his return. He found his comrades melancholy and overstrung, except for Toes; Toes was puzzled at finding nobody willing to rollick with him.

"I say, such a lark!" Toes cried, even before Kim had duly insinuated everyone away from the best place on the cushion in front of the fire. "Such a lark—Tessa's in love! I've been ragging her like anything. Boris is, too, of course, but then you knew about Boris—but you didn't know about Tessa, did you? I'm the first to tell you, aren't I? Shut up, Poppit, why shouldn't I tell him? And who do you think she's in love with?" Kim blinked indifferently at the flames. "Why, with the stranger, the black spaniel, you know—Renny's black spaniel!"

At any other stage of her career, Tessa would have leapt upon Toes and furiously chewed his throat, or the gleaming tips of his long ears; but in her present dreamy, sensitive, lovelorn condition she merely winced and looked appealingly at Boris. Boris, whom a sleepless night had left with thoughtful bumps over his eyes, sighed, wearily swished his tail at a fly, and said: "Don't tease her, Toes!"

But Toes had suffered in the past from Tessa; and though his kind heart, had it understood how love can sting its victims, would have prompted him at once to go away and torment an old boot instead, yet he could not now for the life of him see that Tessa was being anything but funny.

"She's been moping and moaning all day," he went on, nudging Kim. "I say, Kim, you are shaking a lot! Are you cold? You're awfully wet, aren't you? I say, Kim, we had marrowbones for lunch to-day; what a pity you were out, old chap! D'you remember that time when Watty—my poor dear dead father, the late Dr. Watson that *was*"—he mimicked Renny disgracefully—"had a marrowbone under the kitchen table, and you rushed out barking, pretending there were some strange Legs coming up the garden, and we all tore after you, Watty too; and when we came back you were eating the bone? I *did* laugh! I think that was an awfully smart trick—I simply shouted; so did the Legs! Marrowbones for lunch always make me think of it. But Tessa must be frightfully bad to-day, because she only ate her own and didn't try to get anybody else's, and that's not like Tessa, is it? Oh, and I say, Kim, she's been asking for a rhyme to 'spaniel'—I believe she's writing poetry to him!" Toes frisked round the dining-room table in an ecstasy of merriment.

"Oh, leave me *alone!*" begged Tessa in a rapt, far-away voice.

"The only one I could think of was 'flannel'—'Oh, how I love my spannel, I would wrap him up in flannel!' " Toes threw himself over on his back and kicked his plump paws in the air. He chanted these two inspired lines seventeen times. At the eighteenth repetition Kim looked over his shoulder and snapped: "Be quiet, damn you!"

Boris, from the depths of loathing for his privileged rival, growled: "I hate that type of dog! All black curls, and languishing eyes. Romantic rubbish! Can't think what Re—what anyone can see in him besides his looks. Got a touch of the tar-brush in him, I shouldn't wonder."

"How dare you?" flared Tessa, with taut, indignant ears. "He hasn't; and if he had— You're so narrow-minded. What's it matter where a dog was born? We can't all of us afford to be so particular as you, even though *our* ears don't flop sideways. . . ."

Kim began to take enough interest in the discussion to enter it on Boris's side. "I hardly saw the f-f-fellow myself"—his teeth chattered so that he could not speak without stammering—"but I thought him a bit of a l-l-lounge lizard—just the sort of theatrical b-brigand that Tessa *would* fancy, in fact."

"He's not! He's not!" Tessa cried passionately. "Just because he isn't obvious and coarse— You don't understand! I'm on his side, however much it may hurt me. . . ." And a rush of tears forced her to silence just as she was trying to think of something cutting to say about Kim's pedigree—or the lack of it.

Kim took the baiting of Tessa from Toes's clumsy and inefficient paws, into his own. It gave his pain and his loneliness a certain sardonic satisfaction to goad her to a frenzy:

"At Tessa's age," he said, addressing the fire, "it makes very little d-d-difference, of course, whether your love is a real dog or just a c-c-curled and oily boudoir *gentleman*." He subtly stressed the word "gentleman," soothing it, as it were, with a deft gesture of his tongue, into something even more offensive than it actually stood for in animal vocabulary. "P-p-poor Tessa has no discrimination. But that, of course, is no bar to writing bad poetry!"

"I wouldn't talk about *bars* too much if I were you!" fumed Tessa. "My family came over with the Alsatian conquest. . . . They'd be very upset indeed if they knew that I lowered myself to share my meals with a terrier who's got a bar *sinister* and an Italian grandmother!"

. . . The vertical frown between Kim's eyes deepened and his limbs almost imperceptibly grew stiff. "It's very kind of you, Tessa," in murmured deprecation, "even to l-l-lie on the same floor with such an outcast and vagabond as myself; but why worry about *sharing* your meals with me? You don't, you know, nor with anyone else! Qu-quite the other way about. No wonder poor Poppit is thin! As for your Dark Gentleman of the Sonnets—"

"Oh, that's good!" shouted Toes. "Oh, that *is* good! I must tell Pekoe and Baloo that! I must tell Tommy and Gertie and Maudie!

'Dark Gentleman of the Sonnets'—you know, I do think that's stunningly good! Wa-a-aow! *Don't* make me laugh any more—I've got a split lip!"

Kim went on, always imperturbable when most offensive: "I should like to see those verses of yours, Tessa. Honoured if you'd show them to me. They must be p-p-pretty lush."

Tessa, for all her flame and fury, was too juvenile to stand up for long against Kim in a really evil mood. "I hate you! He's not! I won't!" was the nearest she could achieve to a retort; and that, between sobs and rage, was nearly inarticulate. "You're just nothing but a lot of dirty *Legs!* And Poppit's thin because she's only a runt, not because I steal her bones!"

Poppit began to cry. "Oh, I wish dear Mamma was here! Oh, do fetch dear Mamma, somebody!"

This sudden dragging-in of Renny's name had a sobering effect on the quarrelsome group round the fire. They had been acutely conscious of her all day; too conscious of the proximity of her romance with the Dark Spaniel to mention it. Yet the prevalent nerves and bitterness and restless depression, the rags and tags of quarrel, now, at Poppit's heart-broken exclamation, declared themselves significant of the one thought round which they had all the while been draped.
. . . Kim stared into the crumbling ashes and said nothing. Boris remarked, slowly: "It's not, I hope, that I'm conventional, and I don't want to criticize the Legs, but I must say I do think that the whole of this affair is not—well, not strictly according to the Queensberry Rules. We don't know anything about this—this spaniel, and yet they allow him to meet Renny, our Renny"—his voice broke a little—"in a most irregular way, and spend hours alone with her. Sanctioning it. What I'm trying to say is—but, of course, I'm not clever nor artistic nor anything of that sort—what I'm trying to say is, romance is one thing and license is quite another."

Tessa shrilled back: "I think it's fine and brave of animals to live together without a lot of fuss and ceremony and prearrangement. After all, they're married in the sight of Dog. Oh, how I detest these absurd conventions and dog-shows—I would never submit myself to a dog-show, never, never! I'm Tessa! Sometimes the Savoury-Legs calls me *Con*tessa. As for you, Boris, and as for you, Kim, you're simply jealous! That's why you run him down. He's magnificent! He's a hero—anyone can see that by just one look at him; and I—my nature is noble enough to be glad that they're happy, even though it means that I'm unhappy myself!"

"Exit Tessa into the night, with three haloes and a strangled sob," finished Kim. "You simply can't stop seeing yourself, can you, Tessa?—always sublime, and never ridiculous. Funny, and I see you just the other way round!"

. . . Tommy, who had been all this while peacefully asleep in the arm-chair, now opened his shining green eyes, each with the top of a black interrogation mark for pupil, blinked once or twice, rolled over on his back, curving in his soft little paws like the petals of a flower towards their centre, and remarked, with his usual cheerfulness: "Maudie committed suicide half an hour ago. Had you heard? Odd of her, wasn't it?—just to-day, when there's fish for dinner. . . ."

Then he snuggled his little fawn silk nose into his tabby Persian tail, and went to sleep again. . . .

Maudie was the small Italian cat that wasn't Gertie. She was even thinner than Gertie, when Gertie first came up to Casa Lucceola; more moth-eaten and wild and hunted; and she never lost her fear of the Legs. She snatched at her food and then fled, and she grew no fatter. Dog only knows what her past had been! Nobody loved Maudie, who was just a stray, and rubbish; not even a kitchen cat like Gertie. Gertie managed to acclimatize herself among the Italian-Retainer-Legs; she managed to get on without much petting; to grab an adequate, if not a full portion of the food put down for them under the kitchen table; and her white fur, with its black patches, even acquired a certain pierrot jauntiness, although her nose was an unsightly pink stain. But Maudie's ears always looked chewed and bitten, her fur was lustreless, her whiskers hung down, and there was no debonair friendliness about the angle at which she carried her tail. Enviously she watched Gertie—Tommy's position at Casa Lucceola was, of course, as far beyond her aspirations as the milky moon!—but how was it that Gertie had managed to establish herself with more or less security, while Maudie, of the same race and status, still hung on precariously from day to day, from night to night,

never sure when she would be stoned down the hill. . . . Nobody
would have stoned her down the hill, of course, but Maudie was
victim to an agonizing persecution-complex. Her mother had been
a gutter cat, too; and she had never known her father. . . .

"I'm as good as you!" she would say every day to Gertie; and
Gertie would reply: "No, you're not!" Their dialogue never reached
a very high level of wit.

Tommy, being proudly *"il gatto inglese,"* under the delusion that
he was a dog, and not a cat at all, and also a great favourite with the
Legs—Tommy never even bothered to flirt with Gertie or Maudie.
Strangely enough, Maudie minded this, although Gertie didn't.
Maudie thought *"il gatto inglese"* very, very splendid and handsome.
And then . . . and then . . . oh, things grew from bad to worse.
. . . She couldn't get a pantomime engagement for Christmas; and
when at last she thought she had one, they altered the programme
from *Dick Whittington* to *Aladdin*, which hadn't got a cat. . . .
Oh, and her agent wrote to her it was no good trying again: she
wasn't ingratiating enough to play Puss in Boots. . . . Oh, and she
didn't know how long the Legs would keep her—oh, and Gertie
didn't care. Gertie had sidled her way in, somehow; Gertie was
quick-witted. Oh, what did it matter? Maudie knew herself for a
disreputable little drab. . . . They had told her long ago that no
good would come of following the gentleman with the black side-
whiskers into the café, which was so soon and so mysteriously shut
up afterwards. . . . But what did it all matter? Who would care?—
who would notice, even? . . .

. . . Softly, along the branch of olive-tree that overhung the great
rain-water barrel!—one little whimpering mew as she let herself slip
—claws digging frantically into the bark. . . . Too late now. . . .

Kim, in one of his queer flashes of chivalry, of rare decency, made
a formal offer to be one of Maudie's pall-bearers. Gertie's breath was
simply taken away by this, much more than by poor Maudie's watery
end; Kim—the Irish terrier, the most aloof and respected of all the
dogs! . . . What a pity that poor Maudie couldn't be alive to enjoy
the honour—poor dejected Maudie! She hadn't been much good, not

to nobody. How fast it was raining! "I do hate the rain!" squeaked Gertie.

But the sky broke a little towards twilight; and the Legs-in-Authority gave orders to the Savoury-Legs to take the Dark Spaniel for a short walk on the lead. Unfortunately, the Nutritious-Legs, unaware of this, at the same time opened the dining-room door to let the other dogs escape, for a little while, from the confinement that her kindness felt must be so irksome to them.

Kim bolted straight for the Level Crossing again, though he was still throwing one ague after another from the damp that had soaked through his thin skin and into his bones. But he believed in the well-known cure which consisted of the hair of the Legs that bit him. . . .

Boris galloped at a swinging pace up the steps, and up the steep path towards the goat-shed, where his love was immured.

Suddenly he became aware of his enemy.

The Dark Spaniel was just going to submit quietly to the collar and chain; but at the sight of Boris he sprang away from the Savoury-Legs, sprang backwards a couple of paces, and stood there, growling. Boris also remained motionless for a few seconds, his limbs stiffening, his tail slowly lashing from side to side; the hackles rising along the back of his neck in token of hate and of menace; his eyes gleaming like yellow jewels set in the massive matrix of his head.

Then they sprang.

With just such a snarl of rage, too long pent up, Achilles and Hector might have met, forgetting even Helen, for lust of the battle for Helen.

. . . For a second there was a mad swirl and tangle of ugly sound, of jaws snapping, bodies closely locked, gravel and dust rising in choking clouds about the combatants. Then Savoury-Legs, recovering from the paralysis of horror, rushed forward just as the great wolf-hound had rolled his foe over and was sinking his fangs into the curly black throat bared below him. A hard kick in the belly compelled Boris to loose his hold on the Dark Spaniel's windpipe. He had already got in a couple of deep bites, and blood was on the ground. The Legs-in-Authority hurled himself into the fray from the rear, caught hold of Boris round the throat, and tugged him, panting, away.

. . . But, released from the grey wrinkled sheath of misery and inaction which had gathered so tightly round the day, life flowed again for Boris in soft, loose rosy petals. . . . There was a breath of scented coolness in the air. . . . Sirocco was over. Boris was still growling, but mechanically, for his amiable nature, now that it had fulfilled its one elementary need, expanded in genial affection towards his companions, both canine and Legly. He felt tired, but not too tired. He wondered what there was for dinner. . . . He wondered if Renny had heard anything of the great fight. . . .

Renny, from behind her door, had been, indeed, whimpering and barking like mad, hurling herself against the panels, worrying at the wood, terrified. . . . For ah! that all this should have been happening in her service, and she not even able to see it! But Tessa, who breathlessly had watched that primitive scarlet moment when dog met dog, had stood erect among the onions, glorying, glorying!— for her temperament adored strife, and worshipped victory; she was Tessa the Fierce, Tessa the Warrior, Tessa the Selfless!—yes, even selfless enough not to care that it was Renny for whom they fought instead of for her.

"I'm glad, oh, I'm glad!" she whispered in savage triumph, as he who had been for twenty-four hours her hero of romance went down before the powerful paw of Boris, the big wolf.

Chapter V

"—the loveliest little witch you can imagine," rhapsodized the Dark Spaniel, describing his adventure to his great friend, the French poodle, who lived in the next-door villa at San Remo.

They lay side by side, their noses cooling on the broken balustrade of the marble terrace; for the air was warm and languid again, and the scent of freesias stirred in the pergola which led down to the stone fountain. A pepper-tree sprayed its delicate showers of foliage near by; and between an even row of cypresses the Mediterranean gleamed in slices of hot blue.

. . . "Spring is here," sighed the Dark Spaniel; "but my spring is over."

The French poodle was sympathetic, but he did not encourage these vague phrases eloquent of an inexpressive sorrow. Rather was he interested to hear an exact and sophisticated description of Renny —her hair, her figure, her ravishments. Ah, had it but happened to him, this fantastic incident!—Jacquot stuck out his foreleg and complacently gazed upon its rosette—he would have profited himself more particularly of the occasion!

The Dark Spaniel, all unaware that his rhetorical style was being sardonically criticized, went on, as he supposed, creating a tremendous impression. "I tell you, Jacquot, it was like a story from the *Arabian Nights*. I had been chatting with you that morning—it was the same morning, you remember, that we found that new smell, down by the ilexes, at the edge of the fountain."

"Yes, yes, I investigated! It was a nothing, a bagatelle, that smell —a gold-fish that had died young. But continue, I pray. I am all moved by your tale."

The Dark Spaniel went on as bidden. Cruelly parted from his little love, in talking about her he found his only consolation. "Well, and on that same day—how long ago was it? I have lost count . . . a week?—a month?—a year?" He passed a dazed jaw across his eyes.

"It was three days ago," his friend informed him, a trifle impatiently. *Mon Dieu!*—what a *poseur* was this fellow, this sport-dog!"

"Three days ago—three days. . . . A lifetime! Three days cut off and apart; three days of enchantment—less than that, even, for I was there but two nights, and a day enclosed between them, like a shrine between two cypresses. . . ."

"You were there? But *where*, then? You are so mysterious! Where was this place? Who were those Legs? What was your love's name? It is all in the air, that which you tell me. It is nothing of significance."

The Dark Spaniel shook his head; his long black ears flapped mournfully against the marble. "I do not know her name. I do not wish to know it."

"Grace to Dog! You did not even ask? But it is incredible! How are you to find your way back, when again you feel the fascination, the allure?—if, indeed, she had of the allure?" For he could not be-lieve that the spaniel's taste was anything like as fastidious and know-ing as his own. He was a Parisian, this poodle; the original of that popular dance-tune, composed by two Most-Elegant-Legs, "Parisian Poodle." . . .

"I do not want to find my way back," oozed the spaniel in rich, juicy reminiscence. "It would not be the same again. That is not romance—finding one's way back."

"No, but it is life," prosaically from Jacquot, who liked to face facts.

"I prefer it like this—just one solitary, glorious shining episode, suspended in space and in time."

"*Une épisode sans l'addresse, ça ne me sert à rien!*" the poodle con-fided to a tiny cushion of moss pushing up between the cracks in the marble. And then, aloud, "Had she other lovers?"

"Great Spratt!" exclaimed the exasperated spaniel. "You don't understand! This wasn't one of your ordinary fence-by-the-way-side affairs! I tell you, my whole life was in it, and hers too! How would you feel if suddenly you were snatched by stranger Legs away from your own home, and driven through the dark, the shak-ing, rocking dark—who knows in what direction?—then a walk through a strange town, up a strange hill, past a strange house. . . . And then—the supreme miracle: the door opened, and you found yourself in the presence of—but why need I begin to describe her again?"

"But, my faith, you have *not* described her—nothing of what I want to hear! You say that she is all there is of the most adorable—*mais est-ce-qu'elle avait du genre?* Were her eyes soft? Was her mouth of the most seductive? Had she, above all, *une taille svelte?* Did she cede voluntarily and gladly to your desire? Had she tem-perament? Was she coquette?"

But the Dark Spaniel, for all his romantic nature, was a little woolly in the perceptive regions. He could only describe Renny in the English fashion—the colour of her hair, the shape of her nose, the carriage of her tail, and, most eloquently of all, her partiality for himself. The French poodle, an intelligent specimen of his race, put various searching questions about her figure, to which his comrade was quite unable to return coherent answers.

"It was a *fausse maigre*, then? Well, well, you have had of the chance, you! It shows itself from your stupidity to-day it was *un vrai coup de foudre*—a blow of the lightning. But you say you had no rivals? It is droll, that!"

"No rivals?" cried the spaniel. "Great Cæsar, where do you suppose I got these wounds?" He pointed to two deep gashes in his cheek, which had been sewn up directly on his return by the Veterinary-Legs.

"I had figured to myself," remarked Jacquot innocently, "that those were little love-bites!"

The Dark Spaniel sprang to his paws and began to swagger angrily round and round the poodle, as he summoned up a picture of a huge and ferocious wolf-dog, who had been crazy about the pretty brown witch. Yet she rejected him over and over again. "For she was, mark you, extremely cold until I came along—and then she was fire and flame! Ah . . ." He stood still, gazing towards the blue sea. He had once heard Jacquot describe a little witch whom he had met in the streets of Paris as "*feu et flamme*"; and the phrase had caught his fancy. Then, lest Jacquot should still suppose he had won his way without any encounter with jealous and truculent rivals, he threw in a background of assorted bulldogs, borzois and St. Bernards, all madly hating him, all snapping their jaws and lashing their tails; and finally, with infinite relish, he went on to describe the Trojan encounter which had taken place on his last evening. And here Jacquot could not fairly accuse his memory of lacking in detail. He could well describe a fight, if not an embrace. . . .

"And so," he concluded at length, "I left him lying there, prostrate, bleeding, upon the ground."

"*Il était mort?* He was dead?"

"I didn't stay to see—but . . . yes, yes, I think he must have been dead. I had to return to my little love, who was swooning, though I assured her that my wounds were nothing. I've always laughed when real danger came my way," said the Dark Spaniel, perhaps a trifle too exuberantly, "though, of course, you could hardly call this real danger—he wasn't more than three times my size. When I passed that

way again with the stranger Legs, who was taking me home, the
body of the wolf-dog had gone. I expect they had already buried
him. . . ."

Chapter VI

It so happened that that year the feast of St. Sirius, the dog-star,
coincided with the day of days, about a fortnight after the departure
—the rather hasty departure—of the Dark Spaniel, on which Renny
was to be let out from her romantic captivity.

It was Poppit who had overheard the Legs-in-Authority say to the
other Legs: "I think, you know, we can let her out to-morrow, don't
you?" And, all excited, she had trotted away to tell the others.

At first they had received her news with curious indifference.
Poppit had expected, remembering their ragingly impatient attempts
at rescue a fortnight ago, that they would be, as she expressed it to
herself, "beside themselves with glee." But Boris was absorbed in
slowly locating the whereabouts of a parasite that refused to remain
quiet enough on his person to allow him to locate it; and Kim lay
blinking in the hot sun, shivering a little, for he nearly always
shivered nowadays; so that when Poppit frisked on to the lawn, crying: "Dear Mamma will be allowed to join us to-morrow!" Kim only
yawned; and Boris twisted his head round and pressed his nose deep
into his flank till the black leather tip was comically wrinkled; and
Toes cried: "Runt-o! Runt you are!"

"Dear Mamma will be with us again, to-morrow!" cried Poppit
piteously. . . . And Kim and Boris, with guilty starts, realized what
she had said. At once, and as much for the sake of deceiving themselves as for deceiving each other and Poppit and Tessa, they began
to work up enthusiasm; for, of course, their ardour had not in the
least worn off! Of course they had not forgotten Renny's existence,
not for one single second! "Our lovely little Renny—bewitching
Renny—" Could it really be that once again, and so shortly, they were
to see her melting eyes, and her—her—her—what colour *was* her coat?
. . . Well, but if passion had indeed grown sluggish, what with the
fine weather, and the bathing beginning early this year, and one
thing and another—it was bound to revive like a roaring fire, drawn

by a draught up the chimney, directly they saw her again. At least, so Boris reassured himself, loth to renounce an ideal of undying fidelity to his first love. Kim was feeling rather more sceptical, for he had learnt by experience to distrust the permanence of anything, and particularly of his own emotions. Still, he had been strangely moved by Renny's fascination, and charmed by her wit. . . . It might be that she was indeed one of those enchantresses who occur only twice or thrice in the whole history of dog. . . .

"I think," remarked Boris, "that it's up to us to give a party in her honour; especially as it coincides with the feast of St. Sirius. Tradition, you know—what? I'm not exactly a religious dog, but I do like to keep up these ancient rites. There may be something in them, you know."

"Superstition," said Kim, briefly.

"I shouldn't like to say it wasn't," answered Boris, with a profound nod of his head: "but what I said is, you can't tell. I've heard some modern young pups argue that Rome wasn't built by Romulus and Remus at all; but none of this up-to-date tomfoolery and learning would influence me to fail in respect to their memory. But of course we wolves especially have a very strong racial feeling for Romulus and Remus."

"Oh, please, why?" prattled Poppit.

Boris explained, tolerantly: "Is it possible that you don't know that their foster-mother was a wolf? They were always very good to her when she grew old and decrepit, and used to wheel her in a bath-chair, up and down the seven hills of Rome. I've seen a picture of it in a weekly that the Legs take in, called *Punch*."

"*Punch?*" queried Poppit, "*Punch?* Wasn't that the name of the fox-terrier that some Legs from Rapallo brought to see our Legs last autumn?"

"Yes—a very distinguished fellow. He has taken prizes. The weekly was named after him. And that reminds me, Kim, did I ever tell you that rather good one about the curate's dog . . ."

—Ten minutes later Kim said severely: "Take a pull, my good friend, do! Last time I heard *that* old chestnut—well, I remember the occasion clearly, because my eyes hadn't opened yet!"

Boris was a little bit disappointed at this reception of his funny story. But the mental picture conjured up by Kim's remark brought him round to a congenial subject.

"When I have puppies," he announced, "I should very much like to call the two eldest Romulus and Remus." And he moved his tail waggishly towards Tessa.

"I think Fido is a nice name!" said Poppit, timidly.

Boris ignored this trivial suggestion; but Kim, who was always gentle with Poppit, and understood that it was an effort to her to join in the conversation at all, said kindly: "Yes, Fido, and Towzer, too, are good names; good, simple, honest, unpretentious names. I expect Tessa would choose Lancelot and Parsifal!"

But Tessa had risen and walked away a few steps; and lay down again with her back to Boris; for this was one of her loving and amiable habits. Only the back line of her delicately-carved buff and silver head, the two tall ears, sharp conicals cut against the blue sky, expressed her vehement annoyance. Puppies, indeed! Puppies! . . . Yes, and he was the sort of husband who would expect her to have fourteen a year—she, Tessa, Tessa the Free, Tessa the Beautiful, Tessa the Graceful and Defiant, Tessa the Irresistible, Tessa the Fleet of Limb. . . . The slight advantage which Boris had gained in her eyes by his victory a fortnight ago over the Dark Spaniel was now dispelled by his coarse allusions, his ponderous jokes. And they said that marriages were made in the dog-star! One day, perhaps, Tessa reflected, her wiry fierceness subsiding into a gentler shimmer of dreams and hopes—one day, perhaps, Boris and Kim, instead of taking her for granted, as they did now, would find *her* mysteriously fascinating; and that would herald, maybe, like a comet blazing out of nowhere, the sudden arrival of romance itself: a strange wolf, splendid, dogly, heroic, would come loping from the distant hills, drawn by the allure of Tessa, of Tessa, Tessa. . . .

Toes, who was getting terribly bored by Boris's prosy statements regarding faith and superstition, now broke in with: "Oh, I say, let's give a party, anyway! It's ages since we gave a party. Do let's with lots to eat and drink!"

"You care too much about what comes under the table," Poppit reproved her boisterous brother. "Greed is a vice, we are told. I read a *very* pretty tale once, and dear Mamma said it was true, about a dog who, when his Legs was ill, refused all food."

"Very right; very right and proper," Boris nodded approvingly. "I trust that I . . . if the occasion *should* arise, I trust that I should do the same," he added, but his tone was a little doubtful.

"What a hope you've got!" Tessa shot impudently, from over her shoulder.

"You shut up, Tessa! And you too, Poppit. Boris and I aren't likely to stand any tail-wag from either of *you*." And Toes, whose tastes were entirely social, returned undaunted to the subject of the party: "Who shall we invite? Let's invite everybody! Let's invite Pekoe and Baloo!"

. . . Kim emitted a low growl; and Boris turned round and surveyed Toes sternly, through the horn-rimmed spectacles which Nature had painted round his eyes: "Invite those Chows to a party given in our garden in Renny's honour? Toes, you must be mad!"

"I like Pekoe and Baloo," repeated Toes, "and I think it's a shame to leave them out. You're so prejudiced! Why not allow me to ask them, all jolly and easy, and let's all be pals together!"

Boris merely said that he would be sorry for any chow that shoved a blunt nose into his territory. Toes, a little discouraged, yet would not altogether yield his point. It struck him that a feast in honour of St. Sirius of the dog-star was a communal occasion, at which all bones of contention should be decently buried.

"I told them about your fight with Tessa's Dark Gentleman, Boris. They were awfully bucked!"

. . . The faint flicker of a smile played round the corners of Boris's mouth, and he shot out his front paws and howled a little. . . . "Something had to be done. . . . Sanctity of the home. . . . I waited for the Legs to wake up to their responsibilities, but when they didn't—well, I simply horsewhipped the fellow!"

"Quite right!" murmured Kim, who praised but rarely. "I'd have done it myself if I'd been a younger dog!" And with a stir of better feeling he added: "I could have, once, before dope and drink did me in!"

Toes, seeing that he was creating the right effect, made the mis-

take of enlarging a little: "Pekoe said he jolly well wished he could
have seen you knock him out, Boris!"

"I heard what Pekoe really said," murmured dear, innocent little
Tessa. "I was on the wall when they passed underneath, and Toes
didn't see me. Pekoe said: 'Yes, and if Bolis him fight Ploppit, I tink
him velly much win, too!' "

—And that settled the question of whether Pekoe and Baloo were
to be invited to the feast.

There were, however, plenty of dashing young dogs, gay legs,
every one of them, in the neighbourhood around; and they were all
very anxious to be in the Lucceola set, and delighted at the invitations formally issued by the pack, to attend a feast by starlight under
the olives the following night to meet "La Renny." It was etiquette,
whenever dogs gave a party, that every visitor should dig up the best
of his buried hoard, whether bone or biscuit, and bring it along as
contribution, that thus there need be no lack of variety in the viands.
So all through that day and the next, there was a great scratching-up
of earth in the gardens of the villas scattered about San Goffredo;
and much futile anger on the part of all the Legs who cared for
their plants.

The party was due to start at seven-thirty, while the Legs were
at their dinner, and before any of the dogs were shut up in their
kennels for the night. For they would all have had their normal evening feeds by then, which would diminish the force of their first
ravenous onslaught upon the fare contributed, and give an effect
almost of good manners as they dashed here and there, to and fro,
from biscuit to bone, and bone to biscuit.

Renny was not liberated all the next morning, but the Legs had
been heard to say that she was to be allowed to join the others some
time that day, and they trusted blindly in the Legs' statements.
Fortunately for their tranquillity, it never occurred to them that
the Legs were capable of either forgetting or of changing their
minds. They might be tyrannous, or unreasonable, but they were
dependable beings, whose fixed and established government, while
it provided shelter, food, and law, yet came as rarely into actual
conflict with the little animals' personal lives, lived so much nearer

the ground, so much more restlessly than their own, as a country's government interferes with the individual's busy everyday.

But just this very afternoon of the feast the Shapely-Legs must needs make some foolish remark to the Legs-in-Authority; that it was a fine day, and that the dogs were scratching a lot, and that they had not been bathed for at least a month. . . .

Now this was touching the Legs-in-Authority upon his pride. He had an illusion that in a well-conducted household the dogs were bathed systematically once a week. Naturally the dogs encouraged this illusion. It was so much better, Kim argued, that the Legs-in-Authority should believe he bathed them once a week, and, in reality, only bathe them once a month or so, than that he should actually do it every fortnight. There had been one devastating period in their lives, quickly ended, when some evil London Legs had sent the Legs-in-Authority a fat book, relating entirely to the system and routine to be observed for the health and cleanliness of dogs. The Legs-in-Authority absorbed the pages as one who absorbs a fever, which will later come out in a rash. Then he proceeded to reorganize. . . . The dogs still shuddered, remembering what he had done to them; remembering the disinfected, legmatic, trained-to-strict-obedience, sulphur-dosed-every-morning life they had led. All the easy, happy-go-lucky ways, the friendly, give-and-take, existing for the most part between themselves and the Legs, were cancelled and stamped out by the despotism of the unknown writer of that truly horrible book.

At last, unable to bear such super-well-being any longer, they secretly urged on Toes to destroy the four hundred and thirty-seven pages, bound in stout green cloth, which he did, with great glee and thoroughness, early one morning before the Legs were down. Toes was thrashed, of course, when the mutilated fragments of the book were discovered scattered over the garden, for one or two bits of it still adhering to his dew-laps proved him the culprit; and, of course, being Toes, he squealed the very heavens down; but afterwards Boris and Tessa and Kim were all very pleased with him, and called him an excellent, noble, and self-sacrificing Toes. And the Legs-in-Authority, without the printed directions to refer to, gradually forgot all about system and rubbish of that sort; and baths only happened, as now, like a sudden clap of misery out of the blue —but not very often.

Kim, first—

Because he hated it most, and always escaped when he could. He stood bolt upright in the tubful of cloudy and strong-smelling warm water, which stood out in the sunshine on the lawn, and shivered protestingly all the time. Most of Kim's inbred dignity collapsed in the bath. He was just a little light-brown terrier, very miserable and incredibly thin. One big, powerful, relentless hand of the Legs-in-Authority held him down while the other soaped him; canfuls of cold water that blinded and stung like a thousand needles were flung all over him; and, as he leapt out of the tub, he was caught by the Shapely-Legs and the Nutritious-Legs, outposts on the lawn, and enveloped in a big, rough towel, and rubbed hard, till he felt as though his very bones were bursting through their skin. And then the Legs, suddenly become gentle, carried him into the dining-room where, in spite of the warm weather, a big fire had been lit, and Kim was placed on the towel, drawn close to the fire, and allowed to re-cover himself slowly from his dazing and humiliating experience. It took cold water to subdue Kim.

Next, Tessa.

And Tessa, wicked and disobedient in everything else, behaved beautifully in her bath. She held her grateful head very high, and she lifted one dainty paw after another for the soaping; and, beyond a remark flung over her shoulder to Boris that she couldn't understand why they didn't bathe her in asses' milk, which brought out the pointed lustre of her coat to so much greater effect, she did not even grumble. When the experience was over, she bounded lightly from the tub; invited, rather than submitted to, the drying; and then flew round and round the garden, jumping from terrace to terrace; crush-ing stray blossoms, but not heavily, beneath her pads, and frequently burying her nose in her own fur to enjoy the smell—a jungle smell, warm and cosy, battling with the pungent, clean odour of the dis-infectant, and bringing along with it, in the hot rays of the sun, a queer, dream-like whiff that recalled a cave, dug somewhere down under the earth among great rocks, and small, fubsy wolf-cubs playing, and home, and a feeling of being wild yet protected. . . . *Nice* smell! Tessa was happy.

Next, Boris.

Boris did not enjoy being bathed, but it was incompatible with his lordliness to make a fuss over so petty a thing. If it pleased the Legs to inflict this upon him, Boris was too big not to be gentle. The tub seemed a little bit too small as he sat in it, winking his eyes if the soapy hand came near them; shifting his weight from foot to foot; and when he had given his paw once to be soaped, giving it again fourteen times, out of sheer friendliness. Boris took a lot of drying, and when he had finished, he lay down quietly in the sun and spread his massive limbs and went to sleep.

Next, Toes.

And the spaniels, as usual, were more bother than all the rest of the dogs put together. No sooner was Toes caught, skulking behind an olive-tree, and dragged, a dead weight, towards the tub and placed in it, than he leapt out again and scuffled away; and when finally captured, he whimpered, and slipped, and lost his footing, and lay on his back just when they wanted to soap it.—"Be a wolf, Toes!" suggested the Equestrian-Legs. "Be a *wolf!*"—and splashed the water over everybody, and got loose again before he was half dry, and, finding the dirtiest corner of manure and rubbish and earth and old egg-shells, rolled himself in it again and again and again. . . .

"Oh, damn Toes!" said the Legs. "Blast Toes!"

Toes had to be bathed three times that day; and then, for safety, lest he re-dirtied himself, he was shut up, still damp, in the dining-room with Kim, where he immediately lolloped on to a freshly covered arm-chair, and, with a sigh or two, also fell asleep.

Next, Poppit—

Only they forgot all about Poppit, and so she did not get bathed.

Next—

And next, Renny. . . .

Presently Boris awoke from his doze, and snapped at a fly which was tickling one of the fair-hued bumps above his eye. Turning his head, he became aware of Renny, giving trouble in the bath-tub.

He watched the performance without much interest for a few moments, reflecting that spaniels never knew how to behave—they lacked the essential quality of repose; reflecting that the stream of water down the nose and ears caused her, if anything, to look rather plainer than usual. . . . "But a good little soul," murmured Boris drowsily, and closed his eyes again.

When the Legs had finished scrubbing Renny, and swearing at her, and hauling her back into the tub every time she managed, with an effort, to plunge out of it, they gave her a quick and irreverent rubbing with the towel, and then carried her into the dining-room, to prevent her from echoing Toes's performance of promptly rolling her newly washed body in earth.

Kim was still wide-awake, and, of course, occupying the best position in front of the fire. He looked up irritably and began to growl as Renny was tumbled on to the towel beside him: "Oh, hell! Always these spaniels cluttering up the room!" Why was it that two spaniels in the house made themselves seem like twenty? Why couldn't the Legs leave him in peace? First tormenting him, and then—Great Bethgelert!—here was Renny shaking herself all over him, just as he was beginning to get a bit dry and warm! Even Tessa, with all the wicked airs she put on, and her truly marvellous capacity for making mischief, was yet more to his taste in some way than this perpetual plague of spaniels. Tessa, at least, was never clumsy; never tried to propitiate him as Renny was now doing, plunging towards him with her little brown nose full of kisses. . . .

"There, all right! Lie down," said Kim, testily. "Lie down if you must. Not too near, though. And whatever you do, don't *chatter!* I'm not feeling well."

Renny at once was all solicitude and fuss. . . .

"No, it's not *that*, either!" Kim snubbed her. "No, the pain *isn't* there. No, I won't ask the Legs to put a piece of flannel round it. How long have I had it? I don't know—about a fort—"

A dim memory struggled for life. . . . A fortnight. . . . Cold— he had caught cold. . . . Running downhill . . . down again to the Level Crossing—never been right since. . . . Never mind, *will* go . . . teach the Legs . . . teach them to close doors . . . to bring in strangers. . . . About a fortnight—and somewhere, up there at the end of the garden, a beautiful little brown princess in her Tower-room, guarded, unapproachable to all save one. . . . So that she had almost become a legend.

But *this* Renny, tiresome, kind, anxious to please—and oh, so beastly wet!—this Renny surely had been with them all the time?—at least, he was not aware of having missed her. Was there, then, another Renny, who was all a glamour and a dream? . . . Kim was a little fuddled from the drastic bathing he had lately received, and the heat of the fire and the dazzle of the flames. . . . Two Rennys—were there two? That night—yes, they were giving a feast that night, a feast of St. Sirius, because of the promise that a door would be opened again and loveliness released. How they had all longed and agonized for that moment! Well, it was to be to-night, some time. . . . How would she look? Like wonder coming slowly towards them from far-off places? Like a shrine unveiled? Like the embodiment of all that was most tender, most glorious? . . . Renny, Renny would be with them again that night. . . .

And, musing thus, Kim slowly and persistently edged his companion away from the fire; peevishly twitched the towel from under her, so that she lay uncomfortably on the hard string carpet instead of on the thick, fleecy folds which were now warmly gathered up around his own limbs. . . . He sank his head sideways down on to his leg, so that the paw covered his eyes; twitching nerves were soothed at last . . . and Kim slept.

Poppit sat outside her kennel that evening, thinking about Kim. She was waiting till Renny should have finished, and should allow her to enter in. Renny was flurrying round, earthing her shiny brown nose, crimping her ears to bring out their tawny lights, bestowing tremendous pains on her toilet; for she considered that the Legs had taken a most unfair advantage by causing her, after all that long separation, to reappear for the first time, in front of her admirers, during and after a bath, when not the most beautiful animal can ever hope to look her best. It was really not giving her a chance, to plunge her at once into this indignity . . . for Renny had not been slow to perceive her effect, or, rather, lack of effect, upon Boris and Kim, whom she had left, a fortnight ago, craving to be allowed to kiss even the tip of her muzzle. Never mind, there was to be a party to-night in her honour, so she had been told—oh, and in honour of dear St. Sirius, of course! And to-night she would arise before them anew, like Aphrodite from the foam, and they would do her homage.

—So: "Afterwards, my dear, afterwards! Don't bother me now," Renny had said, disposing of Poppit's claims and questions. "No, you can't do your ears now. There's no room. These kennels are terribly cramped, as it is. Wait outside till I call you."

Poppit was sadly apprehensive that this arrangement might not leave her time to get ready for the party; but dear Mamma was still unlike herself: preoccupied, cold to her Poppit's affection, unwilling to give her the usual advice, to help her with deft paws. For Poppit was a little helpless and childish, for her years. She was not even certain whether to loop her ears or to leave them hanging demurely on either side of her piteous little muzzle. How she wished she could devise some striking fashion by which to render herself attractive to Kim, so that he should look at her with new eyes—Kim, who was so mysterious, so thrilling, such a sinner, yet always so carelessly kind to her, and so sarcastic to Tessa; Kim, the philosopher with a cynic's past; Kim, who had even a bar sinister in his family, as well as all his other attractions; Kim, who sullenly, obstinately, defied the Legs, and snarled when he was beaten for it—she had never heard a single whimper from Kim; and yet—here the fussy little mother in Poppit showed itself—he was so small, so light, so thin and little; he was always shivering; he could not be well! . . .

"I wish," mused Poppit, "that I could bear his pain for him!"

Dear Mamma used always to enjoin as a precept:

> Do the work that's nearest,
> Though it's dull at whiles,
> Helping, when you meet them,
> Lame Legs over stiles!

And Poppit was embroidering this verse on her sampler. But for once she did not feel in the mood either for embroidery or for docile observance. She even wished that she were less Poppit and more Tessa. . . .

And at that moment Tessa sauntered by, and paused:

"I wish, dear, that you'd let me do your ears for you, for to-night. They're quite lovely ears, you know, if only . . .

"If only," her ensuing silence indicated, "you didn't contrive to make yourself look quite so hopelessly Victorian."

"I'm very obliged to you, indeed," Poppit thanked her, meekly, "but I doubt if dear Mamma would approve. Supposing you should make me look—fast?"

Tessa merely raised her eyebrows and twitched one ear. It was really not worth taking any trouble with this idiotic little creature.

"I have sometimes wished," Poppit continued, fearfully giving her confidences, "that dear Mamma would allow me to bob my tail!" She was always a trifle out of date, even when most modern. "But dear Mamma says only the common working-class dogs do it: sheep-dogs and dreadful animals like that. Dear Mamma won't allow me to know them."

"Why don't you shingle it?" laughed Tessa; and Poppit cried, shocked: "Oh, I *couldn't!*"

"Have it your own way!" Tessa had no fears, personally, regarding her own appearance.

The party had assembled under the ring of olives at the top of Casa Lucceola garden. Starlight shone above them, but no moon. Sirius flashed green over the western hills; and like tiny echoes in compliment to the distant dog-star, the nearer fireflies flashed the intermittent green of their luminous tails over the little heaps of bone and biscuit that lay on the carpet of wild thyme. The guests only awaited their host's signal that snatching might begin.

But as yet Beauty, in whose honour the feast was given—though ostensibly St. Sirius had been dragged in for the purpose!—Beauty had not yet arrived, and a hush lay over them all. . . . Golden eyes, topaz eyes, sherry eyes, eyes like clear soup or melted amber, were turned towards the path that wound down to the kennels, a black, low line on a sky of indigo velvet.

A rumour had drifted round, of the little witch whose strange charm was so potent that the Legs had been compelled to hold her captive and invisible for many days past. Could it be true, that rumour? Or exaggerated? Was she really to appear at last? Was she all that had been said of her?

On a hillock of broken wall, behind the others, and somewhat raised above them, Kim and Boris stood apart. They were too excited to be sociable; too breathless to stroll about exchanging cordial chat. Bonded, yet solitary, the wolf-hound and the terrier waited for their love.

. . . Soft pad and skip of paws, drawing nearer. Then they saw Renny. She danced towards them, her tail coquettishly tilted, and a rose-pink camellia carried in the corner of her mouth. She danced towards them, knowing well that she was the queen of the party, and that everybody was looking at her. She danced towards them, confident that she was irresistible. . . .

And a sort of snap happened in Kim's brain, and in Boris's simultaneously. . . . And they realized that this was indeed Renny, and that the two Rennys were one, and that Renny of the Tower-room was an illusion. . . . This little dingy frump of a spaniel, with the fussy walk, was the permanent and enduring Renny; the everyday Renny, whom they were used to; Renny, the eternal bore.

. . . But they could not quite understand yet how it had all happened? Torn drifts and wisps of emotion still hung like a vapour between vision and total clarity. . . .

They thought, in amazement: "*What* a fool she's making of herself!"

And did not know that the thought was an epitaph and a dirge!

Epilogue

The white stocks had lasted well that year, blooming all through the winter and spring. And now, in the second week of May, a sweet-smelling mass of them still spread over Watson's grave at the end of the kidney-bean bed.

—Yet Renny was dissatisfied. Her poor, dear, dead husband, the late Dr. Watson that *was*, had so enjoyed a bit of colour; and nobody could deny the sober demeanour of the stocks, when compared with the blaze of orange lilies on the smaller and newer grave beside his.

Renny was a loyal wife. "There's never been anybody but Dr.

Watson, and there never will be. . . ." And she did think—yes, she really did—that the Legs had displayed an unfair partiality in this matter of oral decorations in the dogs' graveyard. Why, the lilies had been already in growth, carefully cherished, in one of the green tubs on the veranda, when the Shapely-Legs had suggested transplanting them; and the Legs-in-Authority had at once agreed to do so: "As it's for Kim . . ." they had said. Well, well, well! Virtue did not count for much in this world! "Common white stocks!" grumbled Renny, watching these operations. . . . White stocks, grown from seed, for the Doctor, a good dog if ever there was one! —and orange lilies for the rake! Expensive orange lilies, grown from the bulb!

All through April this grievance of hers had developed as rapidly as the lilies; and now that they had opened their brilliant spotted petals to stare at the sun, she simply could not bear the comparison any longer. Lilies were such dashing flowers! So off she trotted to the vegetable garden, where she remembered melons had been planted last year; excitedly scratched up one of the plants already in leaf, damaging it considerably in the process; and, refusing even Poppit's help, dragged it down the terraces again and planted it ostentatiously, and very much askew, in the centre of the white stocks. There! her poor, dear, dead husband should have the largest fruit she could think of on his grave: a great big shining yellow melon; and *that* would make the lilies seem but poor, useless, fragile things. . . .

As it happened, it was a tomato which she had dug up by mistake; the Savoury-Legs had put the melons in another bed that year, but as Renny did not know this her triumph was not marred. "There!" she repeated to Poppit, sitting beside her, "and now I must rest. I'm quite exhausted. But I'm never one to mind trouble for those I love."

And, indeed, she felt curiously relieved and happy, now she had done this, as though a heavy burden of injustice had been lifted; as though now she could sleep better, and cease to brood, to nag at Poppit, and to regard the Legs with eyes of unutterable reproach.

"Goodness, how hot it is! I shouldn't wonder if it thundered." Something was going to happen, she was sure. She never remembered before feeling so—so—well, not exactly nervous—no, nor unbalanced either. . . . "Poppit!" sharply, "you're not listening!" A good daughter should never weary of being told of her mother's symptoms.

But Poppit was gazing at the mound of earth from which the orange lilies sprang. She was thinking of her hero, Kim. . . . "Darling Mamma," she sobbed, "do you not remember how quiet he was on the great night of the party? And how he went home early? And we never guessed, even then, that he was so soon to be taken from us."

"My dear," pronounced Renny, very gravely—for though she had been preoccupied with her own emotions and grievances lately, yet nobody could fail to notice that poor little Poppit was even smaller and thinner than before, and showed all the signs of one who, crossed in love, goes into an early decline. "My dear, let this be a lesson to you, and to us all—except me. If poor Kim had not rebelled against virtue, if he had not committed those sad excesses"—she would have said "disgraceful excesses" had Kim been still alive, but even his sins had acquired a certain grace—"he would be with us now. It was all because he went so rapidly downhill, over and over again on that rainy day and afterwards, neglecting his meals and getting his feet wet, and fighting the other dogs, and—and"—but she did not want to shock Poppit, so she compromised with—"and not obeying the Legs when they called, that he lies here now."

"Under the sod!" wept Poppit. Yet she felt that dear Mamma could not quite understand all her grief and secret mourning; and, after all, even her amiable and excellent Mamma had not always answered at once when the Legs called her. . . .

. . . An echo from the early spring rippled faintly over the slope of Diana's hill: "Renny, Renny, *Renny!*" . . . The sound of the chase died away again. . . .

—"So you see, my dear," finished Renny, all unaware of criticism in her docile Poppit's mind, "a moral life always brings contentment in the end, and dogs like good bitches best. And now, as I'm feeling a little faint, I think I will go and lie down in my kennel." And off she waggled, at a slow, encumbered pace, Poppit trotting obediently behind her, with vinaigrette and sal volatile.

As they came round the corner under the wall, they passed Tessa, lazily basking in the sunshine, on the grass of Lower Peckham. She was just visible when the breeze stirred aside the sprays of white and pink roses wantoning over the pergola; but she took no notice of the spaniel's rather pompous little procession, except to be glad of the contrast between Renny's matronly and lustreless appearance, with that hint of a waddle in her unhurrying gait—and her own slim, carefree youth, as she lay outstretched on the warm grass, surrounded by flowers: flame-coloured snapdragons, and yellow poppies, and purple irises. Soft little winds blew over her, brushing her coat from grey to silver, and caressing her nose with whiffs of scent from the small lilac-bush in the centre of the grass plot. Not far away she noticed Golden Toes, lolloping clumsily in the strawberry bed. . . . And her ears began to flatten a little, as she dallied with the delicious, wicked temptation to spring at him and scrunch a portion of him between her sharp, white teeth; but no, not for the moment at any rate—it was not worth while to move. She was Tessa!—Tessa, the capricious; Tessa, the Free and Virginal; Tessa, the Voluptuous; Tessa, the Enchantress. . . .

Boris, loping up the path, paused suddenly underneath the wall . . . paused, and looked up at Tessa, between the hanging clusters of little white roses brushed with glowing pink. "How strangely beautiful Tessa is looking this morning!" he said to himself, but half-aloud, so that she heard him. And then he went on, more slowly.

And Tessa thrilled, for she had heard those words before. They were the archway, and romance was just beyond. Presently, from over the hills. . . .

It was evening, and the straw in Renny's kennel heaved and tumbled with shadowy puppy-shapes.

Renny herself was contented, but puzzled. She could not understand *why*. . . . Certainly, she was a respectable married animal—yes, that part was all right. Her poor, dear, dead husband, the late Dr. Watson, that was—she remembered him clearly; he had been brown—yes, and she was brown. Well then, *why*—?

A lift of far-off memory in her tired-out brain . . . it snatched at a dream, lost it again. . . . Wild flight over the terraces at sunset —scent of thyme and myrtle and mint—then, sharper and more bitter, the tall narcissi, whitely gleaming in the grass under the olives. . . .

Diana running—Diana pursued. . . . Panic! and afterwards, a great flowering. . . .

Yes, but the puppies?

All seven of them were coal-black!

. . . Then, again, memory lifted for a span, just long enough. . . . So it had been real, that unreal and all-but-forgotten romance of her life?

A Dark Spaniel had once passed that way. . . .

A Pair of Lovers

BY

ELSIE SINGMASTER LEWARS

THE first shadows from the western mountains fell upon the little farm at their foot. Often they seemed to chase James down the road. He had gone for the cows alone since he was six years old, but he had never grown accustomed to the queer shapes of the alder bushes in the evenings and to the dark masses which filled the fence corners. Even familiar Mooley and Daisy and Bess took on vast and unfamiliar proportions. James did not often run, and having safely crossed the bridge over the stream which made his mother's land such fine pasture he grew bold. He could see from there the kitchen light, darkened sometimes as his mother passed before it, or he could hear the great tin pails rattling on her arm as she swung open the barnyard gate.

This evening James could not see the kitchen light or hear the pleasant clink of his mother's pails. Already the loud "Gee, Mooley! Haw, Bess!" with which he expressed his return to confidence in himself and in the reasonable structure of the world, was on his lips. But the shout died soundlessly away.

The light of his mother's lamp was lost in a brilliant glare. At first James was certain that the dreaded fire was at last consuming their dwelling and he began to run, crying frantically, "Oh, mother! mother!"

Then he stood still. The light was not in the house, but in the road; it was not the leaping red flame with which fire devours wooden walls and roof. It was a round, still, white light, or, rather, two round,

453

still, white lights which illuminated the road to the bridge. James could count every nail in the railing, every knot in the floor. He could see also, as he looked down to gauge the astonishing power of the fiery eyes, his own bare feet, released to-day from their winter bondage of shoes. He could see the smooth, beautifully colored bodies of the Alderneys, moving placidly up the road in the face of the great light as though they were indifferent to the strange phenomenon.

James stopped so long in amazed contemplation that the cows were halfway to the barn. Then he ran at furious speed.

"It is one of *them!*" he cried, divided between fright and rapture.

At the gate of the house yard he stopped, breathless. The automobile lights were now behind him; he could see that the kitchen lamp was burning and that his mother stood in the doorway, her pails, one inside the other, in one hand, her lantern in the other. Facing her on the step was a stranger, a tall young man with an eager, commanding voice.

"The dairyman told me about you. He said that you loved animals and were kind to them. Robin should be on a farm while we are away. I wouldn't have bought him if I had known we were going so soon. He won't be any trouble, and I will pay you well."

Mrs. Schelling set the lantern on the sill beside her. She was a Pennsylvania German and spoke English with difficulty. She braced herself by putting her hand against the door.

"I could not say his name, to call him."

"Robin! Call him Bob, Bobby; anything you like!"

"I could not talk to him in English."

The young man laughed. "Then talk to him in German!"

Mrs. Schelling answered with a slow "Well." Two dollars a week would be a desirable addition to her income. Suddenly her face brightened. "The little one can talk to him!"

At this mention of himself, James withdrew to the shadows. But it was not at him that the stranger turned to look. The stranger gave a signal, a sharp stroke of middle finger against palm. In answer, a creature leaped in a single, startling curve through the air. It hurled itself from the seat of the automobile and landed on the step between the stranger and James's mother. It was a collie dog, brown as a chestnut.

"Isn't he a beauty?" The young man did not wait for an answer. While James's mother gasped at the suddenness with which the dog had hurled himself at her, his master put him through a series of tricks. He said one word and the collie sat up on his hind legs, another and he leaped higher than his master's head.

"You will keep him?" said he, like one who is accustomed to obedience. "Robin, you are to stay here till I come."

Without another word, the young man stepped into his car. There was a whirring noise, a jolt of wheels, and the car moved. The ribbon of light rolled itself up until it vanished like the gloves of a magician. Loneliness and darkness descended once more upon the little farm; the spring evening seemed like a dark winter night.

"James!" called Mrs. Schelling.

James came out of his hiding-place into the pale light by the door. His blue eyes almost popped from his head. He looked up at his mother and she looked down at him. Between them, the collie turned warm brown eyes from one to the other. Neither mother nor son was given to speech, not because their minds travelled with especial slowness, but because their thoughts were alike.

"It is a dog!" said James's mother slowly in German, as though she could not believe in his presence.

"Will he stay all the time here?" asked James in the English which his mother required.

"Till winter. This was young Harmon from town."

"Will he bite?" asked James in dread.

"No, he is kind." Mrs. Schelling started with pails and lantern toward the barn. "You are to sit with him till I come back."

"He might run away from me!" objected James.

"Then call him! He will come if you call him. His name is Amshel in English. You can say it."

James sat on the door-sill and the dog lay on the step. James was in an ecstasy compounded of delight and terror. If he had ever desired a dog, he had not asked for one. He was a person who accepted the existent as the inevitable. Now he was afraid, not so much that the dog would bite him, as that the beautiful creature would scorn

him. This was a rich dog, a proud dog. The Harmons lived in a great
and wonderful house. James looked down embarrassed at his soiled
bare feet, then solemnly back at the brown eyes.

For a long time he did not move. He could hear the sound of the
milk streaming between his mother's strong fingers into the pails; he
could hear an owl hoot in the distance and a whippoorwill call near
at hand. At the latter dismal sound, accustomed as he was to it, he
moved a little on the step, as though, under pressure of loneliness, he
dared seek acquaintance with his proud companion.

"Robin!" said little James. "You—you doggy!"

Then the dog did a strange thing. James recounted it shyly to his
mother when she came from the barn. Though speech was difficult,
this pleasant experience must be imparted.

"Mother," said he. "I spoke to him by name and he licked me!"

James's mother looked down at the pair. The collie sat with his
head on the little boy's knee, and James's arm was round his neck.
The tears gathered in her eyes as she carried the heavy pails into
the kitchen. Perhaps she thought of the human playmates whom
James might have had if life had been different.

For a week the collie was not allowed to leave the yard. When
James started for the cows, the dog accompanied him to the gate and
waited there till he came back. He did not seem to miss his master, to
whom he had belonged only a short time. When James came in sight,
he barked like mad.

One evening James started later than usual. The shadow of the
mountain lay already on the farm; to go toward it was like entering
a darkening cave. Mrs. Schelling came twice to the door to bid him
go.

"Take him with you!" She never ventured upon the dog's name.
The collie had become "him" as all masters of Pennsylvania German
households are "him."

The little boy leaped and shouted.

"Dare I?"

"Why, yes. He knows enough to come back."

Then was the gate of Paradise opened. The two went down the
lane with the speed of greyhounds, but with the erratic course of
June-bugs. They advanced and they receded, retracing their steps

from pure joy. They screamed and barked together. The little boy was transformed; he behaved as though he had become insane. His mother called to him to drive the cows carefully, and, as though to make up for the soberness of the return, the two behaved all the more crazily. The collie sprang over fences; he sprang over the little boy's head. The little boy, a week ago so sober and quiet, danced like a Maenad or like a fakir of India. He drowned out the cry of the whippoorwill with his wild clamor, his shrieks and song. The stories which his mother had told him were strange, superstitious tales brought almost two centuries ago from Germany; he shouted out the names of their heroes in foolish reiteration, "Old Till Eulenspiegel, Old Sir Devil, Old Till Eulenspiegel!"

The cows walked home slowly, but behind them were strange doings. The little boy danced into the shadows, apostrophizing them scornfully.

"Oh, you nix nutz under the tree! Oh, you black man by the wall! Oh, you fat pig in the corner!" He shrieked with laughter as though his sentiments were the wittiest in the world. He beat at the shadows and kicked them. There was nothing in the universe which he feared.

All the summer Paradise continued. The little boy explored the mountain upon which he had hitherto never dared to set foot. He went far from home along the country roads. When a man spoke to him roughly, the collie leaped at the stranger with the same curving swiftness with which he had leaped from his master's automobile.

When school opened, the dog went with the little boy to the schoolhouse and lay in the corner of the room, being often used as an example by the teacher. The teacher regarded James with astonishment. From the most quiet of her pupils he had become the noisiest.

When September changed to October, the cows were once more fetched at twilight. The progress to the pasture was still as wild as a June-bug's flight. The evenings were cool; the two would have moved swiftly even if life had not danced within them.

The little boy had for some time crossed the bridge by walking on the hand-rail, with the dog barking in admiration or fright below him. The night of the first frost his foot slipped and he plunged head first into the dark pool. He could swim, but the icy water bound him with fetters. He sank and rose and sank again in spite of all his frantic efforts to strike out with feet and hands. Then, beside him, he felt a support at which he could clutch, his fingers sank into a shaggy coat, and in an instant his feet touched the rising bank.

Foolishly, he went on for the cows, not dashing about and shaking himself as the collie did, but walking slowly, and trying to choke back his sobs. He could scarcely pull the pasture bars out of their sockets or follow the slow pace of the cows. They had crossed the bridge before he had left the shadows of the alders.

When he reached the bridge he gave a sharp cry. Again the light in his mother's kitchen was invisible; again there stretched to his feet a broad, shining ribbon up which Daisy, and Mooley and Bess were making their placid way. He called the dog in terror, but he did not come. Already four flying feet had carried the collie up the lane to the side of the young man on the step. Mrs. Schelling faced him, her lantern in one hand, a roll of money in the other.

"I do not like to take it," said she. "He was like a person to us." She could see the little boy creeping along the edge of the lighted road.

"I'm much obliged to you," said the young man. "There is something for your little boy, too." He gave a brisk command and the dog hurled himself into the car. There was a whir, a jolt of wheels, and the ribbon of light rolled itself up once more.

Mrs. Schelling waited for the little boy on the doorstep.

"Come in, little James." She laid her hand on his shoulder. "My child, you are wet!"

The little boy could make no answer, but stood with contorted face, trembling. His mother felt of him, questioning him wildly.

"What has happened? You were in the water? What ails you?"

At last the little boy found his voice.

"I fell in the creek. He pulled me to the bank! Oh, Mother, Mother, Mother!"

Mrs. Schelling stripped off his clothes and began to rub the shivering body. Then she wrapped him in a blanket and took him in her arms. Daisy and Mooley and Bess waited long to be milked.

In the frosty morning the little boy went for the cows. His icy plunge had not hurt him, but he moved slowly. In the evening he cried softly all the way to the pasture and all the way home, too smitten with grief to observe the threatening shadows.

But the next evening the shadows were in their places, darker, more terrible than ever. They seemed like sentient beings who would remember that he had mocked this one, had thrust that one with a sword of wood. They had grown larger; he could scarcely find a path between them and the fence. When he came to the house his face was so white that his mother was frightened.

"I could get you a dog," said she.

"Oh, no!" cried James. "Oh, no, Mother!"

By November, darkness had fallen completely when the little boy came home with the cows. There was still green pasturage in sheltered places, but it was far away. The little boy had to go round the enormous, rustling crown of a fallen tree; he had to encircle a pile of huge boulders. The autumn wind made crackling noises in the underbrush; the shadows thrust out arms to seize him. He dared not run and he was afraid to walk slowly. He tried to keep between the cows, but they wandered uncertainly from side to side, stupidly unaware of his human need.

One evening the cows were restless. James was late, having postponed his journey as long as he dared. The sky was black and the air was full of threatening sounds. When James thought he heard padding feet and panting breath he stood still and screamed. Then his cry changed to a shout.

"Is it thou!" laughed he. "Thou! Thou!"

His mother waited for him at the barn gate and did not see his shining eyes till he came into the kitchen.

"What ails you?" she asked.

"He was here," answered the little boy.

"He? Who?"

"*He*, Mother! He brought me till over the bridge, then he went home."

"It cannot be!"

"He was here," insisted the little boy.

The next evening James came home again with shining eyes. His mother looked at him in terror.

"He was here again," said James quietly. "He was here with me till the bridge. He remembers about the bridge."

In the morning, Mrs. Schelling went out in the starlight to talk to the dairyman who fetched her milk cans.

"Do you think I could buy this dog?" she asked. "My little one is—is—" she could not say the dreadful thing she feared.

The dairyman shook his head.

"That dog cost two hundred dollars. If that young fellow wanted the moon he could have it. All his life he has everything."

Mrs. Schelling was now terrified because she had had in her house so valuable a creature. She wished that she had never seen the young man and his dog.

That afternoon the young man himself rode up the lane and beckoned Mrs. Schelling to the gate.

"My dog runs away every day. Does he come here?"

"The little one says he does." Mrs. Schelling drew a deep breath of relief.

"Where is the little boy?"

"At school."

"Tell him to drive the dog home." The young man spoke angrily. It was easy to see that he had always had everything. "Tell him to throw a stick at him. He's cunning as a fox about getting off."

Having issued his commands, the young man pulled a lever and the car slid down the hill.

Mrs. Schelling gave James the young man's order.

"You are to throw him with a stick and drive him off."

James laughed. "He would only fetch the stick!"

"I will drive him off. The man talked as if we would steal him!"

The next evening Mrs. Schelling crossed the bridge to meet the returning procession. The cows moved placidly along, behind them the little boy laughed and waved his arms, beside him leaped the collie. The little boy did not see his mother until he was almost upon her.

"Mother!" he screamed. "Do not hurt him!"

The collie ran forward and took Mrs. Schelling by her apron and skirt. When he could release her for an instant, he barked for joy.

"You lump!" cried Mrs. Schelling in a furious tone. "You bad dog!" Mrs. Schelling's voice weakened a little. "You rascal! you scoundrel! Go home!" The last words were as weak as the chirp of a sparrow. Mrs. Schelling had seen suddenly over her shoulder the black pool beside the bridge. "Oh, *please* go home!" she cried.

At the end of another week the young man came again. This time he waited until James came from school.

"You must drive him home," he commanded sternly. "I can't keep him penned up night and day. He's growing to be a tramp dog. Do you feed him?"

"No," answered Mrs. Schelling.

"I save him sometimes a little something from dinner," confessed James.

"You're ruining him. He'll have to be beaten if he doesn't stay at home. Remember! I'm determined to conquer him."

That evening the collie waited at the bars.

"To-morrow I will chase him," said the little boy. The next day he said again "to-morrow," and the next. When six days had passed he still had done nothing. Then the collie came panting, walking heavily, with welts from a whip on his back.

"Oh, you must stay home!" wailed the little boy.

To his terror the collie would not leave him at the bridge. But if he did not go home he might be killed. James picked up the end of a fence rail and threw it with all his strength and the collie dropped as though he had been shot.

Somehow the little boy and his mother got the dog to the kitchen. His eyes were open and he breathed, otherwise he gave no sign of life. James sat beside him on the kitchen floor, speechless with woe. Suddenly he began to cry.

"The man is coming!"

Mrs. Schelling met the stranger at the door in the glare of light from the automobile lamps.

"The little boy threw him with a stick," said she.

The young man crossed the room and knelt down and passed his hand over the thick coat and the sleek legs. The cruel welts were still there; it was not the little boy who had hurt the dog.

"He's not badly hurt; he's only tired out."

Then the young man moved his hand quickly away from a wet,

warm, forgiving touch, and got to his feet. He looked about the simple room, bare of everything but the necessities of life, at the hard-working woman and at the little boy in his home-made clothes. He was himself not much more than a boy, and indulgence and prosperity had not yet so hardened him that his heart could not be touched. Now if he conquered anything it was a creature much harder to conquer than a dog.

"You may keep him," said he, in his clear, sharp way.

James gave a startled cry. "For always?"

"Yes," said the young man, "for always."

Garm—A Hostage

BY

RUDYARD KIPLING

ONE night, a very long time ago, I drove to an Indian military encampment called Mian Mir to see amateur theatricals. At the back of the Infantry barracks a soldier, his cap over one eye, rushed in front of the horses and shouted that he was a dangerous highway robber. As a matter of fact, he was a friend of mine, so I told him to go home before any one caught him; but he fell under the pole, and I heard voices of a military guard in search of some one.

The driver and I coaxed him into the carriage, drove home swiftly, undressed him and put him to bed, where he waked next morning with a sore headache, very much ashamed. When his uniform was cleaned and dried, and he had been shaved and washed and made neat, I drove him back to barracks with his arm in a fine white sling, and reported that I had accidentally run over him. I did not tell this story to my friend's sergeant, who was a hostile and unbelieving person, but to his lieutenant, who did not know us quite so well.

Three days later my friend came to call, and at his heels slobbered and fawned one of the finest bull-terriers—of the old-fashioned breed, two parts bull and one terrier—that I had ever set eyes on. He was pure white, with a fawn-colored saddle just behind his neck, and a fawn diamond at the root of his thin whippy tail. I had admired him distantly for more than a year; and Vixen, my own fox-terrier, knew him too, but did not approve.

" 'E's for you," said my friend; but he did not look as though he liked parting with him.

463

"Nonsense! That dog's worth more than most men, Stanley," I said.

" 'E's that and more. 'Tention!"

The dog rose on his hind legs, and stood upright for a full minute. "Eyes right!"

He sat on his haunches and turned his head sharp to the right. At a sign he rose and barked twice. Then he shook hands with his right paw and bounded lightly to my shoulder. Here he made himself into a necktie, limp and lifeless, hanging down on either side of my neck. I was told to pick him up and throw him in the air. He fell with a howl and held up one leg.

"Part o' the trick," said his owner. "You're going to die now. Dig yourself your little grave an' shut your little eye."

Still limping, the dog hobbled to the garden edge, dug a hole and lay down in it. When told that he was cured, he jumped out, wagging his tail, and whining for applause. He was put through half a dozen other tricks, such as showing how he would hold a man safe (I was that man, and he sat down before me, his teeth bared, ready to spring), and how he would stop eating at the word of command. I had no more than finished praising him when my friend made a gesture that stopped the dog as though he had been shot, took a piece of blue-ruled canteen-paper from his helmet, handed it to me and ran away, while the dog looked after him and howled. I read:

Sir—I give you the dog because of what you got me out of. He is the best I know, for I made him myself, and he is as good as a man. Please do not give him too much to eat, and please do not give him back to me, for I'm not going to take him, if you will keep him. So please do not try to give him back any more. I have kept his name back, so you can call him anything and he will answer, but please do not give him back. He can kill a man as easy as anything, but please do not give him too much meat. He knows more than a man.

Vixen sympathetically joined her shrill little yap to the bull-terrier's despairing cry, and I was annoyed, for I knew that a man who cares for dogs is one thing, but a man who loves one dog is quite another. Dogs are at the best no more than verminous vagrants, self-scratchers, foul feeders, and unclean by the law of Moses and Mohammed; but a dog with whom one lives alone for at least six months in the year; a free thing, tied to you so strictly by love that without you he will not stir or exercise; a patient, temperate, humorous, wise soul, who knows your moods before you know them yourself, is not a dog under any ruling.

I had Vixen, who was all my dog to me; and I felt what my friend must have felt, at tearing out his heart in this style and leaving it in my garden.

However, the dog understood clearly enough that I was his master, and did not follow the soldier. As soon as he drew breath I made much of him, and Vixen, yelling with jealousy, flew at him. Had she been of his own sex, he might have cheered himself with a fight, but he only looked worriedly when she nipped his deep iron sides, laid his heavy head on my knee, and howled anew. I meant to dine at the Club that night, but as darkness drew in, and the dog snuffed through the empty house like a child trying to recover from a fit of sobbing, I felt that I could not leave him to suffer his first evening alone. So we fed at home, Vixen on one side, and the stranger-dog on the other; she watching his every mouthful, and saying explicitly what she thought of his table manners, which were much better than hers.

It was Vixen's custom, till the weather grew hot, to sleep in my bed, her head on the pillow like a Christian; and when morning came I would always find that the little thing had braced her feet against the wall and pushed me to the very edge of the cot. This night she hurried to bed purposefully, every hair up, one eye on the stranger, who had dropped on a mat in a helpless, hopeless sort of way, all four feet spread out, sighing heavily. She settled her head on the pillow several times, to show her little airs and graces, and struck up her usual whiney sing-song before slumber. The stranger-dog softly edged towards me. I put out my hand and he licked it. Instantly my wrist was between Vixen's teeth, and her warning *aaarh!* said as plainly as speech, that if I took any further notice of the stranger she would bite.

I caught her behind her fat neck with my left hand, shook her severely, and said:

"Vixen, if you do that again you'll be put into the veranda. Now, remember!"

She understood perfectly, but the minute I released her she mouthed my right wrist once more, and waited with her ears back and all her body flattened, ready to bite. The big dog's tail thumped the floor in a humble and peace-making way.

I grabbed Vixen a second time, lifted her out of bed like a rabbit (she hated that and yelled), and, as I had promised, set her out in the veranda with the bats and the moonlight. At this she howled. Then she used coarse language—not to me, but to the bull-terrier—till she coughed with exhaustion. Then she ran around the house trying every door. Then she went off to the stables and barked as though some one were stealing the horses, which was an old trick of hers. Last she returned, and her snuffing yelp said, "I'll be good! Let me in and I'll be good!"

She was admitted and flew to her pillow. When she was quieted I whispered to the other dog, "You can lie on the foot of the bed." The bull jumped up at once, and though I felt Vixen quiver with rage, she knew better than to protest. So we slept till the morning, and they had early breakfast with me, bite for bite, till the horse came round and we went for a ride. I don't think the bull had ever followed a horse before. He was wild with excitement, and Vixen, as usual, squealed and scuttered and scooted, and took charge of the procession.

There was one corner of a village near by, which we generally pass with caution, because all the yellow pariah-dogs of the place gathered about it. They were half-wild, starving beasts, and though utter cowards, yet where nine or ten of them get together they will mob and kill and eat an English dog. I kept a whip with a long lash for them. That morning they attacked Vixen, who, perhaps of design, had moved from beyond my horse's shadow.

The bull was ploughing along in the dust, fifty yards behind, rolling in his run, and smiling as bull terriers will. I heard Vixen squeal; half a dozen of the curs closed in on her; a white streak came up behind me; a cloud of dust rose near Vixen, and, when it cleared, I saw one tall pariah with his back broken, and the bull wrenching another to earth. Vixen retreated to the protection of my whip, and the bull padded back smiling more than ever, covered with the blood of his enemies. That decided me to call him "Garm of the Bloody Breast," who was a great person in his time, or "Garm" for short; so, leaning forward, I told him what his temporary name would be. He looked up while I repeated it, and then raced away. I shouted "Garm!" He stopped, raced back, and came up to ask my will.

Then I saw that my soldier friend was right, and that that dog knew and was worth more than a man. At the end of the ridge I gave an order which Vixen knew and hated: "Go away and get washed!" I said. Garm understood some part of it, and Vixen interpreted the rest, and the two trotted off together soberly. When I went to the back veranda Vixen had been washed snowy-white, and was very proud of herself, but the dog-boy would not touch Garm on any account unless I stood by. So I waited while he was being scrubbed, and Garm, with the soap creaming on the top of his broad head, looked at me to make sure that this was what I expected him to en- dure. He knew perfectly that the dog-boy was only obeying orders.

"Another time," I said to the dog-boy, "you will wash the great dog with Vixen when I send them home."

"Does *he* know?" said the dog-boy, who understood the ways of dogs.

"Garm," I said, "another time you will be washed with Vixen."

I knew that Garm understood. Indeed, next washing-day, when Vixen as usual fled under my bed, Garm stared at the doubtful dog-boy in the veranda, stalked to the place where he had been washed last time, and stood rigid in the tub.

But the long days in my office tried him sorely. We three would drive off in the morning at half-past eight and come home at six or later. Vixen, knowing the routine of it, went to sleep under my table; but the confinement ate into Garm's soul. He generally sat on the veranda looking out on the Mall; and well I knew what he expected.

Sometimes a company of soldiers would move along on their way to the Fort, and Garm rolled forth to inspect them; or an officer in uniform entered into the office, and it was pitiful to see poor Garm's welcome to the cloth—not the man. He would leap at him, and sniff and bark joyously, then run to the door and back again. One after- noon I heard him bay with a full throat—a thing I had never heard before—and he disappeared. When I drove into my garden at the end of the day a soldier in white uniform scrambled over the wall at the far end, and the Garm that met me was a joyous dog. This happened twice or thrice a week for a month.

I pretended not to notice, but Garm knew and Vixen knew. He would glide homewards from the office about four o'clock, as though he were only going to look at the scenery, and this he did so quietly that but for Vixen I should not have noticed him. The jealous little dog under the table would give a sniff and a snort, just loud enough to call my attention to the flight. Garm might go out forty times in the day and Vixen would never stir, but when he slunk off to see his true master in my garden she told me in her own tongue. That was the one sign she made to prove that Garm did not altogether belong to the family. They were the best of friends at all times, *but*, Vixen explained that I was never to forget Garm did not love me as she loved me.

I never expected it. The dog was not my dog—could never be my dog—and I knew he was as miserable as his master who tramped eight miles a day to see him. So it seemed to me that the sooner the two were reunited the better for all. One afternoon I sent Vixen home alone in the dog-cart (Garm had gone before), and rode over to cantonments to find another friend of mine, who was an Irish soldier and a great friend of the dog's master.

I explained the whole case, and wound up with:

"And now Stanley's in my garden crying over his dog. Why doesn't he take him back? They're both unhappy."

"Unhappy! There's no sense in the little man any more. But 'tis his fit."

"What *is* his fit? He travels fifty miles a week to see the brute, and he pretends not to notice me when he sees me on the road; and I'm as unhappy as he is. Make him take the dog back."

"It's his penance he's set himself. I told him by way of a joke, afther you'd run over him so convenient that night, whin he was drunk— I said if he was a Catholic he'd do penance. Off he went wid that fit in his little head *an'* a dose of fever, an' nothin' would suit but givin' you the dog as a hostage."

"Hostage for what? I don't want hostages from Stanley."

"For his good behaviour. He's keepin' straight now, the way it's no pleasure to associate wid him."

"Has he taken the pledge?"

"If 'twas only that I need not care. Ye can take the pledge for three months on an' off. He sez he'll never see the dog again, an' *so* mark you, he'll keep straight for evermore. Ye know his fits? Well, this is wan of them. How's the dog takin' it?"

"Like a man. He's the best dog in India. Can't you make Stanley take him back?"

"I can do no more than I have done. But ye know his fits. He's just doin' his penance. What will he do when he goes to the Hills? The docthor's put him on the list."

It is the custom in India to send a certain number of invalids from each regiment up to stations in the Himalayas for the hot weather; and though the men ought to enjoy the cool and the comfort, they miss the society of the barracks down below, and do their best to come back or to avoid going. I felt that this move would bring matters to a head, so I left Terrence hopefully, though he called after me:

"He won't take the dog, sorr. You can lay your month's pay on that. Ye know his fits."

I never pretended to understand Private Ortheris; and so I did the next best thing—I left him alone.

That summer the invalids of the regiment to which my friend belonged were ordered off to the Hills early, because the doctors thought marching in the cool of the day would do them good. Their route lay south to a place called Umballa, a hundred and twenty miles or more. Then they would turn east and march up into the Hills to Kasauli or Dugshai or Subathoo. I dined with the officers the night before they left—they were marching at five in the morning. It was midnight when I drove into my garden, and surprised a white figure flying over the wall.

"That man," said my butler, "has been here since nine, making talk to that dog. He is quite mad. I did not tell him to go away because he has been here many times before, and because the dog-boy told me that if I told him to go away, that great dog would immediately slay me. He did not wish to speak to the Protector of the Poor, and he did not ask for anything to eat or drink."

"Kadir Buksh," said I, "that was well done, for the dog would surely have killed thee. But I do not think the white soldier will come any more."

Garm slept ill that night and whimpered in his dreams. Once he sprang up with a clear, ringing bark, and I heard him wag his tail till it waked him and the bark died out in a howl. He had dreamed he was with his master again, and I nearly cried. It was all Stanley's silly fault.

The first halt which the detachment of invalids made was some miles from their barracks, on the Amritsar road, and ten miles distant from my house. By a mere chance one of the officers drove back for another good dinner at the Club (cooking on the line of march is always bad), and there we met. He was a particular friend of mine, and I knew that he knew how to love a dog properly. His pet was a big retriever who was going up to the Hills for his health, and, though it was still April, the round, brown brute puffed and panted in the Club veranda as though he would burst.

"It's amazing," said the officer, "what excuses these invalids of mine make to get back to barracks. There's a man in my company now asked me for leave to go back to cantonments to pay a debt he'd forgotten. I was so taken by the idea I let him go, and he jingled off in an *ekka* as pleased as Punch. Ten miles to pay a debt! Wonder what it was really?"

"If you'll drive me home I think I can show you," I said.

So he went over to my house in his dog-cart with the retriever; and on the way I told him the story of Garm.

"I was wondering where that brute had gone to. He's the best dog in the regiment," said my friend. "I offered the little fellow twenty rupees for him a month ago. But he's a hostage, you say, for Stanley's good conduct. Stanley's one of the best men I have—when he chooses."

"That's the reason why," I said. "A second-rate man wouldn't have taken things to heart as he has done."

We drove in quietly at the far end of the garden, and crept round the house. There was a place close to the wall all grown about with tamarisk trees, where I knew Garm kept his bones. Even Vixen was not allowed to sit near it. In the full Indian moonlight I could see a white uniform bending over the dog.

"Good-bye, old man," we could not help hearing Stanley's voice. "For 'Eving's sake don't get bit and go mad by any measley pi-dog. But you can look after yourself, old man. *You* don't get drunk an' run about 'ittin' your friends. You takes your bones an' eats your biscuit, an' kills your enemy like a gentleman. I'm goin' away—don't 'owl—I'm goin' off to Kasauli, where I won't see you no more."

I could hear him holding Garm's nose as the dog drew it up to the stars.

"You'll stay here an' be'ave, an'—an' I'll go away an' try to be'ave, an' I don't know 'ow to leave you. I don't think—"

"I think this is damn silly," said the officer, patting his foolish fubsy old retriever. He called to the private who leaped to his feet, marched forward, and saluted.

"You here?" said the officer, turning away his head.

"Yes, sir, but I'm just goin' back."

"I shall be leaving here at eleven in my cart. You come with me. I can't have sick men running about all over the place. Report yourself at eleven, *here*."

We did not say much when we went indoors, but the officer muttered and pulled his retriever's ears.

He was a disgraceful, overfed doormat of a dog; and when he waddled off to my cookhouse to be fed, I had a brilliant idea.

At eleven o'clock that officer's dog was nowhere to be found, and you never heard such a fuss as his owner made. He called and shouted and grew angry, and hunted through my garden for half an hour.

Then I said:

"He's sure to turn up in the morning. Send a man in by rail, and I'll find the beast and return him."

"Beast?" said the officer. "I value that dog considerably more than I value any man I know. It's all very fine for you to talk—your dog's here."

So she was—under my feet—and, had she been missing, food and wages would have stopped in my house till her return. But some people grow fond of dogs not worth a cut of the whip. My friend had to drive away at last with Stanley in the back seat; and then the dog-boy said to me:

"What kind of animal is Bullen Sahib's dog? Look at him!"

I went to the boy's hut, and the fat old reprobate was lying on a mat carefully chained up. He must have heard his master calling for twenty minutes, but had not even attempted to join him.

"He has no face," said the dog-boy scornfully. "He is a *punniar-kooter* [a spaniel]. He never tried to get that cloth off his jaws when his master called. Now Vixen-baba would have jumped through the window, and that Great Dog would have slain me with his muzzled mouth. It is true that there are many kinds of dogs."

Next evening who should turn up but Stanley. The officer had sent him back fourteen miles by rail with a note begging me to return the retriever if I had found him, and, if I had not, to offer huge rewards. The last train to camp left at half-past ten, and Stanley stayed till ten talking to Garm. I argued and entreated, and even threatened to shoot the bull-terrier, but the little man was firm as a rock, though I gave him a good dinner and talked to him most severely. Garm knew as well as I that this was the last time he could hope to see his man, and followed Stanley like a shadow. The retriever said nothing, but licked his lips after his meal and waddled off without so much as saying "Thank you" to the disgusted dog-boy.

So that last meeting was over, and I felt as wretched as Garm, who moaned in his sleep all night. When we went to the office he found a place under the table close to Vixen, and dropped flat till it was time to go home. There was no more running out into the verandas, no slinking away for stolen talks with Stanley. As the weather grew warmer the dogs were forbidden to run beside the cart, but sat at my side on the seat. Vixen with her head under the crook of my left elbow, and Garm hugging the left handrail.

Here Vixen was ever in great form. She had to attend to all the moving traffic, such as bullock-carts that blocked the way, and camels, and led ponies; as well as to keep up her dignity when she passed low friends running in the dust. She never yapped for yapping's sake, but her shrill, high bark was known all along the Mall, and other men's terriers ki-yied in reply, and bullock-drivers looked over their shoulders and gave us the road with a grin.

But Garm cared for none of these things. His big eyes were on the horizon and his terrible mouth was shut. There was another dog in the office who belonged to my chief. We called him "Bob the Librarian," because he always imagined vain rats behind the bookshelves, and in hunting for them would drag out half the old newspaper-files. Bob was a well-meaning idiot, but Garm did not encourage him. He would slide his head round the door panting, "Rats! Come along, Garm!" and Garm would shift one forepaw over the other, and curl himself round, leaving Bob to whine at a most uninterested back. The office was nearly as cheerful as a tomb in those days.

Once, and only once, did I see Garm at all contented with his surroundings. He had gone for an unauthorized walk with Vixen early one Sunday morning, and a very young and foolish artilleryman (his battery had just moved to that part of the world) tried to steal both. Vixen, of course, knew better than to take food from soldiers, and, besides, she had just finished her breakfast. So she trotted back with a large piece of the mutton that they issue to our troops, laid it down on my veranda, and looked up to see what I thought. I asked her where Garm was, and she ran in front of the house to show me the way.

About a mile up the road we came across our artilleryman sitting very stiffly on the edge of a culvert with a greasy handkerchief on his knees. Garm was in front of him, looking rather pleased. When the man moved leg or hand, Garm bared his teeth in silence. A broken string hung from his collar, and the other half of it lay, all warm, in the artilleryman's still hand. He explained to me, keeping his eye straight in front of him, that he had met this dog (he called him awful names) walking alone, and was going to take him to the Fort to be killed for a masterless pariah.

I said that Garm did not seem to me much of a pariah, but that he had better take him to the Fort if he thought best. He said he did not care to do so. I told him to go to the Fort alone. He said he did not want to go at that hour, but would follow my advice as soon as I had called off the dog. I instructed Garm to take him to the Fort, and Garm marched him solemnly up to the gate, one mile and a half under a hot sun, and I told the quarter-guard what had happened; but the young artilleryman was more angry than was at all necessary

when they began to laugh. Several regiments, he was told, had tried
to steal Garm in their time.

That month the hot weather shut down in earnest, and the dogs
slept in the bathroom on the cool wet bricks where the bath is placed.
Every morning, as soon as the man filled my bath, the two jumped
in, and every morning the man filled the bath a second time. I said
to him that he might as well fill a small tub especially for the dogs.
"Nay," said he smiling, "it is not their custom. They would not understand. Besides, the big bath gives them more space."

The punkah-coolies who pull the punkahs day and night came
to know Garm intimately. He noticed that when the swaying fan
stopped I would call out to the coolie and bid him pull with a long
stroke. If the man still slept I would wake him up. He discovered,
too, that it was a good thing to lie in the wave of air under the punkah.
Maybe Stanley had taught him all about this in barracks. At any
rate, when the punkah stopped, Garm would first growl and cock his
eye at the rope, and if that did not wake the man—it nearly always
did—he would tiptoe forth and talk in the sleeper's ear. Vixen was
a clever little dog, but she could never connect the punkah and the
coolie; so Garm gave me grateful hours of cool sleep. But he was
utterly wretched—as miserable as a human being; and in his misery
he clung so close to me that other men noticed it, and were envious.
If I moved from one room to another Garm followed; if my pen
stopped scratching, Garm's head was thrust into my hand; if I turned,
half awake, on the pillow, Garm was up at my side, for he knew that
I was his only link with his master, and day and night, and night and
day, his eyes asked one question—"When is this going to end?"

Living with the dog as I did, I never noticed that he was more than
ordinarily upset by the hot weather, till one day at the Club a man
said: "That dog of yours will die in a week or two. He's a shadow."
Then I dosed Garm with iron and quinine, which he hated; and I
felt very anxious. He lost his appetite, and Vixen was allowed to eat
his dinner under his eyes. Even that did not make him swallow, and
we held a consultation on him, of the best man-doctor in the place;
a lady-doctor, who had cured the sick wives of kings; and the Deputy
Inspector-General of the veterinary service of all India. They pro-

nounced upon his symptoms, and I told them his story, and Garm lay on a sofa licking my hand.

"He's dying of a broken heart," said the lady-doctor suddenly.

" 'Pon my word," said the Deputy Inspector-General, "I believe Mrs. Macrae is perfectly right—as usual."

The best man-doctor in the place wrote a prescription, and the veterinary Deputy Inspector-General went over it afterwards to be sure that the drugs were in the proper dog-proportions; and that was the first time in his life that our doctor ever allowed his prescriptions to be edited. It was a strong tonic, and it put the dear boy on his feet for a week or two; then he lost flesh again. I asked a man I knew to take him up to the Hills with him when he went, and the man came to the door with his kit packed on the top of the carriage. Garm took in the situation at one red glance. The hair rose along his back; he sat down in front of me, and delivered the most awful growl I have ever heard in the jaws of a dog. I shouted to my friend to get away at once, and as soon as the carriage was out of the garden Garm laid his head on my knee and whined. So I knew his answer, and devoted myself to getting Stanley's address in the Hills.

My turn to go to the cool came late in August. We were allowed thirty days' holiday in a year, if no one fell sick, and we took it as we could be spared. My chief and Bob the Librarian had their holiday first, and when they were gone I made a calendar, as I always did, and hung it up at the head of my cot, tearing off one day at a time till they returned. Vixen had gone up to the Hills with me five times before; and she appreciated the cold and the damp and the beautiful wood fires there as much as I did.

"Garm," I said, "we are going back to Stanley at Kasauli. Kasauli —Stanley; Stanley—Kasauli." And I repeated it twenty times. It was not Kasauli really, but another place. Still I remembered what Stanley had said in my garden on the last night, and I dared not change the name. Then Garm began to tremble; then he barked; and then he leaped up at me, frisking and wagging his tail.

"Not now," I said, holding up my hand. "When I say 'Go,' we'll go, Garm." I pulled out the little blanket coat and spiked collar that Vixen always wore up in the Hills to protect her against sudden chills and thieving leopards, and I let the two smell them and talk it over.

What they said of course I do not know, but it made a new dog of Garm. His eyes were bright; and he barked joyfully when I spoke to him. He ate his food, and he killed his rats for the next three weeks, and when he began to whine I had only to say "Stanley—Kasauli; Kasauli—Stanley," to wake him up. I wish I had thought of it before.

My chief came back, all brown with living in the open air, and very angry at finding it so hot in the Plains. That same afternoon we three and Kadir Buksh began to pack for our month's holiday, Vixen rolling in and out of the bullock-trunk twenty times a minute, and Garm grinning all over and thumping on the floor with his tail. Vixen knew the routine of travelling as well as she knew my office-work. She went to the station, singing songs, on the front seat of the carriage, while Garm sat with me. She hurried into the railway carriage, saw Kadir Buksh make up my bed for the night, got her drink of water, and curled up with her black-patch eye on the tumult of the platform. Garm followed her (the crowd gave him a lane all to himself) and sat down on the pillows with his eyes blazing, and his tail a haze behind him.

We came to Umballa in the hot misty dawn, four or five men, who had been working hard for eleven months, shouting for our dâks— the two-horse travelling carriages that were to take us up to Kalka at the foot of the Hills. It was all new to Garm. He did not understand carriages where you lay at full length on your bedding, but Vixen knew and hopped into her place at once; Garm following. The Kalka road, before the railway was built, was about forty-seven miles long, and the horses were changed every eight miles. Most of them jibbed, and kicked, and plunged, but they had to go, and they went rather better than usual for Garm's deep bay in their rear.

There was a river to be forded, and four bullocks pulled the carriage, and Vixen stuck her head out of the sliding-door and nearly fell into the water while she gave directions. Garm was silent and curious, and rather needed reassuring about Stanley and Kasauli. So we rolled, barking and yelping, into Kalka for lunch, and Garm ate enough for two.

After Kalka the road wound among the Hills, and we took a curricle with half-broken ponies, which were changed every six miles. No one dreamed of a railroad to Simla in those days, for it was seven thousand feet up in the air. The road was more than fifty miles long, and the regulation pace was just as fast as the ponies could go. Here, again, Vixen led Garm from one carriage to the other; jumped into the back seat and shouted. A cool breath from the snows met us about five miles out of Kalka, and she whined for her coat, wisely fearing a chill on the liver. I had had one made for Garm too, and, as we climbed to the fresh breezes, I put it on, and Garm chewed it uncomprehendingly, but I think he was grateful.

"Hi-yi-yi-yi!" sang Vixen as we shot around the curves; "Toot-toot-toot!" went the driver's bugle at the dangerous places, and "Yow! Yow! Yow! Yow!" bayed Garm. Kadir Buksh sat on the front seat and smiled. Even he was glad to get away from the heat of the Plains that stewed in the haze behind us. Now and then we would meet a man we knew going down to his work again, and he would say: "What's it like below?" and I would shout: "Hotter than cinders. What's it like above?" and he would shout back: "Just perfect!" and away we would go.

Suddenly Kadir Buksh said, over his shoulder: "Here is Solon;" and Garm snored where he lay with his head on my knee. Solon is an unpleasant little cantonment, but it has the advantage of being cool and healthy. It is all bare and windy, and one generally stops at a rest-house near by for something to eat. I got out and took both dogs with me, while Kadir Buksh made tea. A soldier told us we should find Stanley "out there," nodding his head towards a bare, bleak hill.

When we climbed to the top we spied that very Stanley, who had given me all this trouble, sitting on a rock with his face in his hands, and his overcoat hanging loose about him. I never saw anything so lonely and dejected in my life as this one little man, crumpled up and thinking, on the great gray hillside.

Here Garm left me.

He departed without a word, and, so far as I could see, without moving his legs. He flew through the air bodily, and I heard the whack of him as he flung himself at Stanley, knocking the little man clean over. They rolled on the ground together, shouting, and yelping, and hugging. I could not see which was dog and which was man, till Stanley got up and whimpered.

He told me that he had been suffering from fever at intervals, and was very weak. He looked all he said, but even while I watched, both man and dog plumped out to their natural sizes, precisely as dried apples swell in water. Garm was on his shoulder, and his breast and feet all at the same time, so that Stanley spoke all through a cloud of Garm—gulping, sobbing, slavering Garm. He did not say anything that I could understand, except that he had fancied he was going to die, but that now he was quite well, and that he was not going to give up Garm any more to anybody under the rank of Beelzebub.

Then he said he felt hungry, and thirsty, and happy.

We went down to tea at the rest-house, where Stanley stuffed himself with sardines and raspberry jam, and beer, and cold mutton and pickles, when Garm wasn't climbing over him; and then Vixen and I went on.

Garm saw how it was at once. He said good-bye to me three times, giving me both paws one after another, and leaping on to my shoulder. He further escorted us, singing Hosannas at the top of his voice, a mile down the road. Then he raced back to his own master.

Vixen never opened her mouth, but when the cold twilight came, and we could see the lights of Simla across the hills, she snuffled with her nose at the breast of my ulster. I unbuttoned it, and tucked her inside. Then she gave a contented little sniff, and fell fast asleep, her head on my breast, till we bundled out of Simla, two of the four happiest people in all the world that night.

Lassie Come-Home

ERIC KNIGHT

THE dog had met the boy by the school gate for five years. Now she couldn't understand that times were changed and she wasn't supposed to be there any more. But the boy knew.

So when he opened the door of the cottage, he spoke before he entered.

"Mother," he said, "Lassie's come home again."

He waited a moment, as if in hope of something. But the man and woman inside the cottage did not speak.

"Come in, Lassie," the boy said.

He held open the door, and the tricolor collie walked in obediently. Going head down, as a collie when it knows something is wrong, it went to the rug and lay down before the hearth, a black-white-and-gold aristocrat. The man, sitting on a low stool by the fireside, kept his eyes turned away. The woman went to the sink and busied herself there.

"She were waiting at school for me, just like always," the boy went on. He spoke fast, as if racing against time. "She must ha' got away again. I thought, happen this time, we might just ——"

"No!" the woman exploded.

The boy's carelessness dropped. His voice rose in pleading.

"But this time, mother! Just this time. We could hide her. They wouldn't ever know."

"Dogs, dogs, dogs!" the woman cried. The words poured from her as if the boy's pleading had been a signal gun for her own anger. "I'm sick o' hearing about tykes round this house. Well, she's sold and gone and done with, so the quicker she's taken back the better.

Now get her back quick, or first thing ye know we'll have Hynes round here again. Mr. Hynes!"

Her voice sharpened in imitation of the Cockney accent of the south: "Hi know you Yorkshiremen and yer come-'ome dogs. Training yer dogs to come 'ome so's yer can sell 'em hover and hover again.

"Well, she's sold, so ye can take her out o' my house and home to them as bought her!"

The boy's bottom lip crept out stubbornly, and there was silence in the cottage. Then the dog lifted its head and nudged the man's hand, as a dog will when asking for patting. But the man drew away and stared, silently, into the fire.

The boy tried again, with the ceaseless guile of a child, his voice coaxing.

"Look, feyther, she wants thee to bid her welcome. Aye, she's that glad to be home. Happen they don't tak' good care on her up there? Look, her coat's a bit poorly, don't ye think? A bit o' linseed strained through her drinking water—that's what I'd gi' her."

Still looking in the fire, the man nodded. But the woman, as if perceiving the boy's new attack, sniffed.

"Aye, tha wouldn't be a Carraclough if tha didn't know more about tykes nor breaking eggs wi' a stick. Nor a Yorkshireman. My goodness, it seems to me sometimes that chaps in this village thinks more on their tykes nor they do o' their own flesh and blood. They'll sit by their firesides and let their own bairns starve so long as t' dog gets fed."

The man stirred, suddenly, but the boy cut in quickly.

"But she does look thin. Look, truly—they're not feeding her right. Just look!"

"Aye," the woman chattered. "I wouldn't put it past Hynes to steal t' best part o' t' dog meat for himself. And Lassie always was a strong eater."

"She's fair thin now," the boy said.

Almost unwillingly the man and woman looked at the dog for the first time.

"My gum, she is off a bit," the woman said. Then she caught herself. "Ma goodness, I suppose I'll have to fix her a bit o' summat. She can do wi' it. But soon as she's fed, back she goes. And never another dog I'll have in my house. Never another. Cooking and nursing for 'em, and as much trouble to bring up as a bairn!"

So, grumbling and chatting as a village woman will, she moved about, warming a pan of food for the dog. The man and boy watched the collie eat. When it was done, the boy took from the mantelpiece a folded cloth and a brush, and began prettying the collie's coat. The man watched for several minutes, and then could stand it no longer.

"Here," he said.

He took the cloth and brush from the boy and began working expertly on the dog, rubbing the rich, deep coat, then brushing the snowy whiteness of the full ruff and the apron, bringing out the heavy leggings on the forelegs. He lost himself in his work, and the boy sat on the rug, watching contentedly. The woman stood it as long as she could.

"Now will ye please tak' that tyke out o' here?"

The man flared in anger.

"Well, ye wouldn't have me tak' her back looking like a mucky Monday wash, wouldta?"

He bent again, and began fluffing out the collie's petticoats.

"Joe!" the woman pleaded. "Will ye tak' her out o' here? Hynes'll be nosing round afore ye know it. And I won't have that man in my house. Wearing his hat inside, and going on like he's the duke himself—him and his leggings!"

"All right, lass."

"And this time, Joe, tak' young Joe wi' ye."

"What for?"

"Well, let's get the business done and over with. It's him that Lassie runs away for. She comes for young Joe. So if he went wi' thee, and told her to stay, happen she'd be content and not run away no more, and then we'd have a little peace and quiet in the home—though heaven knows there's not much hope o' that these days, things being like they are." The woman's voice trailed away, as if she would soon cry in weariness.

The man rose. "Come, Joe," he said. "Get thy cap."

The Duke of Rudling walked along the gravel paths of his place with his granddaughter, Philippa. Philippa was a bright and know-

ing young woman, allegedly the only member of the duke's family
he could address in unspotted language. For it was also alleged that
the duke was the most irascible, vile-tempered old man in the three
Ridings of Yorkshire.

"Country going to pot!" the duke roared, stabbing at the walk
with his great blackthorn stick. "When I was a young man! Hah!
Women today not as pretty. Horses today not as fast. As for dogs—
ye don't see dogs today like——"

Just then the duke and Philippa came round a clump of rhodo-
dendrons and saw a man, a boy and a dog.

"Ah," said the duke, in admiration. Then his brow knotted.
"Damme, Carraclough! What're ye doing with my dog?"

He shouted it quite as if the others were in the next county, for it
was also the opinion of the Duke of Rudling that people were not
nearly so keen of hearing as they used to be when he was a young
man.

"It's Lassie," Carraclough said. "She runned away again and I
brought her back."

Carraclough lifted his cap, and poked the boy to do the same, not
in any servile gesture, but to show that they were as well brought
up as the next.

"Damme, ran away again!" the duke roared. "And I told that utter
nincompoop Hynes to—where is he? Hynes! Hynes! Damme,
Hynes, what're ye hiding for?"

"Coming, your lordship!" sounded a voice, far away behind the
shrubberies. And soon Hynes appeared, a sharp-faced man in check
coat, riding breeches, and the cloth leggings that grooms wear.

"Take this dog," roared the duke, "and pen her up! And damme,
if she breaks out again, I'll—I'll——"

The duke waved his great stick threateningly, and then, without
so much as a thank you or kiss the back of my hand to Joe Carraclough, he went stamping and muttering away.

"I'll pen 'er up," Hynes muttered, when the duke was gone. "And
if she ever gets awye agyne, I'll——"

He made as if to grab the dog, but Joe Carraclough's hob-nailed
boot trod heavily on Hynes' foot.

"I brought my lad wi' me to bid her stay, so we'll pen her up this time. Eigh—sorry! I didn't see I were on thy foot. Come, Joe, lad."

They walked down the crunching gravel path, along by the neat kennel buildings. When Lassie was behind the closed door, she raced into the high wire run where she could see them as they went. She pressed close against the wire, waiting.

The boy stood close, too, his fingers through the meshes touching the dog's nose.

"Go on, lad," his father ordered. "Bid her stay!"

The boy looked around, as if for help that he did not find. He swallowed, and then spoke, low and quickly.

"Stay here, Lassie, and don't come home no more," he said. "And don't come to school for me no more. Because I don't want to see ye no more. 'Cause tha's a bad dog, and we don't love thee no more, and we don't want thee. So stay there forever and leave us be, and don't never come home no more."

Then he turned, and because it was hard to see the path plainly, he stumbled. But his father, who was holding his head very high as they walked away from Hynes, shook him savagely, and snapped roughly: "Look where tha's going!"

Then the boy trotted beside his father. He was thinking that he'd never be able to understand why grownups sometimes were so bad-tempered with you, just when you needed them most.

After that, there were days and days that passed, and the dog did not come to the school gate any more. So then it was not like old times. There were so many things that were not like old times.

The boy was thinking that as he came wearily up the path and opened the cottage door and heard his father's voice, tense with anger: ". . . walk my feet off. If tha thinks I like——"

Then they heard his opening of the door and the voice stopped and the cottage was silent.

That's how it was now, the boy thought. They stopped talking in front of you. And this, somehow, was too much for him to bear.

He closed the door, ran out into the night, and onto the moor, that great flat expanse of land where all the people of that village walked in lonesomeness when life and its troubles seemed past bearing.

A long while later, his father's voice cut through the darkness.

"What's tha doing out here, Joe lad?"

"Walking."

"Aye."

They went on together, aimlessly, each following his own thoughts. And they both thought about the dog that had been sold.

"Tha maun't think we're hard on thee, Joe," the man said at last. "It's just that a chap's got to be honest. There's that to it. Sometimes, when a chap doesn't have much, he clings right hard to what he's got. And honest is honest, and there's no two ways about it.

"Why, look, Joe. Seventeen year I worked in that Clarabelle Pit till she shut down, and a good collier too. Seventeen year! And butties I've had by the dozen, and never a man of 'em can ever say that Joe Carraclough kept what wasn't his, nor spoke what wasn't true. Not a man in his Riding can ever call a Carraclough mishonest.

"And when ye've sold a man summat, and ye've taken his brass, and ye've spent it—well, then done's done. That's all. And ye've got to stand by that."

"But Lassie was ——"

"Now, Joe! Ye can't alter it, ever. It's done—and happen it's for t' best. No two ways, Joe, she were getting hard to feed. Why, ye wouldn't want Lassie to be going around getting peaked and pined, like some chaps round here keep their tykes. And if ye're fond of her, then just think on it that now she's got lots to eat, and a private kennel, and a good run to herself, and living like a varritable princess, she is. Ain't that best for her?"

"We wouldn't pine her. We've always got lots to eat."

The man blew out his breath, angrily. "Eigh, Joe, nowt pleases thee. Well then, tha might as well have it. Tha'll never see Lassie no more. She run home once too often, so the duke's taken her wi' him up to his place in Scotland, and there she'll stay. So it's good-by and good luck to her, and she'll never come home no more, she won't. Now, I weren't off to tell thee, but there it is, so put it in thy pipe and smoke it, and let's never say a word about it no more—especially in front of thy mother."

The boy stumbled on in the darkness. Then the man halted.

"We ought to be getting back, lad. We left thy mother alone."

He turned the boy about, and then went on, but as if he were talking to himself.

"Tha sees, Joe, women's not like men. They have to stay home and
manage best they can, and just spend the time in wishing. And when
things don't go right, well, they have to take it out in talk and give a
man hell. But it don't mean nowt, really, so tha shouldn't mind when
thy mother talks hard.

"Ye just got to learn to be patient and let 'em talk, and just let it
go up t' chimney wi' th' smoke."

Then they were quiet, until, over the rise, they saw the lights of
the village. Then the boy spoke: "How far away is Scotland,
feyther?"

"Nay, lad, it's a long, long road."

"But how far, feyther?"

"I don't know—but it's a longer road than thee or me'll ever walk.
Now, lad. Don't fret no more, and try to be a man—and don't plague
thy mother no more, wilta?"

Joe Carraclough was right. It is a long road, as they say in the
North, from Yorkshire to Scotland. Much too far for a man to walk
—or a boy. And though the boy often thought of it, he remembered
his father's words on the moor, and he put the thought behind him.

But there is another way of looking at it; and that's the distance
from Scotland to Yorkshire. And that is just as far as from Yorkshire
to Scotland. A matter of about four hundred miles, it would be,
from the Duke of Rudling's place far up in the Highlands, to the
village of Holdersby. That would be for a man, who could go fairly
straight.

To an animal, how much farther would it be? For a dog can study
no maps, read no signposts, ask no directions. It could only go blindly,
by instinct, knowing that it must keep on to the south, to the south.
It would wander and err, quest and quarter, run into firths and lochs
that would send it side-tracking and back-tracking before it could
go again on its way—south.

A thousand miles, it would be, going that way—a thousand miles
over strange terrain.

There would be moors to cross, and burns to swim. And then

those great, long lochs that stretch almost from one side of that dour land to another would bar the way and send a dog questing a hundred miles before it could find a crossing that would allow it to go south.

And, too, there would be rivers to cross, wide rivers like the Forth and the Clyde, the Tweed and the Tyne, where one must go miles to find bridges. And the bridges would be in towns. And in the towns there would be officials—like the one in Lanarkshire. In all his life he had never let a captured dog get away—except one. That one was a gaunt, snarling collie that whirled on him right in the pound itself, and fought and twisted loose to race away down the city street—going south.

But there are also kind people, too; ones knowing and understanding in the ways of dogs. There was an old couple in Durham who found a dog lying exhausted in a ditch one night—lying there with its head to the south. They took that dog into their cottage and warmed it and fed it and nursed it. And because it seemed an understanding, wise dog, they kept it in their home, hoping it would learn to be content. But, as it grew stronger, every afternoon toward four o'clock it would go to the door and whine, and then begin pacing back and forth between the door and the window, back and forth as the animals do in their cages at the zoo.

They tried every wile and every kindness to make it bide with them, but finally, when the dog began to refuse food, the old people knew what they must do. Because they understood dogs, they opened the door one afternoon and they watched a collie go, not down the road to the right, or to the left, but straight across a field toward the south; going steadily at a trot, as if he knew it still had a long, long road to travel.

Ah, a thousand miles of tor and brae, of shire and moor, of path and road and plowland, of river and stream and burn and brook and beck, of snow and rain and fog and sun, is a long way, even for a human being. But it would seem too far—much, much too far—for any dog to travel blindly and win through.

And yet—and yet—who shall say why, when so many weeks had passed that hope against hope was dying, a boy coming out of school, out of the cloakroom that always smelled of damp wool drying, across the concrete play yard with the black, waxed slides, should turn his eyes to a spot by the school gate from force of five years of habit, and see there a dog? Not a dog, this one, that lifted glad ears above a proud, slim head with its black-and-gold mask; but a dog that lay weakly, trying to lift a head that would no longer lift, trying to wag a tail that was torn and blotched and matted with dirt and burs, and managing to do nothing much except to whine in a weak, happy, crying way as a boy on his knees threw arms about it, and hands touched it that had not touched it for many a day.

Then who shall picture the urgency of a boy, running, awkwardly, with a great dog in his arms running through the village, past the empty mill, past the Labor Exchange, where the men looked up from their deep ponderings on life and the dole? Or who shall describe the high tones of a voice—a boy's voice, calling as he runs up a path: "Mother! Oh, mother! Lassie's come home! Lassie's come home!"

Nor does anyone who ever owned a dog need to be told the sound a man makes as he bends over a dog that has been his for many years; nor how a woman moves quickly, preparing food—which might be the family's condensed milk stirred into warm water; nor how the jowl of a dog is lifted so that raw egg and brandy, bought with precious pence, should be spooned in; nor how bleeding pads are bandaged, tenderly.

That was one day. There was another day when the woman in the cottage sighed with pleasure, for a dog lifted itself to its feet for the first time to stand over a bowl of oatmeal, putting its head down and lapping again and again while its pinched flanks quivered.

And there was another day when the boy realized that, even now, the dog was not to be his again. So the cottage rang again with protests and cries, and a woman shrilling: "Is there never to be no more peace in my house and home?" Long after he was in bed that night the boy heard the rise and fall of the woman's voice, and the steady, reiterative tone of the man's. It went on long after he was asleep.

In the morning the man spoke, not looking at the boy, saying the words as if he had long rehearsed them.

"Thy mother and me have decided upon it that Lassie shall stay here till she's better. Anyhow, nobody could nurse her better than us.

But the day that t' duke comes back, then back she goes, too. For she belongs to him, and that's honest, too. Now tha has her for a while, so be content."

In childhood, "for a while" is such a great stretch of days when seen from one end. It is a terribly short time seen from the other.

The boy knew how short it was that morning as he went to school and saw a motorcar driven by a young woman. And in the car was a gray-thatched, terrible old man, who waved a cane and shouted: "Hi! Hi, there! Damme, lad! You there! Hi!"

Then it was no use running, for the car could go faster than you, and soon it was beside you and the man was saying: "Damme, Philippa, will you make this smelly thing stand still a moment? Hi, lad!"

"Yes, sir."

"You're What's-'is-Name's lad, aren't you?"

"Ma feyther's Joe Carraclough."

"I know. I know. Is he home now?"

"No, sir. He's away to Allerby. A mate spoke for him at the pit and he's gone to see if there's a chance."

"When'll he be back?"

"I don't know. I think about tea."

"Eh, yes. Well, yes. I'll drop round about fivish to see that father of yours. Something important."

It was hard to pretend to listen to lessons. There was only waiting for noon. Then the boy ran home.

"Mother! T' duke is back and he's coming to take Lassie away."

"Eigh, drat my buttons. Never no peace in this house. Is tha sure?"

"Aye. He stopped me. He said tell feyther he'll be round at five. Can't we hide her? Oh, mother."

"Nay, thy feyther ——"

"Won't you beg him? Please, please. Beg feyther to ——"

"Young Joe, now it's no use. So stop thy teasing! Thy feyther'll not lie. That much I'll give him. Come good, come bad, he'll not lie."

"But just this once, mother. Please beg him, just this once. Just one lie wouldn't hurt him. I'll make it up to him. I will. When I'm growed up, I'll get a job. I'll make money. I'll buy him things—and you, too. I'll buy you both anything you want if you'll only ——"

For the first time in his trouble the boy became a child, and the mother, looking over, saw the tears that ran openly down his contorted face. She turned her face to the fire, and there was a pause. Then she spoke.

"Joe, tha mustn't," she said softly. "Tha must learn never to want nothing in life like that. It don't do, lad. Tha mustn't want things bad, like tha wants Lassie."

The boy shook his clenched fists in impatience.

"It ain't that, mother. Ye don't understand. Don't yet see—it ain't me that wants her. It's her that wants us! Tha's wha made her come all them miles. It's her that wants us, so terrible bad!"

The woman turned and stared. It was as if, in that moment, she were seeing this child, this boy, this son of her own, for the first time in many years. She turned her head down toward the table. It was surrender.

"Come and eat, then," she said. "I'll talk to him. I will that, all right. I feel sure he won't lie. But I'll talk to him, all right. I'll talk to Mr. Joe Carraclough. I will indeed."

At five that afternoon, the Duke of Rudling, fuming and muttering, got out of a car at a cottage gate to find a boy barring his way. This was a boy who stood, stubbornly, saying fiercely: "Away wi' thee! Thy tyke's net here!"

"Damme, Philippa, th' lad's touched," the duke said. "He is. He's touched."

Scowling and thumping his stick, the old duke advanced until the boy gave way, backing down the path out of the reach of the waving blackthorn stick.

"Thy tyke's net here," the boy protested.

"What's he saying?" the girl asked.

"Says my dog isn't here. Damme, you going deaf? I'm supposed to be deaf, and I hear him plainly enough. Now, ma lad, what tyke o' mine's net here?"

As he turned to the boy, the duke spoke in broadest Yorkshire, as he did always to the people of the cottages—a habit which the

Duchess of Rudling, and many more members of the duke's family, deplored.

"Coom, coom, ma lad. Whet tyke's net here?"

"No tyke o' thine. Us hasn't got it." The words began running faster and faster as the boy backed away from the fearful old man who advanced. "No tyke could have done it. No tyke can come all them miles. It isn't Lassie. It's another one that looks like her. It isn't Lassie!"

"Why, bless ma heart and sowl," the duke puffed. "Where's thy father, ma lad?"

The door behind the boy opened, and a woman's voice spoke.

"If it's Joe Carraclough ye want, he's out in the shed—and been there shut up half the afternoon."

"What's this lad talking about—a dog of mine being here?"

"Nay," the woman snapped quickly. "He didn't say a tyke o' thine was here. He said it wasn't here."

"Well, what dog o' mine isn't here, then?"

The woman swallowed, and looked about as if for help. The duke stood, peering from under his jutting eyebrows. Her answer, truth or lie, was never spoken, for then they heard the rattle of a door opening, and a man making a pursing sound with his lips, as he will when he wants a dog to follow, and then Joe Carraclough's voice said: "This is t' only tyke us has here. Does it look like any dog that belongs to thee?"

With his mouth opening to cry one last protest, the boy turned. And his mouth stayed open. For there he saw his father, Joe Carraclough, the collie fancier, standing with a dog at his heels—a dog that sat at his left heel patiently, as any well-trained dog should do—as Lassie used to do. But this dog was not Lassie. In fact, it was ridiculous to think of it at the same moment as you thought of Lassie.

For where Lassie's skull was aristocratic and slim, this dog's head was clumsy and rough. Where Lassie's ears stood in twin-lapped symmetry, this dog had one ear draggling and the other standing up Alsatian fashion in a way to give any collie breeder the cold shivers. Where Lassie's coat was rich tawny gold, this dog's coat had ugly patches of black; and where Lassie's apron was a billowing stretch of snow-white, this dog had puddles of off-color blue-merle mixture.

Besides, Lassie had four white paws, and this one had one paw white, two dirty-brown, and one almost black.

That is the dog they all looked at as Joe Carraclough stood there, having told no lie, having only asked a question. They all stood, waiting the duke's verdict.

But the duke said nothing. He only walked forward, slowly, as if he were seeing a dream. He bent beside the collie, looking with eyes that were as knowing about dogs as any Yorkshireman alive. And those eyes did not waste themselves upon twisted ears, or blotched marking, or rough head. Instead they were looking at a paw that the duke lifted, looking at the underside of the paw, staring intently at five black pads, crossed and recrossed with the scars where thorns had lacerated, and stones had torn.

For a long time the duke stared, and when he got up he did not speak in Yorkshire accents any more. He spoke as a gentleman should, and he said: "Joe Carraclough. I never owned this dog. 'Pon my soul, she's never belonged to me. Never!"

Then he turned and went stumping down the path, thumping his cane and saying: "Bless my soul. Four hundred miles! Damme, wouldn't ha' believed it. Damme—five hundred miles!"

He was at the gate when his granddaughter whispered to him fiercely.

"Of course," he cried. "Mind your own business. Exactly what I came for. Talking about dogs made me forget. Carraclough! Carraclough! What're ye hiding for?"

"I'm still here, sir."

"Ah, there you are. You working?"

"Eigh, now. Working," Joe said. That's the best he could manage.

"Yes, working, working!" The duke fumed.

"Well, now——" Joe began.

Then Mrs. Carraclough came to his rescue, as a good housewife in Yorkshire will.

"Why, Joe's got three or four things that he's been considering," she said, with proper display of pride. "But he hasn't quite said yes or no to any of them yet."

"Then say no, quick," the old man puffed. "Had to sack Hynes. Didn't know a dog from a drunken filly. Should ha' known all along no damn Londoner could handle dogs fit for Yorkshire taste. How much, Carraclough?"

"Well, now," Joe began.

"Seven pounds a week, and worth every penny," Mrs. Carraclough chipped in. "One o' them other offers may come up to eight," she lied, expertly. For there's always a certain amount of lying to be done in life, and when a woman's married to a man who has made a lifelong cult of being honest, then she's got to learn to do the lying for two.

"Five," roared the duke—who, after all, was a Yorkshireman, and couldn't help being a bit sharp about things that pertained to money.

"Six," said Mrs. Carraclough.

"Five pound ten," bargained the duke, cannily.

"Done," said Mrs. Carraclough, who would have been willing to settle for three pounds in the first place. "But, o' course, us gets the cottage too."

"All right," puffed the duke. "Five pounds ten and the cottage. Begin Monday. But—on one condition. Carraclough, you can live on my land, but I won't have that thick-skulled, screw-lugged, gay-tailed eyesore of a misshapen mongrel on my property. Now never let me see her again. You'll get rid of her?"

He waited, and Joe fumbled for words. But it was the boy who answered, happily, gaily: "Oh, no, sir. She'll be waiting at school for me most o' the time. And, anyway, in a day or so we'll have her fixed up and coped up so's ye'd never, never recognize her."

"I don't doubt that," puffed the duke, as he went to the car. "I don't doubt ye could do just exactly that."

It was a long time afterward, in the car, that the girl said: "Don't sit there like a lion on the Nelson column. And I thought you were supposed to be a hard man."

"Fiddlesticks, m'dear. I'm a ruthless realist. For five years I've sworn I'd have that dog by hook or crook, and now, egad, at last I've got her."

"Pooh! You had to buy the man before you could get his dog."

"Well, perhaps that's not the worst part of the bargain."

The Voice of Bugle Ann

BY

MacKINLAY KANTOR

1

H ER VOICE was something to dream about, on any night when she was running through the hills. The first moment she was old enough to boast an individual voice, Springfield Davis swore that she would be a great dog, and within another month he had given her the name she carried so proudly.

One of her great-grandfathers, many generations removed, had followed Spring Davis away from home when he went off to join General Claiborne Jackson and his homespun army among the prickly-orange hedges, so there was logic in the inheritance which put that trumpet in her throat.

She was slender, like hounds of the Spaulding line, and not as sprawling or cumbersome as the good-natured, long-tongued Walkers. Any one in Missouri who knew anything about fox-hounds had heard of the Davis dogs, but somehow there never came to be a Davis line. It was all in the family, and there existed a haughtiness in the old man which wouldn't permit him to have Davis dogs running anywhere except in the ranges along Heaven Creek. That was why Bugle Ann was still a maiden at five years, long after old Calhoun Royster or the Lanceys would have seen to it that she carried on her business in life.

And Spring Davis was prudish past the point of ridicule, though no one would have dared to laugh at him. He hated the common

493

word for a female dog, and would not let it touch his tongue. He
called his she-dogs ladies or girls, and there was a firm beauty about
him when he spoke to them. You wouldn't think that a man like
that could ever be tried for murder, or become a convict.

Those things did happen to Spring Davis, at eighty-two. They
didn't affect him as they would have affected most men of eighty-
two. Whenever he heard the gongs and whistles which sent him about
his gray routine at Jefferson City, he must have banished those sounds
from his consciousness. He must have imagined instead that he was
sitting by a fire at the edge of Bachelor's timber, listening to the dogs
as they hunted out of Chilly Branch Hollow, with Bugle Ann's cry
echoing against the blackness of the sky.

2

"Bake," said Old Cal Royster, "put some wood on."

Baker went to the woodpile beyond the red circle and found a
piece of rotten stump. "We'll have a good moon by next week," he
said, and jammed the wood upon the coals.

"I don't give shucks for moonlight," exclaimed Cal Royster. "Give
me a black-dark night, when the fox ain't shadow-shy. Any fool
ought to know that. I don't know where my boys get such notions
as moonlight nights."

Across the fire, Spring Davis tapped his pipe against the heel of
his boot. He stopped, suddenly, head tilted to one side. The firelight
turned his shaggy mustache and eyebrows to fluid metal.

"Listen," he said. "Getting sweet."

His son, Benjy Davis, rose to his feet. He moved like an Indian;
so did his father. There was something of the Indian in Benjy's
twenty-year-old face, tanned and narrow and bony.

His black eyes glittered. "He's a mighty sweet fox if they've had
him away over toward the river! We ain't heard a sound for twenty
minutes."

There were five men around that fire at the edge of Bachelor's
timber. Four of them—Spring Davis and his only son Benjy, and
Calhoun Royster and his oldest son, Baker—were the most ardent
fox-hound men in the county. The fifth man was no hound man at

all; he was a new insurance agent from Wolf Center. He had eaten supper at the Davises', and he was beside that fire only by invitation and sufferance.

He inquired, "What do you mean, Mr. Davis? 'Getting sweet.' "

"It sweats," Spring told him. "The fox does. They can smell him better after he's been running awhile. That's 'getting sweet.' "

Now even the agent's untrained ears could detect a faint distraction amid the common night sounds—the hush of sleeping forests that never sleep, and which is really no hush at all. The sound came from over past the Armstrong place, far past Chilly Branch and across the ridge beyond, and it was as eerie and elusive as the calling of wild geese.

"You'll hear her in a minute," whispered Springfield Davis.

The confused murmur became a tiny baying: the tongues of many dogs, eager and striving in spite of their two-hour run.

"That's Toul Sector," Bake Royster declared. Bake had been in the war, and all the Royster dogs were named Toul Sector or Border Service or General Bullard or some such name.

"It's not Toul Sector," said Benjy. "Not that nearest one."

Calhoun Royster's tone showed the jealous annoyance which he displayed frequently with the self-assured Davises. "It's no Bugle Ann, neither," he snorted. "Nor no Bill Bryan, nor Cox, nor Frances Cleveland, nor any Davis dog."

"Reckon it is a bit turkey-mouthed for one of ours."

Old Spring Davis loved to hear Cal swear in his beard. So he continued, "I'll tell you, Cal. It's an Armstrong dog. They've picked up an Armstrong as they come past."

Royster stood with head wiggling on his humped shoulders, his bearded lips hanging open as he tried to take that baying apart and examine it.

"What Armstrong dog?" he demanded. He seemed to be weakening.

"I'd say it was Jackie Cooper, that little pale-faced two-year-old."

Old man Royster listened a moment longer. He gave a defeated snort. Then his ire mounted. "Where in hell's Bugle Ann, anyway?"

"Maybe she'll quit, and come in," muttered his son.

Benjy whirled, and for a moment the insurance agent thought that he was going to strike Bake Royster. "No Davis dog ever come in without being called, before a fox holed," Benjy said. "Except one. You remember him. We shot him the next day."

Spring nodded. "Easy boy. . . . Guess there's bound to be a black sheep in every tribe, though this dog was white. Don't you folks worry about Bugle Ann. You'll hear her soon enough."

"Pshaw, scat," said Bake, uneasily, "I was just joking."

On such a night as this, with clouds covering the stars and no southeast wind smothering the scent, you could tell that the hounds were running with their heads high. They skirted the eastern boundary of Chilly Branch Hollow, and straightened out along the higher ridge which swung toward Bachelor's woods.

All the men were on their feet.

"You talk moonlight," Royster chided his son. "Never get a fox to keep the high ground except on this kind of night. Lose half the sound when them dogs get in a gulley."

There was a turkey-mouth among those ringing voices; old Spring had been right about the Armstrong dog. The Royster dogs were mainly chop-mouthed, and they sent their clipped bristling bay like a volley across the wooded plateau.

"I don't hear her, Pa," whispered Benjy Davis, with some concern.

The old man held up his hand. Suddenly a new cry was born amid all the hissing of excited crickets.

For some reason, the Wolf Center insurance agent felt the hair prickle on his neck. . . . This was no hound-voice such as he had ever heard before, and he would never hear its like again. It was a bugle—the Davises had a rare poetry in their make-up, thought young Mr. Mayor of the National Emblem Liability. He stood there with his nails cutting his palms, and listened.

"That's her, all right," came Cal Royster's admission, "but why's she kiting off by herself? If she hain't lost it, I'm loony."

Spring Davis repeated the word, "Lost," and smiled into the fire. . . . There had never been a sound like that in the Heaven Creek country until Bugle Ann was born; even now the trumpet-cry knew its own pride, and swung off toward the southeast, far ahead of the *owk-owk-owk-owk* with which the Royster dogs threatened.

The old man whooped, without any warning: "Now, there they go after her!"

Left, around the last spur of Bachelor's woods, the welter of hounds went sweeping after Bugle Ann. Her cry soared ahead—high, round, with that queer and brassy resonance which made you think that ghosts were out there somewhere, sounding Taps without any armies to follow them.

Springfield Davis came back to the fire and squatted on his heels. "You see," he told the insurance agent, "Bugle Ann was running that same fox night-before-last. I reckon she remembered how he likes to feint west along a little draw that's over there, and then double back and cut his own trail. It's a common fox trick if the fox has got the nerve to try it, and easy for him to work when the scent's heavy."

"I'm afraid," said Mr. Mayor, "that I don't understand."

"Well," said Cal Royster, somewhat reluctantly, "the average dog is bound to foller the way he's headed, if the smell is hauling him."

They were silent for a moment, listening to the baying as it swam fainter and fainter into the darkness.

"I'm afraid I don't understand any of this," Mr. Mayor cried with honesty. "I came from the East, just this year. They gave me this Missouri territory and—Fox-hunting! If you hunt every night or two, I don't see how you have any foxes left."

Bake Royster added more wood to the fire, and Benjy Davis brought up the sandwich sack. "We never kill the fox," said Spring, sharply. "We don't ride no horses, nor wear funny coats, and caps. We raise dogs, and train them."

Waken, lords and ladies gay, thought Mr. Mayor in his baffled mind. *All the jolly chase is here, with* . . . "But it's really just a race between fox and dogs, then?"

"Fox holes up when he gets tired, and the dogs come home."

"And the same fox will run again, another night?"

"There's quite a slew of them around. Plenty of mice and ground-squirrels for them to eat; they never bother no hen roosts. Yes, they run again. Night after night, and year after year."

Benjy opened a battered vacuum bottle and poured a cup of coffee for his father. The gray-headed man touched the hot tin cup with cautious fingers. "Year after year," he repeated, dreamily.

The insurance agent choked over a bacon sandwich. "Are you folks—and you also, Mr. Royster—the only people who do this sort of thing?"

Spring Davis looked up from the fire. "Young man, did you ever hear of Old Man Spaulding? Reckon not. Or Gentry German, or Alex Parrish, or Colonel Trigg?"

"I suppose," Mr. Mayor replied, "that those are dogs."

"Those are men who made fox-hound history in America. And Wash Maupin, and Robert Rodes, and James Kanatzar. You see, sir, it's a matter of breeding good dogs—and understanding them—and—kind of loving them. It—" He broke off suddenly.

Cal Royster blinked at the gems of flame which shone through the whisky flask in his hand. "Speaking of names, Spring," he began, "you ought to take our friend here, over to the Armstrongs. You see, mister, Ed Armstrong is mighty religious and his boys are mighty the other way."

"Always going to town," put in Bake, "to dances and moving pictures and rotation pool, and things."

His father insisted, "But they do hunt. They name their dogs after moving picture actors. Old Ed Armstrong, he names his after religious folks. Until you've heard the Armstrong pack after a good, sweet fox, you hain't heard a thing. All turkey-mouthed, or squawl-horn-chop-mouthed at the best. Until you've heard Billy Sunday and Jackie Cooper and Dwight L. Moody and Zasu Pitts and Hoot Gibson and Mary Magdalene all driving a fox at once, you never have had no treat give to you."

"They're good bench dogs," said Spring Davis. He didn't like to hear too much laughter directed at the Armstrongs. "They mostly got stylish tails and compact feet and good stifles. If you like bench, the Armstrong dogs just hustle in the points."

He held up his hand, and Cal Royster put away the whisky bottle.

"Coming in," Davis prophesied. "I can get it, from 'way south, at the top of Heaven Creek."

Benjy swore; his face was very dark. "Blame fox won't give them more'n three hours any more."

"That's a fact," nodded his father. "We'll have to try farther up Heaven Creek to-morrow."

Mr. Mayor burst out, "Good Lord, do you do this all night, every night? When do you do your farm work?" He began to understand why Spring Davis had been unable to renew his fire insurance policy.

"Not every night," said Springfield. "Sometimes it rains. Or just the opposite, sometimes the weather's been too dry. Or we get long damp spells—too damp—or we get low southeast winds. We don't come out every night."

"Mr. Davis," cried Mr. Mayor of the National Emblem Liability, "how old are you?"

Spring smiled into the fire. "Seventy years ago this season, I ran off to join the Confederate army. I was only twelve, but I had done a sight of fox-hunting before that."

The hounds came closer, and once more Bugle Ann's blare was riding high above their hooted chorus.

"He's striking for his hole," Bake said. "In a minute he'll hand them the raspberry."

Spring Davis leaned back and closed his eyes. He drew a deep breath. "Waited seventy years to have a dog like that," he whispered to nobody in particular.

The fox uttered his shout of defiance—that strange yelp which was half a cat-cry, half a dog-bark, and wholly insulting. Then baffled shrieks told that he had holed.

"Fetch the horn, Benjy," ordered old Davis. "I don't want her sporting around."

Cal Royster bristled. "This ain't August nor yet February. You talk like our dogs was a pack of hoodlums."

"I just like to have her to home, Cal."

From beside a rolled up sweater, Benjy Davis brought a battered army bugle and gave it to his father. The old man wet his lips, fitted the mouthpiece carefully beneath his shaggy mustache, and blew two notes: the *ta-da* of galloping Valkyries, forever a summons and a challenge.

"Will she come for that?" Mr. Mayor asked in amazement.

"Always."

Benjy peered toward the crossing at Heaven Creek. "Looks like some other folks are coming, too."

The dull, yellow lights of an old Ford were rocking toward them, and they could hear the chatter of its motor. "That'll be Tom and Delbert, I reckon," said Cal Royster. "Don't know what's got into them. Been to see the Lancey girls again. They'd ruther spark around with two flibberty-jibbets than be out with the dogs."

Slowly the Ford rattled up the hill, and stopped at the wood road. The two younger Royster boys got out with cheers of greeting, which were stilled hastily when they saw a stranger at the fire.

"How's the calf market?" taunted their elder brother.

"Never you mind," grunted Delbert Royster. He and Tom were sunburned, strapping youngsters who would have looked happier in overalls than in the Sunday suits they had worn for their squiring.

Their faces were unwontedly serious, and neither of them headed for the sandwiches.

"What in time ails you two?" demanded Cal.

"You heard about the old Camden place?" countered Delbert.

Every one except the insurance agent looked automatically toward the northwest. A mile down the valley of Heaven Creek stood an abandoned house and farm buildings, which in daylight showed plainly from their hill.

"I did hear that somebody was moving on it," said the father.

"Some of the Camdens, coming back," added Baker.

Old Spring Davis stood fingering his bugle. "The Camdens was great dog people in their day. That's twenty-thirty year ago."

"Well," said Tom, "we heard about it over at Lancey's. It's a son-in-law of the old Camdens, and his name is Terry, and he aims to raise sheep."

For a long moment no one spoke.

"Fence," said Spring Davis. There was an odd whine in his tone.

Delbert brought out a sack of Bull Durham, and began to make a cigarette. "Martin Lancey was at the lumberyard to-day, and this Terry was there. He was ordering posts and wire. Wove-wire, Lancey said."

"Hog-tight, bull-strong and horse-high," added Tom.

A coal popped in the fire, and a shower of sparks blew up.

Spring Davis said, thoughtfully: "Man's name is Jacob Terry. I remember him."

"Sure enough," agreed Calhoun Royster, "and he married Effie

Camden. I heard she died, up in Jackson County. Had one daughter, seems to me."

Spring Davis put down the bugle. His knee-joints creaked as he stood up. "I wouldn't call this Jake Terry a pleasant man. Once he whipped a horse with a piece of board . . . going to put up a wove-wire fence, hey?"

"They're moving in, this week," went on Delbert. "Mrs. Lancey said there was a light in the house early to-night."

Something twitched outside the last reaches of firelight, and Spring Davis went down on one knee. "Come on, little lady," he cried. Bugle Ann trotted into the light, her long ears flapping, her elbows plastered with mud. She was a small hound, but with a strong, well-arched coupling, and she carried her tail like a banner.

Davis took her in his arms. "This here's the angel song you heard, Mr. Mayor."

"She didn't come very prompt," scoffed old Royster.

"Prompt enough," said the veteran. "She set out there past the light, until she was sure about that car. You didn't know the Royster boys would come driving up in their smoke-wagon, did you, honey?"

She wiped his chin with her limp tongue.

"What do you feed her?" asked Mr. Mayor.

"Best cornmeal, bran, and pork cracklings," answered Benjy. "Ma boils it to a thick mush. All our dogs get that."

His father rubbed Bugle Ann's head with his stubbled chin. "I puke out," growled the saturnine neighbor. "Spring, you're plumb foolish over that dog."

The older man shrugged. "I've run dogs for seventy-odd year, but I never heard a voice like this. Nor did you, Cal, nor anybody else. She's galloped forty-five miles to-night. She's the sweetest-mouthed hound in Missouri, and sometimes I reckon I don't deserve her."

Baker asked, "What do you say about the fence, Spring?"

The other hounds were coming in—tan and white, wet ears, drooling jowls—a muddle of tails and snorts and sneezes in the firelight. Benjy took charge of the Davises. There were six of them out, this night, and he handled them with skill and deference and firmness . . . his father still held Bugle Ann wrapped in his gaunt arms.

"I reckon," decided Spring, "that we'd better make a visit on this Jake Terry to-morrow. Call the Armstrongs and Lanceys and everybody together; even get the Pettigrews down from Big Panther Creek. Nobody has ever put up such a fence in these parts, and this is a mighty poor time to start."

Again Mr. Frank Mayor prayed for information.

"First place," explained Davis, "a fox hates such a fence. He's liable to shy off and leave the country because of it. But some of the foxes do like it, and that's even worse. Because a dog runs about fifteen mile an hour—and he hits a wove-wire fence in the dark. The fox is little—he's gone through without choking to death. The dog is liable to get killed."

He rubbed the home-made collar on Bugle Ann's neck. The collar plate was made from a silver dollar stamped flat, and silver dollars were none too plentiful with Springfield Davis any more.

"You can't get good hunting in a country where they put such fences across the fox range," Baker Royster summed up.

Bugle Ann was snoring happily in old Spring's arms.

Mr. Mayor had to drive all the way to Wolf Center, and he didn't arrive at home until four A.M., and his wife was worried to death. He told her that he had just attended the strangest fox hunt in the world; it was a kind of fox-hunting in which no killing took place. He was a discerning man, but in this case he spoke too soon.

The men of the Heaven Creek neighborhood waited upon Jacob Terry the next day.

3

That was June. By July, everybody knew that young Benjy Davis was tarnishing some mysterious code which existed among them all, and which no one of them could have explained or accounted for. Benjy was keeping company with Jacob Terry's daughter, and he made no secret of it.

She was named after her mother's people: Camden. She was eighteen, and she had the shaded hazel eyes of her mother's family, the dainty nostrils and firm lower lip which had marked the Camdens as quality folks when they first came to that country on horseback.

From her father Camden inherited the Terry stature, the Terry red hair. All Heaven Creek hoped that she hadn't inherited his surliness, loose tongue and ugly disposition. Benjy believed that she hadn't.

The crisis began to develop, one night when the grass still reeked from a July flood, and the southeast wind would have drowned any fox-smell which rose from last autumn's leaves. Springfield Davis sat on the front porch with his shoes off, and Bugle Ann dreamed on the step beside him.

Spring noticed that Benjy disappeared immediately after the evening chores were done, and later he smelled shoe polish. About eight o'clock Benjy came around the corner of the house, and he was wearing his good trousers and the blue necktie which Grandma Duncan had sent him for Christmas, and which he had never worn.

"It's a wet night," Spring said. He began to fill his pipe.

"I reckon the wind will change," said Benjy. "But anyway it's unlike to dry off the grass before midnight."

Spring put his hand on Bugle Ann. "If it does dry up enough, Cal will be out."

"I'll listen when I get back," Benjy told him. "If I hear you up in the woods, I'll come over. I thought," he said, "that I might go with Camden Terry to see the moving pictures in town."

McKee's Crossing was five miles to the north. . . . Spring thought, "I've counted, each time they was together. This is eight times." He said aloud, "That's a long way for a buggy. You plowed pretty steady all day, too."

"I wanted to lay-by that slow corn," Benjy said. "Camden can drive her Ford. We talked about it out in the field, when she came past to-day."

"Well," his father muttered. He thought, "So I was wrong. Nine times." He cleared his throat. "You might bring me a sack of Sweet Burley from town."

Benjy waved good-by. "I'll bring it," he said, and went away like a war-chief in the dusk.

A long while later, Spring leaned down and blew softly against Bugle Ann's ear, and she roused up to wash his face for him. The April pups, by Billy Bryan out of Miss Wilson, came to tumble across his lap. "I reckon there would be no way to stop that," decided old Davis, "even if I wanted to. She looks more like the Camdens, and they was fine folks. Used to have a beautiful line of Irish-Maryland stock. I hope Benjy has sense enough to pay for the gasoline, if he rides in a Terry car. He will, though."

He sat for hours, thinking of Jacob Terry and how he had greeted the deputation which waited on him a few weeks before. They were men with sober faces, but they were not men who would shoot unless they were called by a certain name, and that was one curse which Jacob Terry had not dared to invoke. He had talked some of shooting dogs, but people didn't believe he really meant it. No man who had married a Camden could be perverted enough to shoot a fox-hound wantonly, they thought.

The fence was solidly in place: bull-strong, hog-tight and horse-high, just as the Royster boys had foretold. It ran across the creek, up the west slope of Heaven Hump, swung its yellow posts to the north and went down hill for another half mile. On the other two sides it paralleled Heaven Creek and Welsh Run. Jake Terry hadn't bought many sheep yet, but folks said that he was dickering here and there.

It seemed that recently he had inherited some money from an elderly aunt, and likely he would run through with that just as he had done with his wife's share of the Camden property.

When that woven belt of wire encompassed the slope of Heaven Hump, the Davises and Roysters had gone up into the woods and had dug out all the nearer fox dens. Several foxes were captured alive, and later were liberated miles away, east of the Armstrong farm. Their dens were broken in, or stopped with bowlders and saturated with chemicals. Now it was hoped that no fox would venture toward that menacing wire sash. The north range of Heaven Creek became a victory for Jacob Terry.

As a matter of fact, the foxes were quick to learn what Terry had done to the hills. Certain of them seemed to take a fiendish delight in slipping through the meshes, whereat the dogs would howl and scramble perilously, knotting themselves in the wire squares.

This night, Spring Davis dozed on the steps until after eleven, and his wife slept on the sofa in the living room. Mrs. Davis was thirty years younger than her husband, eighteen inches shorter, a few degrees less talkative, and she knew that after his dogs Spring loved her well. . . . The breeze did change, and when the old man awoke he found a steady west wind breathing its dryness against his face.

He went out into the yard and felt of the ground. He sniffed several times. Bugle Ann came behind him, stretching and yawning.

"I think a fox would hang on the high ground, after all. The scent'd be fairly free. Reckon you wouldn't have to grind your nose against the ground, little girl," said the master.

She swung her tail, and lifted her muzzle. "Now, hush!" he said, and waited with delight for her to disobey him.

She blew her trumpet.

"What is it?" called Mrs. Davis, sleepily.

The other hounds were answering, from out by the barn, and far in the southwest you could hear the Royster hounds casting about. "We had bugles in the rebel army," said Spring, "but I tell you, Adelaide, I waited a long time to hear the noise that this little girl has got snuggled inside her, all ready to let out when God is willing."

"Are you going up the creek?" asked his wife. They didn't say "down the creek" any more.

"I reckon I will. Cal is out. I hear General Bullard; sounds like he's striking. Will you fetch me a snack, while I get the lantern?"

She had a lunch ready when the old man came up from the corn-crib, with his hands full of Frances Cleveland and Billy Bryan and Old Hickory. "I can't mind more than four, what with Benjy gone," he told Adelaide, and put his lunch in his pocket and the bugle under his suspender strap. He went across the cabbage patch, with the rest of the Davis dogs wailing their grief behind him.

"Poor little folks," he commiserated. "You'll just have to be patient, I reckon. Benjy sure is gone a long time. It must be a mighty good moving picture."

He saw the Royster lanterns opposite the line fence, and he let the dogs loose, one by one. Bugle Ann shot into the lead. "You find the pack, little lady!" Spring shouted at her. "Find the pack if they come high. They got a long jump on you."

Cal Royster chuckled in the shadows. "Talk like she understood every word you said."

"I wager she'll be up with them inside thirty minutes," Spring responded. "And anyway, likely she does know what's what. How could she help it, with that silver cornet the Lord bequeathed her?"

Del and Thomas were off with the Lancey girls again, but Bake and old Cal and Spring Davis all waded Heaven Creek and went up on the south end of the Divide to build their fire. The bugs were bad, and it was more of a smudge than a camp-blaze.

"What's become of Benjy?" asked Bake, who knew well enough what had become of Benjy. "Is he still taking that mail-school lesson about new ways of farming?"

"No, that's been done up for some time," Spring replied. He hesitated, then said: "He's gone to McKee's Crossing to the Wednesday night moving picture." This seemed neither the time nor the place to elaborate on his statement.

4

The hounds came down the valley soon after midnight, with the fox at a tantalizing short lead. The men descended the Divide when the baying sounded first from above them, and they felt rather than saw the truant varmint squeeze past them into the north.

White blur after white blur—like snowy hands whisking before the eyes—the dogs went by.

Cal Royster voiced the apprehension of the others when he spoke. "Fox'll go right up Chilly Branch Holler," he said, and Spring hoped that he was right, for it was hard to forget the menace of the wire which lay beyond.

They heard the dogs crossing Chilly Branch near its mouth, and then Bugle Ann singled out ahead of them all, booming up the steep terraces of Heaven Hump. And Springfield Davis recognized another sound in the universe beyond: the faint clatter of an old Ford rocking along a narrow lane.

He thought, "So they're back from the moving pictures. I hope to God the fox switches east to the hill-top. The girl looks more like the Camdens than she does like Jacob. I reckon most of my dogs would be small enough to squeeze through that fence without getting hung up."

Then Bake cracked out, savagely, "They never went up the Hollow. Let's get over there!" and he lumbered away through the darkness. The two older men fumbled after him until their feet touched a deep cattle trail at the base of the hill, and then they could travel rapidly.

They splashed through the rapids near the mouth of Chilly Branch, and far ahead the hounds were rearing and yelling against Jacob Terry's hog-tight fence. One dog (he must have been Wound Stripe, and well-named, for Bake Royster swore about it) kiyied, and told the world that an end of the wire had been sharp and gashing.

When the men reached the fence, waving their lanterns, the fox was long since gone. The pack danced and strutted in hysteria beside the barrier.

Wound Stripe's left fore-leg was drenched with blood.

"Bugle Ann ain't here," muttered Cal Royster.

The lantern beams had gone their anxious round.

"No," Spring Davis replied, "reckon she sailed right through." He walked up to the fence and tested its strength with his shoe, and prepared to climb over. You couldn't see his face in the lantern light.

Bake was thirty-four, and heavy enough, but he was standing inside Terry's sheep pasture before old Springfield had managed to put his stiff legs astride the fence. Baker was thinking that Benjy should be there, and probably the others were thinking the same thing. . . . The far-away chugging of the Ford car had ceased, but a bright light moved rapidly toward them from the Terry farmhouse.

Sheep scampered here and there in distracted little coteries, appearing suddenly, and vanishing into the thick night amid a rattle of hillside pebbles.

"She'd come up to me, if she was inside the lot," said Spring. "It's possible she squeezed out at the other side, too."

Cal Royster put his arms in the fence meshes, trying vainly to stop their trembling. "She ain't giving voice no more. Maybe you better use your horn, Spring."

The old soldier had the bugle against his lips when Jacob Terry loomed up the hillside, an electric flashlight in his fist.

"Get out of this pasture," Terry said. He did not yell, and there was added menace in his voice on that account.

"Look out," Cal Royster warned. He saw a shotgun in the curve of the farmer's arm.

Spring Davis turned around and took down the bugle. He rubbed a finger across his mouth. "Jacob," he said, "I come in here after my dog."

"If your damn dog is here, he's got no good business among my sheep." Terry held the flashlight steadily on old Springfield's face, and somehow Bake Royster thought of big searchlights he had seen weaving above the Argonne woods, on another night when hatred paraded on a grander scale.

Spring told Terry, "It's Bugle Ann. She wouldn't hurt your sheep, but she's small enough to come through your fence when a fox brings her here."

In the next silence, they listened for her voice, but could hear only the thudding of sheep which scampered along the slope. The rest of the dogs panted and mourned outside the fence.

"Get this straight, old boy." The flashlight held its unblinking stare in Terry's hand. "I'm gonna raise sheep, and I don't care a stink for all the dogs in Missouri. You keep yours off of my land, or they'll get a dose of Number Ten shot in the high end."

Benjy got there a moment later. He had left Camden at the lane entrance, and he had started across a spur of the Davis timber when he heard the hounds working straight down the creek. He had no lantern; the woods were black, so was the creek valley, and it had taken him longer than he anticipated.

Somehow there had been a menace in the entire evening, from the moment when Camden first cried against his clean green shirt.

He asked, "What's the matter?" and his voice sounded like a youth's voice, breaking as it essayed the inflection. He snatched Cal Royster's lantern and investigated the hounds outside the pen. "Pa," he called, "where's Bugle Ann?" and then he came over.

Terry took a couple of steps closer. "There's more than just dogs that give me a peeve, anyway, and you know what I mean. Get out, all of you, and don't bend down my fence when you go over it, neither."

"One of my hounds got cut open," said Bake Royster. "I don't reckon you could be decent enough to staple down those ragged ends of wire, could you? Well, I'll sure come around and staple them for you."

Terry called him a name, and turned the muzzle of the gun toward him, but Benjy stepped out to meet it. He swung wide and openly, for he was not a trained boxer, but he was quicker than a cat in any movement. His fist lifted Terry off his heels and threw him heavily.

The shotgun flew wide; it was still uncocked, and that kept it from going off.

"Take care, Benjy," was all his father said. There were grief and resignation in Spring's voice.

Terry rolled over and got up on his haunches.

"Don't you make a pass at me!" Benjy cried. "If you've killed Bugle Ann, I'll sure kill you."

"No," Spring said, "that'd be my job. But he hasn't, Benjy, he hasn't. . . . I'm plumb certain she went out the other side." Then, all in an instant, he stepped back and flung his arms high; one hand held the bugle.

He appealed, huskily, "For God's sake, listen to that!"

. . . She was far beyond Heaven Hump, far in the timber that blanketed Welsh Run. And she must have passed successfully through the north fence of Terry's pasture, for she had found the fox-smell again, and she was telling the whole state of Missouri about it.

It was a bugle, and every man knew that he would never hear its like again after she died.

Bake Royster had Terry's shotgun, and Benjy had his flashlight, and together they eyed the big farmer. "Terry," said Bake, "it's mighty fortunate for you that she's out there running safe and sound."

"You talk smart enough," whispered Jacob Terry. "Four against one! It's easy to talk smart."

"Your having this gun kind of evened it up."

"I'll even up any of your dogs, if they come on my land again." He went on to say what kind of dogs they were.

The hunters returned across the fence—all except Benjy.

"Come on, boy," Spring ordered him.

"Here's your light," said Benjy to Jacob. "I reckoned you had something else to say."

Terry came close to him. "I'm not afraid of no Davises," he bellowed, "but I like to choose my friends! Don't you come near Camden no more—hear me? I'm particular about who my little girl goes places with."

"I reckoned that was it," replied Benjy. The others knew from the drawl with which he spoke that he was enraged almost beyond control. "Well, you can go to hell and fry in your own lard. You know well enough that fox-hounds don't go around pulling the hide off of sheep."

The man's voice rose in one shouting shriek. "Why, you young blacksnake, I'll kill every God damn cur that steps on this grass!"

"Jacob," Spring called to him, steadily enough, "I can't speak for the Roysters or Lanceys or Armstrongs or anybody else. But if you shoot a Davis dog, I'll blow you clean to glory. Now come out of that hog-pen, Benjy Davis."

Benjy climbed over the fence. Terry turned off the flashlight, and stood there like the black stub of a tree, watching him. "How about my gun?" he asked. "Are you folks going around stealing honest people's guns, too?"

"Here," said Bake. He clicked the breech and threw something far into the valley. He passed the shotgun back through the fence. "Both barrels empty. If you look careful, down by the creek, you'll maybe find the shells."

"Remember what I said!" yelled Jacob Terry. "I got an old cistern needs filling in, and I'd just as soon fill it up with dog-meat."

Spring Davis said nothing more, but Cal Royster spat out his tobacco and declared that nobody would forget a word that had been said. He doubted Spring Davis's ability to blow Jacob Terry to glory, and remarked that another destination would be more easy to promise.

They gathered up the dogs and went back to the Divide. Their fire was nearly out, but Bake soon kicked it into activity, and his father found some dry wood stowed away in a hollow basswood at the head of the ravine.

They waited until two-thirty o'clock, and still Bugle Ann didn't come back, nor did they hear her metal baying any more. Baker took all the Royster dogs home to their straw beds, and then returned to the fireside. The Davis animals lay near the fire and sprawled like the dead, as only hounds can ever do, but there was a nervousness haunting their dreams and you could imagine that the eldest of them moaned in his sleep for Bugle Ann.

Benjy sat like bronze, his arms locked around his knees. From where he watched, Cal Royster studied him and wondered if a strain of Shawnee had not been dropped into the Davis blood a century before. . . . The whisky got lower and lower in Cal's flask.

Spring Davis walked up and down outside the firelight, tramping a path from the basswood to the nearest clump of hickory sprouts. Once he came back to the fire and spat into the coals.

"Wonder how far the gamest fox would travel, if he set his mind to go in a bee-line?" he asked, but Cal Royster couldn't tell him. Then Spring climbed to the highest point of the Divide, and awakened the dozing whippoorwills with his urgent bugle.

5

In the darkest half-hour, immediately before the sky above the Armstrong farm turned gray, the men heard Jacob Terry's Ford beginning to hiccough. By that time they were scattered far and wide through the hills, but Bake Royster was on top of the Divide. He saw the car lights twist out of Terry's barnyard, and stop for awhile, and then go on, smudging away toward the county road.

Bake listened until the car had chugged in the direction of McKee's Crossing. He had started back toward the fire, when a gnome with a lantern waylaid him at the edge of the timber.

"Bake," whispered his father's voice, "I heard a yip."

He asked, "What kind of a yip?" with the unreasoning annoyance of a young man who shuns the mumbling vagaries of the aged.

"A dog yip," said Cal. "I was down the crick, plumb inside Terry's pasture again. And I heard it, up toward the house."

"Just once?"

In the growing fog of dawn, the old man clutched Baker's arm;

his fingers tightened and relaxed. "The dog was struck dead, if you ask me. Terry might of done it with an ax, so's Spring wouldn't hear the gun."

Far along the upper twist of Chilly Branch Hollow, Spring Davis's bugle chanted stubbornly. . . . Bake felt stuffed up inside, as he considered what his father had just told him. "Benjy went to take his dogs home, Pa. You wait here for Spring, and I'll go for Del and Tom."

"Don't bring 'em back direct," commanded his father. "Send Tom across fields for the Lanceys, and have Del take the car and go up to the Armstrong place. He can ring the Pettigrews from there. I wish to God I was rich and could afford a telephone."

Bake swallowed. "You want the whole tribe?"

"We can't go off half-cocked, boy. Maybe it was just a notion I had, or something. I would of sworn it was a yip—just one quick one. Don't you dare tell Spring about it. But if that little bitch—"

"Lady," muttered Bake, not realizing he had said it.

"If she's hung up on bob-wire somewhere, we got to find her soon. It'll take a sight of searching. She never was one to try and dig up a fox-hole. Maybe she got clear over east on the slab, and some foreigners picked her up in a car."

Bake started for home like a good soldier, with crisp obedience in his mind. At all this talk of killing, he began to tremble inside with a nervousness which had never possessed him since his discharge from the U. S. Veterans' hospital in 1921. *Too much* . . . his big feet found the trampled mire beside Heaven Creek . . . *too much of that sort of thing.* Just now he didn't like the name Springfield. It didn't make him think of a town there in Missouri, but it did make him think of a rifle. Cartridges began to glint in his mind: pointed clips of them, clicking one against the other in a webbed pouch.

Suddenly, he thought he could feel the cold stolidity of a Springfield bolt in the curve of his right index-finger.

He decided, "She's got to be caught in the wire somewhere. It'll be the best thing that could happen."

He routed Tom and Delbert out, and sent them flying. His mother and Lucy stood in their nightgowns and stared at him with cold, pale eyes, and said they'd do the milking if the men weren't back in an

hour and a half. . . . There was a mess of cornmeal in the smelly
summer kitchen, stirred up in a huge crock, and Bake took it out to
the hounds. Halfway to the barn, he imagined that he heard a frightened voice yapping: "I'm runner—Brigade Headquarters—where's
Sixtieth Infantry?" and the rifle bolts clicked in a machine-gun
chorus. His throat was dusty, and he smelled pepper in his nose, as
if some one had given him a blow that fractured the little blood ves-
sels inside. . . . Then he pulled his nerves together, and went on
to feed the dogs.

On the Divide behind his farm, Spring Davis came back to the
dead fire with the sunrise smoking behind him. He walked, not like
an old man who has been up and on his feet all night, but like a solemn
pontiff who has sat in the cruelest judgment.

"It's the first time she ever disobeyed the horn," he said to Cal
Royster and Benjy, who were waiting for him.

Cal kicked his empty bottle into the ashes. "Spring, you ought to
drink at least a cup of coffee and maybe have a snack, before you
go further."

"Why," said Spring, "I don't need—"

Benjy said: "They'll be gathering at the house. Bake and Tom
and Del are getting folks."

"I heard her," said Spring. "So did you. She had got through that
second fence. I heard her plain, over past the outside of his pasture."

"Sure we heard her," crooned old Royster, "and if she ain't found
by high noon—maybe just got a toe caught somewhere, or something,
like when she was a pup—I'll give you a four-headed Shorthorn
rooster!"

Benjy looked at his father. "Anyway, you got to stop by the house
first."

Spring nodded. "Guess that's so. Come along with you."

Roy and Joe Lancey were sitting on the well-curb when they
got to the house, and Tom Royster was up at the kitchen door, talking with Mrs. Davis. The Lanceys stood up, awkwardly, as un-
tutored men do at funerals, when Spring strode across the yard.

"Ma," asked Benjy, "you got some coffee?"

She nodded. "I kept hearing the horn, even after you was here,
Benjy. The dogs have been just wild. I got a big coffeepot on the

stove, and a couple skillets of eggs for anybody that wants them."

Bake Royster was coming across the south pasture, and another Lancey—Patterson, the sixteen-year-old one—was advancing up the front road on horseback.

At the back step, Spring Davis surveyed the men in his yard. His eyes were hot enough, but it was a slow and sturdy heat, infinitely ferocious. . . . An orange sun lifted above the Divide and found a whole jewelry store scattered over the clover behind the yard fence. All the remaining Davis dogs seemed to sense the import of this hour, except the April pups. They were smelling around Roy Lancey's legs.

"How about the ears on this one?" muttered Roy.

"They're well set," said Joe, "but she'll never have a stylish tail."

Cal Royster cackled, "Don't ask me! I ain't much on bench, but I'm the darndest Home-plate Judge you kids ever seen." The men all tried to laugh, as if he had said something very funny.

They heard the drone of the Armstrongs' old Studebaker from the road, and the rattle of Delbert Royster's Ford behind it. . . . When Spring Davis came out of the house five minutes later, there were thirteen men in the yard, including Benjy.

Spring had a lever action 30-30 Winchester in his hands. He tried it a couple of times, sliding shells into the breech, lowering the hammer with his thumb while he released the trigger, and flicking the cartridges out again. The sun discovered the Winchester; for a moment its barrel looked like mother-of-pearl.

"I'd just as soon go alone," Spring said, mildly.

Benjy cried, "No."

"You might say I'd prefer it."

Benjy said, "I'll go with you."

Cal Royster tried to make an explosion of laughter, but it was only a vague squawl. "Why, of course we all got to go with you, Spring. It'll take all the men we can raise, to comb real thorough. Maybe that fox took her—" His throat crackled.

"Maybe the fox went clean to the Indian River," supplied young Tom, and there was a murmur of assent.

Spring clamped the rifle under his arm. "Very well, neighbors. . . . I might be wrong, but I reckon I can learn in a hurry when I

get there." He stepped down into the yard. "Good-by, Mother," he
said to his wife, and in the doorway she made a sound. The pups
scampered to meet him, ears flopping and tails swinging. "Get 'em
into the crib or kitchen or somewhere," he requested of the world,
and kept going.

The unkempt mob of men started after him. Benjy hustled the
pups into the kitchen, and his mother hooked the sagging screen
door.

Down in the barn, Frances Cleveland began to bay, and her relatives took up the song. Benjy sprinted ahead and opened the plank
gate for his father; the old man headed along the edge of the cornfield,
but after twenty yards he struck off between the green fronds, his
feet sinking deep into the damp earth and leaving the prints of his
heel-corners bright and compressed.

The neighbors followed, all of them; they talked a little about
corn. The thinnest corner of the Davis timber swayed forward to
meet them, and beyond that lay the lane, and beyond that the Terry
house.

They came out into the jet lane, with its golden, morning pools
of mud and the grooved ruts where Terry's Ford had plowed
through. Nobody tried to avoid the deeper mire; the farmers
marched in uneven phalanx behind Spring Davis, and anybody
would have guessed that the old man didn't know whether he was
walking through mud or last year's oat stubble.

Cal Royster had fallen to the rear, but not through choice. A little
pageant walked with him, and impeded his footsteps . . . it was
when he was eighteen, some fifty years earlier, and the neighbors all
went up Welsh Run to prosecute Big Cass Strickland when he beat
his two children to death. They prosecuted him at the end of his
own wagon-harness, wrapped around the limb of a white-oak tree,
and he hung there seven hours before any one cut him down. . . .

You couldn't see a soul moving in the Terry yard, and now the
men believed most certainly that Jacob Terry had gone far away
in the Ford, before dawn. Bake Royster and his father began to watch
for tracks, as soon as they came opposite the weed-grown orchard,
and it was impossible for them to conceal their search.

Cal felt Spring Davis turning and staring at him, and he held his face closer than ever to the ground.

Then all the men had stopped. Benjy Davis came back and stood between the two Roysters, with his hands clamped over his hip-bones.

"The pack never got up this high," he said. "They weren't out of the creek valley, except on the other side."

"No," whispered old Cal. "We was just a-looking."

Benjy grabbed Bake's shoulder and turned him around. "What do you know, Bake?"

"It ain't me," said Bake. "It's Pa. He heard it. I didn't."

Cal stammered, "Now, Benjy Davis. My ears are mighty old and mighty tricky. I can't depend on them no way."

"You better speak up," drawled Benjy. Spring Davis had come back to stand beside them; the rest of the neighbors waited in uneasy silence beyond.

"Well," Cal told them, "it did sound like a yip."

"Up here?" persisted Benjy.

"It was kind of in this general direction. I guess it was a short while before sun-up."

Benjy turned to his father, and tried to take the gun. The old man pushed him away with sudden and amazing strength. "You remember, boy," he said, as if there wasn't another man within twenty miles, "how she got her foot caught in that rat-trap before she was weaned."

Bake Royster yowled, without being asked, "Sure, sure! Every-body knows that. But one gone toe never bothered her, because it happened when she was young enough. You'd never pick her as belonging to a Casual Outfit."

"All right, Father," Benjy Davis said. Nobody had ever heard him say Father before. "I reckon any tracks that are here would be like cement in the mud. Quite—" He hunted for the word. "Quite un-mistakable."

"I'll warrant you," his father replied. Spring drew down the lever of his Winchester the barest part of its arc: there was a shell in the breech. He clicked it back. Then he turned and started east along the lane, with his eyes boring against the ground.

Benjy looked at him as if he were just seeing him for the first time. "Wait," he cried, and the old man turned. Benjy brought out a sack of Sweet Burley, its blue seal blazing in the fresh sunlight. "I just remembered that you wanted me to bring this from town, and I been carrying it in my pants all this time."

Spring nodded. "I'm obliged, Benjy." He thrust the tobacco into his hip pocket. "Before Cal talked about that yip," he told his neighbors, "I had been quite divided. I thought that probably she was in wire, or else somebody had stole her, over on the slab highway. Just possibly."

They didn't find any tracks until they came to the yard gate, almost directly in front of the house. Then there were a few. The imprints were made by the feet of a hound coming from the east, coming slowly and wearily a few inches outside the thick grass which bordered the wood road.

Everybody moved off upon the turf, and let the Davises handle this matter in their own way.

Benjy stood looking into the deserted barnyard, but his father got down on his knees and examined the smoother patches of drying mud near the intersection of the wheel ruts.

"How about that toe?" asked the boy.

"I think so," answered Spring, haltingly. "I'm not right certain: so many car wheels, and other tracks. She must of turned off on the grass at this point. . . . Wait'll I find a good one."

Then at last he stood up, and took the rifle in both hands. "Oh, I reckon it would stand in court," he declared. "Just like fingerprints and such. That gone toe is as plain as copper plate. And the tracks don't pass this gateway. She did get this far, on the way home."

A drop of water bobbed over his crusty eyelid and spent itself in a quick streak on his face, dividing and splitting when it came to a nest of wrinkles.

Benjy said, "She was all alone, and likely the fox holed over in Lester's timber near the creek mouth. She knew this old wood road come back, and was easier traveling. She knew enough not to go through those wove-wire fences unless a fox took her that way."

"Cal Royster," said Spring, "you owe me a four-headed Shorthorn rooster." He faced the Terry house for the first time.

Old Ed Armstrong cried, "Now, Springfield. Now, Brother, wait a spell! The Lord don't smile on wrath in unguarded moments of haste."

"You and the Lord can hold your horses," Spring said, without turning his head. "If I'm looking for rats in my granary, I don't set down and pray on it."

Benjy pleaded, "Give me that Winchester, Pa."

"Pshaw, scat," said his father, and started into the farmyard. "You never bred her, did you? She was mine."

Benjy swung around and glared at the neighbors. "He don't want to go in with a whole parade. I'll stay by this gate. Don't nobody try to come past me."

"Spring!" howled Cal Royster. "He's gone! Spring, I tell you he went away in the car. We all heard it go. We—"

"If he ain't at home," said Benjy, "Pa'll wait."

Jacob Terry came out on the kitchen porch. In the barn lot, his two cows were lowing: they had not yet been milked, and none of the neighbors was surprised to know that Jacob had put off his milking until that hour. There were young chickens on the porch, and in the yard below.

Terry held his shotgun in his hands; of course there had been plenty of other shells in the house. Number Ten shot, Baker remembered. Little bright lights flickered in Bake's eyes, and again he smelled that pepper of a painful smash against his nose.

"Get out of here, you old devil," said Terry.

"What'd you do with her?" asked Spring. His tone was flat. "The tracks are to the gate. Did you haul her inside, then?"

Terry mouthed, "I never killed your damn dog, but I'll put some slugs through you if you don't get out of here." He began to hoist the shotgun toward his shoulder.

Springfield Davis fired from his hip. Terry dropped the shotgun and looked surprised and horrified; a dishpan behind him rang like a gong, and fell from its nail, rolling unsteadily across the floor of the porch. Terry's knees bent; he tried to get hold of his chest, and failed. He fell forward into the mud below the porch, with his arms doubled under him.

A lot of half-feathered chickens scurried away from him, peeping shrilly. When the men had rolled him over, they found that one chicken was dead beneath him—crushed flat when he fell upon it.

Benjy went into the house, but Camden wasn't there, and he was dumbly grateful—even in this calamity, and in the mystery of her absence. But the Ford was gone. She must have driven away in it.

That afternoon, after Springfield Davis had ridden to Wolf Center with the Sheriff, the authorities were able to telephone to the Camdens up in Jackson County. Camden Terry had arrived there about noon, but had driven on to an isolated farm belonging to a bachelor uncle. It was twenty-four hours before she could be notified and could complete the return trip as far as Wolf Center.

On the first day when people sat in the big, hot room among the scarred oak desks, Benjy Davis thought Camden looked prettier than she had ever looked before. Her pallor was the cold pallor of hepaticas; her eyes were excessively deep and shaded and secret.

Benjy didn't look her way when he thought she might be looking at him, but he studied her often when she was watching old Spring and the Coroner and the other people. Her story was calm, distant, told without emotion—it might have been translated from some ancient book. Yes, she had been with Benjy Davis the night before the shooting. Yes, she knew that her father had had trouble with the neighbors over his fence and their fox-hounds. She knew that there had been threats. . . . After her father came back to the house from the sheep pasture, they had engaged in an argument.

He had slapped her; just once, she said; not very hard. She packed some clothes, and took the Ford. He dared not stop her, because the Ford was hers—not his. Her Aunt Nancy had given it to her after Uncle Newt died; Aunt Nancy couldn't drive.

(She didn't look at Benjy, either, when she thought that he might be observing her. Sometimes their glances crossed, but never seemed to meet and hold. Each understood that Jacob Terry was still between them, standing or lying dead, it didn't make any difference. In a way, Spring Davis also was between them now. And Bugle Ann.)

Her voice continued soberly, a little-girl voice. She thought that she wouldn't stay with her father any more, after that night. She drove up to Jackson County, and went out to Uncle Elnathan's place, and that was where the news had reached her.

Benjy Davis and the Royster boys spent days in going over the Terry farm, both before and after the sale of farm animals and machinery and household goods. They couldn't find a trace of Bugle Ann's body, even though they took up wooden slabs and explored the old cistern. She could have been buried in any loose earth of the barnyard or hog-lot, and no one would have known the difference.

Spring Davis was tried in September; the trial was in no way notable except for the oration on fox-hounds by a young attorney who volunteered to assume the defense without pay. The young attorney quoted, "Senator Vest's Tribute to the Dog," and added tributes of his own. He discussed fox-hunting as practiced in Missouri, and offered a biographical sketch of Old Man Spaulding, who was still alive in those days. In the eastern part of these great United States, said the young attorney, fox-hunting was an Anglicized pose of the idle rich, and they had many strange fetishes, not the least of which was the custom never to refer to a fox-hound as a "dog." They were all "hounds." Most of his listeners thought that very odd, but they did remember with interest how Spring Davis always called his female dogs Little Ladies or Little Girls.

Fifty years before, certainly, he would never have been convicted. But in this age you must not kill a man, even when another man talks of shooting and has a shotgun in his hands. It was proved that Spring Davis went into the Terry yard armed and ready to kill—he said as much himself. It was proved that Jacob Terry did not fire the first shot, nor did he have his gun at his shoulder when he was struck down.

The most important *corpus delicti*—the body of Bugle Ann—was not available. In short, no one could swear beyond all doubt that Jacob Terry had killed her. Spring Davis had usurped the prerogatives of the Sovereign State of Missouri, and the Sovereign State of Missouri brought that out very pointedly.

Girls made fudge for Spring while he was in jail; women sent in basket dinners. He gave the fudge away, of course, and some of the dinners. There was muttering at his conviction, and men talked darkly of a jail delivery. But such a rebellion belonged fifty years in the past. Springfield Davis went to Jefferson City and served three years, eight months and twenty-one days, and then he was pardoned by the governor.

6

During the first June which Spring spent in prison, the voice of Bugle Ann came back to ring across the dark valleys. Adelaide Davis was the first to hear this banshee, and she ran and told Benjy, and then they were both awake. Over on the next farm, Cal Royster started from his bed screaming, "Bake! Bake! It's her—" and even the youngest Lancey, who was up with a toothache, declared that there was no mistake in the identity.

And from that night rose the sprout of a legend which spread itself over the whole county, and farther than that. It was the legend of a white dog—lean, like hounds of the Spaulding line—who bugled her way through the brush at night, who ran with her head high, calling and hunting for the master who had been carried away from the hills he loved.

They said she ran at the head of a silent pack in which there were thirty-four dogs, all the great and noble sires who had galloped those ranges before the Civil War. There were the hounds brought into Missouri when Daniel Boone came, great sword-mouthed brutes who could pull down a deer if they wanted to. But they all ran silently—their feet made not even a whisper in the dryest leaves of last year, and their baying was not the kind which ordinary people could hear. Only if you were about to die, you might hear them crying all at once.

But the Davises and the Roysters and one Lancey, and even old Ed Armstrong's hired man—all had heard Bugle Ann on that solitary night, and though they didn't hear her again, it was said that Benjy Davis spent more hours roving the woods than was wise for a young man with a farm on his hands.

No one lived at the Terry farm now. Shortly after Springfield Davis had gone to the penitentiary, men from McKee's Crossing came and took down the hog-tight wire fence. When questioned, they declared that a lawyer had told them they could have the wire and posts if they'd take them down. It was easy to pry out the staples, and they bore the wire away in huge rolls atop their trucks. But the posts were another matter; they quit digging after they had uprooted a few. Still, the wire was the main thing.

And there were those who swore that the pack led by Bugle Ann could go through a hog-tight fence like so much dishwater, but young Benjy Davis was hard to convince. After he had searched and yelled through every ravine between the Indian River and Big Panther Hollow, he declared that it had all been a mistake. Bugle Ann lay somewhere beneath the fresh weeds that grew in Terry's hog-lot, and as for her baying—it was another dog, that was all.

"It was her," insisted Adelaide Davis. "If your Pa had been here, he would of got up out of bed and gone for his lantern."

"Well," said Benjy, "I did that, didn't I?"

"But she quit giving voice," his mother said, "and whoever stole her took her away again." Her hands shook, in their cerements of bread dough. "Or else—"

He chided, awkwardly, "I got to get out to the field. . . . It's mighty unnatural to believe in ghosts."

Then he returned to his cultivator seat, and combed the black earth of the cornfield; he combed the rows early and late, and this year he had planted extra acreage. It was too bad, perhaps, for the price of corn got lower—so low that Benjy said there was no sense in selling. He didn't sell his corn, but he did sell the April pups of the year before, to the Lanceys. He took a corn-crib in payment— one fairly new. They moved it over to the Davis place with teams and cables and turnstiles: a three-day job. The Davises were hard put to scratch for a living, and that new corn-crib did look like a lot of foolishness.

Benjy stored his 1933 corn, too, and then came the next summer and the drouth, and corn at seventy cents. . . . Benjy carried an important slip of pink paper out of the office of the Wolf Center Farmers' Grain Company, and shoved it under a grille at the Wolf Center Savings Bank.

Mr. Mayor came after him and talked of insurance, but the only expenditures which Benjy was known to have made were subscriptions to *The Red Ranger* and *The Hunter's Horn*. You couldn't expect the library at the state prison to have those periodicals in stock.

It was the night of Wednesday, September 26th, when Bake Royster came around to the Davis place and got Benjy out of bed. Bake could remember the date forever; that day, sixteen years removed, marked the opening of the Meuse-Argonne offensive. Bake had a great head for names and dates.

He looked green around the gills when Benjy padded out across the kitchen in his night-shirt, and wanted to know what was up.

"I've found something," announced Bake. "Found it in the dark, and I guess you better come and see it."

Benjy's sharp glance made a hole in Royster's face. "I'll get my clothes, Bake. Keep soft, so's not to wake Ma. Her sciatica has been bothering her again."

He came out promptly, and sat on the back step to draw on his shoes. "Where is this—what you found?"

"It's clear in the east side of Bachelor's timber, where the Bachelor used to have a shack. It's a smart piece, but I got my lantern."

"I better take mine, too," said Benjy. He brought a square, scarlet-enameled electric lantern from the porch shelf; Bake thought of that check for the seventy-cent corn.

They went across the yard, with the white disk dancing around their feet and ahead of them. "Maybe you'll want a spade, too," muttered Bake.

"A spade?" Benjy stopped and looked at him in the dark.

Bake said, "Or else a grain sack."

After a moment, Benjy replied, "I'll get a sack, I think," and he found one hanging inside the barn door. Together they crossed the garden patch, and up across the Divide they could hear the Royster dogs and a couple of Armstrongs working intently north into the tangles along Chilly Branch. One or two of the Davis hounds wailed at them, but half-heartedly: the Davis hounds had forgotten what a black-dark night was like, with a fox spraying his oily perfume through the thickets.

"Wound Stripe and Toul Sector had him across the corner of Bachelor's," explained Royster. "Some young dogs was along with them, and that little Elsie Janis got herself twisted in some rusty wire. That's how I come to go down there and—"

He gargled in the dimness, and added with an attempt at being casual, "Tom and Pa are there now."

When they crossed Heaven Creek (its widest pool could have flowed between your shoes, after the drouth) Baker began to remonstrate with Benjy Davis.

"I don't see what ails you, Benjy. It's a shame to have good stock tied up and molting away the way yours are."

"You can't sashay around the woods all night, if you're busy farming," the younger man told him.

Bake growled, "Now, I know all about that corn! You don't need to rub it into me. But you ain't had nothing but dried-up crops to worry you, this year, and since the fall rains began to come there's been *beaucoup* fox around here."

For a while Benjy climbed the incline without speaking, loose pebbles rolling down around Bake Royster as he plodded an arm's length behind. "No stomach for it," Benjy said, at last, and Baker knew that was really the explanation. "Not until he's out of that damn place. I can't set beside a fire and listen to the baying, and know he's at Jefferson City in a cell-house."

It was eerie, passing through the oak woods, with a few katydids throbbing in secret dens under the stiff green leaves, and occasional yellow leaves sailing down into the straight electric ray. There was a feel of frost in the air, and Bake kept thinking of what he had found an hour before . . . a dog like Bugle Ann could take a thousand ghost hounds across the prairies among the stars, and still her baying would come back to you. Bake had ceased worrying about Springfield rifles and cartridges in webbed pouches, long before; sometimes still he thought of Jacob Terry and the chicken which had been crushed beneath his tumbling body, and he wouldn't get enthusiastic about half-feathered chickens ever again, especially if they made a shrill peeping.

But the death of Jacob Terry had come with its own certain violence, justified and canceled by a rifle bullet, the same as the many deaths Baker had seen in the valley of the Meuse. In Bugle Ann's passing there was too much mystery for any man to ponder. Any man who had ever been a patient in a government hospital.

The Bachelor's cabin was nothing but a heap of mossy shingles and broken crockery among the hickory saplings, for the Bachelor had left the country before Bake Royster was born. Some of his wire existed still: thick, old-fashioned plaits of bent rust amid the stumps. And near one of those barricades Cal Royster and young Tom waited with their lantern.

"Pa," called Bake.

"I'm right here," said the old man. "Evening, Benjy." Tom Royster didn't offer any greeting; embarrassment had frozen him into silence.

Benjy stood beside them and took what Cal Royster handed him. It was a leather collar, now stiff as iron with winter and summer and rain and mold, but the flattened silver dollar on it was unmistakable —you could even scrape away what had gathered over it, and see the Liberty head all flatly distorted, with its crudely-scratched legend.

The men waited silently.

"Where's the rest?" asked Benjy, after a long time. He slid the collar, with leaves still clinging to it, inside his shirt.

"Right here, in the bushes. They're a little scattered."

Benjy got down on his knees. If you had seen him, and had not known why he was there, you would have thought that he was praying. . . . Cal Royster had a vague notion that he ought to re-move his hat, but Cal had never done such a thing for a dog.

"How long would you say?" asked Benjy presently.

The others murmured, hazarding several opinions. You couldn't tell much about bones. Maybe a doctor could. Animals had been there, probably, and birds. Maybe a year, maybe two, or three, or—

It was the collar which first had attracted Bake's attention. He saw it sticking up out of the leaves while he was releasing Elsie Janis from the wire. The young hound had left some of her blood there, from a lacerated elbow, and it seemed strangely appropriate to have that ground moistened with the blood of a fox-hound, even if she wasn't a Davis dog.

"The point is," said Benjy, speaking slowly and gravely, "whether she was here all the time, that night, or whether she come later. Somehow or other. The point is whether we heard her voice two year ago last June, or whether—"

Cal Royster said, "By God, it was her voice. Reckon I heard it." "And by God," whispered Benjy, "those were her tracks at the edge of Terry's barnyard, in July of 'thirty-one."

"So what?" asked young Tom. It was slang such as he always picked up at the moving pictures, but it seemed unusually apt.

Benjy said, "I reckon there's nothing I can do except tote her home in the grain sack. I'm glad I didn't bring the spade, Bake, because now I'd be tempted to use it: just seem like a lot of old sticks, somehow, and I always did think a dog skull was powerful ugly."

They helped him pick up the relics, and he carried them back home while Bake Royster went ahead with the electric lantern. The men brought a shovel from the woodshed and buried the fragments, grain sack and all, beneath the sweet-crab tree at the corner of Mrs. Davis's little orchard. Benjy washed the collar and wiped it clean, using several dish towels in the process, and then he took it upstairs and hung it over the pointed, upright support of his bureau mirror, on top of his five neckties.

He told his mother the next morning, and of course through the Roysters the story was well around the neighborhood before noon. But Benjy and his mother were positive that no word of it would reach the ears of Springfield Davis at Jefferson City, and they were correct. It was the sort of a tale which might not be welcomed in print, so the *Weekly Clarion-Advocate* held no mention of it. No person except members of the family carried on any correspondence with Spring Davis, anyway, and thus the old man did not learn of how Bugle Ann's skeleton had been found until after he was released from prison.

It gave Bake Royster a fever, however, and he spent four days in bed. His family thought it was a kind of flu, but Baker knew the truth. He'd lie there at night, until he got over it, and watch the whole insane puzzle exploding before his eyes. Desperately he tried to align the formations—to put each separate element in the nook where it belonged; and this was lunacy to attempt.

Camden Terry: take her, now. She was living up in Jackson

County, folks said, and she had never offered to sell the farm. Just let it grow to weeds. Nobody seemed to know whether or not she was married, and naturally it would take a hardy soul to mention her name to Benjy. Bake reckoned that Benjy had been mighty sweet on Camden.

Everybody had seen the tracks at Jake Terry's gate; there was no doubt about that missing toe. Not another hound in the neighborhood had a toe gone. So there were her tracks, and why would Bugle Ann have gone across Heaven Creek from the Terry farm—why would she have climbed Heaven Hump, or gone through Chilly Branch Hollow, and south into the timber land to get herself strangled in the Bachelor's wire? Spring Davis was making the hills quiver with his trumpet, and people all knew how Bugle Ann would come to such a summons.

No, she must have lived somehow, somewhere—and then she must have come back to the woods she loved, on another night, in June of 1932. Then they had heard her calling, and then she had met her death, alone beside the windfall of curling shingles.

No, she must have been a ghost, all along. It was not natural for any dog to have a voice like hers, and perhaps she had been sired by one of the silent pack which followed her so willingly in popular imagination. Even now her bones lay wadded in the Davis orchard, but Bugle Ann was up and gone, baying in ranges where no horns could ever summon her, and it would be death to hear her bugling again. . . . It was this surmise, however hysterical, which comforted Baker Royster and let him sleep with no more fever. Yet it was hard for him to forget how Benjy Davis had looked in the lantern light, coming down from the Divide with that sack of bones swinging from his shoulder and Bugle Ann's collar nestling inside his shirt.

7

They had less than twenty-four hours' warning, the next June when Springfield Davis was sent home from the penitentiary. There hadn't been such a tornado of festivity in the neighborhood since Delbert Royster and LaVonne Lancey were married two years before, and even then the Davises could not have felt very festive.

At five-thirty P.M. of the great day, Benjy and Bake started for McKee's Crossing in the old Royster car, but the fan-belt parted and as a result the train was just pulling out when they careened up to the station. They saw Spring Davis sitting there with a straw suitcase beside him.

His hair and mustache were snow-white and his face sagged, as if its fleshy sub-structure had dried up. His pointed shoulders came forward more noticeably and tried to meet across the front of his chest, but otherwise his appearance was the same as it had been. Benjy expected him to be as pale as a tallow candle, but he was not; Spring explained later that he had worked out of doors a good deal. The worst thing about the whole prison experience, he thought, was having so many of the convicts call him Pop.

He was eighty-six years old, and walked stiffly, and sometime he'd open his mouth for a moment before he could say anything when he wanted to talk.

They got him into the car, with twenty townspeople staring quietly at him, and started for home. Spring didn't talk much on the way. He took off his old slouch hat and let the wind blow his hair— soft as milkweed silk. Once he said, "I see they've cut down that willow-row on the Collins place," and again, "Well, there's no use in my not saying that I was surprised—terribly surprised. It come so sudden! I didn't expect them to let me out for years and years."

He glanced keenly toward the Terry place as they passed its bur-dock-grown lane, and he seemed about to ask a question. But the next moment the north field of the Davises had swum past, and the car was crunching in at the gate. Adelaide Davis was just opening the screen door: others of the neighborhood women huddled behind her, and a lot of men were squatting on their heels beneath the cotton-wood tree. Benjy always remembered how Cal Royster snapped his knife shut and put it into his pocket before he turned. Cal had been whittling a toy dart for one of the Lancey kids.

A long table had been arranged beside the peony bushes, and you could smell everything from fried chicken to beet pickles. After the greetings were made, Spring said that he'd like to put on some other clothes, and Benjy went behind him as he toiled up the narrow stair-way to the hot rooms under the eaves. Spring's old work-clothes were there, but washed and smooth and foreign to him; he would not feel at home until his crooked knees and elbows had made their appropriate dents in the cloth.

Mrs. Davis had disposed of his old suspenders, and he couldn't get a satisfactory adjustment on the ones he was wearing. He came into Benjy's room for help, and the first thing he saw was Bugle Ann's collar hanging beside the mirror.

If he lived to be a hundred, Benjy would never cease blaming himself for that.

Finally, after working his mouth for a long time, Spring managed to say, "Then you did find her. You never wrote it to me."

"Pa," Benjy groaned, "now you set down, Pa. Set down." And at last the old man sank deep into the narrow feather-bed.

He wanted to know, "Where was it? Where?"

"Up in Bachelor's timber. We never found her until last September."

"Bachelor's," echoed Spring. And then: "No, no, couldn't have been there."

"It was right beside the old shack," said his son, as gently as he could.

Spring stared for a while. Downstairs they were yelling and laughing, and LaVonne Lancey Royster was ringing a dinner bell. Out in the yard, old Billy Bryan began to challenge with excitement.

"Then Terry never did it," said Spring.

"Maybe she run up there—after he shot her—or—"

The old man hissed, "Ah, stop your foolish talk!" His eyes were wet and blazing. "Nevertheless," he declared in a rapid whisper, "I'm thankful I done it when I did, for certainly I'd had to do it sometime. He meant it, Benjy. He would of killed her in a minute."

"Sure he would!" cried Benjy. "You don't think anybody in this world is blaming you, do you?"

Springfield had the collar in his hand, turning it slowly around and around.

Benjy mopped his perspiring forehead. "Pa," he began, "that ain't the whole story. There was a time, first June after you went up there—"

He told briefly of the dog's bugling which had echoed in the woods beyond Heaven Creek, and how the neighborhood had taken it, and of the phantom pack which was said to hunt so silently at night, unattended by any hunters.

Spring blew his nose when Benjy was through. "There was a time when I would of laughed my head off at that," he said, simply enough, "but I've had plenty of time to think, these last four years. There were funny things in the War, boy, and there's been funny things other times. My mother knew that brother Rufus was killed by a snapped log-cabin, long before they ever brung her the news. She saw it in a kind of dream. . . . I don't say you heard Bugle Ann up there in the timber, that night, but you did hear something. Mighty often I thought I heard her, clear off in Jefferson City."

Then they went downstairs and out into the yard, to the fried chicken and other food, and all the talk, and all the people.

Supper stretched far into the dusk; then the table was cleared, and women began chattering and packing their baskets in the vicious heat of the kitchen. The men sat on the front porch and on the grass, and children shrieked at mysterious games among the berry bushes.

They had tried to enthrone Springfield Davis in the big splint-bottomed rocker, but he preferred to sit with his angular spine against a porch post. The dogs came to pay their respects; there was no one of them that he loved well enough to let it sleep across his lap, though Benjy watched hopefully.

In the first hush of twilight, when conversation had labored away from fox-hunting a dozen times, Spring astonished the crowd by rising to his feet and walking slowly down into the yard to feel the grass.

"It's not real wet," he said, so distinctly that all could hear him, "but there's a promising feel of dampness between the blades. When did it rain here?"

Somebody coughed. "Must of been night-before-last."

The pipes and cigarettes glowed spasmodically, and in the kitchen the younger Lancey girls were trying to harmonize with *Sometimes I'm happy, sometimes I'm blue.*

"This night'll be black-dark and that's a fact," came from Cal Royster.

Spring stood listening to the girls' song. "Radio," he muttered.

"Well, we had radio music up there, too." He called to Royster, "Cal, I've been smelling at black-dark nights for nigh onto four years."

"I didn't think you'd feel—" Bake started to say, and then he chewed his nervous lip.

Spring Davis echoed, "Feel what?" He looked like a tall, guerrilla ghost in the thickening dusk, and the scent of June flowers was heavy as at a funeral. "Why, when a relative dies we all go on living, don't we? We all have to. I'd like, just as quick as possible, to set beside a fire again."

Benjy stood up. He felt his knees quivering. "The dogs are rusty, Pa. You know I've been farming pretty steady."

"They'll get the kinks out of their noses, once a fox is good and sweet," said Spring. It was as if he alone were trying to whistle up the courage of his neighbors. "I hate to see a good, sticky night go to waste. And there ain't any southeast wind."

There was a stir among the farmers, and more than one stood up. But for all their eagerness a certain delicacy possessed them now. They realized that this pathetic rite—the first journeying of old Spring to the hills of Heaven Creek—was something sacred to the Davises and Roysters, who had hunted together time out of mind.

"I'm afraid Gabe won't look after that colt proper," said old Ed Armstrong. "Awful hard to keep a hock bandaged." The Lanceys spoke of a big day in the field to-morrow, and Henry Pettigrew made lugubrious mention of his rheumatic knee.

"Well," Bake Royster announced, in a sweeping gesture of exclusion, "looks like everybody else has to go home and do chores or go to bed early, but Pa and I might trail up in the timber a spell with you, Spring."

Davis said, "Fetch the hounds, Benjy. I don't reckon we'll need a snack to-night, we're so full of good supper."

In half an hour the four of them had crossed the narrow clover field and were wading the valley darkness: Spring, Benjy, Cal and Baker. A solid bank of clouds rose slowly out of the west, and rain would come before morning. The air was one great, mossy cellar of humidity.

On the high crest of the Divide, the hounds went loose—four Davis dogs and five Roysters. All of the Davis dogs were elderly hounds whose voices Spring Davis knew as well as his own name. The white blots went speeding, zigzagging toward the shadows where foxes most often made their path.

The men sat on their haunches and waited.

"One's struck," said Cal, when a haunting moan came from the hilltop. The moan stopped suddenly. "No," Benjy grunted, "you just thought so. If that was Toul Sector . . . has he run on his own trail lately, Bake?"

Bake grinned, in spite of himself. "Not for a good month. Wait awhile."

The insects skirmished around them. At last little Elsie Janis found exciting evidence; she talked about it. Billy Bryan and Old Hickory joined her, and the whole mob went hooting melodiously toward the south slope.

"Good voice she's got," said Spring. "She one of your new ones, Cal?"

"Just small fry," replied Royster, with pride which he couldn't conceal, "and she'll run as long as a fox makes tracks."

Baker thought, "Good voice? Well, the old guy said so," and yet Bake was well aware that her yelps were not qualified for a chorus of the best Royster voices, let alone to bring praise from the man who had bred Bugle Ann. He wondered whether it was merely a mistaken kindness on Spring's part, or whether the old man had really lost his ear. Three years, eight months and twenty-one days were an awful long time.

Bake began to hum *I stood in the jailhouse,* and stopped in horror when he realized what he was humming.

He heard the bubbling of his father's whisky bottle. "Let's have a fire," Cal ordered.

The first curling flame, nursed tenderly through drying twigs, showed Benjy Davis something which made him catch his breath. He had to build the fire higher before he was sure. . . . Yes, old Springfield had gone upstairs before he left the house, but Benjy hadn't given it any thought at the time. And now he saw that the old man wore the battered bugle, tucked neatly beneath his suspender strap.

Stiff little needles rose on Benjy's scalp. He kept fooling with the fire.

"They're well toward Big Panther Holler," Cal estimated.

Spring inclined his head critically. "Yes, that's a bee-line fox tonight. Doesn't let no crops grow under his feet." He spoke without a tremor of madness, but this old bugle glowed and shimmered and caught dull flashes from the firelight at every snap of the flames.

Then Benjy saw the shaking of Baker Royster's hands, and he knew that Bake too had seen the trumpet. . . . The son thought crazily, "Christ in the Mountains, what would we do if he stood up and started to blow that thing?"

Bake was shivering with the same wonder. This was June . . . he knew the month, and the year, and the farm—he knew every scrap of sod beneath his feet—and yet the first blast of that horn would turn the commonplace world to madness. No person could estimate what tribes might come sweeping through the underbrush in answer.

After a few moments, it was impossible to hear the dogs any more. They had gone deep into the crooked defile of Big Panther Creek; there was no telling just when they might return. The Roysters knew this fox well enough: their dogs had run him frequently during the year. He was a bee-liner from the word Go, as Cal often remarked, and he'd just as soon venture into the next county as not. But always he holed at the south end of Bachelor's timber, so they knew the pack would come howling back eventually.

No one talked. The log on the fire shrank to the thinness of a charred bone, and Benjy arose to see whether he could find another one dry enough to burn. There was a V of discarded fence posts nearby, and under their shelter perhaps—

He stopped, frozen in his tracks as the sound pierced him. It was a faint and elvish cry, half lost amid the buzz of tree-toads, and it might have been fathered by one of those nighthawks which rode high overhead. . . . Still, it never came from the throat of a bird, and in the first second Benjy wondered what sort of a throat it had come from.

Before the sudden blurring of his gaze, he watched his father's head lifting, nodding. Spring's mouth had opened slightly, in the reflex of one who listens without half knowing. . . .

Again the thin, silver measure—the horn of something which

searched the forest away over beyond Heaven Hump. Bake Royster
crawled up on his elbow, and his face became yellow instead of red
in the firelight.

"Benjy," whispered Spring Davis, "I reckon she's struck."

The young man made a harsh sound. "It's a dog," he said. "Fox-
hound that belongs to— Running all off by himself, that way. I
reckon he's an Armstrong."

The sockets beneath Spring's eyebrows were blank and dark and
empty; the weaving shadows did strange things to the contour of
his face. He said, "No Armstrong ever had that kind of music in
him." Then, creakily, he was on his feet and fingering the lip of his
bugle.

"For pity sake," mumbled Cal Royster, "it's just a kind of
echo. . . ."

"Cal," said Spring, "if she comes real close to us, I'll blow the
bugle for her."

Benjy didn't know why she should have been up again, loping
through that timber. It was her voice, of course—no other dog had
ever lived with such a melody hidden in its throat. He ventured to
suppose that Bugle Ann had loved Spring Davis, much as a woman
might have loved him, but it was a cruel and selfish devotion which
would rob them all of their sanity, and never let them live in the
same world with other men again.

He was repeating, again and again, "Pa! Pa—set down—set down—"
and that was the same plea he had made in the bedroom.

Old Spring laughed at them all, and he seemed to tower against
the sky. "Are you plumb certain that was her collar, Benjy? . . . I
reckon nobody but God seen her bones hop up out of the orchard
to-night."

He ceased speaking, then, because the dog's howling was closer
and more distinct, as if the trail had swung toward the Hollow; even
now the fox might be leaping the gorge of Chilly Branch. But Bugle
Ann had learned the last trick of any fox that ever jumped.

Bake Royster was trying to stand up, but for the moment his legs
wouldn't support him. He thought, "She won't need any help to-
night. Spring Davis is in the woods, and naturally she knows it."
When he was far off in the penitentiary it had been kind of the

Boone dogs, the hounds buried and dust a hundred years ago, to come out and hunt with her and cast in enormous circles to locate the scent . . . big, gobbling shapes, they could drag down the fastest deer in the hills. They could make the black bears afraid of them, and every catamount would slink along the tree-tops when they went by.

In sudden relief, Bake wanted to laugh out loud. He had hoped that she was a ghost, all along, for that made the whole tale so much easier to understand.

"Sweet mouth," he heard old Davis saying, "the sweetest mouth that ever lived."

Cal groped for his friend's arm. "Now, Spring," he quavered, "you got to get holt of yourself."

Spring laughed.

That clear, baying voice rocketed against the cloudy ceiling, and came down to wash all around them.

"Get holt? Why, I bred the most beautiful tune ever played in these parts, and I ain't ashamed! Maybe you laughed when you seen me bring this bugle, but I reckoned it would come handy." He paused, grinning slyly, and nodding again as the round pealing broke loose anew.

Then, from blackest distance and seeming to rise behind the hound notes, sounded the yell of a bugle. It blew the same chords which Springfield Davis had always blown for his dog.

The hound's cry ceased, quickly, and the woods seemed to hold out empty hands.

The men looked at one another, pale face reflecting pale face, and for the first time you could see Springfield's eyes. They were bright with bewilderment, and with rage.

Once more the *ta-da*, the shrill witchery and command of it. The strings of old Davis's neck stood out tight against his skin. "I never done it," he cried. "I never gave no one else leave to blow her in!"

"Where was it?" asked Bake, hoarsely.

"Up on Heaven Hump, or past," Benjy answered him. Then he started away through the timber like a runaway steer, with Bake after him.

8

Spring and Cal stumbled cruelly in the underbrush, until the younger
men called to each other, remembering, and came back to help them.
Only when they had worked their way across Chilly Branch and
had crept to the summit beyond, did any one say a complete sentence.
It was Spring who spoke.

"Put out your lights," he ordered. "I see another fire."

A faint ruddiness lived in the north and east, and they went
toward it. Benjy grasped his father's arm, pulling him along. The old
man moved like a wooden image, but he breathed steadily, and
Benjy was certain he'd never drop dead in those woods, no matter
who or what they found beside that fire.

Again the tree-toads buzzed; the crickets sawed and chuckled,
and betty-millers came to kiss the hunters' perspiring faces; these
creatures could be merry and could exalt their whispers again, with
all those mighty trumpet notes echoed beyond recall.

The woods thinned away. Here was a clearing, stockaded with
lonely fence posts, where once Jacob Terry's sheep had lain down
in a green pasture.

A black shape grew against the distant core of firelight.

"It's a woman," said Bake.

For a moment he weaved, dizzy, as in the dawn before Jacob
Terry was killed.

Camden Terry sat beside the blaze. She was motionless, even as the
dry sticks crackled under approaching feet; she must have been expecting this invasion, all along. A dog was with her. The dog bayed,
briefly, and Springfield Davis whispered, ". . . World, and they
that dwell therein," and his arm tried to twist out of Benjy's mana-
cling grasp.

The girl looked up at them. Benjy thought that she was more
beautiful than ever—more beautiful than that day in court, for the
fire made red gilt of her hair. Her eyes held dignity and fearlessness,
but undoubtedly she was waiting for some immense judgment.

Spring stepped up against the fire, and looked down at the hound
which crouched within the curve of the girl's arm. "You blew them

notes," were the first words he said, for he saw the bugle in Camden Terry's lap.

She said, "Yes. Twice. Yes, I did."

"That hound . . ." His throat went to pieces on the word. He seemed to build it up again. "What dog is that?"

"I raised her."

"But it's got—her voice."

"Yes, I know. I used to hear her."

He said, scornfully, "I tell you, God never made no two hound-voices alike. Same kind of mouth, and all. He never."

The girl looked up at him. "This— She was hers. She's Bugle Ann's. She's by Proctor Pride out of Bugle Ann. There were four more, but only this one had the real bugle-mouth."

Springfield staggered. Benjy held him. "She never had no pups," said Spring, thickly.

Camden passed her hand over the little hound's ears, and the dog watched Spring Davis with soft, sad eyes. Her nostrils reached out for the smell of him. . . . Camden Terry stood up; the bugle rolled across the ground. Firelight made her blue dress seem purple, and it did kindly with her eyes, and for a moment Benjy couldn't breathe.

"Mr. Davis," the girl said, "my father never killed her."

Spring cried, "Aw, we know that! The boys found her skeleton over by Bachelor's, and they heard her voice in the woods, but I still say she never was bred to any dog."

"That night—" Camden's voice was very low; her hands struggled together. "I drove out of the yard, just like I told in court. She was coming past the gate; I couldn't see her in time. I couldn't— It was an awful sharp turn. . . . I got out and picked her up. . . . She wasn't dead, and even—hurt—she— She didn't seem to blame me. I was afraid there'd be trouble over it: Bugle Ann's being hurt."

Somewhere in the world beyond, Cal Royster was saying, "Car lights. They stopped for a minute. Then they went on. It was when I heard the yip."

"This hound never was hers," Spring Davis snarled. "Where in hell did it get her voice?"

"Wait, Pa," said Benjy.

The girl's hands separated; the fingers flattened stiffly together. "I took her along in the car. The rest of my folks didn't know I'd brought her; just Uncle Elnathan. I told them I had found a run-over dog, on the way, and I hustled her out to Uncle's place. . . . After we heard what had happened, I didn't dare tell the truth. It would have been worse for you, if the jury knew Bugle Ann wasn't really dead at all."

She gasped, "Oh, I hated Pa. He killed my mother with pure mean-ness. It's the awfulest thing in the world to have a father you've got to hate."

Spring eyed her grimly, and told her to go on.

"Well, it was Bugle Ann's shoulder and leg. . . . She was kind of crippled, but I nursed her to health. When she came in heat in February, I bred her to Proctor Pride. He was a Spaulding hound; the only good one Uncle had, any more. There were five pups. But this was the one—like her."

Camden paused, and there were tears all over her face, but this time it was Benjy who asked her to go on.

"She waited till they were weaned. Then she left one night— there was a moon— She wasn't dried up yet, and she wasn't strong enough to run. But she did go away. We traced her fifteen miles, next day, and then lost her for good. Likely she was heading for home when she struck a fox, and you folks heard her. We never knew she was dead, for sure, but I always thought she'd been killed trying to get back home."

Spring exclaimed, "Benjy, I got to set," and his son eased him quickly to the ground. . . . Cal Royster fumbled around. It took him a long while to find his flask, but at last he did find it.

Soon, Spring opened his eyes and nodded at the girl. "You see," he murmured, "they let me out of Jefferson City."

Her chin trembled. "I knew. That's how I come to be here to-night. I thought you'd maybe be out in the timber."

Benjy stared at her with fierce intensity. "*You* knew. How did you know? They don't talk those things around."

"Well," she told him, "I knew beforehand."

Benjy said, "It wasn't a parole. He was pardoned."

"Yes. The parole board. Sometimes they—kind of recommend. Folks write letters. And talk."

He had taken her hand—both of her hands. He came between her and the Roysters, and he seemed even to have forgotten his father. Camden said, rapidly: "Jacob Terry was my father. I'd like to forget that, but it counted for something when they come to considering and— All my folks weren't Terrys," she cried at him. "Half of them were Camdens, and Camdens mean something in this state, even yet. Some of them are in the legislature."

Bake Royster exploded, "My God! You done it, didn't you?"

She shook her head. "No. I couldn't of done it myself. I just—did what I could. They all knew what kind of a man my father was. And I told them about Mr. Davis."

Inch by inch, the hound had hitched forward to sniff around Spring Davis's feet. At first the old man twisted his legs away, but finally he lay still and watched the dog. "I'm all right, boy," he muttered to Benjy, and then he raised up on his elbow. His eyes took in the whole color and shape and hide of the hound; they studied her slenderness, her strong and well-arched coupling, the stifle built far out from her body. . . . The hound sneezed. She looked at old Davis with curiosity, and then stepped across his legs with tail waving politely, and smelled him from the other side.

"I reckon she could run," said Spring.

"I trained her to the horn. Same as— It seemed like the best thing to do." Camden looked at Benjy, and he nodded slowly, and his face came close to hers.

Spring asked, "What do you call her?"

"Little Lady."

The old man said, "Got a deeper tan, but it's spotted much the same." Stiffly, reluctantly, he put out his hand and touched the hound's muzzle. His eyes were still hard and dry, but he whispered, "Little Lady. You got quite a mouth, Little Lady."

Cal Royster was crying like his own grandchild, but more quietly. Bake took him away from the fire. "Come on, Pa," he grunted, "we got to get out of here. I think I hear the pack coming north again." Baker was certain in his heart that before the other hounds had ever come in, Spring Davis would have sent Little Lady out with

Camden and Benjy, to see what she was made of. He prophesied to himself that she would run as long as any fox made tracks; she would be a twenty-hour dog, given to mighty journeyings and chasings, but always she would come back to those black-dark hills when the bugle called her home.

Some Sunnybank Dogs

BY

ALBERT PAYSON TERHUNE

A SCHOOLTEACHER, looking back over his experiences with more than a thousand pupils, would find himself dwelling with special interest in recollections of at least nine or ten of them; nine or ten personalities so outstanding, for one reason or another, that they will not let themselves be forgotten or grouped with the vast majority.

It is so with my memories of the long line of Sunnybank dogs.

Soon or late, every dog master's memory becomes a graveyard; peopled by wistful little furry ghosts that creep back unbidden, at times, to a semblance of their olden lives. To outsiders, the past deeds and misdeeds of these loved canine wraiths may hold no great interest.

With this somewhat windy apology, which really is no apology at all, let's go:

Lad stands out as foremost of the dogs of Sunnybank. I have written his life saga; stretching its exploits through no fewer than three "Lad" books. So I need not go in for a wearisome retelling of his biography. A few episodes and characteristics, and then we'll pass on to the next cage.

He was a big and incredibly powerful collie, with a massive coat of burnished mahogany-and-snow and with absurdly small forepaws (which he spent at least an hour a day in washing) and with deepset dark eyes that seemed to have a soul behind them. So much for the outer dog. For the inner: he had a heart that did not know the meaning of fear or of disloyalty or of meanness.

541

But it was his personality, apart from all these things, which made —and still makes—him so impossible to forget. As I have tried clumsily to bring out in my three books about him.

He was immeasurably more than a professionally loyal and heroic collie. He had the most elfin sense of fun and the most humanlike reasoning powers I have found in any dog.

Suppose we talk about those traits for a minute or two.

The Mistress and I went to pay a call of sympathy on a lachrymose old woman whose arm had been broken. The fracture had knit. The victim was almost as well as ever. But she reveled in giving dramatic recitals of her mishap to anyone and everyone who would listen.

We took Lad along with us when we dropped in on the invalid-emeritus. Before we had been there five minutes, we had every reason to wish we had left him at home.

Not that he failed to behave with entire outward decorum. But he took much uncalled-for part in the conversation. The woman launched forth on a detailed report of her accident. She sprinkled the lamentable recital thickly with moans and groans and belching sighs.

Lad was enormously pleased with the performance. So much so that he elected to turn the dolorous solo into a still more doleful duet. Every time our hostess gave forth one of the many successive sounds of grief, Lad copied it with startling realism and in precisely the same key. In perfect imitation, he moaned and whimpered and sighed and emitted ghastly groanings.

Throughout, he was lying demurely at the Mistress's feet. But his eyes were a-dance. The plumed tip of his tail twitched uncontrollably. Lad was having a beautiful time. The Mistress and I were not.

We sought to keep our faces straight, as the woman's narrative waxed in noisy intensity and as Lad's accompaniment swelled to a crescendo.

Groan for groan he gave her and moan for moan. Carried away by his own brilliant enactment, his ululations increased in volume until they all but drowned out the sufferer's performance. It was a horrible duel of emotional expression. And Lad won it. For the woman paused in her jeremiad, and stared down at the statuesquely couchant collie in tearful admiration. "Oh, he's wonderful!" she exclaimed. "Just *wonderful!* He understands all the agonies I've been through! And it almost breaks his heart. I wish some people were half as sympathetic as this poor dumb beast."

Lad, who for five minutes had been anything but dumb, eyed her in happy expectation; waiting for her to strike the next imitable note of grief, and yearning for a chance to resume his own performance. But there was no opening. The lament had shifted to clamorous praise of the dog's unbelievable comprehension and sympathy. And in the hymn of praise there were no alluring groans to copy.

We got away as soon as we could. If ever a dog merited rebuke for disgraceful impudence, Lad was that dog. But neither the Mistress nor myself had the heart to scold him for it.

With uncanny wisdom the collie had realized from the outset that the old lady was in no pain, in no real distress, that she was just airing her past trouble in maudlin quest for sympathy and in an orgy of self-pity. And he had joined blithely in the scene; in a spirit of straight ridicule.

In cases of genuine human distress or pain or misfortune, Lad's sympathy was ever eager and heartsick. But he had a whole-souled disgust for any form of faking; a disgust he took pleasure in showing most unmistakably.

Sometimes his guying took a subtler form. As when a man came here to see me on business—a man Lad disliked and distrusted as much as did I. The day was hot. The visitor took off his new pongee coat and laid it on the edge of the veranda. Then he began to talk.

He had an unpleasant manner and he was saying unpleasant things. I was hard put to it to remember I was his host, and to behave civilly to him. I found the effort more and more difficult as the talk went on.

Lad was lying beside my chair. As always, he sensed my mood.

With a collie's odd psychic powers he knew I was increasingly angry and that I yearned to kick the visitor off my land. The dog looked worriedly up into my face. Then he eyed my caller, and the tip of one of his long white eyeteeth peeped from under the lip that had begun to curl ever so slightly.

I could see the tiger muscles go taut beneath Lad's coat. I laid my hand on his head and whispered sharply:

"*Quiet*, Lad. Let him *alone!*"

All his adult life the dog had known the meaning of both those commands and the stark necessity of obeying them. Yet the Master was pestered by this obnoxious stranger. And, with Lad, that was not on the free list. Glumly he lay down, his eyes fixed alertly on the guest.

Then, stealthily, he got to his feet. With catlike softness of foot he crossed to the veranda edge where was draped the visitor's imported white coat—a garment of much value, even if not of many colors. To my shame I admit I saw the collie's progress without checking it. I had used up my whole day's stock of hospitality.

Lad lifted the snowy and costly coat from its place. He carried it out onto the muddy gravel of the driveway as tenderly as though it were a sick puppy. The owner was too busy orating to notice the rape of the garment. And I had not the good breeding to call Lad back.

On the driveway, Lad sought out a spot where was a smear of surface mud and silt as wide as a dining-room table—the effluvia of that morning's heavy rain.

With the same exaggerated tenderness he laid the coat atop the area of mud. Then, in very evident relish, he proceeded to roll on it, back and forth, several times. After which he proceeded to rub one of his heavy shoulders into the muddily crumpled British imported pongee, and then the other shoulder. He ended the desecration by rolling once more upon it.

Now to an outsider this shoulder rubbing and rolling might have had no significance, apart from crass mischief. A dogman would have understood the unspeakable black insult implied. For only into carrion—liquescent and putrescent carrion—does a dog roll and rub his body in that fashion. It is the foulest affront he can offer.

It was when Lad had completed his task of defilement as I have told it and was pacing back in majestic dignity to his place beside my chair, that the visitor's eye chanced to rest—first inquisitively and then in swift horror—upon his treasured white coat; or at the be-fouled bunch of muddy cloth which had been that coat.

Again I should have reprimanded Lad right ferociously. Again I did not.

In October of 1912 the Mistress was stricken with a long and perilous attack of pneumonia. It was a time of horror which even yet I don't like to recall. Through the endless days and the interminable nights Lad crouched against the door of her sickroom. He would not eat. If he were put out of the house, he would smash a cellar window, and, two minutes later, he would be back at his post outside the shut door.

Day and night he lay there, shivering, moaning softly under his breath. Doctor and nurse, coming or going, would tread accidentally on his sensitive body a dozen times a day.

Outside, the October woods were full of chaseable rabbits and squirrels: Lad's lifelong pacemakers in wild-forest chases. But the dog paid no heed. Miserable and sick with dread, he lay there.

Then, of a glorious Sunday morning, the death danger was past. I called Lad into the sickroom. Trembling, ecstatic, he made his way to the side of the bed, moving as softly as any nurse or mother. The Mistress was told of his long vigil. And she patted his classic head and told him what a grand dog he was.

Then I told him to go outdoors. He obeyed.

Once outside, he proceeded to comport himself in a manner unworthy of a three-months puppy.

For the next ten hours complaints came pouring in on me: complaints ranging from tearful to blasphemous; complaints I was too happy to heed.

Lad had broken into the dairy, by hammering open its door with his head. There he had pulled, one by one, every milk or cream pan from the shelves, and had left the stone floor deep in a white covering.

Lad had chased the Mistress's cat up a tree. And the poor little feline was stranded out on the end of a wabbly bough whence only a long ladder could rescue her.

Lad had gushed forth among the cows and had driven them into stampede flight. One of them, tethered to a long chain, he had chased in a circle till the chasee was too exhausted to stand.

Lad had cantered up to the gate lodge. There he had slipped into the kitchen and had yanked from the open cover a ten-pound leg of mutton designed for the Sunday dinner of my superintendent and his family. This hotly savory trophy he had been burying deep in a flowerbed when the superintendent's wife rescued it in sorry plight.

Lad had nipped the heels of an elderly horse which drew a carryall wherein his owner and the latter's children were driving to church. The horse had run away, more in conscientiousness than in terror, for several yards, before the driver could rein him in.

Meantime, Lad had sprung upward and had caught between his teeth the corner of an elaborate laprobe. He had dragged this for a quarter mile, and at last had deposited it in the dead center of a half-impenetrable berry patch.

Lad had hunted up three neighbors' dogs and had routed them out of their kennels and had bestowed on them a series of terrific thrashings.

Lad had ripped the nurse's best newly starched uniform from the clothesline (he hated the antiseptic-smelling and abhorredly efficient nurse from the first) and had deposited it in the black lakeside mud.

In brief, Lad had misbehaved as never before in all his stately life had he dreamed of misbehaving. He had been, for ten hours, a Scourge, a neighborhood Pest.

Fast and furious poured in the complaints from everywhere. To my lasting discredit, I must say I made the same reply to every weeping or cursing complainant:

"Let him alone. Send me the bill and I'll settle it. Lad and I have been through the red flames of hell, this past fortnight. Today he's doing the things I'd do if I had the nerve. We're celebrating, he and I."

(I don't need to point out to any of you that this was an inanely drunken speech for any grown man to keep on repeating as I repeated it on that golden Day of Deliverance.)

A year later, Lad took upon himself, of his own accord, a man's size job. Namely, the task of shaping his harum-scarum young son, Wolf, into a decent canine citizen. Patiently, the big dog wrought at this chore. At first the results were slow and uncertain.

For one thing, Wolf's inborn sense of mischief made his sedate sire's life a burden. The worst form of plaguing was the stealing by Wolf of Lad's most cherished meat bones.

At first the older collie suffered these thefts without resentment or punishment. Lad could thrash (and *did* thrash) every dog of his size, or much larger, which attacked him. But against a silly half-grown pup he would not employ his fearsome punitive powers. He hit on a better trick for keeping his beloved bones from Wolf's thieving teeth. I was lucky enough to be on hand, at a distance, to see this ruse carried out more than once. And, to me, it savors, not of blind atavistic canine instinct, but of true human sense of reasoning.

Lad received, as part of his dinner, a gorgeously meatful beef bone. He had eaten to repletion. Thus he planned to bury this delicious two-pound morsel for future exhuming and gnawing. First, he took preliminary steps.

Then with no show of caution at all he carried the red-streaked bone to a sheltered spot in a flower border. There he laid it down and proceeded to dig a hole in the soft loam—a hole deeper than he usually dug.

In the bottom of this pit he placed the bone. With his nose, he shoved an inch or so of earth atop the buried treasure. (A dog digs holes with his forepaws, you know. But he uses his nose, never his paws, for filling such holes. I don't know why.)

After the bone was comfortably if lightly covered, Lad dived into a clump of shrubbery hard by, and reappeared carrying a bare and sterile bone he had hidden there—a bone which long ago had lost its last iota of dog appeal and which had been bleached white by many rains.

This forlorn relic he dropped into the cavity. Then he proceeded to push back all the displaced dirt, up to the level of the rest of the ground; and walked unconcernedly away, not once turning to glance back at the cache.

Wolf had been watching from a safe distance, and with avid interest. As soon as Lad left the scene of interment, the puppy danced over to it and began to dig. Thus, often, he had rifled his sire's underground bone-repositories. Presently, Wolf had dug down to the first bone.

In disgust he sniffed at its meatless aridity. Then he turned away. Apparently he had had all his toil for nothing, for less than nothing, for a bone a starving coyote would have turned up its nose at. Off trotted the baffled puppy without the faintest suspicion that a right toothsome meat-fringed bone was lying less than two inches beneath the decoy bone he had disinterred.

Now, unless I am more in error than usual, that ruse of old Lad's called for something like human reasoning and powers of logic. Assuredly it was not based on mere instinct. Every move was thought out and executed in crafty sequence.

I have heard of two other dogs, since then, whose owners saw them do the same thing.

Let's go back to an aftermath of Lad's crazy spree of relief when he knew the Mistress was out of danger. A week or so later, the convalescent was carried downstairs, one Indian summer morning, and ensconced in a porch hammock. Lad, as always, lay on the veranda floor beside her.

During the forenoon, two or three neighbors came to see the Mistress, to congratulate her on her recovery and to bring her gifts of flowers and candy and fruit and the like. These presents they placed in her lap for inspection. Lad watched interestedly. Soon he got up and loped away toward the woods.

Somewhere far back in the forests he found—much more likely *re*found—the carcass of an excessively dead horse. From it he wrenched part of a rib. Then, dragging his heavy burden, he made his way home.

None of us noticed the collie's approach; the wind blowing from the wrong direction. Our first knowledge of his return to the porch was when he came alongside the hammock and dropped his awful gift across the Mistress' lap.

And why not? To a dog, such far-gone carrion is a rare delicacy. Not for food, but to roll in. To him the odor must seem delicious, if one may judge by his joy in transferring it to his own coat.

Lad had followed the example of the morning's visitors by bringing his dear deity a present—the choicest he could find.

After all, the reek of carrion cannot be much more offensive to us than is the smell of tobacco and of booze and of costly imported perfumes, to dogs. Yet for the incomprehensible pleasure of being near us, our dogs endure those rank smells; while we banish from the house any dog whose fur has even the faintest reek of carrion.

Of all my countless ignorances of dog nature, the densest is his yearning to be near his master or mistress.

I don't know why my collies will leave their dozing in front of the living-room hearth for the privilege of following me out into a torrent of winter rain. They hate rain.

I don't know why all folk's dogs risk gladly a scolding or a whipping by breaking out of a room or a kennel into which they have been shut, and galloping down the street or over the fields to catch up with the master who purposely has left them behind.

Today (for another and non-thrilling instance) I am writing at my hammock desk, a hundred yards or more from the house. Seven dogs are with me. It is a cool, brilliant afternoon; just the weather for a romp. The lawns and the woods and the lake all offer allurement to my collies.

What are the seven doing? Each and every one of them is lounging on the ground, close to the hammock.

Even crippled and ancient Sandy (Sunnybank Sandstorm) has left the veranda mat where he was so comfortable. To him all movement nowadays is a source of more or less keen discomfort. Yet he limped painfully down the six steps from the veranda to the driveway, and came slowly over to me, as soon as he found I was here; stretching himself at my feet, on bumpy ground much less comfortable than his porch bed. And here for the past two hours he has been drowsing with the others.

Why? *I* don't know. There must be some mysterious lure in the presence of their human gods which gives dogs that silly yearning to stay at their sides; rather than to do more amusing and interesting things.

When I chance to go from the house toward the stables, a cloud of the white doves of Sunnybank fly to meet me and to escort me in winnowing flight to my destination. There is no mystery about this semblance of devotion. They know their food box is in a shed there.

The same cause was assignable to the welcoming whinnies of my horses (when I still kept horses) that greeted me as I passed in through the stable doors in the early mornings.

It is the same with the goldfish, when a hundred of them converge in fiery streams to where I halt at the curb of the wide lily pool; and when they wriggle fearlessly in and out among my dabbling fingers. They know—or hope—I am there to feed them.

No, none of those phenomena holds a single half-grain of mystery, any more than does human fawning on a rich relative. But the dogs—mine and everyone's—stick around where we are and go where we go, through no graft motive at all.

They are absurd enough to want to be with us, and with no hope of reward. That is an impulse I have sought hard and vainly to explain to myself.

In the bunch of Sunnybank collies, as they lie around me here on the grass, there is no trace of the flattering attention they show toward the maids, who love to feed them surreptitiously from the kitchen windows; none of the still more rapt interest they bestow on my superintendent as he prepares their one ample daily meal.

There is no such patently self-seeking tinge in their attitude toward me as they lie here on the lawn. There was none of it in the canine procession which followed me to the house, three minutes ago, when I went to my study for a new supply of typewriter paper, and which waited at the door for me and then convoyed me back here to the hammock.

No, it is a trait I can't figure out. As I think I have said several times in the past page or two.

Which is a long digression from our story. I like to hope it hasn't bored you overmuch. And now let's get back to Lad:

I have dealt here only with a few of the queerly human and mischievous and logic-guided happenings in Laddie's life. Not with his actual history.

His death battle with two younger and stronger dogs in the snow-choked forests back of Sunnybank, his deeds of dashingly worshipful service to the Mistress and to myself during his full sixteen years of life, the series of stark adventures that starred his long career—are not these chronicled to perhaps tiresome length in my three books about him?

Foremost among the Sunnybank dogs of my childhood and young boyhood was my father's oversized pointer, Shot. He is worth your notice. Naturally, in any modern dog show Shot would be "gated" most unmercifully.

He was of royally pure blood. But his head lacked the so-styled refinement of today's show pointer. His mighty chest and shoulders and hindquarters that carried him tirelessly for ten hours a day through the stiffest kinds of shooting country, and the harsh coat and thick skin which served as armor against briar and bramble and kept him unscathed through the thorniest copses—these were at laughable variance with the silken skin and dainty narrow-chested body lines of the show-type pointer of nowadays.

At "laughable" variance. But to me the laugh would not be on Shot. For, to me, he still is, in memory, the grandest pointer of my rather long experience.

My mother's health broke. My father took her and all of us to Europe, in the hope of curing her. (The cure was made. She lived more than forty healthy years longer.)

Sunnybank was rented during our two-year absence from America. Shot was sent to one of my uncles to be cared for until we should come back for him.

This uncle, Colonel G. P. Hawes, Sr., was an ideal sportsman. He understood dogs as it is given to few men to understand them. He and Shot had been good friends, since the pointer came to us as a just-weaned puppy. The dog could not have had a better home and a more congenial guardian.

Yet Colonel Hawes wrote my father that the usually gay dog had grown sullen and mopey and spiritless. Shot went through his duties in the hunting field as honestly as ever, but with no interest. He was grieving sorely for his absent master and for Sunnybank.

After our two-year exile we came back to America. One of my father's first moves was to go to my uncle's home and bring Shot to Sunnybank. He took me along on this errand. Its details are as clear in my memory as if they had occurred last month.

As soon as we were seated, Colonel Hawes sent a man to bring Shot into the house. The dog was kenneled some distance away and had not seen or scented our arrival. Into the living room plodded the pointer, at my uncle's summons.

He was thinner, much thinner, than I remembered him. His gait and his every line and motion were listless. He seemed wholly without spirit and devoid of any interest in life. My father had arranged the scene beforehand. He had told me what to do. I did it.

He and I sat motionless and without speaking. We were at the end of the room farthest from the door, and we were seated perhaps ten feet from each other.

Lifelessly, Shot came through the doorway. Just inside the threshold he halted. Up went his splendid head. His eyes sought out my father's mute and moveless figure. For a second or more the dog stood so.

Then he began to creep toward my father, hesitantly, one slow step at a time, crouching low and shuddering as with ague. Never did his dazed eyes leave my father's face. Inch by inch he continued that strangely crawling advance.

He did not so much as glance toward where I was sitting. His whole mind was focussed on the unmoving and unspeaking man in the chair ahead of him. So might a human move toward the ghost of a loved one; incredulous, hypnotized, awed. Then my father spoke the one word:

"*Shot!*"

The dog screamed; as though he had been run over. He hurled himself on his long-lost master, sobbing and shrieking, insane with joy. Then the sedate pointer whirled around him in galloping circles, and ended the performance by dropping to my father's feet; laying his head athwart his shoe and chattering and sobbing.

I drew a shaky breath. At the sound Shot raised his head from its place of adoration.

He dashed over to me and accorded me a welcome which ordinarily would have seemed tumultuous, but which was almost indifferent, compared to the greeting he had accorded my father. Then, all at once, he was back to his master again, laying his head on the man's knee and still sobbing in that queerly human fashion.

(Yet not long ago I read a solemn scientific preachment to the effect that no dog could remember a lost master's face and scent for the space of eighteen months! Shot beat that record by half a year. And I believe he could have beaten it by a decade.)

To Sunnybank we came; Shot with us. The dog's sullen apathy was gone—gone for all time. He was jubilantly happy at his return to the home of his earliest memories. But for weeks he would not willingly let my father out of his sight. He seemed to fear he would lose his master again.

My father taught me to shoot. A few years after our return to America he and I went out quail-hunting with Shot. At the base of a steep hill there was a brambly meadow. The meadow was cut midway by a railroad track. As he neared the track, the dog came to a dead point. He was facing a clump of low bushes on the far side of the rails.

Statue-still, Shot stood, at point, waiting my father's signal to move forward toward the clump. Before that signal could be spoken, an express train came whizzing around the curve at the foot of the hill, and bore down toward us. Under its wheels and in its wake was a fog of dust and of flying hot cinders.

Shot stood, rocklike, on his point. The train roared past, not ten inches from his nose. The dog did not stir or falter, though he was peppered with burning cinders and choked by the whirlwind of dust and soot.

After the train had rattled its ill-smelling length out of the way, my father signaled Shot to move forward. The pointer took two stealthy steps ahead: steps that carried him to the center of the railroad track. From the clump just in front of him three quail whirred upward like a trio of fluffy little bombs. I suppose they had been too scared by the passage of the train to break cover until then.

Shot dropped to the ground, tense and waiting. My father brought down two of the birds in one of his customary brilliant left-and-right volleys.

I missed the third.

I was too shaky over the dog's peril and his plucky ignoring of it to do any creditable shooting just then. Shot lived to a ripe—an over-ripe—old age. We buried him in a strip of lakeside land a furlong or more from the house: a strip where sleep the Sunnybank dogs of almost eight decades. He was interred next to a grave whose little marble headstone's blurred lettering still may be deciphered as

FRANK Our Dog. For Thirteen Years
Our Faithful Friend. Died 1876.

Frank was Shot's immediate predecessor as my father's hunting companion.

Frank bit me when I was at the age of two. I had tried to bite off one of his floppy ears. It was a punitive nip Frank gave me rather than a real incision. I am told I wept loudly at the scare and hurt of it.

(If "when a man bites a dog, that's *news*," I wonder if it is tabloid news when a two-year-old boy chews a dog's ear.)

It was long before my birth that my father bought Frank. The dog was just past puppyhood. The time was winter. So my parents were at Newark, where my father was pastor of the old First Reformed Church. Not at Sunnybank. (Even as, to my sorrow, I was not born at Sunnybank like three of my nephews, but at Newark; because my birth date fell on December 21st—my mother's forty-second birthday.)

Young Frank was restless in his new home. On the day after his arrival he ran away. My father and my mother and my two elder sisters and the servants went to look for him. All in different directions.

My mother wandered about for an hour, calling the pointer's name from time to time. At last, just in front of her, in the twilight, she saw him emerge from an alleyway. She called to him. He paid no heed, but walked away. She gave chase and overhauled him. The dog showed his teeth as she grabbed him by the collar. This though he had seemed to take a genuine liking to her after his arrival at our home.

She ripped a flounce or something from an underskirt—women wore a labyrinth of underskirts and petticoats in those prehistoric days—and fastened it to his collar. Then she proceeded to drag him homeward.

"Drag" is the right word. For the pointer fought and held back every step of the way. A small but enthusiastic crowd formed, and followed the pair with shouts of gay encouragement. After a mile of hard going they reached our house, at 476 High Street.

In triumph, if in much weariness, my mother hauled the snappingly protesting dog indoors and into the firelit living room.

There, in front of the hearth, lounged my father. Frank was asleep on the rug at his feet.

The runaway dog had tired of his roamings and, half an hour earlier, had come back home of his own accord; just as my father was returning from a fruitless search for him.

The dog my mother had kidnapped was enough like him to have been Frank's twin brother. They never knew who the other pointer belonged to. But when they let him escape into the night he bounded off as with some evident destination in view. For weeks thereafter my mother dreaded arrest on a charge of dog stealing.

Never again did Frank run away, throughout the thirteen happy years of his life. Every winter he stayed on at Sunnybank when the family returned to Newark. There, in the absence of his gods, he made himself a member of the superintendent's family at the gate lodge; waiting in weary impatience for the family's return home.

When in early spring our carriage and the baggage wagon turned in at the gate, Frank would follow them down the winding furlong driveway to Sunnybank House. Here, till our departure in late autumn, he remained. And he would bark harrowingly at the superintendent or at anyone of the gate-lodge household who might venture to come near our door.

He was a peerless field dog and a peerless watchdog. To the inch, he knew the boundaries of our land. No unauthorized outsider might pass those boundaries without instant challenge and assault from Frank. He treed several innocent (if any of their foul breed can merit the term, "innocent") sightseers. He was a Neighborhood Terror.

Nightly, at stated intervals, he would leave his porch mat and would patrol the outside of the house and every part of Sunnybank's home tract. He was perhaps the best of all the great Sunnybank watchdogs we have had over a period of nearly eighty years.

I never liked him. And he didn't like me. Thus, my praise of his worth comes from my brain and from my conscience, not from my heart. He was bitterly and justly resentful, too, when in his old age young Shot came here to take his place in the field work he no longer had the strength or endurance to perform. I can't blame the ancient dog for that.

It was soon after Frank's death that someone gave my mother a miniature black-and-tan terrier. She named her "Jip," after Dora Copperfield's tiny dog. Though Jip nominally was my mother's, yet the little terrier chose my father as her only god. Her devotion to him was all-engrossing. She insisted on going everywhere with him. Sometimes this was not wholly pleasant.

As when, one Sunday, she was locked safely at home in his study while the rest of us went to church. My father was in the midst of his sermon when Jip came strutting proudly up the aisle.

A servant had gone into the study to replenish its fire. Jip had sneaked out, unseen. Somehow she had made her way to the street. There she had had no trouble at all in picking up my father's trail and following it.

Happy at the reunion with her adored master, Jip eluded easily the grabbing hands of the sexton and of one or two of the worshipers whose pews she went past. Up the pulpit steps she bounded, and leaped to the pulpit itself, landing squarely if scramblingly on the open Bible.

My father did not so much as pause in the delivery of his sermon, nor did he heed the snickers of the congregation. Which showed fairly good self-control, I think, as he had not noticed the terrier's progress up the aisle, and as his first intimation of her presence was when she appeared, wagging her tail and wriggling with joy, on the top of the pulpit's Bible.

Without checking his discourse, my father picked up the little morsel of caninity very gently and thrust her into one of the flowing sleeves of his black clerical gown.

From that exalted position, her beady eyes surveyed the congregation in triumph. Throughout the rest of the long church service she did not stir. She just cuddled deep in the folds of her master's silken sleeve, her alert head alone visible to the grinning onlookers.

If she shamed us on that day, she more than atoned for her sin a few nights later.

Always she slept on the foot of my father's bed. He woke to hear her growling with falsetto intensity far down in her throat. Then she sprang to the floor and scampered out of the room and downstairs.

A moment later, the house re-echoed to her furious barking. My father went down to investigate. For never before had the good little dog done such a thing as to disturb the slumbers of the family. Others of the household also went downstairs to find what it was all about. As a result, a burglar was nabbed and jailed. In his cell, later, the man gave this testimony:

"The thing we're most scared of in a house is a·small dog that barks and keeps backing away, like that black cur at Dominie Terhune's last night. You can't make them shut up and you can't get close enough to them to land a kick. They wake up everybody."

So much for gallant and adoring Jip. I don't remember what became of her. And now, a good deal more than a half-century later, there is nobody I can ask. Peace to her, anyhow! She stood patiently for a godless lot of mauling from my grubby childish hands. I recall that much, very distinctly.

Jock and Jean were son and mother. Both were children of my great collie, Bruce, "The Dog without a Fault"; the hero of my book that bears his name.

Usually a mother dog loses all special interest in her pups soon after she has weaned them. That was what Jean did, in regard to most of her many offspring. But never with Jock.

To the day of Jock's death he was still her cherished baby. Daily—though he grew to be almost twice her size—she would make him lie down, first on one side and then on the other, while with her untiring pink tongue she washed him from nose to tail tip.

She superintended his eating. Daintily she would transfer from her own food dish to his the choicest tidbits of her dinner.

It was pretty: this love and care of the little brown collie mother for her big brown collie son. And Jock reciprocated it all to the utmost. He and Jean were wretchedly unhappy when either was forced to be away from the comradeship of the other for more than an hour at a time.

Jock was one of the best collies, from a show point, I have bred. Close he was to complete perfection. In his only dog show he cleaned up everything in his classes against strong competition; and he was beaten for "Best of Breed" only by his own peerless sire, Bruce.

This meant immeasurably less to me than did my success in breeding into him a clever and gay and courageous spirit and a flavor of wise "folksiness" which made him an ideal companion. Mentally, spiritually, in disposition, he was a replica of Bruce. I asked (and ask) better of no dog on earth. As to his jolly pluck:

From the time he could leave the brood nest, Jock feared nothing. He would tackle any peril, any adversary, with a queerly happy and defiant high-pitched bark whose duplicate I have yet to hear.

That queer bark of glad defiance was ever his war cry.

On a day, while I sat writing in my outdoor hammock, young Jock lounged at my feet. He leaped up, suddenly, with that jocund challenge bark of his.

I looked behind me. There I saw on the lawn a big and thick-girthed copperhead snake. The serpent had been gliding through the grass toward the hammock and toward my unheeding ankles, when Jock either had sighted him or else had become aware of the nauseous viperine odor—a stench as of stale cucumbers—which clings to such venomous snakes.

In some occult way, Jock had seemed to divine my possible peril. He had sprung up from his doze and had rushed at the copperhead, sounding his glad battle cry. The snake checked its own slithery advance. It coiled, and prepared itself to face this plangent new adversary.

Many a fool dog would have plunged forward to death. Many a more prudent dog would have avoided the issue. Jock was neither a fool nor prudent.

It was a new experience to me to watch his duel with the copperhead. Never before, I think, had he encountered a snake. Yet he fought with consummate skill. In and out he flashed, tempting the copperhead to strike, and then dodging back, barely an inch out of reach of the death-dealing fangs; and immediately flashing in with an effort to slay the serpent before it could coil afresh.

Each combatant was a shade too swift for the other. Back and forth for some seconds waged the death duel. Neither adversary scored the fatal bite, though more than once each was within a hair's breadth of it. And ever rang forth that odd battle bark of my young collie.

Then I had sense enough to realize that I was allowing an untried paragon to pit his skill, for life or for death, against the most deadly type of viper in this region. And I went to his help.

I smashed the copperhead's ugly triangular skull under my heel. This with no zest at all. For I was wearing low shoes of canvas at the time. And if I had missed, the snake might well have scored on my unprotected ankle. I had a twinge of mental nausea as I gauged the distance and the required speed and accuracy for my head blow.

(There is little of the hero and a goodly modicum of the coward in my make-up. I detest danger and all its by-products. But Jock was my chum. And he was risking his life for me.)

The heel came down fatally on the fat copperhead. The fight was ended. So was the snake's life. And for two days thereafter Jock would have nothing whatever to do with me. I had spoiled his jolly life battle by butting in on it and by slaying his very entertaining opponent. He viewed me with cold aversion, until his youth and his inborn love for me overcame his disapproval.

But we were chums, he and I, for a pitifully short time after that.

For, a week later, like the fool I was, I took him to the dog show I have mentioned. He had been inoculated twice against distemper, and I used every other preventive and safeguard I knew of. (Doses of Delcreo in advance, a sponging of mouth and of pads with grain alcohol directly after the show, followed by the rubbing of flaked naphthaline into his luxuriant coat and a liberal dosage of castor oil.)

But a distemper-sickening chow had touched noses with him briefly at the big show. And that was enough. Jock was the more delicate because he was so closely inbred. He was infected. Ten days afterward he developed a dry cough and a wet nose.

The disease had set in. The malady which kills more pure-bred dogs than do all other diseases put together; the malady which took horrible toll from that same show and which has killed more than a thousand dogs a month, in its flood tide, after other shows.

Distemper practically never kills a mongrel (cross-breed is a better term) which it assails. The afflicted dog crawls under the barn or into some other cool and dark hiding place. Thence he emerges a few days later, bone thin and weak, but cured. But it slays at least fifty per cent of the thoroughbreds it attacks. Sometimes more.

It is a disease which, like typhoid, its human counterpart, calls for twenty-four hours a day of nursing. And, as in typhoid, nursing is 90 per cent of the cure.

Not often does actual distemper kill its victims. Oftener they die of its sequel illnesses: pneumonia or pleurisy or chorea. Chorea is a form of St. Vitus's dance. With dogs, almost always it is fatal.

Jock weathered the distemper itself. I nursed him, twenty-four hours a day, through the pneumonia which followed upon it. Then through the long siege of chorea which came after pneumonia. I cured him of each successive one of these scourges, though I waxed dead on my feet from sleeplessness and from eternal vigilance during every one of them.

I gave up all attempt to work. And I spent my days and my eternally long nights in the wide box stall that was Jock's sickroom. Then, just as success seemed ahead, the youngster somehow acquired "re-infection." At least that is what the two vets named it.

At gray dawn of one November morning I sat on the floor in a dim corner of the box stall, with Jock's head and shoulders pillowed on my aching knees. I had had seven weeks of the conflict, with not one night's rest. Yet I was thrilled at the idea I gradually was winning the battle for the good collie comrade I loved.

Jock had been sleeping peacefully for hours. Suddenly he lurched to his feet. His fevered eyes were fixed on something in the black shadows at the far opposite corner of the wide stall; something my own gross human gaze could not see.

Forward he sprang, voicing that same strange high challenge bark of his. Then he fell dead, across my outstretched feet.

What did he see—if anything—lurking there in the stall's far corner? Probably nothing. Perhaps "the Arch Fear in visible shape."

Whatever It was, brave young Jock had no dread of It. With his olden glad bark of defiance he had staggered forward to meet It.

Perhaps some of us soul-possessing humans may die a less valiant death.

At sunrise I had my men dig a grave for Jock, far from the house, and in the center of the line of Sunnybank dogs' graves I have spoken of, at the lake edge and on the border of the more distant woods. There we buried the fearless young collie; buried him almost six feet deep, before we fumigated his box-stall sickroom.

For the past weeks Jean had been shut up in her own spacious kennel yard. That day I let her out, for the first time since her loved son had fallen ill. Eagerly, unwearingly, the little she-collie searched every inch of the forty-acre Place. Back and forth and in narrowing circles she coursed and cast, in quest of Jock.

After several hours she came to the grave of her puppy. There she halted; first sniffing about, then waving happily her plumed tail and nestling down beside the mound of new earth.

There was nothing sad or hopeless in her attitude and aspect. It was as if, after long search, she had arrived by chance at a spot nearer her precious son than she had been for weeks.

Presently she got up and ran to find me. Then she led me joyously to the grave; and once more she snuggled down to it, with waving tail and happy, smiling eyes. There she stayed all day. Not mournfully, but in pleasant expectation.

There was no taint of exhibitionism or of the role of professional mourner, or even of grief, in her bearing. She had missed her dear son all these weeks. Now at last she was nearer to him than she had been throughout that long time of waiting. Her sense of smell told her that.

Several times before settling down there she circled the ground, nose to earth, for a radius of perhaps thirty feet, as if in search of some newer trail to follow. There was none. She realized she was closer to him, at his grave, than anywhere else. Presumably she believed Jock would come back to her, there, in course of time. So she waited, in happy eagerness.

She did not establish a senseless twenty-four-hour-a-day vigil. But every morning, as soon as she was let out of her kennel yard, she

would canter to Jock's grave in that same blithe expectation of finding he had returned. There she would stand or lie for a few minutes
before going back to the day's usual routine.

She was a strangely lovable little collie, was Sunnybank Jean; with
a hundred pretty ways that were all her own. The Mistress, whose
property she was, used to say:

"Any burglar could steal Jean if only he'd pat her while he was
doing it."

Unlike most of our collies, she loved petting, even from strangers.
And she delighted in the arrival of guests.

At sight or sound of a car coming down the furlong of winding
wooded driveway from the highroad above, Jean would run to the
foot of the drive at the veranda's edge and stand wriggling with jolly
anticipation, thrusting forward one of her white fore paws in an
effort to shake hands with the approaching visitors—even while their
car still was many yards away.

Two minor mishaps were forever befalling Jean. One was the
wedging of some fragment of bone into the hinges of her jaw at the
very back of her mouth. This propped her jaws wide apart and she
could not close them or get rid of the obstacle. The other was throwing her shoulder out of joint during a gallop or a romp.

Both these things happened again and again. But they did not
bother her. Invariably she would come straight to me with a flatteringly trustful expression on her visage; an aspect which said as
plainly as could any shouted words:

"Boss, I'm in a jam again. But it's all right, now that you're here.
You'll fix it for me. You always do."

With plumed tail awag, she would stand patiently and even gaily
while I pried loose the lump of knuckle-bone from between her jaw
hinges, or pulled the dislocated shoulder joint back into place.

One morning, when she was let out for a run, she went as always
to Jock's grave. On her way back to the house she heard a car starting
down the drive from the highroad. In her role of Reception Committee, she raced to her usual place of welcome and stood with fore
paw outthrust in a handshaking gesture.

The car, laden with sightseeing strangers from far away, had
crashed the gates at the lodge and had sped down the drive at per-

haps forty miles an hour. This with the customary sweet disregard for the several "Please Drive Slowly" signs which disfigure our trees along the way.

Perhaps the driver did not notice the beautiful little collie near the veranda; the canine Reception Committee with waving tail and politely extended fore paw, waiting so happily to welcome the newcomers.

The car went over Jean, disemboweling her and breaking most of her bones.

She must have been in hideous agony during the few minutes before she died. But not so much as a whimper escaped her. She was as plucky as they make them.

When I ran out of the house, toward her, Jean lifted her head and turned it toward me with the same flatteringly trustful expression that always had been hers when her jaw hinge was blocked by a bone or when her shoulder was out of joint; the expression that said:

"It's all right, now that *you're* here. *You'll* fix it for me."

A large woman in bright blue was among the tourists who debarked tumultuously from the killer car. Breezing over to where I knelt beside my dead little collie friend she made graceful amends for everything by assuring me with a gay smile:

"I am really VERY sorry this has happened."

(What a heaven-sent gift it must be, to know how to say just the right thing at just the right time! Hers was a talent to be envied. Yet for the only time in my life I replied to a woman's words with a torrent of indescribably foul blasphemy.)

A local magistrate fined the head of the party one hundred dollars for trespass and for malicious mischief or for some such fault. He wanted to make the sum much larger. I persuaded him not to. I told him the mischief had not been malicious, but idiotic. Which was far worse, but not so heinous in the eyes of the law. Also that if he should fine every unwarranted sightseer motorist who trespasses on Sunnybank's posted grounds the national debt could be wiped out in no time at all.

I told him to divide the hundred dollars between two village charities. Which he did. I wanted no part of the blood money that he imposed for my collie chum's killing.

As far as I was concerned I thought the rotten incident was closed. It was not.

A syndicated newspaper column's space, two days later, was devoted to the affair and to denouncing me venomously for my boorishness in penalizing a party of "kindly meaning hero worshippers who had traveled so far to see me." Several papers throughout the country—one of them a religious weekly—printed editorials along the same general line of invective.

Thus I lost not only good little Jean, but much popular approval and, doubtless, many readers.

The Whistle

BY

HUGH WALPOLE

Mrs. Penwin gave one of her nervous little screams when she
saw the dog.

"Oh Charlie!" she cried. "You surely haven't bought it!" And
her little nose, that she tried so fiercely to keep smooth, wrinkled
into its customary little guttering of wrinkles.

The dog, taking an instant dislike to her, slunk, his head between
his shoulders. He was an Alsatian.

"Well—" said Charlie, smiling nervously. He knew that his im-
pulsiveness had led him once more astray. "Only the other evening
you were saying that you'd like another dog."

"Yes, but *not* an Alsatian! You *know* what Alsatians are. We read
about them in the paper every day. They are simply *not* to be trusted.
I'm sure he looks as vicious as anything. And what about Mopsa?"

"Oh, Mopsa—" Charlie hesitated. "He'll be all right. You see,
Sibyl, it was charity really. The Sillons are going to London as you
know. They simply can't take him—it wouldn't be fair. They've
found it difficult enough in Edinburgh as it is."

"I'm sure they are simply getting rid of him because he's vicious."

"No. Maude Sillon assured me he's like a lamb—"

"Oh, Maude! She'd say anything!"

"You know that you've been wanting a companion for Mopsa—"

"A companion for Mopsa! That's good!" Sibyl laughed her shrill
little laugh that was always just out of tune.

"Well, we'll try him. We can easily get rid of him. And Blake
shall look after him."

565

"Blake?" She was scornful. She detested Blake, but he was too good a chauffeur to lose.

"And he's most awfully handsome. You can't deny it."

She looked. Yes, he was most awfully handsome. He had laid down his head on his paws, staring in front of him, quite motionless. He seemed to be waiting scornfully until he should be given his next command. The power in those muscles, moulded under the skin, must be terrific. His long wolf ears lay flat. His color was lovely, here silver gray, there faintly amber. Yes, he was a magnificent dog. A little like Blake in his strength, silence, sulkiness.

She turned again to the note that she was writing.

"We'll try him if you like. Anyway there are no children about. It's Blake's responsibility—and the moment he's tiresome he goes."

Charlie was relieved. It hadn't been so hard after all.

"Oh, Blake says he doesn't mind. In fact he seemed to take to the dog at once. I'll call him."

He went to the double windows that opened into the garden and called: "Blake! Blake!" Blake came. He was still in his chauffeur's uniform, having just driven his master and the dog in from Keswick. He was a very large man, very fair in coloring, plainly of great strength. His expression was absolutely English in its complete absence of curiosity, its certainty that it knew the best about everything, its suspicion, its determination not to be taken in by anybody, and its latent kindliness. He had very blue eyes and was clean-shaven; his cap was in his hand and his hair, which was fair almost to whiteness, lay roughly across his forehead. He was not especially neat but of a quite shining cleanliness.

The dog got up and moved towards him. Both the Penwins were short and slight; they looked now rather absurdly small beside the man and the dog.

"Look here, Blake," said Charlie Penwin, speaking with much authority, "Mrs. Penwin is nervous about the dog. He's your responsibility, mind, and if there's the slightest bit of trouble, he goes. You understand that?"

"Yes, sir," said Blake, looking at the dog, "but there won't be no trouble."

"That's a ridiculous thing to say," remarked Mrs. Penwin sharply, looking up from her note. "How can you be sure, Blake? You know how uncertain Alsatians are. I don't know what Mr. Penwin was thinking about."

Blake said nothing. Once again, and for the hundred-thousandth time, both the Penwins wished that they could pierce him with needles. It was quite terrible the way that Blake didn't speak when expected to, but then he was so wonderful a chauffeur, so good a driver, so excellent a mechanic, so honest—and Clara, his wife, was an admirable cook.

"You'd better take the dog with you now, Blake. What's its name?"

"Adam," said Charlie.

"Adam! What a foolish name for a dog! Now don't disturb Clara with him, Blake. Clara hates to have her kitchen messed up."

Blake, without a word, turned and went, the dog following closely at his heels.

Yes, Clara hated to have her kitchen messed up. She was standing now, her sleeves rolled back, her plump hands and wrists covered with dough. Mopsa, the Sealyham, sat at her side, his eyes, glistening with greed, raised to those doughy arms. But at sight of the Alsatian he turned and flew at his throat. He was a dog who prided himself on fighting instantly every other dog. With human beings he was mild and indifferently amiable. Children could do what they would with him. He was exceedingly conceited, and cared for no one but himself.

He was clever, however, and hid this indifference from many sentimental human beings.

Blake, with difficulty, separated the two dogs. The Alsatian behaved quite admirably, merely noticing the Sealyham and looking up at Blake to say, "I won't let myself go here although I should like to. I know that you would rather I didn't." The Sealyham, muttering deeply, bore the Alsatian no grudge. He was simply determined that he should have no foothold here.

Torrents of words passed from Clara. She had always as much to say as her husband had little. She said the same thing many times over as though she had an idiot to deal with. She knew that her husband was not an idiot—very far from it—but she had for many years been trying to make some impression on him. Defeated beyond hope, all she could now do was to resort to old and familiar tactics. What was this great savage dog? Where had he come from? Surely the Mistress didn't approve, and she wouldn't have her kitchen messed up, not for anybody, and as Harry (Blake) very well knew, nothing upset her like a dog fight, and if they were going to be perpetual, which, knowing Mopsa's character, they probably would be, she must just go to Mrs. Penwin and tell her that, sorry though she was after being with her all these years, she just couldn't stand it and would have to go, for if there was one thing more than another that really upset her it was a dog fight, and as Harry knew having the kitchen messed up was a thing that she couldn't stand. She paused and began vehemently to roll her dough. She was short and plump with fair hair and blue eyes like her husband's.

When she was excited, little glistening beads of sweat appeared on her forehead. No one in this world knew whether Blake was fond of her or no, Clara Blake least of all. She wondered perpetually; this uncertainty and her cooking were her principal interests in life. There were times when Blake seemed very fond of her indeed, others when he appeared not to be aware that she existed.

All he said now was, "The dog won't be no trouble," and went out, the dog at his heels. The Sealyham thought for a moment that he would follow him, then, with a little sniff of greed, settled himself down again at Clara Blake's feet.

The two went out into the thin, misty autumn sunshine, down through the garden into the garage. The Alsatian walked very closely beside Blake as though some invisible cord held them together. All his life, now two years in length, it had been always his constant principle to attach himself to somebody. For, in this curious world where he was, not his natural world at all, every breath, every movement, rustle of wind, sound of voices, patter of rain, ringing of bells, filled him with nervous alarm. He went always on guard, keeping his secret soul to himself, surrendering nothing, a captive in the country of the enemy. There might exist a human being to whom he would surrender himself. Although he had been attached to several people, he had not in his two years yet found one to whom he could give himself. Now as he trod softly over the amber and rosy leaves he was not sure that this man, beside whom he walked, might not be the one.

In the garage Blake took off his coat, put on his blue overalls and began to work. The dog stretched himself out on the stone floor, his head on his paws and waited. Once and again he started, his pointed ears pricked, at some unexpected sound. A breeze blew the brown leaves up and down in the sun, and the white road beyond the garage pierced like a shining bone the cloudless sky.

Blake's thoughts ran, as they always did, with slow assurance. This was a fine dog. He'd known the first moment that he set eyes on him that this was the dog for him. At that first glance something in his heart had been satisfied, something that had for years been unfulfilled. For they had had no children, he and Clara, and a motor car was fine to drive and look after, but after all it couldn't give you everything, and he wasn't one to make friends (too damned cautious), and the people he worked for were all right but nothing extra, and he really didn't know whether he cared for Clara or no. It was so difficult after so many years married to tell. There were lots of times when he couldn't sort of see her at all.

He began to take out the spark plugs to clean them. That was the worst of these Daimlers, fine cars, as good as any going, but you had to be forever cleaning the spark plugs. Yes, that dog was a beauty. He was going to take to that dog.

The dog looked at him, stared at him as though he were saying something. Blake looked at the dog. Then, with a deep sigh, as though some matter, for long uncertain, was at last completely settled, the dog rested again his head on his paws, staring in front of him, and so fell asleep. Blake, softly whistling, continued his work.

A very small factor, in itself quite unimportant, can bring into serious conflict urgent forces. So it was now when this dog, Adam, came into the life of the Penwins.

Mrs. Penwin, like so many English wives and unlike all American wives, had never known so much domestic power as she descried. Her husband was, of course, devoted to her, but he was forever just escaping her, escaping her into that world of men that is so important in England, that is, even in these very modern days, still a world in the main apart from women.

Charlie Penwin had not very many opportunities to escape from his wife, and he was glad that he had not, for when they came he took them. His ideal was the ideal of most English married men (and of very few American married men), namely, that he should be a perfect companion to his wife. He fulfilled this ideal; they were excellent companions, the two of them, so excellent that it was all the more interesting and invigorating when he could go away for a time and be a companion to someone else, to Willie Shaftoe, for instance, with whom he sometimes stayed in his place near Carlisle, or even for a few days' golf with the Reverend Thomas Bird, rector of a church in Keswick.

Mrs. Penwin in fact had nerves quite in spite of his profound devotion to her, never entirely captured the whole of her husband—a small fragment eternally escaped her, and this escape was a very real grievance to her. Like a wise woman she did not make scenes—no English husband can endure scenes—but she was always attempting to stop up this one little avenue of escape. But most provoking! So soon as one avenue was closed another would appear.

She realized very quickly (for she was not at all a fool) that this Alsatian was assisting her husband to escape from her because his presence in their household was bringing him into closer contact with Blake. Both the Penwins feared Blake had admired him; to friends and strangers they spoke of him with intense pride. "What we should do without Blake I can't think!" "But aren't we lucky in *these* days to have a chauffeur whom we can completely trust?"

Nevertheless, behind these sentiments there was this great difference, that Mrs. Penwin disliked Blake extremely (whenever he looked at her he made her feel a weak, helpless, and idiotic woman) while Charlie Penwin, although he was afraid of him, in his heart liked him very much indeed.

If Blake only were human, little Charlie Penwin, who was a sentimentalist, used to think—and now suddenly Blake *was* human. He had gone "dotty" about this dog, and the dog followed him like a shadow. So close were they the one to the other that you could almost imagine that they held conversations together.

Then Blake came into his master's room one day to ask whether Adam could sleep in his room. He had a small room next to Mrs,

Blake's because he was often out late with the car at night or must rise very early in the morning. Clara Blake liked to have her sleep undisturbed.

"You see, sir," he said, "he won't sort of settle down in the out-house. He's restless. I know he is."

"How do you know he is?" asked Charlie Penwin.

"I can sort of feel it, sir. He won't be no sort of trouble in my room, and he'll be a fine guard to the house at night."

The two men looked at one another and were in that moment friends. They both smiled.

"Very well, Blake. I don't think there's anything against it."

Of course, there *were* things against it. Mrs. Penwin hated the idea of the dog sleeping in the house. She did not really hate it; what she hated was that Blake and her husband should settle this thing without a word to her. Nor, when she protested, would her husband falter. Blake wanted it. It would be a good protection for the house.

Blake developed a very odd whistle with which he called the dog. Putting his fingers into his mouth he called forth this strange melancholy note that seemed to penetrate into endless distance and that had in it something mysterious, melancholy, and dangerous. It was musical and inhuman; friends of the Penwins, comfortably at tea, would hear this thin whistling cry, coming, it seemed, from far away beyond the fells, having in it some part of the lake and the distant sea trembling on Drigg sands and of the lonely places in Eskdale and Ennerdale.

"What's that?" they would say, looking up.

"Oh, it's Blake calling the dog."

"What a strange whistle!"

"Yes, it's the only one the dog hears."

The dog did hear it, at any distance, in any place. When Blake went with the car the Alsatian would lie on the upper lawn whence he could see the road and wait for his return.

He would both see and hear the car's return, but he would not stir until Blake, released from his official duties, could whistle to him —then with one bound he would be up, down the garden, and with his front paws up against Blake's chest would show him his joy.

To all the rest of the world he was indifferent. But he was not hostile. He showed indeed an immense patience, and especially with regard to the Sealyham.

The dog Mopsa attempted twice at least every day to kill the Alsatian. He succeeded in biting him severely but so long as Blake was there he showed an infinite control, letting Blake part them although every instinct in him was stirred to battle.

But after a time, Blake became clever at keeping the two dogs separate; moreover, the Sealyham became afraid of Blake. He was clever enough to realize that when he fought the Alsatian he fought Blake as well—and Blake was too much for him.

Very soon, however, Blake was at war not only with the Sealyham but with his wife and Mrs. Penwin too. You might think that the words "at war" were too strong when nothing was to be seen on the surface. Mrs. Blake said nothing, Mrs. Penwin said nothing, Blake himself said nothing.

Save for the fights with the Sealyham, there was no charge whatever to bring against the Alsatian. He was never in anyone's way, he brought no dirt in the house; whenever Charlie Penwin took him in the car he sat motionless on the back seat, his wolf ears pricked up, his large and beautiful eyes sternly regarding the outside world, but his consciousness fixed only upon Blake's back, broad and masterly above the wheel.

No charge could be brought against him except that the devotion between the man and the dog was in this little house of ordered emotions, routine habits, quiet sterility, almost terrible. Mrs. Blake, as her husband left her one night to return to his own room, broke out: "If you'd loved me as you love that dog I'd have had a different life."

Blake patted her shoulder, moist beneath her nightdress. "I love you all right, my girl," he said.

And Mrs. Penwin found that here she could not move her husband. Again and again she said: "Charlie, that dog's got to go."

"Why?"

"It's dangerous."

"I don't see it."

"Somebody will be bitten one day, and then you *will* see it."

"There's a terrible lot of nonsense talked about Alsatians—"

And then, when everyone was comfortable, Mrs. Blake reading

her "Home Chat," Mrs. Penwin her novel, Mrs. Fern (Mrs. Penwin's best friend) doing a "cross-word," over the misty, dank garden, carried it seemed by the muffled clouds that floated above the fell, would sound that strange melancholy whistle, so distant and yet so near, Blake calling his dog.

For Blake himself life was suddenly, and for the first time, complete. He had not known, all this while, what it was that he missed although he had known that he missed something. Had Mrs. Blake given him a child he would have realized completion. Mrs. Blake alone had not been enough for his heart. In this dog he found fulfilment because here were all the things that he admired—loyalty, strength, courage, self-reliance, fidelity, comradeship, and, above all, sobriety of speech and behavior. Beyond these there was something more—love. He did not, even to himself, admit the significance of this yet deeper contact. And he analyzed nothing.

For the dog, life in this dangerous menacing country of the enemy was at last secure and simple. He had only one thing to do, only one person to consider.

But, of course, life is not so simple as this for anybody. A battle was being waged, and it must have an issue.

The Penwins were not in Cumberland during the winter. They went to their little place in Sussex, very close to London and to all their London friends. Mrs. Penwin would not take the Alsatian to Sussex. "But why not?" asked Charlie. She hated it, Mrs. Blake hated it. That, Charlie objected, was not reason enough.

"Do you realize," said Mrs. Penwin theatrically, "that this dog is dividing us?"

"Nonsense," said Charlie.

"It is not nonsense. I believe you care more for Blake than you do for me." She cried. She cried very seldom. Charlie Penwin was uncomfortable but some deep male obstinacy was roused in him. This had become an affair of the sexes. Men must stand together and protect themselves or they would be swept away in this feminine flood.

Blake knew, Mrs. Blake knew, Mrs. Penwin knew that the dog would go with them to Sussex unless some definite catastrophe gave Mrs. Penwin the victory.

Lying on his bed at night, seeing the gray wolf-like shadow of the dog stretched on the floor, Blake's soul for the first time in its history trembled, at the thought of the slight movement, incident, spoken word, sound that might rouse the dog beyond his endurance and precipitate the catastrophe. The dog was behaving magnificently, but he was surrounded by his enemies. Did he know what hung upon his restraint?

Whether he knew or no, the catastrophe arrived and arrived with the utmost, most violent publicity. On a sun-gleaming, russet October afternoon, on the lawn while Charlie was giving Blake instructions about the car and Mrs. Penwin put in also her word, Mopsa attacked the Alsatian. Blake ran to separate them, and the Alsatian, sharply bitten, bewildered, humiliated, snapped and caught Blake's leg between his teeth. A moment later he and Blake knew, both of them, what he had done. Blake would have hidden it, but blood was flowing. In the Alsatian's heart remorse, terror, love, and a sense of disaster—a confirmation of all that, since his birth, knowing the traps that his enemies would lay for him, he had suspected—leapt to life together.

Disregarding all else, he looked up at Blake.

"And that settles it!" cried Mrs. Penwin, triumphantly. "He goes!"

Blake's leg was badly bitten in three places; there would be scars for life. And it was settled. Before the week was out the dog would be returned to his first owners, who did not want him—who would give him to someone else who also, in turn, through fear or shyness of neighbors, would not want him.

Two days after this catastrophe, Mrs. Blake went herself to Mrs. Penwin.

"My husband's that upset—I wouldn't care if the dog stays, Mum."

"Why, Clara, you hate the dog."

"Oh well, Mum, Blake's a good husband to me. I don't like to see him—"

"Why, what has he said?"

"He hasn't said *anything*, Mum."

But Mrs. Penwin shook her head. "No, Clara, it's ridiculous. The dog's dangerous."

And Blake went to Charlie Penwin. The two men faced one

another and were closer together, fonder of one another, man caring for man, than they had ever been before.

"But, Blake, if the dog bites *you* whom he cares for—I mean, don't you see? he really *is* dangerous—"

"He wasn't after biting me," said Blake slowly. "And if he *had* to bite somebody, being aggravated and nervous, he'd not find anyone better to bite than me who understands him and knows he don't mean nothing by it."

Charlie Penwin felt in himself a terrible disloyalty to his wife. She could go to— Why should not Blake have his dog? Was he forever to be dominated by women? For a brief rocking, threatening moment his whole ordered world trembled. He knew that if he said the dog was to remain the dog would remain and that something would have broken between his wife and himself that could never be mended.

He looked at Blake, who with his blue serious eyes stared steadily in front of him. He hesitated. He shook his head.

"No, Blake, it won't do. Mrs. Penwin will never be easy now while the dog is here."

Later in the day Blake did an amazing thing. He went to Mrs. Penwin.

During all these years he had never voluntarily, himself, gone to Mrs. Penwin. He had never gone unless he was sent for. She looked at him and felt, as she always did, dislike, admiration, and herself a bit of a fool.

"Well, Blake?"

"If the dog stays I'll make myself responsible. He shan't bite nobody again."

"But how can you tell? You said he wouldn't bite anyone before and he did."

"He won't again."

"No, Blake, he's got to go. I shan't have a moment's peace while he's here."

"He's a wonderful dog. I'll have him trained so he won't hurt a fly. He's like a child with me."

"I'm sure he is. Irresponsible like a child. That's why he bit you."

"I don't make nothing of his biting me."

"You may not, but next time it will be someone else. There's something in the paper about them every day."

"He's like a child with me."

"I'm very sorry, Blake. I can't give way about it. You'll see I'm right in the end. My husband ought never to have accepted the dog at all."

After Blake had gone she did not know why, but she felt uneasy, as though she had robbed a blind man, or stolen another woman's lover. Ridiculous! There could be no question but that she was right.

Blake admitted that to himself. She was right. He did not criticise her, but he did not know what to do. He had never felt like this in all his life before as though part of himself were being torn from him.

On the day before the dog was to go back to his original owners Blake was sent into Keswick to make some purchases. It was a soft blooming day, one of those North English autumn days when there is a scent of spices in the sharp air and a rosy light hangs about the trees. Blake had taken the dog with him, and driving back along the lake, seeing how it lay, a sheet of silver glass upon whose surface the islands were painted in flat colors of auburn and smoky gray, a sudden madness seized him. It was the stillness, the silence, the breathless pause—

Instead of turning to the right over the Grange bridge, he drove the car straight on into Borrowdale. It was yet early in the afternoon —all the lovely valley lay in gold leaf at the feet of the russet hills, and no cloud moved in the sky. He took the car to Seatoller and climbed with the dog the steep path towards Honister.

And the dog thought that at last what he had longed for was to come to pass. He and Blake were at length free, they would go on and on, leaving all the stupid, nerve-jumping world behind them, never to return to it.

With a wild, fierce happiness such as he had never yet shown he bounded forward, drinking in the cold streams, feeling the strong turf beneath his feet, running back to Blake to assure him of his comradeship. At last he was free, and life was noble as it ought to be.

At the turn of the road Blake sat down and looked back. All around him were hills. Nothing moved; only the stream close to him slipped murmuring between the boulders. The hills ran ranging from horizon to horizon, and between gray clouds a silver strip of sky, lit by an invisible sun, ran like a river into mist. Blake called the dog to him and laid his hand upon his head. He knew that the dog thought that they both had escaped forever now from the world. Well, why not? They could walk on, on to the foot of the hill on whose sky-line the mining hut stood like a listening ear, down the Pass to Butter-mere, past the lake, past Crummock Water to Cockermouth. There would be a train. It would not be difficult for him to get work. His knowledge of cars (he had a genius for them) would serve him any-where. And Clara? She was almost invisible, a tiny white blot on the horizon. She would find someone else. His hand tightened about the dog's head.

For a long while he sat there, the dog never moving, the silver river spreading in the sky, the hills gathering closer about him.

Suddenly he shook his head. No, he could not. He would be run-ning away, a poor kind of cowardice. He pulled Adam's sharp ears; he buried his face in Adam's fur. He stood up, and Adam also stood up, placed his paws on Blake's chest, licked his cheeks. In his eyes there shone great happiness because they two were going alone to-gether.

But Blake turned back down the path, and the dog realizing that there was to be no freedom, walked close behind him, brushing with his body sometimes the stuff of Blake's trousers.

Next day Blake took the dog back to the place whence he had come.

Two days later, the dog, knowing that he was not wanted, sat watching a little girl who played some foolish game near him. She had plump bare legs; he watched them angrily. He was unhappy, lonely, nervous, once more in the land of the enemy, and now with no friend.

Through the air, mingling with the silly laughter of the child and other dangerous sounds came, he thought, a whistle. His heart ham-mered. His ears were up. With all his strength he bounded towards the sound. But he was chained. To-morrow he was to be given to a Cumberland farmer.

Mrs. Penwin was entertaining two ladies at tea. This was the last day before the journey south. Across the dank lawns came that irritating, melancholy whistle disturbing her, reproaching her—and for what?

Why, for her sudden suspicion that everything in life was just ajar—one little push and all would be in its place—but would she be married to Charlie, would Mrs. Plang then be jealous of her pretty daughter, would Miss Tennyson, nibbling now at her pink pieces of icing, be nursing her aged and intemperate father? She looked up crossly.

"Really, Charlie, that must be Blake whistling. I can't think why now the dog's gone. To let us know what he thinks about it, I suppose." She turned to her friends, "Our chauffeur—a splendid man—we *are* so fortunate. Charlie, do tell him. It's such a hideous whistle anyway—and now the dog is gone—"

The Character of Dogs

BY

ROBERT LOUIS STEVENSON

THE civilisation, the manners, and the morals of dog-kind are to a great extent subordinated to those of his ancestral master, man. This animal, in many ways so superior, has accepted a position of inferiority, shares the domestic life, and humors the caprices of the tyrant. But the potentate, like the British in India, pays small regard to the character of his willing client, judges him with listless glances, and condemns him in a byword. Listless have been the looks of his admirers, who have exhausted idle terms of praise, and buried the poor soul below exaggerations. And yet more idle and, if possible, more unintelligent has been the attitude of his express detractors; those who are very fond of dogs "but in their proper place"; who say "poo' fellow, poo' fellow," and are themselves far poorer; who whet the knife of the vivisectionist or heat his oven; who are not ashamed to admire "the creature's instinct"; and flying far beyond folly, have dared to resuscitate the theory of animal machines. The "dog's instinct" and the "automaton-dog," in this age of psychology and science, sound like strange anachronisms. An automaton he certainly is; a machine working independently of his control, the heart like the mill-wheel, keeping all in motion, and the consciousness, like a person shut in the mill garret, enjoying the view out of the window and shaken by the thunder of the stones; an automaton in one corner of which a living spirit is confined: an automation like man. Instinct again he certainly possesses. Inherited aptitudes are his, inherited frailties. Some things he at once views and understands, as though

579

he were awakened from a sleep, as though he came "trailing clouds of glory." But with him, as with man, the field of instinct is limited; its utterances are obscure and occasional; and about the far larger part of life both the dog and his master must conduct their steps by deduction and observation.

The leading distinction between dog and man, after and perhaps before the different duration of their lives, is that the one can speak and that the other cannot. The absence of the power of speech confines the dog in the development of his intellect. It hinders him from many speculations, for words are the beginning of metaphysic. At the same blow it saves him from many superstitions and his silence has won for him a higher name for virtue than his conduct justifies. The faults of the dog are many. He is vainer than man, singularly greedy of notice, singularly intolerant of ridicule, suspicious like the deaf, jealous to the degree of frenzy, and radically devoid of truth. The day of an intelligent small dog is passed in the manufacture and the laborious communication of falsehood; he lies with his tail, he lies with his eye, he lies with his protesting paw; and when he rattles his dish or scratches at the door his purpose is other than appears. But he has some apology to offer for the vice. Many of the signs which form his dialect have come to bear an arbitrary meaning, clearly understood both by his master and himself; yet when a new want arises he must either invent a new vehicle of meaning or wrest an old one to a different purpose; and this necessity frequently recurring must tend to lessen his idea of the sanctity of symbols. Meanwhile the dog is clear in his own conscience, and draws, with a human nicety, the distinction between formal and essential truth. Of his punning perversions, his legitimate dexterity with symbols, he is even vain; but when he has told and been detected in a lie, there is not a hair upon his body but confesses guilt. To a dog of gentlemanly feeling theft and falsehood are disgraceful vices. The canine, like the human, gentleman demands in his misdemeanours Montaigne's "*je ne sais quoi de généreux.*" His is never more than half ashamed of having barked or bitten; and for those faults into which he has been led by the desire to shine before a lady of his race, he retains, even under physical correction, a share of pride. But to be caught lying, if he understands it, instantly uncurls his fleece.

Just as among dull observers he preserves a name for truth, the dog has been credited with modesty. It is amazing how the use of language blunts the faculties of man—that because vainglory finds no vent in words, creatures supplied with eyes have been unable to detect a fault so gross and obvious. If a small spoiled dog were suddenly to be endowed with speech, he would prate interminably, and still about himself; when we had friends, we should be forced to lock him in a garret; and what with his whining jealousies and his foible for falsehood, in a year's time he would have gone far to weary out our love. I was about to compare him to Sir Willoughby Patterne, but the Patternes have a manlier sense of their own merits; and the parallel, besides, is ready. Hans Christian Andersen, as we behold him in his startling memoirs, thrilling from top to toe with an excruciating vanity, and scouting even along the street for shadows of offence—here was the talking dog.

It is just this rage for consideration that has betrayed the dog into his satellite position as the friend of man. The cat, an animal of franker appetites, preserves his independence. But the dog, with one eye ever on the audience, has been wheedled into slavery, and praised and patted into the renunciation of his nature. Once he ceased hunting and became man's plate-licker, the Rubicon was crossed. Thenceforth he was a gentleman of leisure; and except the few whom we keep working, the whole race grew more and more self-conscious, mannered and affected. The number of things that a small dog does naturally is strangely small. Enjoying better spirits and not crushed under material cares, he is far more theatrical than average man. His whole life, if he be a dog of any pretension to gallantry, is spent in a vain show, and in the hot pursuit of admiration. Take out your puppy for a walk, and you will find the little ball of fur clumsy, stupid, bewildered, but natural. Let but a few months pass, and when you repeat the process you will find nature buried in convention. He will do nothing plainly; but the simplest processes of our material life will all be bent into the forms of an elaborate and mysterious etiquette. Instinct, says the fool, has awakened. But it is not so. Some dogs—some, at the very least—if they be kept separate from others, remain quite natural; and these, when at length they meet with a companion of experience, and have the game explained to them, distinguish themselves by the severity of their devotion to its rules. I wish I were allowed to tell a story which would radiantly illuminate the point; but men, like dogs, have an elaborate and mysterious etiquette. It is their bond of sympathy that both are the children of convention.

The person, man or dog, who has a conscience is eternally condemned to some degree of humbug; the sense of law in their members fatally precipitates either towards a frozen and affected bearing. And the converse is true; and in the elaborate and conscious manners of the dog, moral opinions and the love of the ideal stand confessed. To follow for ten minutes in the street some swaggering, canine cavalier, is to receive a lesson in dramatic art and the cultured conduct of the body; in every act and gesture you see him true to a refined conception; and the dullest cur, beholding him, pricks up his ear and proceeds to imitate and parody that charming ease. For to be a high-mannered and high-minded gentleman, careless, affable, and gay, is the inborn pretension of the dog. The large dog, so much lazier, so much more weighed upon with matter, so majestic in repose, so beautiful in effort, is born with the dramatic means to wholly represent the part. And it is more pathetic and perhaps more instructive to consider the small dog in his conscientious and imperfect efforts to outdo Sir Philip Sidney. For the ideal of the dog is feudal and religious; the ever-present polytheism, the whip-bearing Olympus of mankind, rules them on the one hand; on the other, their singular difference of size and strength among themselves effectually prevents the appearance of the democratic notion. Or we might more exactly compare their society to the curious spectacle presented by a school—ushers, monitors, and big and little boys—qualified by one circumstance, the introduction of the other sex. In each, we should observe a somewhat similar tension of manner, and somewhat similar points of honor. In each the large animal keeps a contemptuous good humor; in each the smaller annoys him with wasp-like impudence, certain of practical immunity; in each we shall find a double life producing double characters, and an excursive and noisy heroism combined with a fair amount of practical timidity. I have known dogs, and I have known school heroes that, set aside the fur, could hardly have been told apart; and if we desire to understand the chivalry of old, we must turn to the school playfields or the dung-heap where the dogs are trooping.

Woman, with the dog, has been long enfranchised. Incessant massacre of female innocents has changed the proportions of the sexes and perverted their relations. Thus, when we regard the manners of the dog, we see a romantic and monogamous animal, once perhaps as delicate as the cat, at war with impossible conditions. Man has much to answer for; and the part he plays is yet more damnable and parlous than Corin's in the eyes of Touchstone. But his intervention has at least created an imperial situation for the rare surviving ladies. In that society they reign without a rival: conscious queens; and in the only instance of a canine wife-beater that has ever fallen under my notice, the criminal was somewhat excused by the circumstances of his story. He is a little, very alert, well-bred, intelligent Skye, as black as a hat, with a wet bramble for a nose and two cairngorms for eyes. To the human observer, he is decidedly well-looking; but to the ladies of his race he seems abhorrent. A thorough elaborate gentleman, of the plume and sword-knot order, he was born with a nice sense of gallantry to women. He took at their hands the most outrageous treatment; I have heard him bleating like a sheep, I have seen him streaming blood, and his ear tattered like a regimental banner; and yet he would scorn to make reprisals. Nay more, when a human lady upraised the contumelious whip against the very dame who had been so cruelly misusing him, my little greatheart gave but one hoarse cry and fell upon the tyrant tooth and nail. This is the tale of a soul's tragedy. After three years of unavailing chivalry, he suddenly, in one hour, threw off the yoke of obligation; had he been Shakespeare he would then have written *Troilus and Cressida* to brand the offending sex; but being only a little dog, he began to bite them. The surprise of the ladies whom he attacked indicated the monstrosity of his offence; but he had fairly beaten off his better angel, fairly committed moral suicide; for almost in the same hour, throwing aside the last rags of decency, he proceeded to attack the aged also. The fact is worth remark, showing, as it does, that ethical laws are common both to dogs and men; and that with both a single deliberate violation of the conscience loosens all. "But while the lamp holds on to burn," says the paraphrase, "the greatest sinner may return." I have been cheered to see symptoms of effectual penitence in my sweet ruffian; and by the handling that he accepted uncomplainingly the other day from an indignant fair one, I began to hope the period of *Sturm und Drang* is closed.

All these little gentlemen are subtle casuists. The duty to the female dog is plain; but where competing duties rise, down they will sit and study them out, like Jesuit confessors. I knew another little Skye, somewhat plain in manner and appearance, but a creature compact of amiability and solid wisdom. His family going abroad for a winter, he was received for that period by an uncle in the same city. The winter over, his own family home again, and his own house (of which he was very proud) reopened, he found himself in a dilemma between two conflicting duties of loyalty and gratitude. His old friends were not to be neglected, but it seemed hardly decent to desert the new. This was how he solved the problem. Every morning, as soon as the door was opened, off posted Coolin to his uncle's, visited the children in the nursery, saluted the whole family, and was back at home in time for breakfast and his bit of fish. Nor was this done without a sacrifice on his part, sharply felt; for he had to forego the particular honor and jewel of his day—his morning's walk with my father. And, perhaps from this cause, he gradually wearied of and relaxed the practice, and at length returned entirely to his ancient habits. But the same decision served him in another and more distressing case of divided duty, which happened not long after. He was not at all a kitchen dog, but the cook had nursed him with unusual kindness during the distemper; and though he did not adore her as he adored my father—although (born snob) he was critically conscious of her position as "only a servant"—he still cherished for her a special gratitude. Well, the cook left, and retired some streets away to lodgings of her own; and there was Coolin in precisely the same situation with any young gentleman who has had the inestimable benefit of a faithful nurse. The canine conscience did not solve the problem with a pound of tea at Christmas. No longer content to pay a flying visit, it was the whole forenoon that he dedicated to his solitary friend. And so, day by day, he continued to comfort her solitude until (for some reason which I could never understand and cannot approve) he was kept locked up to break

him of the graceful habit. Here, it is not the similarity, it is the difference, that is worthy of remark; the clearly marked degrees of gratitude and the proportional duration of his visits. Anything further
removed from instinct it were hard to fancy; and one is even stirred
to a certain impatience with a character so destitute of spontaneity,
so passionless in justice, and so priggishly obedient to the voice of
reason.

There are not many dogs like this good Coolin, and not many
people. But the type is one well marked, both in the human and the
canine family. Gallantry was not his aim, but a solid and somewhat
oppressive respectability. He was a sworn foe to the unusual and
the conspicuous, a praiser of the golden mean, a kind of city uncle
modified by Cheeryble. And as he was precise and conscientious in
all the steps of his own blameless course, he looked for the same
precision and an even greater gravity in the bearing of his deity, my
father. It was no sinecure to be Coolin's idol: he was exacting like a
rigid parent; and at every sign of levity in the man whom he respected, he announced loudly the death of virtue and the proximate
fall of the pillars of the earth.

I have called him a snob; but all dogs are so, though in varying
degrees. It is hard to follow their snobbery among themselves; for
though I think we can perceive distinctions of rank, we cannot grasp
what is the criterion. Thus in Edinburgh, in a good part of the town,
there were several distinct societies or clubs that met in the morning
to—the phrase is technical—to "rake the backets" in a troop. A friend
of mine, the master of three dogs, was one day surprised to observe
that they had left one club and joined another; but whether it was
a rise or a fall, and the result of an invitation or an expulsion, was more
than he could guess. And this illustrates pointedly our ignorance of
the real life of dogs, their social ambitions and their social hierarchies.
At least, in their dealings with men they are not only conscious of
sex, but of the difference of station. And that in the most snobbish
manner; for the poor man's dog is not offended by the notice of the
rich, and keeps all his ugly feeling for those poorer or more ragged
than his master. And again, for every station they have an ideal of
behavior, to which the master, under pain of derogation, will do
wisely to conform. How often has not a cold glance of an eye in-

formed me that my dog was disappointed; and how much more gladly would he not have taken a beating than to be thus wounded in the seat of piety!

I knew one disrespectable dog. He was far liker a cat; cared little or nothing for men, with whom he merely coexisted as we do with cattle, and was entirely devoted to the art of poaching. A house would not hold him, and to live in a town was what he refused. He led, I believe, a life of troubled but genuine pleasure, and perished beyond all question in a trap. But this was an exception, a marked reversion to the ancestral type; like the hairy human infant. The true dog of the nineteenth century, to judge by the remainder of my fairly large acquaintance, is in love with respectability. A street-dog was once adopted by a lady. While still an Arab, he had done as Arabs do, gambolling in the mud, charging into butchers' stalls, a cat-hunter, a sturdy beggar, a common rogue and vagabond; but with his rise into society he laid aside these inconsistent pleasures. He stole no more, he hunted no more cats; and conscious of his collar, he ignored his old companions. Yet the canine upper class was never brought to recognize the upstart, and from that hour, except for human countenance, he was alone. Friendless, shorn of his sports and the habits of a lifetime, he still lived in a glory of happiness, content with his acquired respectability, and with no care but to support it solemnly. Are we to condemn or praise this self-made dog? We praise his human brother. And thus to conquer vicious habits is as rare with dogs as with men. With the most part, for all their scruple-mongering and moral thought, the vices that are born with them remain invincible throughout; and they live all their years, glorying in their virtues, but still the slaves of their defects. Thus the sage Coolin was a thief to the last; among a thousand peccadilloes, a whole goose and a whole cold leg of mutton lay upon his conscience; but Woggs,[1] whose soul's shipwreck in the matter of gallantry I have recounted above, has only twice been known to steal, and has often nobly conquered the temptation. The eighth is his favorite commandment. There is something painfully human in

---

[1] Walter, Watty, Woggy, Woggs, Wogg, and lastly Bogue; under which last name he fell in battle some twelve months ago. Glory was his aim and he attained it; for his icon, by the hand of Caldecott, now lies among the treasures of the nation.

these unequal virtues and moral frailties of the best. Still more painful is the bearing of those "stammering professors" in the house of sickness and under the terror of death. It is beyond a doubt to me that, somehow or other, the dog connects together, or confounds, the uneasiness of sickness and the consciousness of guilt. To the pains of the body he often adds the tortures of the conscience; and at these times his haggard protestations form, in regard to the human deathbed, a dreadful parody or parallel.

I once supposed that I had found an inverse relation between the double etiquette which dogs obey; and that those who were most addicted to the showy street life among other dogs were less careful in the practice of home virtues for the tyrant man. But the female dog, that mass of carneying affectations, shines equally in either sphere; rules her rough posse of attendant swains with unwearying tact and gusto; and with her master and mistress pushes the arts of insinuation to their crowning point. The attention of man and the regard of other dogs flatter (it would thus appear) the same sensibility; but perhaps, if we could read the canine heart, they would be found to flatter it in very different degrees. Dogs live with man as courtiers round a monarch, steeped in the flattery of his notice and enriched with sinecures. To push their favor in this world of pickings and caresses is, perhaps, the business of their lives; and their joys may lie outside. I am in despair at our persistent ignorance. I read in the lives of our companions the same processes of reason, the same antique and fatal conflicts of the right against the wrong, and of unbitted nature with too rigid custom; I see them with our weaknesses, vain, false, inconstant against appetite, and with our one stalk of virtue, devoted to the dream of an ideal; and yet, as they hurry by me on the street with tail in air, or come singly to solicit my regard, I must own the secret purport of their lives is still inscrutable to man. Is man the friend, or is he the patron only? Have they indeed forgotten nature's voice? or are those moments snatched from courtiership when they touch noses with the tinker's mongrel, the brief reward and pleasure of their artificial lives? Doubtless, when man shares with his dog the toils of a profession and the pleasures of an art, as with the shepherd or the poacher, the affection warms and

1909, 1937, reprinted by permission from Doubleday, Doran & Company, Inc.; "The Whistle" from *All Souls' Night* by Hugh Walpole, copyright, 1933, by Doubleday, Doran & Company, Inc.; "Memoirs of a Yellow Dog" from *The Four Million* by O. Henry, copyright, 1905, 1933, by Doubleday, Doran & Company, Inc. The two articles: "Being a Public Character" from *The Revolt of the Oyster* by Don Marquis, copyright, 1912, 1913, 1922, by Doubleday, Doran & Company, Inc.; and "Some Sunnybank Dogs" from *A Book of Famous Dogs* by Albert Payson Terhune, copyright, 1937, reprinted by permission from Doubleday, Doran & Company, Inc.

E. P. DUTTON & COMPANY, INC. The story "Dandy, The Story of a Dog" from *A Traveller in Little Things* by W. H. Hudson, published by E. P. Dutton & Company, Inc.

HARCOURT, BRACE & COMPANY. The story "A Dog of Pompeii" from *The Donkey of God* by Louis Untermeyer, copyright, 1932, by Harcourt, Brace & Company.

HARPER & BROTHERS. The articles "A Dog's Nervous System" and "The Care and Training of a Dog," which appeared originally in *Harper's Magazine*, July, 1939, and January, 1941, respectively.

HENRY HOLT & COMPANY, INC. The radio play "The Odyssey of Runyon Jones" by Norman Corwin from *Thirteen by Corwin*, published by Henry Holt & Company, Inc. Dramatic rights are reserved for the author by Henry Holt & Company, Inc.

ALFRED A. KNOPF, INC. The two stories "A Dark Brown Dog" from *Midnight Sketches* by Stephen Crane, reprinted by permission of and special arrangement with Alfred A. Knopf, Inc., authorized publishers; "Bashan" ("A Man And His Dog") reprinted from *Stories of Three Decades* by Thomas Mann, by permission of and special arrangement with Alfred A. Knopf, Inc. Copyright 1930, 1931, 1934, 1935, 1936 by Alfred A. Knopf, Inc.

FRIEDA LAWRENCE. The story "Rex" by D. H. Lawrence, published by Dial Press.

MRS. ELSIE SINGMASTER LEWARS. The story "A Pair of Lovers."

THE MACMILLAN COMPANY. The story "For the Love of a Man" from *The Call of the Wild* by Jack London. By permission of The Macmillan Company, publishers.

MATSON AND DUGGAN. The story "The Biscuit Eater" by James Street, which appeared originally in *The Saturday Evening Post*, May 13, 1939.

HAROLD OBER. The two stories: "Moses" by Walter D. Edmonds, copyright, 1938, reprinted by permission of the author; "Brag Dog" by Vereen Bell, copyright, 1939, by the Curtis Publishing Company, reprinted by permission of the author.

SIDNEY A. SANDERS. The story "My Talks with Dean Spanley," copyright, 1936, by Lord Dunsany.

CHARLES SCRIBNER'S SONS. The two stories: "The Bar Sinister" by Richard Harding Davis, and "memories" by John Galsworthy.

SIMON AND SCHUSTER, INC. The article "Pillar to Post" from *How to do Practically Anything,* copyright, 1942, by Jack Goodman and Alan Green.

MR. JAMES THURBER. For "The Hound and the Hat." The story "The Dog that Bit People" from *My Life and Hard Times,* copyright, 1933, by James Thurber, and the article "Snapshot of a Dog" from *The Middle-Aged Man on the Flying Trapeze.*

MR. E. B. WHITE. The article "Obituary" which appeared originally in *The New Yorker,* March 12, 1932.